VISUAL
dictionary

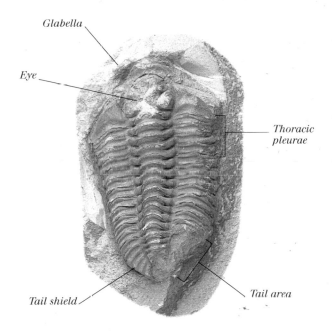

Glabella

Eye

Thoracic pleurae

Tail shield

Tail area

PREHISTORIC TRILOBITE

DIGITAL VIDEO CAMERA

Liquid crystal display (LCD)

Viewfinder

Power switch

Battery

Cassette compartment lid

OVERHEAD VIEW OF OUR GALAXY

Location of Solar System

Nucleus

First electron shell

Second electron shell

Nucleus

ANATOMY OF A FLUORINE–19 ATOM

Fault plane

Dip of fault plane

Hade of fault plane

STRUCTURE OF A FAULT

Windshield

Steering wheel

Radiator

Headlight

Ford

Ford

102-14

MODEL T FORD

Exhaust port

VELOCETTE OHV ENGINE

Floral design

MOSAIC DESIGN

VISUAL
dictionary

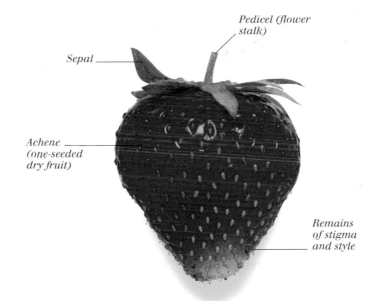

Pedicel (flower stalk)

Sepal

Achene (one-seeded dry fruit)

Remains of stigma and style

STRAWBERRY

DK PUBLISHING

LONDON, NEW YORK, MUNICH, MELBOURNE, AND DELHI

Revised Editions
Art Editor Hugh Schermuly
Designers Phil Gamble, Simon Oon, Pamela Shiels,
Steve Woosnam-Savage, Lee Riches
Jacket Designer John Dinsdale
Project Editor Cathy Meeus
Editor Paul Docherty
Jacket Editor Adam Powley
Editorial Consultant Sarah Angliss
Senior Art Editor Ina Stradins
Senior Editor Angeles Gavira
Production Elizabeth Cherry, Tony Phipps
Managing Art Editor Phil Ormerod
Category Publisher Jonathan Metcalf

Anatomical And Botanical Models Supplied By Somso Modelle, Coburg, Germany

Original Edition *Ultimate Visual Dictionary*
Project Art Editors Heather McCarry, Johnny Pau, Chris Walker, Kevin Williams
Designer Simon Murrell
Project Editors Luisa Caruso, Peter Jones, Jane Mason, Geoffrey Stalker
Editor Jo Evans
DTP Designer Zirrinia Austin
Picture Researcher Charlotte Bush
Managing Art Editor Toni Kay
Senior Editor Roger Tritton
Managing Editor Sean Moore
Production Manager Hilary Stephens

FIRST AMERICAN EDITION PUBLISHED UNDER THE TITLE
ULTIMATE VISUAL DICTIONARY, 1994
07 08 09 10 11 10 9 8 7 6 5 4 3 2 1

THIS REVISED EDITION PUBLISHED 2006 BY
DK PUBLISHING
375 HUDSON STREET
NEW YORK, NEW YORK 10014

A CATALOGING IN PUBLICATION RECORD IS AVAILABLE FROM THE LIBRARY OF CONGRESS

ISBN 978-0-7566-3079-9

REPRODUCED BY COLOURSCAN, SINGAPORE
PRINTED AND BOUND IN SINGAPORE BY STAR STANDARD

Discover more at
www.dk.com

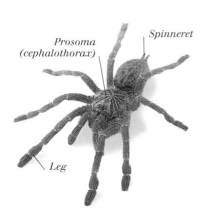

Prosoma (cephalothorax)   *Spinneret*

Leg

EXTERNAL FEATURES OF A SPIDER

Canopy   *Fin*

G-BNHB

Main landing gear

SIDE VIEW OF ARV SUPER 2 AIRPLANE

Heat shield

JPL

PAM-D upper stage booster

Launch vehicle

MARS PATHFINDER

CONTENTS

Barrel

Permanent black ink

FOUNTAIN PEN AND INK

Face light emitting diodes (LEDs)   *Movable tail*

SONY AIBO ROBOT DOG

Parallel bands

ONYX

Low pressure gases

Central electrode

BALL CONTAINING HIGH TEMPERATURE GAS (PLASMA)

Nonbreakable plastic

Riddell

Shock absorber

FOOTBALL HELMET

Introduction

THE VISUAL DICTIONARY is a completely new kind of reference book. It provides a link between pictures and words in a way that no ordinary dictionary ever has. Most dictionaries simply tell you what a word means, but the *Visual Dictionary* shows you—through a combination of detailed annotations, explicit photographs, and illustrations. In the *Visual Dictionary*, pictures define the annotations around them. You do not read definitions of the annotated words, you see them. The highly accessible format of the *Visual Dictionary*, the thoroughness of its annotations, and the range of its subject matter make it a unique and helpful reference tool.

How to use the Visual Dictionary

You will find the *Visual Dictionary* simple to use. Instead of being organized alphabetically, it is divided by subject into 14 sections—The Universe, Prehistoric Earth, Plants, Animals, The Human Body, etc. Each section begins with a table of contents listing the major entries within that section. For example, The Visual Arts section has entries on *Drawing, Tempera, Fresco, Oils, Watercolor, Pastels, Acrylics, Calligraphy, Printmaking, Mosaic,* and *Sculpture*. Every entry has a short introduction explaining the purpose of the photographs and illustrations, and the significance of the annotations.

If you know what something looks like, but don't know its name, find the term you need by turning to the annotations surrounding the pictures; if you know a word, but don't know what it refers to, use the comprehensive index to direct you to the appropriate page.

Suppose that you want to know what the bone at the end of your little finger is called. With a standard dictionary, you wouldn't know where to begin. But with the *Visual Dictionary* you simply turn to the entry called *Hands*—within The Human Body section—where you will find four fully annotated, color photographs showing the skin, muscles, and bones of the human hand. In this entry you will quickly find that the bone you are searching for is called the distal phalanx, and for good measure you will discover that it is attached to the middle phalanx by the distal interphalangeal joint.

Perhaps you want to know what a catalytic converter looks like. If you look up "catalytic converter" in an ordinary dictionary, you will be told what it is and possibly what it does—but you will not be able to tell what shape it is or what it is made of. However, if you look up "catalytic converter" in the index of the *Visual Dictionary*, you will be directed to the *Modern engines* entry on page 344—where the introduction gives you basic information about what a catalytic converter is—and to page 350—where there is a spectacular exploded-view photograph of the mechanics of a Renault Clio. From these pages you will find out not only what a catalytic converter looks like, but also that it is attached at one end to an exhaust downpipe and at the other to a silencer.

Whatever it is that you want to find a name for, or whatever name you want to find a picture for, you will find it quickly and easily in the *Visual Dictionary*. Perhaps you need to know where the vamp on a shoe is; or how to tell obovate and lanceolate leaves apart; or what a spiral galaxy looks like; or whether birds have nostrils. With the *Visual Dictionary* at hand, the answers to each of these questions, and thousands more, are readily available.

The *Visual Dictionary* does not just tell you what the names of the different parts of an object are. The photographs, illustrations, and annotations are all specially arranged to help you understand which parts relate to one another and how objects function.

With the *Visual Dictionary* you can find in seconds the words or pictures that you are looking for; or you can simply browse through the pages of the book for your own pleasure. The *Visual Dictionary* is not intended to replace a standard dictionary or conventional encyclopedia, but is instead a stimulating and valuable companion to ordinary reference volumes. Giving you instant access to the language that is used by astronomers and architects, musicians and mechanics, scientists and sportspeople, it is the ideal reference book for specialists and generalists of all ages.

Sections of the VISUAL DICTIONARY

The 14 sections of the *VISUAL DICTIONARY* contain a total of more than 30,000 terms, encompassing a wide range of topics:

•In the first section, THE UNIVERSE, spectacular photographs and illustrations are used to show the names of the stars and planets and to explain the structure of solar systems, galaxies, nebulae, comets, and black holes.

•PREHISTORIC EARTH tells the story in annotations of how our own planet has evolved since its formation. It includes examples of prehistoric flora and fauna, and fascinating dinosaur models—some with parts of the body stripped away to show anatomical sections.

•PLANTS covers a huge range of species—from the familiar to the exotic. In addition to the color photographs of plants included in this section, there is a series of micrographic photographs illustrating plant details—such as pollen grains, spores, and cross-sections of stems and roots— in close-up.

•In the ANIMALS section, skeletons, anatomical diagrams, and different parts of animals' bodies have been meticulously annotated. This section provides a comprehensive guide to the vocabulary of zoological classification and animal physiology.

•The structure of the human body, its parts, and its systems are presented in THE HUMAN BODY. The section includes lifelike, three-dimensional models and the latest false-color images. Clear and authoritative annotations indicate the correct anatomical terms.

•GEOLOGY, GEOGRAPHY, AND METEOROLOGY describes the structure of the Earth—from the inner core to the exosphere—and the physical phenomena—such as volcanoes, rivers, glaciers, and climate—that shape its surface.

•PHYSICS AND CHEMISTRY is a visual journey through the fundamental principles underlying the physical universe, and provides the essential vocabulary of these sciences.

•In RAIL AND ROAD, a wide range of trains, trams and buses, cars, bicycles, and motorcycles are described. Exploded-view photographs show mechanical details with striking clarity.

•SEA AND AIR gives the names for hundreds of parts of ships and airplanes. The section includes civil and fighting craft, both historical and modern.

•THE VISUAL ARTS shows the equipment and materials used by painters, sculptors, printers, and other artists. Well-known compositions have been chosen to illustrate specific artistic techniques and effects.

•ARCHITECTURE includes photographs of exemplary architectural models and illustrates dozens of additional features such as columns, domes, and arches.

•MUSIC provides a visual introduction to the special language of music and musical instruments. It includes clearly annotated photographs of each of the major groups of traditional instruments—brass, woodwind, strings, and percussion—together with modern electronic instruments.

•The SPORTS section is a guide to the playing areas, formations, equipment, and techniques needed for many of today's most popular sports.

•In THE MODERN WORLD, items that are a familiar part of our daily lives are taken apart to reveal their inner workings and give access to the language used by their manufacturers. It also includes systems and concepts, such as the internet, that increasingly influence our 21st century world.

THE UNIVERSE

Anatomy of the Universe

Fireball of rapidly expanding, extremely hot gas lasting about one million years

THE UNIVERSE CONTAINS EVERYTHING that exists, from the tiniest subatomic particles to galactic superclusters (the largest structures known). Nobody knows how big the Universe is, but astronomers estimate that it contains about 100 billion galaxies, each comprising an average of 100 billion stars. The most widely accepted theory about the origin of the Universe is the Big Bang theory, which states that the Universe came into being in a huge explosion—the Big Bang—that took place between 10 and 20 billion years ago. The Universe initially consisted of a very hot, dense fireball of expanding, cooling gas. After about one million years, the gas probably began to condense into localized clumps called protogalaxies. During the next five billion years, the protogalaxies continued condensing, forming galaxies in which stars were being born. Today, billions of years later, the Universe as a whole is still expanding, although there are localized areas in which objects are held together by gravity; for example, many galaxies are found in clusters. The Big Bang theory is supported by the discovery of faint, cool background radiation coming evenly from all directions. This radiation is believed to be the remnant of the radiation produced by the Big Bang. Small "ripples" in the temperature of the cosmic background radiation are thought to be evidence of slight fluctuations in the density of the early Universe, which resulted in the formation of galaxies. Astronomers do not yet know if the Universe is "closed," which means it will eventually stop expanding and begin to contract, or if it is "open," which means it will continue expanding forever.

COMPUTER-ENHANCED MICROWAVE MAP OF COSMIC BACKGROUND RADIATION

Pink indicates "warm ripples" in background radiation

Pale blue indicates "cool ripples" in background radiation

Deep blue indicates background radiation corresponding to -454.5°F (remnant of the Big Bang)

Red and pink band indicates radiation from our galaxy

Low-energy microwave radiation corresponding to about -454°F

High-energy gamma radiation corresponding to about 5,400°F

ORIGIN AND EXPANSION OF THE UNIVERSE

*Quasar (probably the center
of a galaxy containing a
massive black hole)*

*Universe one to five
billion years after
Big Bang*

*Protogalaxy
(condensing gas cloud)*

*Galaxy spinning and
flattening to become
spiral shaped*

*Dark cloud
(dust and gas
condensing
to form a
protogalaxy)*

*Elliptical
galaxy in
which stars
form rapidly*

*Universe today
(10–20 billion years
after Big Bang)*

*Cluster of
galaxies held
together by gravity*

*Elliptical galaxy
containing old stars
and little gas and dust*

Irregular galaxy

*Spiral galaxy
containing gas,
dust, and young stars*

OBJECTS IN THE UNIVERSE

**CLUSTER OF
GALAXIES IN VIRGO**

**COLOR-ENHANCED IMAGE
OF 3C273 (QUASAR)**

**NGC 4406
(ELLIPTICAL GALAXY)**

**NGC 5256
(SPIRAL GALAXY)**

**NGC 6822
(IRREGULAR GALAXY)**

**THE ROSETTE NEBULA
(EMISSION NEBULA)**

**THE JEWEL BOX
(STAR CLUSTER)**

**THE SUN
(MAIN SEQUENCE STAR)**

EARTH

THE MOON

Galaxies

SOMBRERO,
A SPIRAL GALAXY

A GALAXY IS A HUGE MASS OF STARS, nebulae, and interstellar material. The smallest galaxies contain about 100,000 stars, while the largest contain up to 3,000 billion stars. There are three main types of galaxy, classified according to their shape: elliptical, which are oval shaped; spiral, which have arms spiraling outward from a central bulge; and irregular, which have no obvious shape. Sometimes, the shape of a galaxy is distorted by a collision with another galaxy. Quasars (quasi-stellar objects) are thought to be galactic nuclei but are so far away that their exact nature is still uncertain. They are compact, highly luminous objects in the outer reaches of the known Universe; while the farthest known "ordinary" galaxies are about 10 billion light-years away, the farthest known quasar is about 15 billion light-years away. Active galaxies, such as Seyfert galaxies and radio galaxies, emit intense radiation. In a Seyfert galaxy, this radiation comes from the galactic nucleus; in a radio galaxy, it also comes from huge lobes on either side of the galaxy. The radiation from active galaxies and quasars is thought to be caused by black holes (see pp. 28-29).

**OPTICAL IMAGE OF NGC 4486
(ELLIPTICAL GALAXY)**

Globular cluster containing very old red giants

Central region containing old red giants

Less densely populated region

Neighboring galaxy

OPTICAL IMAGE OF LARGE MAGELLANIC CLOUD (IRREGULAR GALAXY)

Tarantula Nebula

Dust cloud obscuring light from stars

Emission nebula

Light from stars

OPTICAL IMAGE OF NGC 2997 (SPIRAL GALAXY)

Glowing nebula in spiral arm

Spiral arm containing young stars

Galactic nucleus containing old stars

Dust in spiral arm reflecting blue light from hot young stars

Hot, ionized hydrogen gas emitting red light

Dust lane

OPTICAL IMAGE OF CENTAURUS A (RADIO GALAXY)

Dust lane crossing elliptical galaxy

Galactic nucleus containing powerful source of radiation

Light from old stars

COLOR-ENHANCED RADIO IMAGE OF CENTAURUS A

Radio lobe

Red indicates high-intensity radio waves

Blue indicates low-intensity radio waves

Radiation from galactic nucleus

Outline of optical image of Centaurus A

Radio lobe

Yellow indicates medium-intensity radio waves

COLOR-ENHANCED RADIO IMAGE OF 3C273 (QUASAR)

Radiation from jet of high-energy particles moving away from quasar

Quasar nucleus

White indicates high-intensity radio waves

Blue indicates low-intensity radio waves

OPTICAL IMAGE OF NGC 1566 (SEYFERT GALAXY)

Nebula in spiral arm

Compact nucleus emitting intense radiation

Spiral arm

COLOR-ENHANCED OPTICAL IMAGE OF NGC 5754 (TWO COLLIDING GALAXIES)

Blue indicates low-intensity radiation

Red indicates medium-intensity radiation

Spiral arm distorted by gravitational influence of smaller galaxy

Large spiral galaxy

Smaller galaxy colliding with larger galaxy

Yellow indicates high-intensity radiation

The Milky Way

VIEW TOWARD GALACTIC CENTER

THE MILKY WAY IS THE NAME GIVEN TO THE FAINT BAND OF LIGHT that stretches across the night sky. This light comes from stars and nebulae in our galaxy, known as the Milky Way Galaxy or simply as "the Galaxy." The Galaxy is shaped like a spiral, with a dense central bulge that is encircled by four arms spiraling outward and surrounded by a less dense halo. We cannot see the spiral shape because our Solar System is in one of the spiral arms, the Orion Arm (also called the Local Arm). From our position, the center of the Galaxy is completely obscured by dust clouds; as a result, optical maps give only a limited view of the Galaxy. However, a more complete picture can be obtained by studying radio, infrared, and other radiation. The central bulge of the Galaxy is a relatively small, dense sphere that contains mainly older red and yellow stars. The halo is a less dense region in which the oldest stars are situated; some of these stars may be as old as the Galaxy itself (possibly 15 billion years). The spiral arms contain mainly hot, young, blue stars, as well as nebulae (clouds of dust and gas, inside which stars are born). The Galaxy is vast—about 100,000 light-years across (a light-year is about 5,879 billion miles); in comparison, the Solar System seems small, at about 12 light-hours across (about 8 billion miles). The entire Galaxy is rotating in space, although the inner stars travel faster than those further out. The Sun, which is about two-thirds out from the center, completes one lap of the Galaxy about every 220 million years.

PANORAMIC OPTICAL MAP OF OUR GALAXY AND NEARBY GALAXIES

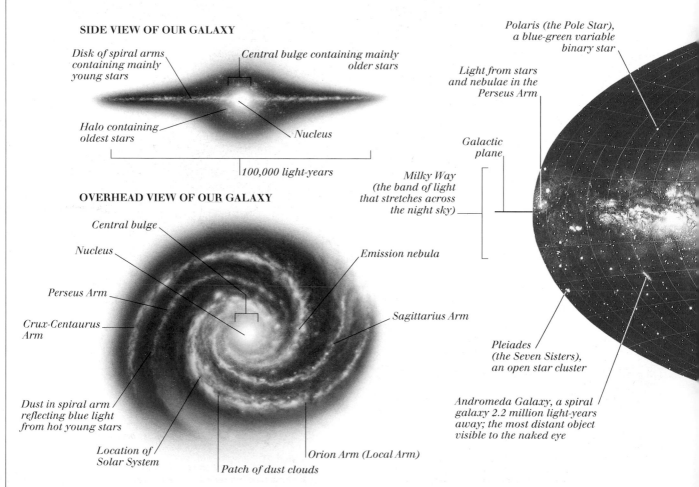

SIDE VIEW OF OUR GALAXY

Disk of spiral arms containing mainly young stars

Central bulge containing mainly older stars

Halo containing oldest stars

Nucleus

100,000 light-years

OVERHEAD VIEW OF OUR GALAXY

Central bulge

Nucleus

Perseus Arm

Crux-Centaurus Arm

Dust in spiral arm reflecting blue light from hot young stars

Location of Solar System

Patch of dust clouds

Emission nebula

Sagittarius Arm

Orion Arm (Local Arm)

Polaris (the Pole Star), a blue-green variable binary star

Light from stars and nebulae in the Perseus Arm

Galactic plane

Milky Way (the band of light that stretches across the night sky)

Pleiades (the Seven Sisters), an open star cluster

Andromeda Galaxy, a spiral galaxy 2.2 million light-years away; the most distant object visible to the naked eye

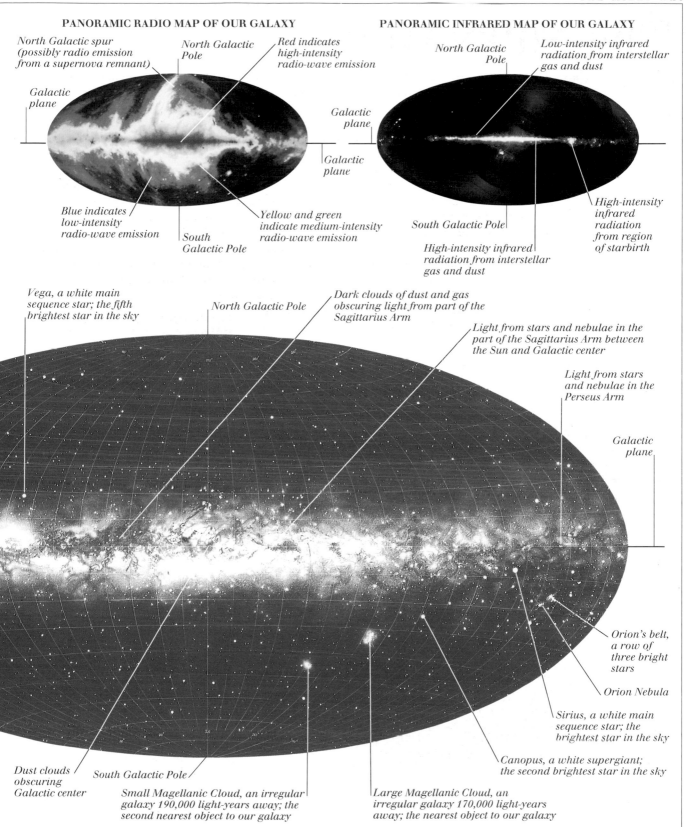

PANORAMIC RADIO MAP OF OUR GALAXY

North Galactic spur (possibly radio emission from a supernova remnant)

North Galactic Pole

Red indicates high-intensity radio-wave emission

Galactic plane

Galactic plane

Galactic plane

Blue indicates low-intensity radio-wave emission

South Galactic Pole

Yellow and green indicate medium-intensity radio-wave emission

PANORAMIC INFRARED MAP OF OUR GALAXY

North Galactic Pole

Low-intensity infrared radiation from interstellar gas and dust

High-intensity infrared radiation from region of starbirth

South Galactic Pole

High-intensity infrared radiation from interstellar gas and dust

Vega, a white main sequence star; the fifth brightest star in the sky

North Galactic Pole

Dark clouds of dust and gas obscuring light from part of the Sagittarius Arm

Light from stars and nebulae in the part of the Sagittarius Arm between the Sun and Galactic center

Light from stars and nebulae in the Perseus Arm

Galactic plane

Orion's belt, a row of three bright stars

Orion Nebula

Sirius, a white main sequence star; the brightest star in the sky

Canopus, a white supergiant; the second brightest star in the sky

Dust clouds obscuring Galactic center

South Galactic Pole

Small Magellanic Cloud, an irregular galaxy 190,000 light-years away; the second nearest object to our galaxy

Large Magellanic Cloud, an irregular galaxy 170,000 light-years away; the nearest object to our galaxy

Nebulae and star clusters

**HODGE 11, A
GLOBULAR CLUSTER**

A NEBULA IS A CLOUD OF DUST AND GAS inside a galaxy. Nebulae become visible if the gas glows or if the cloud reflects starlight or obscures light from more distant objects. Emission nebulae shine because their gas emits light when it is stimulated by radiation from hot young stars. Reflection nebulae shine because their dust reflects light from stars in or around the nebula. Dark nebulae appear as silhouettes because they block light from shining nebulae or stars behind them. Two types of nebula are associated with dying stars: planetary nebulae and supernova remnants. Both consist of expanding shells of gas that were once the outer layers of a star. A planetary nebula is a gas shell drifting away from a dying stellar core. A supernova remnant is a gas shell moving away from a stellar core at great speed following a violent explosion called a supernova (see pp. 26-27). Stars are often found in groups known as clusters. Open clusters are loose groups of a few thousand young stars that were born in the same cloud and are drifting apart. Globular clusters are densely packed, roughly spherical groups of hundreds of thousands of older stars.

TRIFID NEBULA (EMISSION NEBULA)

Reflection nebula

Emission nebula

Dust lane

Starbirth region (area in which dust and gas combine to form stars)

**PLEIADES (OPEN STAR CLUSTER)
WITH A REFLECTION NEBULA**

Wisps of dust and hydrogen gas remaining from cloud in which stars formed

Young star in an open cluster of 300–500 stars

Reflection nebula

HORSEHEAD NEBULA (DARK NEBULA)

Glowing filament of hot, ionized hydrogen gas

Alnitak (star in Orion's belt)

Dust lane

Emission nebula

Star near southern end of Orion's belt

Emission nebula

Horsehead Nebula

Reflection nebula

Dark nebula obscuring light from distant stars

ORION NEBULA (DIFFUSE EMISSION NEBULA)

Glowing cloud of dust and hydrogen gas forming part of Orion Nebula

Gas cloud emitting light because of ultraviolet radiation from the four young Trapezium stars

Dust cloud

Trapezium (group of four young stars)

Green light from hot, ionized oxygen gas

Glowing filament of hot, ionized hydrogen gas

Red light from hot, ionized hydrogen gas

VELA SUPERNOVA REMNANT

Supernova remnant (gas shell consisting of outer layers of star thrown off in supernova explosion)

Hydrogen gas emitting red light due to being heated by supernova explosion

Glowing filament of hot, ionized hydrogen gas

HELIX NEBULA (PLANETARY NEBULA)

Planetary nebula (gas shell expanding outward from dying stellar core)

Stellar core at a temperature of about 180,000°F

Red light from hot, ionized hydrogen gas

Blue-green light from hot, ionized oxygen and nitrogen gases

Stars of northern skies

WHEN YOU LOOK AT THE NORTHERN SKY, you look away from the densely populated Galactic center, so the northern sky generally appears less bright than the southern sky (see pp. 20-21). Among the best-known sights in the northern sky are the constellations Ursa Major (the Great Bear) and Orion. Some ancient civilizations believed that the stars were fixed to a celestial sphere surrounding the Earth, and modern maps of the sky are based on a similar idea. The North and South Poles of this imaginary celestial sphere are directly above the North and South Poles of the Earth, at the points where the Earth's axis of rotation intersects the sphere. The celestial North Pole is at the center of the map shown here, and Polaris (the Pole Star) lies very close to it. The celestial equator marks a projection of the Earth's equator on the sphere. The ecliptic marks the path of the Sun across the sky as the Earth orbits the Sun. The Moon and planets move against the background of the stars because the stars are much more distant; the nearest star outside the Solar System (Proxima Centauri) is more than 50,000 times farther away than the planet Jupiter.

ORION

VISIBLE STARS IN THE NORTHERN SKY

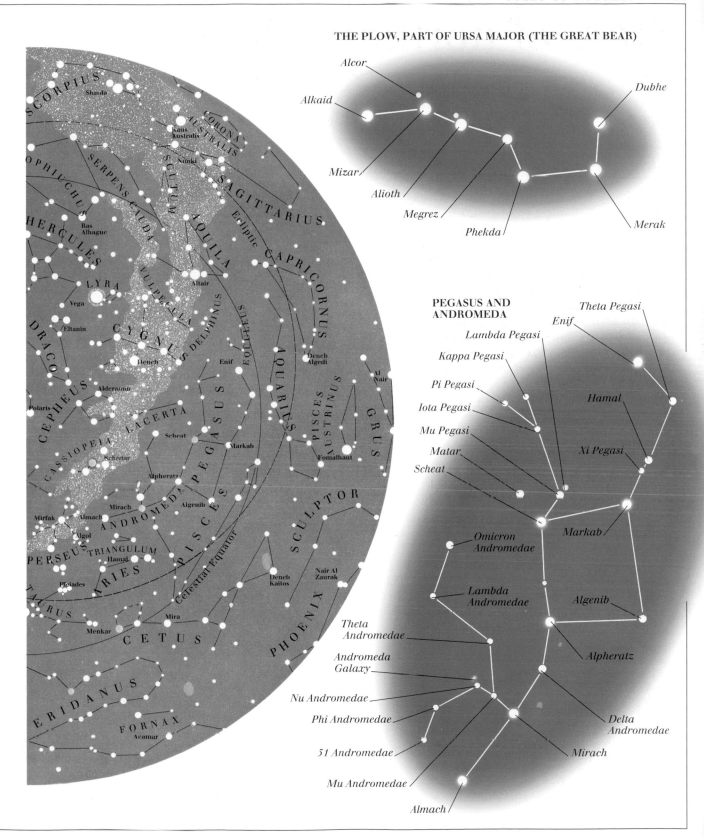

THE PLOW, PART OF URSA MAJOR (THE GREAT BEAR)

Alcor
Alkaid
Dubhe
Mizar
Alioth
Megrez
Phekda
Merak

PEGASUS AND ANDROMEDA

Theta Pegasi
Enif
Lambda Pegasi
Kappa Pegasi
Pi Pegasi
Hamal
Iota Pegasi
Mu Pegasi
Xi Pegasi
Matar
Scheat
Markab
Omicron Andromedae
Lambda Andromedae
Algenib
Theta Andromedae
Alpheratz
Andromeda Galaxy
Nu Andromedae
Delta Andromedae
Phi Andromedae
Mirach
51 Andromedae
Mu Andromedae
Almach

SCORPIUS
Shaula
CORONA
AUSTRALIS
Kaus Australis
SAGITTARIUS
Nunki
OPHIUCHUS
SERPENS CAUDA
SCUTUM
AQUILA
CAPRICORNUS
Ecliptic
Ras Alhague
HERCULES
Altair
VULPECULA
DELPHINUS
Deneb Algedi
LYRA
Vega
EQUULEUS
AQUARIUS
Al Nair
Eltanin
CYGNUS
Enif
PISCES AUSTRINUS
GRUS
DRACO
Deneb
PEGASUS
CEPHEUS
Alderamin
LACERTA
Markab
Fomalhaut
Polaris
Scheat
CASSIOPEIA
Schedar
Alpheratz
SCULPTOR
Mirach
Aigenib
Mirfak
Almach
ANDROMEDA
PISCES
Algol
Nair Al Zaurak
PERSEUS
TRIANGULUM
Hamal
PHOENIX
ARIES
Pleiades
Deneb Kaitos
TAURUS
Mira
Menkar
CETUS
Celestial Equator
ERIDANUS
FORNAX
Acamar

Stars of southern skies

WHEN YOU LOOK AT THE SOUTHERN SKY, you look toward the Galactic center, which has a huge population of stars. As a result, the Milky Way appears brighter in the southern sky than in the northern sky (see pp. 18-19). The southern sky is rich in nebulae and star clusters. It contains the Large and Small Magellanic Clouds, which are the two nearest galaxies to our own. Stars make fixed patterns in the sky called constellations. The constellations, however, are only apparent groupings of stars, because the distances to the stars in a constellation may vary enormously. The shapes of constellations may change over many thousands of years because of the relative motions of stars. The apparent movement of entire constellations across the sky is due to the Earth's motion in space. The daily rotation of the Earth causes the constellations to move across the sky from east to west, and the orbit of the Earth around the Sun causes different areas of sky to be visible in different seasons. The visibility of areas of sky also depends on the location of the observer. For instance, stars near the celestial equator may be seen from either hemisphere at some time during the year, while stars close to the celestial poles (the celestial South Pole is at the center of the map shown here) can never be seen from the opposite hemisphere.

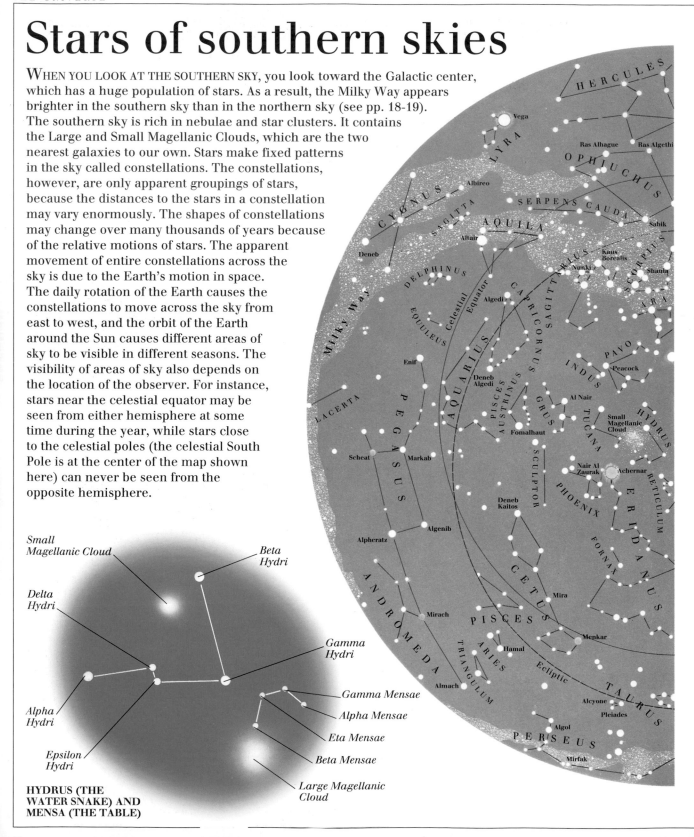

HYDRUS (THE WATER SNAKE) AND MENSA (THE TABLE)

Small Magellanic Cloud

Beta Hydri

Delta Hydri

Gamma Hydri

Gamma Mensae

Alpha Mensae

Eta Mensae

Beta Mensae

Alpha Hydri

Epsilon Hydri

Large Magellanic Cloud

VISIBLE STARS IN THE SOUTHERN SKY

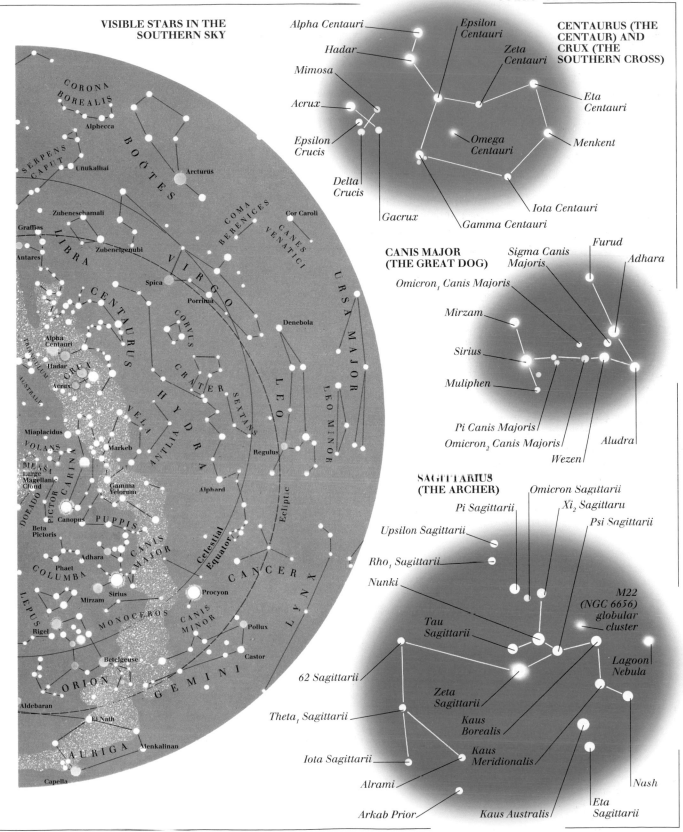

CENTAURUS (THE CENTAUR) AND CRUX (THE SOUTHERN CROSS)

Alpha Centauri
Epsilon Centauri
Hadar
Zeta Centauri
Mimosa
Eta Centauri
Acrux
Omega Centauri
Menkent
Epsilon Crucis
Delta Crucis
Gacrux
Iota Centauri
Gamma Centauri

CANIS MAJOR (THE GREAT DOG)

Sigma Canis Majoris
Furud
Adhara
Omicron₁ Canis Majoris
Mirzam
Sirius
Muliphen
Pi Canis Majoris
Omicron₂ Canis Majoris
Wezen
Aludra

SAGITTARIUS (THE ARCHER)

Pi Sagittarii
Omicron Sagittarii
Xi₂ Sagittarii
Upsilon Sagittarii
Psi Sagittarii
Rho₁ Sagittarii
Nunki
M22 (NGC 6656) globular cluster
Tau Sagittarii
Lagoon Nebula
62 Sagittarii
Zeta Sagittarii
Theta₁ Sagittarii
Kaus Borealis
Iota Sagittarii
Kaus Meridionalis
Alrami
Arkab Prior
Kaus Australis
Eta Sagittarii
Nash

CORONA BOREALIS
Alphecca
SERPENS CAPUT
Unukalhai
BOÖTES
Arcturus
Zubeneschamali
COMA BERENICES
Cor Caroli
Graffias
CANES VENATICI
Antares
LIBRA
Zubenelgenubi
VIRGO
URSA MAJOR
Spica
Porrima
Alpha Centauri
CENTAURUS
Denebola
Hadar
CORVUS
LEO
Acrux
CRUX
CRATER
SEXTANS
LEO MINOR
TRIANGULUM AUSTRALE
HYDRA
VELA
Miaplacidus
ANTLIA
Regulus
VOLANS
Markeb
MENSA
Large Magellanic Cloud
CARINA
Gamma Velorum
Alphard
Ecliptic
DORADO
PICTOR
PUPPIS
Beta Pictoris
Canopus
CANIS MAJOR
Celestial Equator
CANCER
LYNX
Adhara
Phact
COLUMBA
Mirzam
Sirius
Procyon
MONOCEROS
CANIS MINOR
Pollux
LEPUS
Rigel
Castor
Betelgeuse
ORION
GEMINI
Aldebaran
El Nath
Menkalinan
AURIGA
Capella

21

Stars

OPEN STAR CLUSTER AND DUST CLOUD

STARS ARE BODIES of hot glowing gas that are born in nebulae (see pp. 24-27). They vary enormously in size, mass, and temperature: diameters range from about 450 times smaller to over 1,000 times bigger than that of the Sun; masses range from about a twentieth to over 50 solar masses; and surface temperatures range from about 5,500°F to over 90,000°F. The color of a star is determined by its temperature: the hottest stars are blue and the coolest are red. The Sun, with a surface temperature of 10,000°F, is between these extremes and appears yellow. The energy emitted by a shining star is produced by nuclear fusion in the star's core. The brightness of a star is measured in magnitudes—the brighter the star, the lower its magnitude. There are two types of magnitude: apparent magnitude, which is the brightness seen from Earth, and absolute magnitude, which is the brightness that would be seen from a standard distance of 10 parsecs (32.6 light-years). The light emitted by a star may be split to form a spectrum containing a series of dark lines (absorption lines). The patterns of lines indicate the presence of particular chemical elements, enabling astronomers to deduce the composition of the star's atmosphere. The magnitude and spectral type (color) of stars may be plotted on a graph called a Hertzsprung-Russell diagram, which shows that stars tend to fall into several well-defined groups. The principal groups are main sequence stars (those which are fusing hydrogen to form helium), giants, supergiants, and white dwarfs.

STAR SIZES

Red giant (diameters between about 10 million and 100 million miles)

The Sun (main sequence star with diameter about 870,000 miles)

White dwarf (diameters between about 2,000 and 30,000 miles)

ENERGY EMISSION FROM THE SUN

Nuclear fusion in core produces gamma rays and neutrinos

Neutrinos travel to Earth directly from Sun's core in about 8 minutes

Lower-energy radiation travels to Earth in about 8 minutes

Earth

Sun

High-energy radiation (gamma rays) loses energy while traveling to surface over 2 million years

Lower-energy radiation (mainly ultraviolet, infrared, and light rays) leaves surface

STAR MAGNITUDES

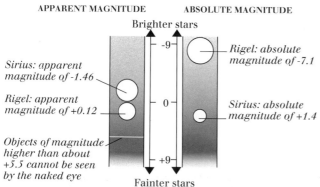

APPARENT MAGNITUDE

ABSOLUTE MAGNITUDE

Brighter stars

-9

0

+9

Fainter stars

Sirius: apparent magnitude of -1.46

Rigel: apparent magnitude of +0.12

Objects of magnitude higher than about +5.5 cannot be seen by the naked eye

Rigel: absolute magnitude of -7.1

Sirius: absolute magnitude of +1.4

NUCLEAR FUSION IN MAIN SEQUENCE STARS LIKE THE SUN

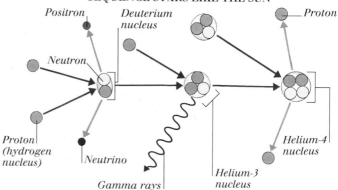

Positron

Deuterium nucleus

Proton

Neutron

Proton (hydrogen nucleus)

Neutrino

Gamma rays

Helium-3 nucleus

Helium-4 nucleus

HERTZSPRUNG-RUSSELL DIAGRAM

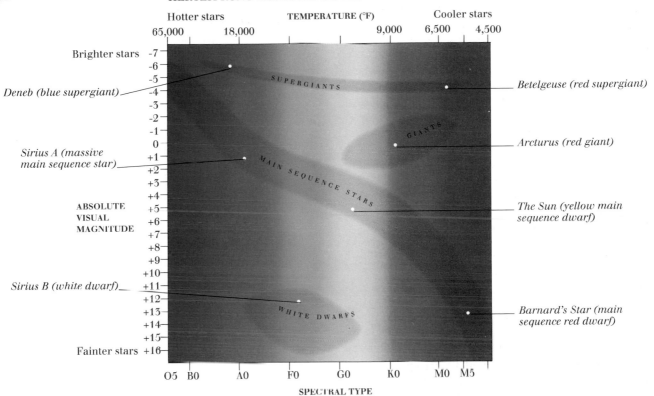

Hotter stars   TEMPERATURE (°F)   Cooler stars

65,000   18,000   9,000   6,500   4,500

Brighter stars

SUPERGIANTS

Deneb (blue supergiant)

Betelgeuse (red supergiant)

GIANTS

Arcturus (red giant)

Sirius A (massive main sequence star)

MAIN SEQUENCE STARS

ABSOLUTE VISUAL MAGNITUDE

The Sun (yellow main sequence dwarf)

Sirius B (white dwarf)

WHITE DWARFS

Barnard's Star (main sequence red dwarf)

Fainter stars

O5   B0   A0   F0   G0   K0   M0   M5

SPECTRAL TYPE

STELLAR SPECTRAL ABSORPTION LINES

Calcium line   Hydrogen gamma line   Hydrogen beta line   Helium line   Sodium lines   Hydrogen alpha line

STAR OF SPECTRAL TYPE A (e.g., SIRIUS)

STAR OF SPECTRAL TYPE G (e.g., THE SUN)

Hydrogen beta line   Magnesium lines   Sodium lines   Hydrogen alpha line

Small stars

REGION OF STAR FORMATION IN ORION

SMALL STARS HAVE A MASS of up to about one and a half times that of the Sun. They begin to form when a region of higher density in a nebula condenses into a huge globule of gas and dust that contracts under its own gravity. Within a globule, regions of condensing matter heat up and begin to glow, forming protostars. If a protostar contains enough matter, the central temperature reaches about 27 million °F. At this temperature, nuclear reactions in which hydrogen fuses to form helium can start. This process releases energy, which prevents the star from contracting further, and also causes it to shine; it is now a main sequence star. A star of about one solar mass remains in the main sequence for about 10 billion years, until the hydrogen in the star's core has been converted into helium. The helium core then contracts again, and nuclear reactions continue in a shell around the core. The core becomes hot enough for helium to fuse to form carbon, while the outer layers of the star expand, cool, and shine less brightly. The expanding star is known as a red giant. When the helium in the core runs out, the outer layers of the star may drift off as an expanding gas shell called a planetary nebula. The remaining core (about 80 percent of the original star) is now in its final stages. It becomes a white dwarf star that gradually cools and dims. When it finally stops shining altogether, the dead star will become a black dwarf.

STRUCTURE OF A MAIN SEQUENCE STAR

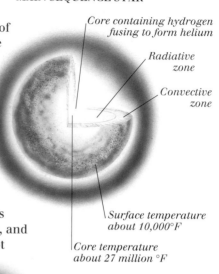

Core containing hydrogen fusing to form helium

Radiative zone

Convective zone

Surface temperature about 10,000°F

Core temperature about 27 million °F

STRUCTURE OF A NEBULA

Young main sequence star

Dense region of dust and gas (mainly hydrogen) condensing under gravity to form globules

Hot, ionized hydrogen gas emitting red light due to stimulation by radiation from hot young stars

Dark globule of dust and gas (mainly hydrogen) contracting to form protostars

LIFE OF A SMALL STAR OF ABOUT ONE SOLAR MASS

Cool cloud of gas (mainly hydrogen) and dust

Dense globule condensing to form protostars

NEBULA

Glowing ball of gas (mainly hydrogen)

Natal cocoon (shell of dust blown away by radiation from protostar)

PROTOSTAR
Duration: 50 million years

About 870,000 miles

Star producing energy by nuclear fusion in core

MAIN SEQUENCE STAR
Duration: 10 billion years

STRUCTURE OF A RED GIANT

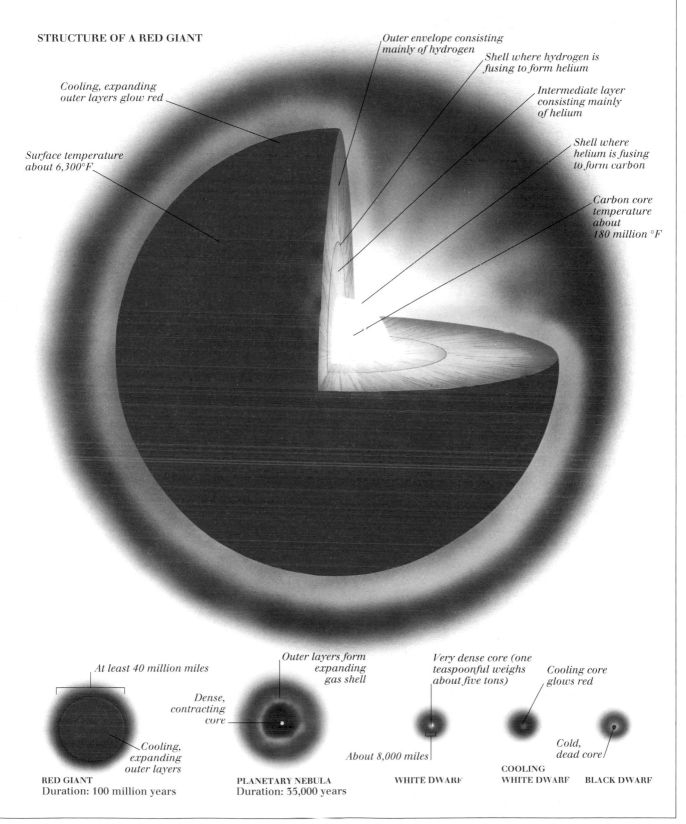

Outer envelope consisting mainly of hydrogen

Shell where hydrogen is fusing to form helium

Intermediate layer consisting mainly of helium

Shell where helium is fusing to form carbon

Carbon core temperature about 180 million °F

Cooling, expanding outer layers glow red

Surface temperature about 6,300°F

At least 40 million miles

Dense, contracting core

Cooling, expanding outer layers

RED GIANT
Duration: 100 million years

Outer layers form expanding gas shell

PLANETARY NEBULA
Duration: 35,000 years

Very dense core (one teaspoonful weighs about five tons)

About 8,000 miles

WHITE DWARF

Cooling core glows red

COOLING WHITE DWARF

Cold, dead core

BLACK DWARF

Massive stars

MASSIVE STARS HAVE A MASS AT LEAST THREE TIMES that of the Sun, and some stars are as massive as about 50 Suns. A massive star evolves in a similar way to a small star until it reaches the main sequence stage (see pp. 24-25). During the main sequence, a star shines steadily until the hydrogen in its core has fused to form helium. This process takes billions of years in a small star, but only millions of years in a massive star. A massive star then becomes a red supergiant, which initially consists of a helium core surrounded by outer layers of cooling, expanding gas. Over the next few million years, a series of nuclear reactions form different elements in shells around an iron core. The core eventually collapses in less than a second, causing a massive explosion called a supernova, in which a shock wave blows away the outer layers of the star. Supernovae shine brighter than an entire galaxy for a short time. Sometimes, the core survives the supernova explosion. If the surviving core is between about one and a half and three solar masses, it contracts to become a tiny, dense neutron star. If the core is considerably greater than three solar masses, it contracts to become a black hole (see pp. 28-29).

SUPERNOVA

TARANTULA NEBULA BEFORE SUPERNOVA

STRUCTURE OF A RED SUPERGIANT

Outer envelope consisting mainly of hydrogen

Layer consisting mainly of helium

Layer consisting mainly of carbon

Layer consisting mainly of oxygen

Layer consisting mainly of silicon

Shell of hydrogen fusing to form helium

Shell of helium fusing to form carbon

Shell of carbon fusing to form oxygen

Shell of oxygen fusing to form silicon

Shell of silicon fusing to form iron core

Surface temperature about 5,500°F

Cooling, expanding outer layers glow red

Core of mainly iron at a temperature of 5.4–9 billion °F

LIFE OF A MASSIVE STAR OF ABOUT 10 SOLAR MASSES

Dense globule condensing to form protostars

Cool cloud of gas (mainly hydrogen) and dust

NEBULA

Glowing ball of gas (mainly hydrogen)

Natal cocoon (shell of dust blown away by radiation from protostar)

PROTOSTAR
Duration: a few hundred thousand years

About 2 million miles

Star producing energy by nuclear fusion in core

MAIN SEQUENCE STAR
Duration: 10 million years

FEATURES OF A SUPERNOVA

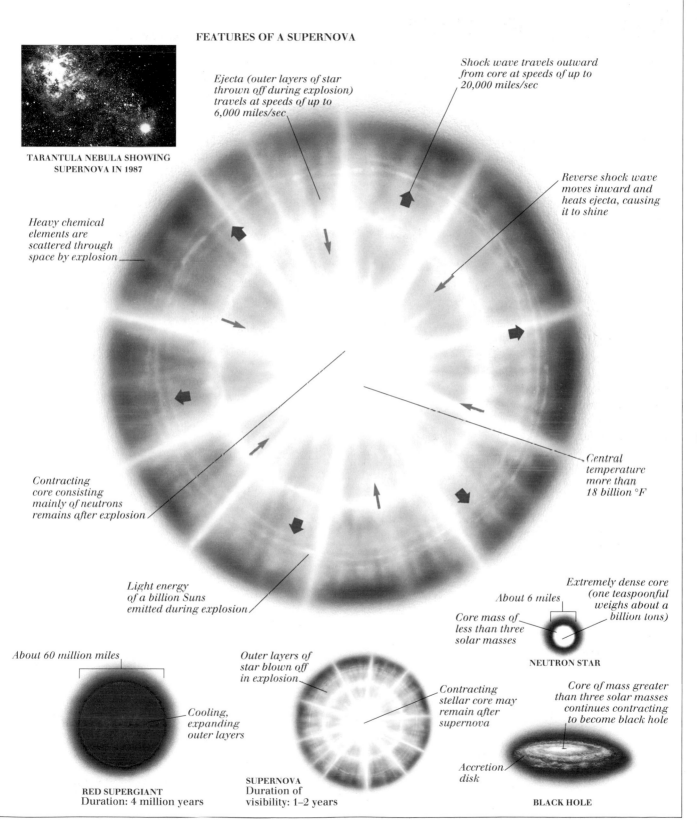

TARANTULA NEBULA SHOWING SUPERNOVA IN 1987

Ejecta (outer layers of star thrown off during explosion) travels at speeds of up to 6,000 miles/sec

Shock wave travels outward from core at speeds of up to 20,000 miles/sec

Reverse shock wave moves inward and heats ejecta, causing it to shine

Heavy chemical elements are scattered through space by explosion

Contracting core consisting mainly of neutrons remains after explosion

Central temperature more than 18 billion °F

Light energy of a billion Suns emitted during explosion

About 60 million miles

Cooling, expanding outer layers

RED SUPERGIANT
Duration: 4 million years

Outer layers of star blown off in explosion

Contracting stellar core may remain after supernova

SUPERNOVA
Duration of visibility: 1–2 years

About 6 miles

Core mass of less than three solar masses

Extremely dense core (one teaspoonful weighs about a billion tons)

NEUTRON STAR

Core of mass greater than three solar masses continues contracting to become black hole

Accretion disk

BLACK HOLE

Neutron stars and black holes

NEUTRON STARS AND BLACK HOLES form from the stellar cores that remain after stars have exploded as supernovae (see pp. 26-27). If the remaining core is between about one and a half and three solar masses, it contracts to form a neutron star. If the remaining core is considerably greater than about three solar masses, it contracts to form a black hole. Neutron stars are typically only about six miles in diameter and consist almost entirely of subatomic particles called neutrons. These stars are so dense that a teaspoonful would weigh about a billion tons. Neutron stars are observed as pulsars, so-called because they rotate rapidly and emit two beams of radio waves, which sweep across the sky and are detected as short pulses. Black holes are characterized by their extremely strong gravity, which is so powerful that not even light can escape; as a result, black holes are invisible. However, they may be detected if they have a close companion star. The gravity of the black hole pulls gas from the other star, forming an accretion disk that spirals around the black hole at high speed, heating up and emitting radiation. Eventually, the matter spirals in to cross the event horizon (the boundary of the black hole), finally disappearing from the visible Universe.

X-ray emission from pulsar (neutron star rotating 30 times each second)

X-ray emission from center of nebula

X-RAY IMAGE OF THE CRAB NEBULA (SUPERNOVA REMNANT)

PULSAR (ROTATING NEUTRON STAR)

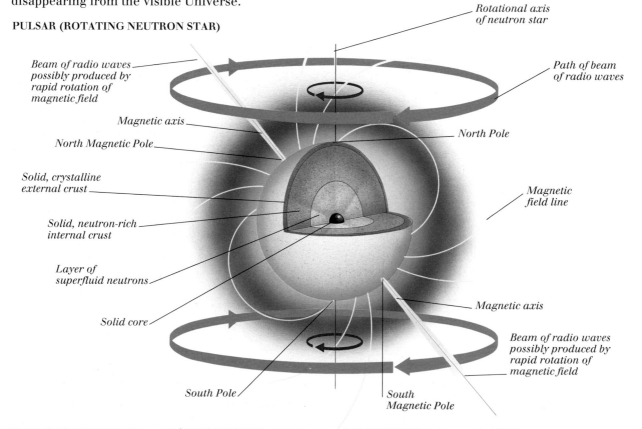

Rotational axis of neutron star

Beam of radio waves possibly produced by rapid rotation of magnetic field

Path of beam of radio waves

Magnetic axis

North Magnetic Pole

North Pole

Solid, crystalline external crust

Magnetic field line

Solid, neutron-rich internal crust

Layer of superfluid neutrons

Solid core

Magnetic axis

Beam of radio waves possibly produced by rapid rotation of magnetic field

South Pole

South Magnetic Pole

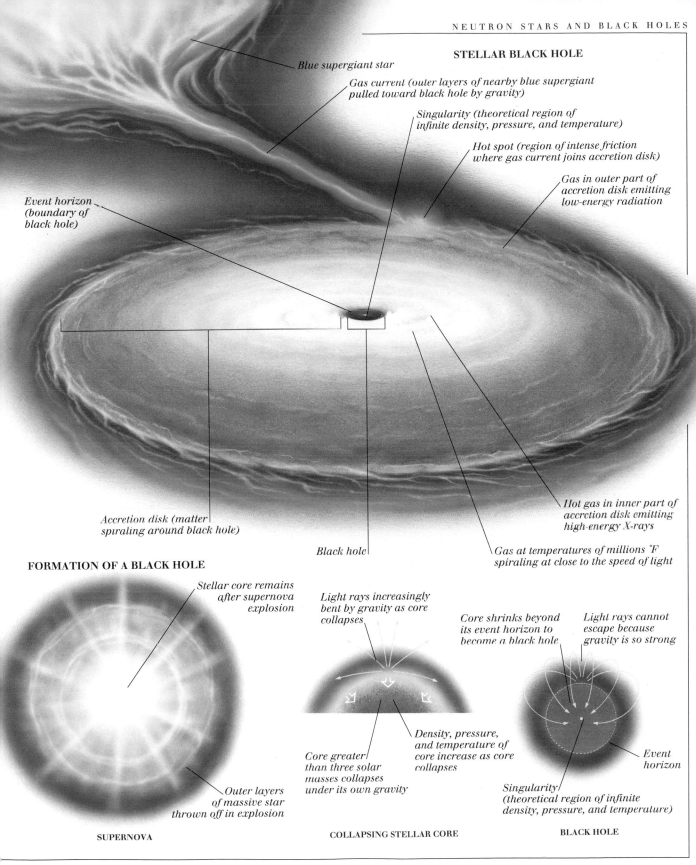

STELLAR BLACK HOLE

Blue supergiant star

Gas current (outer layers of nearby blue supergiant pulled toward black hole by gravity)

Singularity (theoretical region of infinite density, pressure, and temperature)

Hot spot (region of intense friction where gas current joins accretion disk)

Gas in outer part of accretion disk emitting low-energy radiation

Event horizon (boundary of black hole)

Hot gas in inner part of accretion disk emitting high-energy X-rays

Accretion disk (matter spiraling around black hole)

Black hole

Gas at temperatures of millions °F spiraling at close to the speed of light

FORMATION OF A BLACK HOLE

Stellar core remains after supernova explosion

Light rays increasingly bent by gravity as core collapses

Core shrinks beyond its event horizon to become a black hole

Light rays cannot escape because gravity is so strong

Density, pressure, and temperature of core increase as core collapses

Event horizon

Core greater than three solar masses collapses under its own gravity

Outer layers of massive star thrown off in explosion

Singularity (theoretical region of infinite density, pressure, and temperature)

SUPERNOVA

COLLAPSING STELLAR CORE

BLACK HOLE

The Solar System

THE SUN

THE SOLAR SYSTEM consists of a central star (the Sun) and the bodies that orbit it. These bodies include nine planets and their 61 known moons, asteroids, comets, and meteoroids. The Solar System also contains interplanetary gas and dust. Most of the planets fall into two groups: four small rocky planets near the Sun (Mercury, Venus, Earth, and Mars), and four planets farther out, the gas giants (Jupiter, Saturn, Uranus, and Neptune). Pluto belongs to neither group—it is very small, solid, and icy. Pluto is the outermost planet, except when it passes briefly inside Neptune's orbit. Between the rocky planets and gas giants is the asteroid belt, which contains thousands of chunks of rock orbiting the Sun. Most of the bodies in the Solar System move around the Sun in elliptical orbits located in a thin disk around the Sun's equator. All the planets orbit the Sun in the same direction (counterclockwise when viewed from above) and all but Venus, Uranus, and Pluto also spin around their axes in this direction. Moons also spin as they, in turn, orbit their planets. The entire Solar System orbits the center of our galaxy, the Milky Way (see pp. 14-15).

Perihelion (orbital point closest to Sun)

Sun

Elliptical orbit

Planet orbiting Sun

Direction of planetary rotation

Aphelion (orbital point farthest from Sun)

Aphelion of Neptune: 2,819 million miles

ORBITS OF INNER PLANETS

Average orbital speed of Venus: 21.8 miles/sec

Average orbital speed of Mercury: 29.8 miles/sec

Average orbital speed of Earth: 18.5 miles/sec

Average orbital speed of Mars: 15 miles/sec

Mercury

Perihelion of Mercury: 28.5 million miles

Perihelion of Venus: 66.7 million miles

Perihelion of Earth: 91.4 million miles

Mars

Perihelion of Mars: 128.4 million miles

Earth

Venus

Sun

Aphelion of Mercury: 43.3 million miles

Aphelion of Venus: 67.7 million miles

Aphelion of Earth: 94.5 million miles

Aphelion of Mars: 154.8 million miles

Asteroid belt

Aphelion of Pluto: 4,583 million miles

MERCURY
Year: 87.97 Earth days
Mass: 0.055 Earth masses
Diameter: 3,031 miles

VENUS
Year: 224.7 Earth days
Mass: 0.81 Earth masses
Diameter: 7,521 miles

EARTH
Year: 365.26 days
Mass: 1 Earth mass
Diameter: 7,926 miles

MARS
Year: 1.88 Earth years
Mass: 0.11 Earth masses
Diameter: 4,217 miles

JUPITER
Year: 11.86 Earth years
Mass: 318 Earth masses
Diameter: 88,850 miles

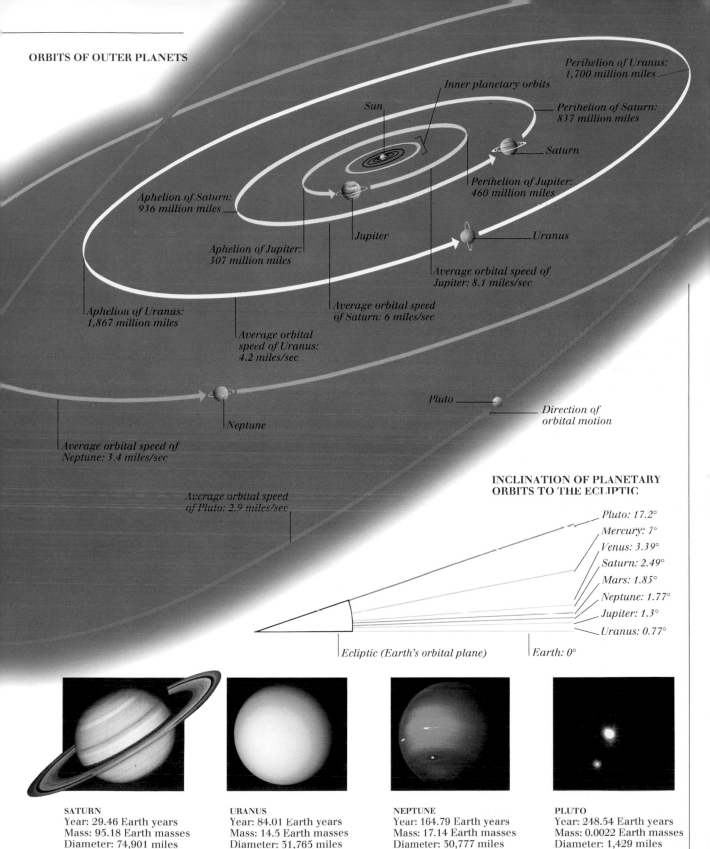

ORBITS OF OUTER PLANETS

Perihelion of Uranus: 1,700 million miles

Inner planetary orbits

Perihelion of Saturn: 837 million miles

Sun

Saturn

Perihelion of Jupiter: 460 million miles

Aphelion of Saturn: 936 million miles

Uranus

Jupiter

Aphelion of Jupiter: 507 million miles

Average orbital speed of Jupiter: 8.1 miles/sec

Aphelion of Uranus: 1,867 million miles

Average orbital speed of Saturn: 6 miles/sec

Average orbital speed of Uranus: 4.2 miles/sec

Pluto

Direction of orbital motion

Neptune

Average orbital speed of Neptune: 3.4 miles/sec

Average orbital speed of Pluto: 2.9 miles/sec

INCLINATION OF PLANETARY ORBITS TO THE ECLIPTIC

Pluto: 17.2°

Mercury: 7°

Venus: 3.39°

Saturn: 2.49°

Mars: 1.85°

Neptune: 1.77°

Jupiter: 1.3°

Uranus: 0.77°

Ecliptic (Earth's orbital plane)

Earth: 0°

SATURN
Year: 29.46 Earth years
Mass: 95.18 Earth masses
Diameter: 74,901 miles

URANUS
Year: 84.01 Earth years
Mass: 14.5 Earth masses
Diameter: 31,765 miles

NEPTUNE
Year: 164.79 Earth years
Mass: 17.14 Earth masses
Diameter: 30,777 miles

PLUTO
Year: 248.54 Earth years
Mass: 0.0022 Earth masses
Diameter: 1,429 miles

The Sun

SOLAR
PHOTOSPHERE

THE SUN IS THE STAR AT THE CENTER of our Solar System. It is about five billion years old and will probably continue to shine as it does now for about another five billion years. The Sun is a yellow main sequence star (see pp. 22-23) about 870,000 miles in diameter. It consists almost entirely of hydrogen and helium. In the Sun's core, hydrogen is converted to helium by nuclear fusion, releasing energy in the process. The energy travels from the core through the radiative and convective zones to the photosphere (visible surface), where it leaves the Sun in the form of heat and light. On the photosphere there are often dark, relatively cool areas called sunspots. These usually appear in pairs or groups and are thought to be caused by magnetic fields. Other types of solar activity are flares, which are usually associated with sunspots, and prominences. Flares are sudden discharges of high-energy radiation and atomic particles. Prominences are huge loops or filaments of gas extending into the solar atmosphere; some last for hours, others for months. Beyond the photosphere is the chromosphere (inner atmosphere) and the extremely rarified corona (outer atmosphere), which extends millions of miles into space. Tiny particles that escape from the corona give rise to the solar wind, which streams through space at hundreds of miles per second. The chromosphere and corona can be seen from Earth when the Sun is totally eclipsed by the Moon.

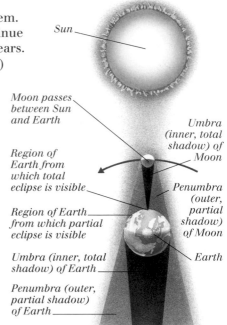

Sun

Moon passes between Sun and Earth

Umbra (inner, total shadow) of Moon

Region of Earth from which total eclipse is visible

Penumbra (outer, partial shadow) of Moon

Region of Earth from which partial eclipse is visible

Umbra (inner, total shadow) of Earth

Earth

Penumbra (outer, partial shadow) of Earth

SURFACE FEATURES

Gas loop (looped prominence)

Prominence (jet of gas at edge of Sun's disk up to hundreds of thousands of miles high)

Spicule (vertical jet of gas)

Photosphere (visible surface)

Chromosphere (inner atmosphere)

TOTAL SOLAR ECLIPSE

Corona (outer atmosphere of extremely hot diffuse gas)

Moon covers Sun's disk

SUNSPOTS

Granulated surface of Sun

Penumbra (lighter, outer region) containing radial fibrils

Umbra (darker, inner region) temperature about 7,200°F

Photosphere temperature about 9,900°F

**EXTERNAL FEATURES AND
INTERNAL STRUCTURE OF THE SUN**

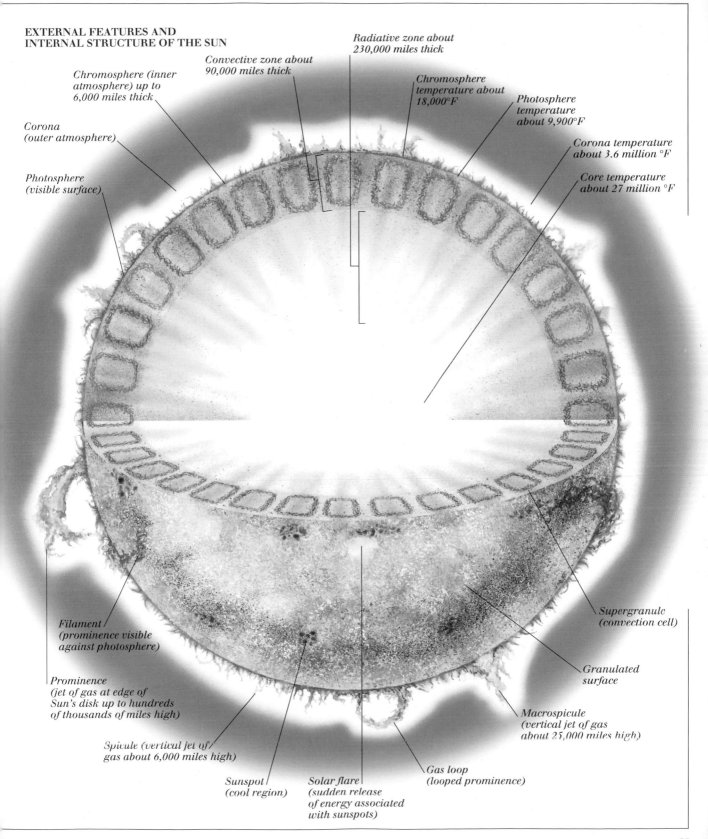

*Chromosphere (inner
atmosphere) up to
6,000 miles thick*

*Convective zone about
90,000 miles thick*

*Radiative zone about
230,000 miles thick*

*Chromosphere
temperature about
18,000°F*

*Photosphere
temperature
about 9,900°F*

*Corona
(outer atmosphere)*

*Corona temperature
about 3.6 million °F*

*Core temperature
about 27 million °F*

*Photosphere
(visible surface)*

*Supergranule
(convection cell)*

*Filament
(prominence visible
against photosphere)*

*Granulated
surface*

*Prominence
(jet of gas at edge of
Sun's disk up to hundreds
of thousands of miles high)*

*Macrospicule
(vertical jet of gas
about 25,000 miles high)*

*Spicule (vertical jet of
gas about 6,000 miles high)*

*Sunspot
(cool region)*

*Solar flare
(sudden release
of energy associated
with sunspots)*

*Gas loop
(looped prominence)*

Mercury

MERCURY

MERCURY IS THE NEAREST PLANET to the Sun, orbiting at an average distance of about 36 million miles. Because Mercury is the closest planet to the Sun, it moves faster than any other planet, traveling at an average speed of nearly 30 miles per second and completing an orbit in just under 88 days. Mercury is very small (only Pluto is smaller) and rocky. Most of the surface has been heavily cratered by the impact of meteorites, although there are also smooth, sparsely cratered plains. The Caloris Basin is the largest crater, measuring about 800 miles across. It is thought to have been formed when a rock the size of an asteroid hit the planet and is surrounded by concentric rings of mountains thrown up by the impact. The surface also has many ridges, called rupes, that are thought to have been formed when the hot core of the young planet cooled and shrank about four billion years ago, buckling the planet's surface in the process. The planet rotates about its axis very slowly, taking nearly 59 Earth days to complete one rotation. As a result, a solar day (sunrise to sunrise) on Mercury is about 176 Earth days—twice as long as the 88-day Mercurian year. Mercury has extreme surface temperatures, ranging from a maximum of 800°F on the sunlit side to -270°F on the dark side. At nightfall, the temperature drops very quickly because the planet's atmosphere is almost nonexistent. It consists only of minute amounts of helium and hydrogen captured from the solar wind, plus traces of other gases.

TILT AND ROTATION OF MERCURY

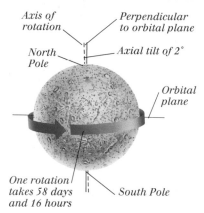

Axis of rotation
Perpendicular to orbital plane
North Pole
Axial tilt of 2°
Orbital plane
One rotation takes 58 days and 16 hours
South Pole

DEGAS AND BRONTË (RAY CRATERS)

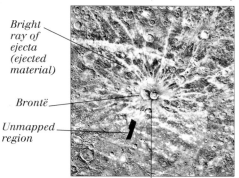

Bright ray of ejecta (ejected material)
Brontë
Unmapped region
Degas with central peak

FORMATION OF A RAY CRATER

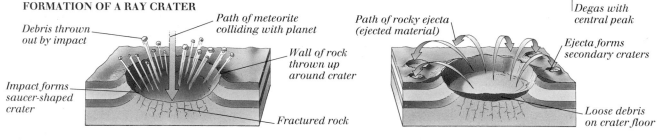

Debris thrown out by impact
Path of meteorite colliding with planet
Wall of rock thrown up around crater
Impact forms saucer-shaped crater
Fractured rock

METEORITE IMPACT

Path of rocky ejecta (ejected material)
Ejecta forms secondary craters
Loose debris on crater floor

SECONDARY CRATERING

Wall of rock forms ring of mountains
Ray of ejecta (ejected material)
Small secondary crater
Loose ejected rock
Central mountain rings form if floor of large crater recoils from meteorite impact
Falling debris forms ridges on side of wall

RAY CRATER

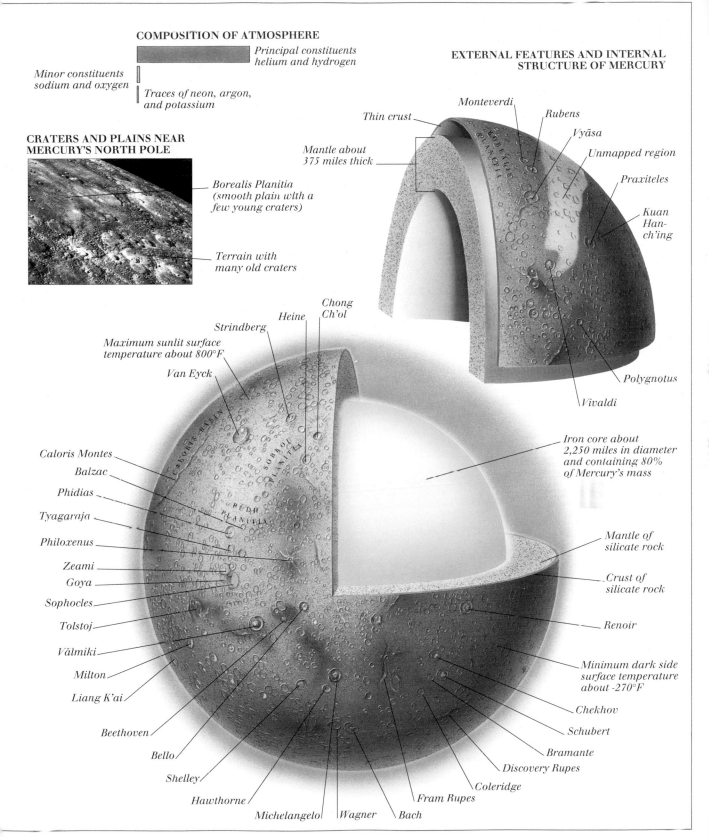

COMPOSITION OF ATMOSPHERE

Principal constituents
helium and hydrogen

Minor constituents
sodium and oxygen

Traces of neon, argon,
and potassium

**EXTERNAL FEATURES AND INTERNAL
STRUCTURE OF MERCURY**

Monteverdi

Rubens

Vyãsa

Unmapped region

Praxiteles

Kuan
Han-
ch'ing

Thin crust

Mantle about
375 miles thick

Polygnotus

Vivaldi

**CRATERS AND PLAINS NEAR
MERCURY'S NORTH POLE**

Borealis Planitia
(smooth plain with a
few young craters)

Terrain with
many old craters

Chong
Ch'ol

Heine

Strindberg

Maximum sunlit surface
temperature about 800°F

Van Eyck

Caloris Montes

Balzac

Phidias

Tyagaraja

Philoxenus

Zeami

Goya

Sophocles

Tolstoj

Välmiki

Milton

Liang K'ai

Beethoven

Bello

Shelley

Hawthorne

Michelangelo

Wagner

Bach

Fram Rupes

Coleridge

Discovery Rupes

Bramante

Schubert

Chekhov

Minimum dark side
surface temperature
about -270°F

Renoir

Crust of
silicate rock

Mantle of
silicate rock

Iron core about
2,250 miles in diameter
and containing 80%
of Mercury's mass

35

Venus

RADAR IMAGE OF VENUS

VENUS IS A ROCKY PLANET and the second planet from the Sun. Venus spins slowly backward as it orbits the Sun, causing its rotational period to be the longest in the Solar System, at about 243 Earth days. It is slightly smaller than Earth and probably has a similar internal structure, consisting of a semisolid metal core surrounded by a rocky mantle and crust. Venus is the brightest object in the sky after the Sun and Moon because its atmosphere reflects sunlight strongly. The main component of the atmosphere is carbon dioxide, which traps heat in a greenhouse effect far stronger than that on Earth. As a result, Venus is the hottest planet, with a maximum surface temperature of about 900°F. The thick cloud layers contain droplets of sulfuric acid and are driven around the planet by winds at speeds of up to 220 miles per hour. Although the planet takes 243 Earth days to rotate once, the high-speed winds cause the clouds to circle the planet in only four Earth days. The high temperature, acidic clouds, and enormous atmospheric pressure (about 90 times greater at the surface than that on Earth) make the environment extremely hostile. However, orbiting satellites have managed to land on Venus and photograph its dry, dusty surface. The Venusian surface has also been mapped by probes with radar equipment that can "see" through the cloud layers. Such radar maps reveal a terrain with craters, mountains, volcanoes, and areas where craters have been covered by plains of solidified volcanic lava. There are two large highland regions called Aphrodite Terra and Ishtar Terra.

TILT AND ROTATION OF VENUS

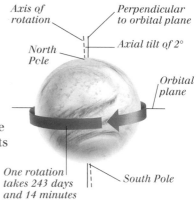

Axis of rotation

Perpendicular to orbital plane

North Pole

Axial tilt of 2°

Orbital plane

One rotation takes 243 days and 14 minutes

South Pole

CLOUD FEATURES

Polar hood

Dark, mid-latitude band

Cloud features swept around planet by winds of up to 220 mph

Dirty yellow hue due to sulfuric acid in atmosphere

Bright polar band

VENUSIAN CRATERS

Danilova

Ejecta (ejected material)

Central peak

Howe

COMPUTER-ENHANCED RADAR MAP OF THE SURFACE OF VENUS

Metis Regio

Maxwell Montes

Bell Regio

Tethus Regio

Atalanta Planitia

Sedna Planitia

Leda Planitia

Eisila Regio

Tellus Regio

Guinevere Planitia

Niobe Planitia

Phoebe Regio

Alpha Regio

Ovda Regio

Themis Regio

Thetis Regio

Lavinia Planitia

Aino Planitia

Helen Planitia

Lada Terra

ISHTAR TERRA

APHRODITE TERRA

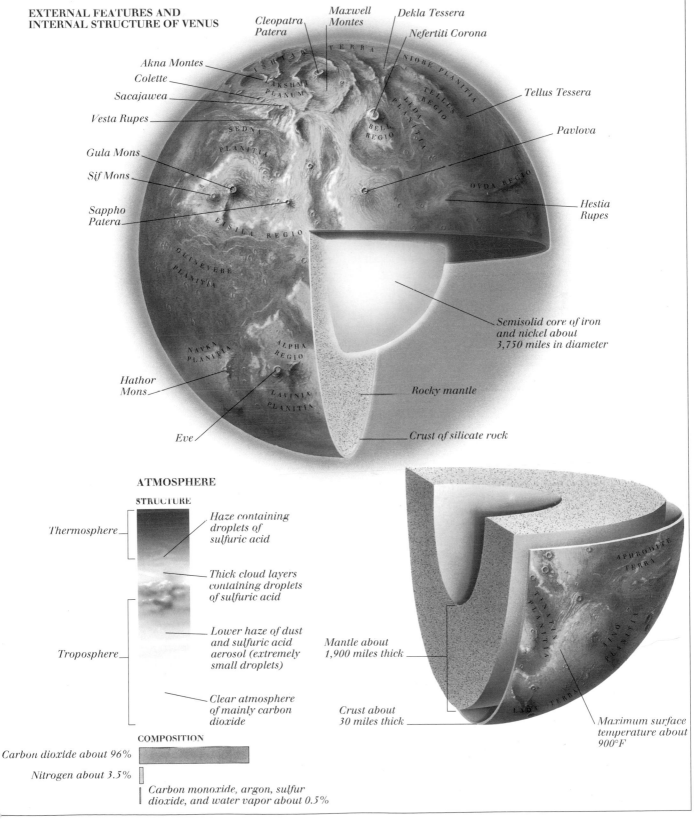

**EXTERNAL FEATURES AND
INTERNAL STRUCTURE OF VENUS**

Cleopatra Patera

Maxwell Montes

Dekla Tessera

Nefertiti Corona

Akna Montes

Colette

Sacajawea

Vesta Rupes

Gula Mons

Sif Mons

Sappho Patera

Hathor Mons

Eve

Tellus Tessera

Pavlova

Hestia Rupes

Semisolid core of iron and nickel about 3,750 miles in diameter

Rocky mantle

Crust of silicate rock

ATMOSPHERE

STRUCTURE

Thermosphere

Troposphere

Haze containing droplets of sulfuric acid

Thick cloud layers containing droplets of sulfuric acid

Lower haze of dust and sulfuric acid aerosol (extremely small droplets)

Clear atmosphere of mainly carbon dioxide

Mantle about 1,900 miles thick

Crust about 30 miles thick

Maximum surface temperature about 900°F

COMPOSITION

Carbon dioxide about 96%

Nitrogen about 3.5%

Carbon monoxide, argon, sulfur dioxide, and water vapor about 0.5%

The Earth

THE EARTH

THE EARTH IS THE THIRD of the nine planets that orbit the Sun. It is the largest and densest rocky planet, and the only one known to support life. About 70 percent of the Earth's surface is covered by water, which is not found in liquid form on the surface of any other planet. There are four main layers: the inner core, the outer core, the mantle, and the crust. At the heart of the planet the solid inner core has a temperature of about 7,230°F. The heat from this inner core causes material in the molten outer core and mantle to circulate in convection currents. It is thought that these convection currents generate the Earth's magnetic field, which extends into space as the magnetosphere. The Earth's atmosphere helps screen out some of the harmful radiation from the Sun, stops meteorites from reaching the planet's surface, and traps enough heat to prevent extremes of cold. The Earth has one natural satellite, the Moon, which is large enough for both bodies to be considered a double-planet system.

TILT AND ROTATION OF THE EARTH

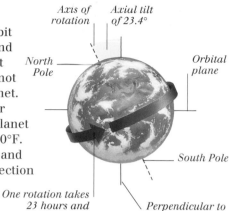

Axis of rotation

Axial tilt of 23.4°

North Pole

Orbital plane

South Pole

One rotation takes 23 hours and 56 minutes

Perpendicular to orbital plane

THE FORMATION OF THE EARTH

The heat of the collisions caused the planet to glow red

The cloud broke up into particles of ice and rock, which stuck together to form planets

Microorganisms began to photosynthesize, creating a supply of oxygen

4,600 YEARS AGO, THE SOLAR SYSTEM FORMED FROM A CLOUD OF GAS AND DUST

THE EARTH WAS FORMED FROM COLLIDING ROCKS

4,500 YEARS AGO THE SURFACE COOLED TO FORM THE CRUST

THE CONTINENTS BROKE UP AND REFORMED, GRADUALLY TAKING THEIR PRESENT POSITIONS

Solar wind enters atmosphere and produces aurora

Magnetosphere (magnetic field)

Solar wind (stream of electrically charged particles)

THE EARTH'S MAGNETOSPHERE

Van Allen radiation belt

Earth

Axis of geographic poles

Axis of magnetic poles

EXTERNAL FEATURES AND INTERNAL STRUCTURE OF THE EARTH

COMPOSITION OF THE EARTH

Greenland

Atmosphere about 310 miles deep

Crust 4–25 miles thick

Mantle about 1,740 miles thick

Outer core about 1,430 miles thick

Cyclonic storm

Other elements less than 1%

Aluminum 0.4%

Calcium 0.6%

Sulfur 2.7%

Nickel 2.7%

Silicon 13%

Magnesium 17%

Oxygen 28%

Iron 35%

Surface temperature between about -126°F and 136°F

Core temperature about 7,230°F

Molten core of iron and nickel

Solid inner core of iron and nickel about 1,490 miles in diameter

Gutenberg discontinuity (boundary between outer core and mantle)

Atlas Mountains

Sahara (desert region)

Mantle of mostly solid silicate material

Mohorovicic discontinuity (boundary between mantle and crust)

Congo Basin (tropical rain forest)

Crust of silicate rock

Amazon Basin (tropical rain forest region)

Andes (mountain range near crustal plate boundary)

Earthquake region along crustal plate boundary

Land forms about 30% of surface

Cloud typically covers about 50% of surface

Oceans cover about 70% of surface

39

The Moon

THE MOON FROM EARTH

THE MOON IS THE EARTH'S only natural satellite. It is relatively large for a moon, with a diameter of about 2,155 miles—just over a quarter that of the Earth. The Moon takes the same time to rotate on its axis as it takes to orbit the Earth (27.3 days), and so the same side (the near side) always faces us. However, the amount of the surface we can see—the phase of the Moon—depends on how much of the near side is in sunlight. The Moon is dry and barren, with no atmosphere or water. It consists mainly of solid rock, although its core may contain molten rock or iron. The surface is dusty, with highlands covered in craters caused by meteorite impacts, and lowlands in which large craters have been filled by solidified lava to form dark areas called maria or "seas." Maria occur mainly on the near side, which has a thinner crust than the far side. Many of the craters are rimmed by mountain ranges that form the crater walls and can be thousands of feet high.

TILT AND ROTATION OF THE MOON

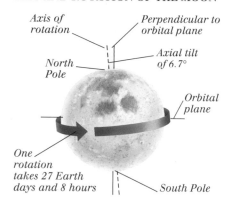

Axis of rotation

Perpendicular to orbital plane

Axial tilt of 6.7°

North Pole

Orbital plane

One rotation takes 27 Earth days and 8 hours

South Pole

CRATERS ON OCEANUS PROCELLARUM

Aristarchus

Cobra Head (head of Schröter's Valley)

Herodotus

NEAR SIDE OF THE MOON

Aristoteles

De la Rue

Hercules

Atlas

Montes Apenninus

Aristillus

Plato

Archimedes

Montes Jura

Sinus Iridum

Cleomedes

Macrobius

Julius Caesar

Bright rays of ejected material

Copernicus

Aristarchus

Langrenus

Vendelinus

Cyrillus

Petavius

Fracastorius

Furnerius

Catharina

Rupes Altai

Albategnius

Ptolemaeus

Arzachel

Walter

Stöfler

Deslandres

Kepler

Encke

Flamsteed

Fra Mauro

Grimaldi

Letronne

Gassendi

Mersenius

Pitatus

Schickard

Alphonsus

Bailly

Tycho

Clavius

Maginus

MARE FRIGORIS

MARE IMBRIUM

MARE SERENITATIS

MARE CRISIUM

MARE VAPORUM

MARE TRANQUILLITATIS

MARE FECUNDITATIS

OCEANUS PROCELLARUM

MARE NECTARIS

MARE NUBIUM

MARE HUMORUM

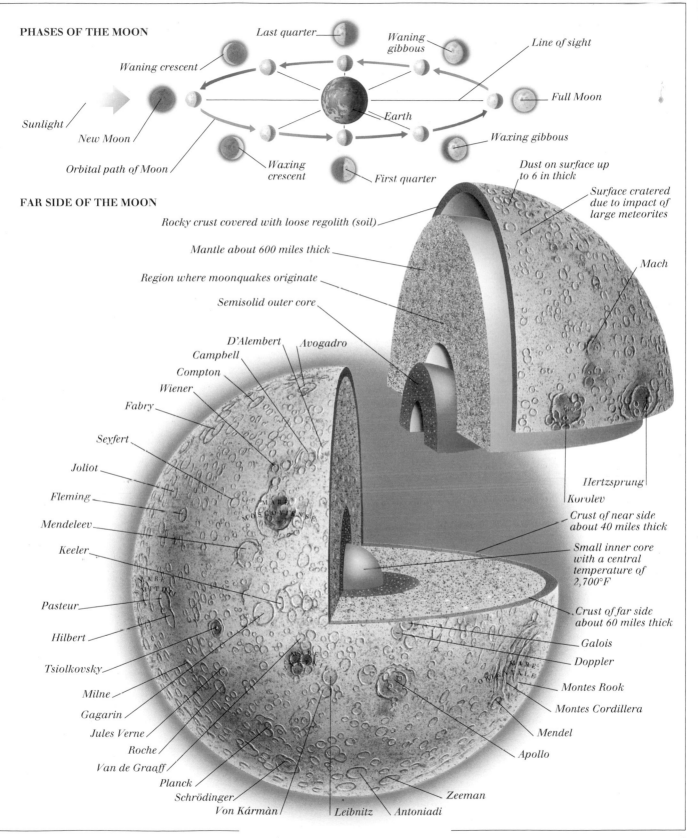

PHASES OF THE MOON

Last quarter

Waning gibbous

Waning crescent

Line of sight

Sunlight

New Moon

Full Moon

Orbital path of Moon

Earth

Waxing gibbous

Waxing crescent

First quarter

FAR SIDE OF THE MOON

Rocky crust covered with loose regolith (soil)

Dust on surface up to 6 in thick

Surface cratered due to impact of large meteorites

Mantle about 600 miles thick

Region where moonquakes originate

Mach

Semisolid outer core

D'Alembert

Avogadro

Campbell

Compton

Wiener

Fabry

Seyfert

Joliot

Fleming

Hertzsprung

Mendeleev

Korolev

Keeler

Crust of near side about 40 miles thick

Small inner core with a central temperature of 2,700°F

Pasteur

Hilbert

Crust of far side about 60 miles thick

Tsiolkovsky

Galois

Milne

Doppler

Gagarin

Montes Rook

Jules Verne

Montes Cordillera

Roche

Mendel

Van de Graaff

Apollo

Planck

Schrödinger

Zeeman

Von Kármàn

Leibnitz

Antoniadi

MARE MOSCOVIENSE

MARE SMYTHII

MARE INGENII

MARE ORIENTALE

Mars

MARS

MARS, KNOWN AS THE RED PLANET, is the fourth planet from the Sun and the outermost rocky planet. In the 19th century, astronomers first observed what were thought to be signs of life on Mars. These signs included apparent canal-like markings on the surface, and dark patches that were thought to be vegetation. It is now known that the canals are an optical illusion and the dark patches are areas where the red dust that covers most of the planet has blown away. The fine dust particles are often whipped up by winds into dust storms that occasionally obscure almost all Mars's surface. Residual dust in the atmosphere gives the Martian sky a pinkish hue. The northern hemisphere of Mars has many large plains formed of solidified volcanic lava, while the southern hemisphere has many craters and large impact basins. There are also several huge, extinct volcanoes, including Olympus Mons, which at 370 miles wide and 15 miles high is the largest known volcano in the Solar System. The surface also has many canyons and branching channels. The canyons were formed by movements of the surface crust, but the channels are thought to have been formed by flowing water that has now vaporized almost completely and escaped from the atmosphere. The Martian atmosphere is much thinner than Earth's, with only a few clouds and morning mists. Mars has two tiny irregularly shaped moons, Phobos and Deimos. Their small size indicates that they may be asteroids that have been captured by the gravity of Mars.

TILT AND ROTATION OF MARS

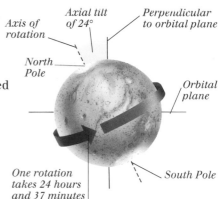

Axis of rotation

Axial tilt of 24°

Perpendicular to orbital plane

North Pole

Orbital plane

One rotation takes 24 hours and 37 minutes

South Pole

SURFACE FEATURES OF MARS

Bright water-ice fog

Fog in canyon about 12 miles wide at end of Valles Marineris

Syria Planum

NOCTIS LABYRINTHUS (CANYON SYSTEM)

Summit caldera consisting of overlapping collapsed volcanic craters

Crater

Gentle slope produced by lava flow

Cloud formation

OLYMPUS MONS (EXTINCT SHIELD VOLCANO)

THE SURFACE OF MARS

Dark area where dust has been blown away by wind

South polar ice cap

Surface covered with red-colored iron oxide dust

MOONS OF MARS

PHOBOS
Average diameter: 14 miles
Average distance from planet: 5,800 miles

DEIMOS
Average diameter: 8 miles
Average distance from planet: 14,600 miles

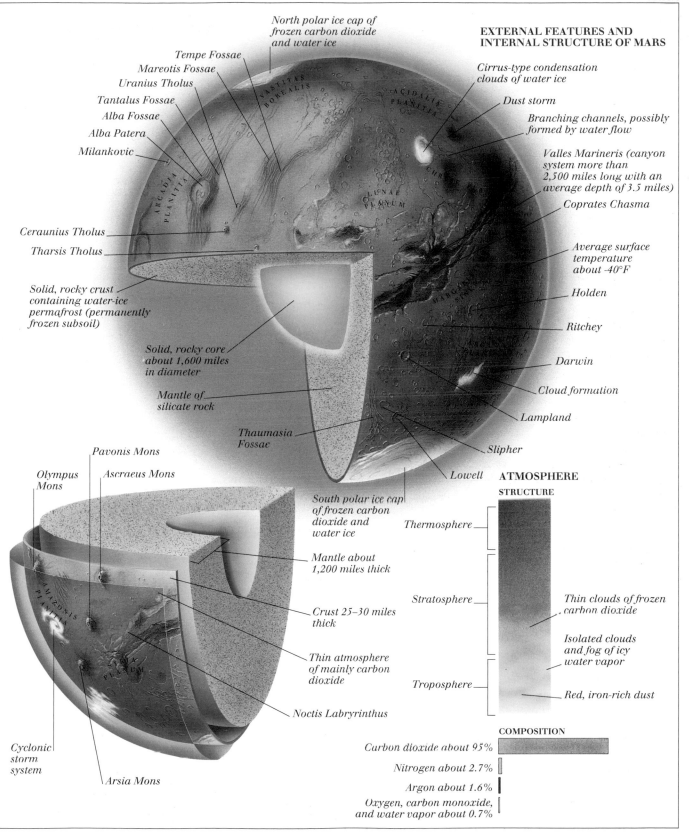

EXTERNAL FEATURES AND INTERNAL STRUCTURE OF MARS

North polar ice cap of frozen carbon dioxide and water ice

Tempe Fossae

Mareotis Fossae

Uranius Tholus

Tantalus Fossae

Alba Fossae

Alba Patera

Milankovic

Ceraunius Tholus

Tharsis Tholus

Solid, rocky crust containing water-ice permafrost (permanently frozen subsoil)

Solid, rocky core about 1,600 miles in diameter

Mantle of silicate rock

Thaumasia Fossae

Cirrus-type condensation clouds of water ice

Dust storm

Branching channels, possibly formed by water flow

Valles Marineris (canyon system more than 2,500 miles long with an average depth of 3.5 miles)

Coprates Chasma

Average surface temperature about -40°F

Holden

Ritchey

Darwin

Cloud formation

Lampland

Slipher

Lowell

South polar ice cap of frozen carbon dioxide and water ice

Olympus Mons

Pavonis Mons

Ascraeus Mons

Mantle about 1,200 miles thick

Crust 25–30 miles thick

Thin atmosphere of mainly carbon dioxide

Noctis Labryrinthus

Cyclonic storm system

Arsia Mons

ATMOSPHERE

STRUCTURE

Thermosphere

Stratosphere

Troposphere

Thin clouds of frozen carbon dioxide

Isolated clouds and fog of icy water vapor

Red, iron-rich dust

COMPOSITION

Carbon dioxide about 95%

Nitrogen about 2.7%

Argon about 1.6%

Oxygen, carbon monoxide, and water vapor about 0.7%

Jupiter

JUPITER

JUPITER IS THE FIFTH PLANET from the Sun and the first of the four gas giants. It is the largest and the most massive planet, with a diameter about 11 times that of the Earth and a mass about 2.5 times the combined mass of the eight other planets. Jupiter is thought to have a small rocky core surrounded by an inner mantle of metallic hydrogen (liquid hydrogen that acts like a metal). Outside the inner mantle is an outer mantle of liquid hydrogen and helium that merges into the gaseous atmosphere. Jupiter's rapid rate of rotation causes the clouds in its atmosphere to form belts and zones that encircle the planet parallel to the equator. Belts are dark, low-lying, relatively warm cloud layers. Zones are bright, high-altitude, cooler cloud layers. Within the belts and zones, turbulence causes the formation of cloud features such as white ovals and red spots, both of which are huge storm systems. The most prominent cloud feature is a storm called the Great Red Spot, which consists of a spiraling column of clouds three times wider than the Earth that rises about five miles above the upper cloud layer. Jupiter has one thin, faint, main ring, inside of which is a halo ring of tiny particles extending toward the planet. There are 16 known Jovian moons. The four largest moons (called the Galileans) are Ganymede, Callisto, Io, and Europa. Ganymede and Callisto are cratered and probably icy. Europa is smooth and icy and may contain water. Io is covered in bright red, orange, and yellow splotches. This coloring is caused by sulfurous material from active volcanoes that shoot plumes of lava hundreds of miles above the surface.

TILT AND ROTATION OF JUPITER

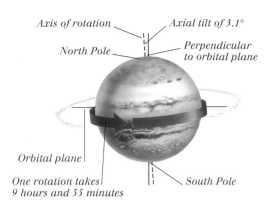

Axis of rotation

Axial tilt of 3.1°

North Pole

Perpendicular to orbital plane

Orbital plane

One rotation takes 9 hours and 55 minutes

South Pole

GREAT RED SPOT AND WHITE OVAL

Great Red Spot (anticyclonic storm system)

Red color probably due to phosphorus

White oval (temporary anticyclonic storm system)

GALILEAN MOONS OF JUPITER

EUROPA
Diameter: 1,950 miles
Average distance from planet: 416,900 miles

CALLISTO
Diameter: 2,983 miles
Average distance from planet: 1,168,200 miles

GANYMEDE
Diameter: 3,270 miles
Average distance from planet: 664,900 miles

IO
Diameter: 2,263 miles
Average distance from planet: 262,100 miles

RINGS OF JUPITER

Main ring

Halo ring

ATMOSPHERE

STRUCTURE

EXTERNAL FEATURES AND INTERNAL STRUCTURE OF JUPITER

Stratosphere

Troposphere

White clouds of ammonia crystals

Dark orange clouds of ammonium hydrosulfide crystals

Bluish clouds of water ice and water droplets

COMPOSITION

Hydrogen about 90%

Helium about 10%

Traces of ammonia, methane, and water vapor

Atmosphere of mainly hydrogen and helium

Outer mantle merging into atmosphere

Inner mantle about 18,500 miles thick

Zone (high-pressure region of rising gases)

Red spot

Plume (trailing cloud)

High-altitude white cloud

North polar aurora

North Temperate Zone

North Temperate Belt

North Tropical Zone

North Equatorial Belt

Equatorial Zone

South Equatorial Belt

South Tropical Zone

South Temperate Belt

South Temperate Zone

Flash of lightning

Great Red Spot (anticyclonic storm system)

Outer mantle of liquid hydrogen and helium

Inner mantle of metallic hydrogen

Rocky core about 17,500 miles in diameter

Core temperature about 54,000°F

Belt (low-pressure region of sinking gases)

White oval (temporary anticyclonic storm system)

Cloud-top temperature about -180°F

Saturn

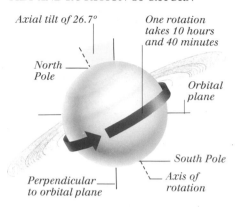

TILT AND ROTATION OF SATURN

Axial tilt of 26.7°

One rotation takes 10 hours and 40 minutes

North Pole

Orbital plane

South Pole

Axis of rotation

Perpendicular to orbital plane

COLOR-ENHANCED IMAGE OF SATURN

SATURN IS THE SIXTH PLANET from the Sun. It is a gas giant almost as big as Jupiter, with an equatorial diameter of about 74,900 miles. Saturn is thought to consist of a small core of rock and ice surrounded by an inner mantle of metallic hydrogen (liquid hydrogen that acts like a metal). Outside the inner mantle is an outer mantle of liquid hydrogen that merges into a gaseous atmosphere. Saturn's clouds form belts and zones similar to those on Jupiter, but obscured by overlying haze. Storms and eddies, seen as red or white ovals, occur in the clouds. Saturn has an extremely thin but wide system of rings that is less than one mile thick but extends outward to about 260,000 miles from the planet's surface. The main rings comprise thousands of narrow ringlets, each made of icy lumps that range in size from tiny particles to chunks several yards across. The D, E, and G rings are very faint, the F ring is brighter, and the A, B, and C rings are bright enough to be seen from Earth with binoculars. Saturn has 18 known moons, some of which orbit inside the rings and are thought to exert a gravitational influence on the shapes of the rings. Unusually, seven of the moons are co-orbital—they share an orbit with another moon. Astronomers believe that such co-orbital moons may have originated from a single satellite that broke up.

COLOR-ENHANCED IMAGE OF SATURN'S CLOUD FEATURES

Ribbon-shaped striation caused by winds of up to 335 mph

Oval (rotating storm system)

INNER RINGS OF SATURN

D ring

C ring ("crepe ring")

B ring

Cassini Division

A ring

Encke Division

F ring

MOONS OF SATURN

ENCELADUS
Diameter: 309 miles
Average distance from planet: 148,000 miles

TETHYS
Diameter: 652 miles
Average distance from planet: 183,000 miles

DIONE
Diameter: 695 miles
Average distance from planet: 234,000 miles

MIMAS
Diameter: 247 miles
Average distance from planet: 115,600 miles

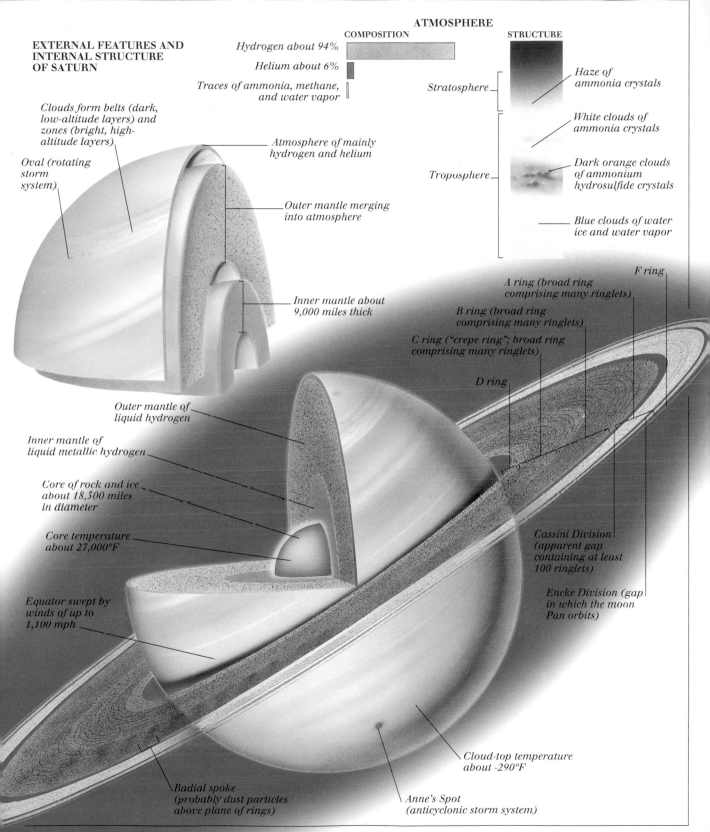

ATMOSPHERE

COMPOSITION

Hydrogen about 94%

Helium about 6%

Traces of ammonia, methane, and water vapor

STRUCTURE

EXTERNAL FEATURES AND INTERNAL STRUCTURE OF SATURN

Clouds form belts (dark, low-altitude layers) and zones (bright, high-altitude layers)

Oval (rotating storm system)

Atmosphere of mainly hydrogen and helium

Outer mantle merging into atmosphere

Inner mantle about 9,000 miles thick

Stratosphere

Troposphere

Haze of ammonia crystals

White clouds of ammonia crystals

Dark orange clouds of ammonium hydrosulfide crystals

Blue clouds of water ice and water vapor

F ring

A ring (broad ring comprising many ringlets)

B ring (broad ring comprising many ringlets)

C ring ("crepe ring"; broad ring comprising many ringlets)

D ring

Outer mantle of liquid hydrogen

Inner mantle of liquid metallic hydrogen

Core of rock and ice about 18,500 miles in diameter

Core temperature about 27,000°F

Cassini Division (apparent gap containing at least 100 ringlets)

Encke Division (gap in which the moon Pan orbits)

Equator swept by winds of up to 1,100 mph

Cloud-top temperature about -290°F

Radial spoke (probably dust particles above plane of rings)

Anne's Spot (anticyclonic storm system)

Uranus

URANUS IS THE SEVENTH PLANET from the Sun and the third largest, with a diameter of about 32,000 miles. It is thought to consist of a dense mixture of different types of ice and gas around a solid core. Its atmosphere contains traces of methane, giving the planet a blue-green hue, and the temperature at the cloud tops is about -350°F. Uranus is the most featureless planet to have been closely observed: only a few icy clouds of methane have been seen so far. Uranus is unique among the planets in that its axis of rotation lies close to its orbital plane. As a result of its strongly tilted rotational axis, Uranus rolls on its side along its orbital path around the Sun, while other planets spin more or less upright. Uranus is encircled by 11 rings that consist of rocks interspersed with dust lanes. The rings contain some of the darkest matter in the Solar System. They are extremely narrow, making them difficult to detect: nine of them are less than six miles wide, whereas most of Saturn's rings are thousands of miles in width. There are 15 known Uranian moons, all of which are icy and most of which are farther out than the rings. The 10 inner moons are small and dark, with diameters of less than 100 miles, and the five outer moons are between about 290 and 1,000 miles in diameter. The outer moons have a wide variety of surface features. Miranda has the most varied surface, with cratered areas broken up by huge ridges and cliffs 12 miles high.

TILT AND ROTATION OF URANUS

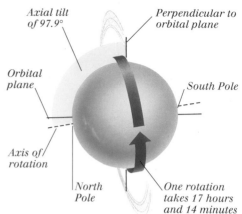

Axial tilt of 97.9°

Perpendicular to orbital plane

Orbital plane

South Pole

Axis of rotation

North Pole

One rotation takes 17 hours and 14 minutes

OUTER MOONS

MIRANDA
Diameter: 293 miles
Average distance from planet: 80,700 miles

TITANIA
Diameter: 981 miles
Average distance from planet: 270,900 miles

RINGS OF URANUS

Epsilon ring

Ring 1986 U1R

Delta ring

Gamma ring

Eta ring

Beta ring

Alpha ring

Rings 4 and 5

Ring 6

Ring 1986 U2R

RINGS AND DUST LANES

ARIEL
Diameter: 720 miles
Average distance from planet: 118,800 miles

UMBRIEL
Diameter: 726 miles
Average distance from planet: 165,300 miles

OBERON
Diameter: 946 miles
Average distance from planet: 362,000 miles

EXTERNAL FEATURES AND
INTERNAL STRUCTURE
OF URANUS

COMPOSITION OF
ATMOSPHERE

Hydrogen 85%

Helium 12%

Methane 3%

Atmosphere of
hydrogen,
helium, and
methane gases

Dense mantle of
icy and gaseous
water, ammonia,
and methane

Core temperature
about 12,600°F

Solid rocky core
up to 10,500 miles
in diameter

Mantle about
6,000 miles thick

Atmosphere
merging into
mantle

Icy clouds of
frozen methane
blown by winds
of up to 185 mph

Sharply defined
outer Epsilon ring

Blue-green hue due to
presence of methane
in atmosphere

South Pole

Cloud-top
temperature
about 350°F

Rings of dark
rocks interspersed
with dust lanes

Neptune and Pluto

COLOR-ENHANCED IMAGE OF NEPTUNE

NEPTUNE AND PLUTO are the two farthest planets from the Sun, at an average distance of about 2,800 million miles and 3,700 million miles, respectively. Neptune is a gas giant and is thought to consist of a small rocky core surrounded by a mixture of liquids and gases. The atmosphere contains several prominent cloud features. The largest of these are the Great Dark Spot, which is as wide as the Earth, the Small Dark Spot, and the Scooter. The Great and Small Dark Spots are huge storms that are swept around the planet by winds of about 1,200 miles per hour. The Scooter is a large area of cirrus cloud. Neptune has four tenuous rings and eight known moons. Triton is the largest Neptunian moon and the coldest object in the Solar System, with a temperature of -391°F. Unlike most moons in the Solar System, Triton orbits its mother planet in the opposite direction to the planet's rotation. Pluto is usually the outermost planet, but its elliptical orbit causes it to pass inside the orbit of Neptune for 20 years of its 248-year orbit. Pluto is so small and distant that little is known about it. It is a rocky planet, probably covered with ice and frozen methane. Pluto's only known moon, Charon, is large for a moon, at half the size of its parent planet. Because of the small difference in their sizes, Pluto and Charon are sometimes considered to be a double-planet system.

TILT AND ROTATION OF NEPTUNE

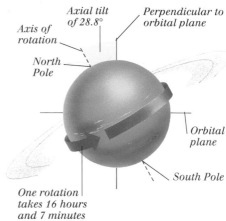

Axial tilt of 28.8°

Perpendicular to orbital plane

Axis of rotation

North Pole

Orbital plane

South Pole

One rotation takes 16 hours and 7 minutes

CLOUD FEATURES OF NEPTUNE

Great Dark Spot (anticyclonic wind storm)

Scooter (cirrus cloud)

Small Dark Spot (cyclonic wind storm)

HIGH-ALTITUDE CLOUDS

Methane cirrus clouds 25 miles above main cloud deck

Cloud shadow

Main cloud deck blown by winds at speeds of about 1,200 mph

RINGS OF NEPTUNE

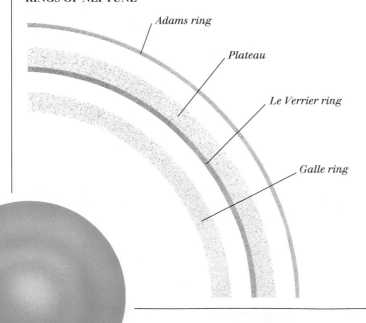

Adams ring

Plateau

Le Verrier ring

Galle ring

MOONS OF NEPTUNE

TRITON
Diameter: 1,681 miles
Average distance from planet: 220,500 miles

PROTEUS
Diameter: 259 miles
Average distance from planet: 73,100 miles

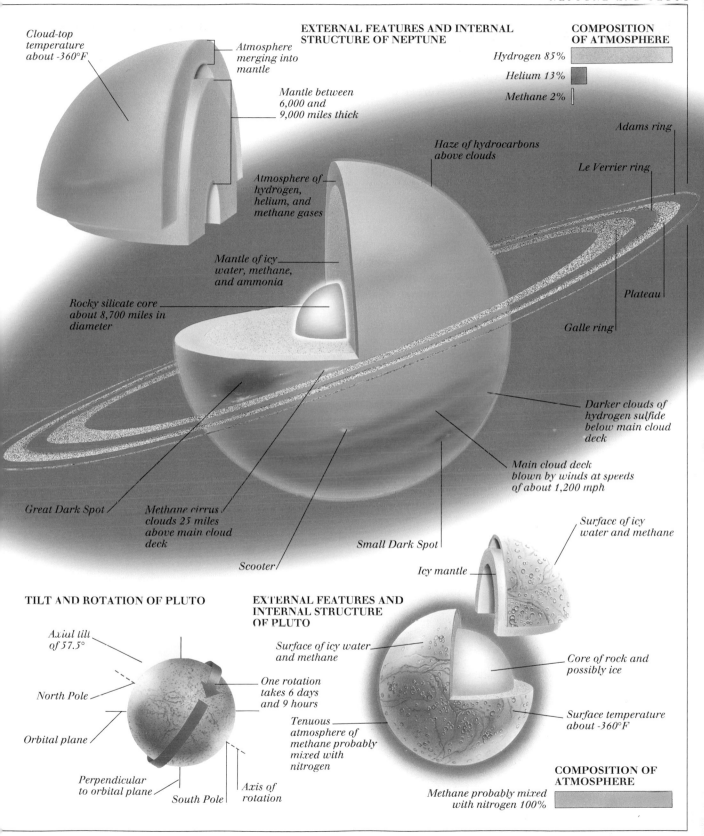

EXTERNAL FEATURES AND INTERNAL STRUCTURE OF NEPTUNE

Cloud-top temperature about -360°F

Atmosphere merging into mantle

Mantle between 6,000 and 9,000 miles thick

COMPOSITION OF ATMOSPHERE

Hydrogen 85%

Helium 13%

Methane 2%

Haze of hydrocarbons above clouds

Adams ring

Le Verrier ring

Atmosphere of hydrogen, helium, and methane gases

Mantle of icy water, methane, and ammonia

Plateau

Rocky silicate core about 8,700 miles in diameter

Galle ring

Darker clouds of hydrogen sulfide below main cloud deck

Main cloud deck blown by winds at speeds of about 1,200 mph

Great Dark Spot

Methane cirrus clouds 25 miles above main cloud deck

Small Dark Spot

Scooter

Surface of icy water and methane

Icy mantle

TILT AND ROTATION OF PLUTO

EXTERNAL FEATURES AND INTERNAL STRUCTURE OF PLUTO

Surface of icy water and methane

Core of rock and possibly ice

Axial tilt of 57.5°

North Pole

One rotation takes 6 days and 9 hours

Orbital plane

Surface temperature about -360°F

Perpendicular to orbital plane

South Pole

Axis of rotation

Tenuous atmosphere of methane probably mixed with nitrogen

COMPOSITION OF ATMOSPHERE

Methane probably mixed with nitrogen 100%

51

Asteroids, comets, and meteoroids

ASTEROID 951 GASPRA

ASTEROIDS, COMETS, AND METEOROIDS are all debris remaining from the nebula in which the Solar System formed 4.6 billion years ago. Asteroids are rocky bodies up to several hundred miles in diameter, although most are much smaller. Most of them orbit the Sun in the asteroid belt, which lies between the orbits of Mars and Jupiter. Comets may originate in a huge cloud, called the Oort Cloud, that is thought to surround the Solar System. They are made of frozen gases and dust, and are a few miles in diameter. Occasionally, a comet is deflected from the Oort Cloud to orbit the Sun in a long, elliptical path. As the comet approaches the Sun, the comet's surface starts to vaporize in the heat, producing a brightly shining coma (a huge sphere of gas and dust around the nucleus), a gas tail, and a dust tail. Meteoroids are small chunks of stone or stone and iron, some of which are fragments of asteroids or comets. Meteoroids range in size from tiny dust particles to objects tens of yards across. If a meteoroid enters the Earth's atmosphere, it is heated by friction and appears as a glowing streak of light called a meteor (also known as a shooting star). Meteor showers occur when the Earth passes through the trail of dust particles left by a comet. Most meteors burn up in the atmosphere. The few that are large enough to reach the Earth's surface are termed meteorites.

COLOR-ENHANCED IMAGE OF HALLEY'S COMET

High-intensity light emission

Nucleus

Medium-intensity light emission

Low-intensity light emission

COLOR-ENHANCED IMAGE OF A LEONID METEOR SHOWER

METEORITES

DEVELOPMENT OF COMET TAILS

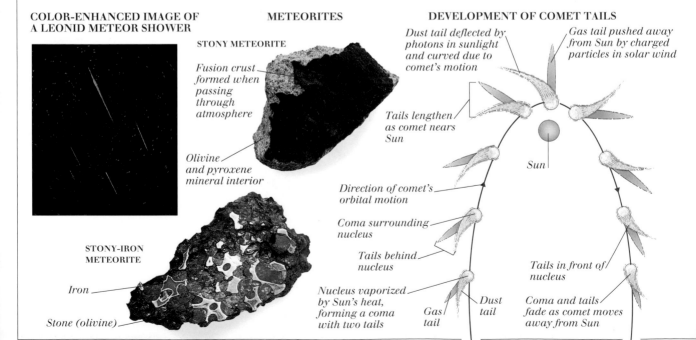

STONY METEORITE

Fusion crust formed when passing through atmosphere

Olivine and pyroxene mineral interior

STONY-IRON METEORITE

Iron

Stone (olivine)

Dust tail deflected by photons in sunlight and curved due to comet's motion

Gas tail pushed away from Sun by charged particles in solar wind

Tails lengthen as comet nears Sun

Sun

Direction of comet's orbital motion

Coma surrounding nucleus

Tails behind nucleus

Tails in front of nucleus

Nucleus vaporized by Sun's heat, forming a coma with two tails

Gas tail

Dust tail

Coma and tails fade as comet moves away from Sun

FEATURES OF A COMET

Thin, straight
gas tail

Broad, curved
dust tail

Gas molecules
heated by Sun
and emitting
light

Comet tails up to
62 million miles long

Thin, straight gas
tail blown by
solar wind

Head (coma and nucleus)

Coma
surrounding
nucleus

Nucleus a few
miles across

**STRUCTURE OF
A COMET**

Glowing coma
up to 600,000
miles across
surrounding
nucleus

Possible
core of
silicate
dust

Crust
with active
areas emitting
jets of gas
and dust

Jet of gas
and dust produced
by vaporization on
sunlit side of nucleus

Ices, including
water ice, and frozen carbon
dioxide, methane, and ammonia

Broad dust
tail curved along
comet's orbital path

Dust particles
reflecting sunlight

53

PREHISTORIC EARTH

The changing Earth

THE EARTH FORMED FROM A CLOUD OF DUST and gas drifting through space about 4,600 million years ago. Dense minerals sank to the center while lighter ones formed a thin rocky crust. However, the first known life forms—bacteria and blue-green algae—did not appear until about 3,400 million years ago, and it was only about 700 million years ago that more complex plants and animals began to develop. Since then, thousands of animal and plant species have evolved. Some, such as the dinosaurs, survived for millions of years, while others died out quickly. The Earth itself is continually changing. Although continents neared their present locations about 50 million years ago, they are still drifting slowly over the planet's surface, and mountain ranges such as the Himalayas—which began to form 40 million years ago—are continually being built up and worn away. Climate is also subject to change: the Earth has undergone a series of ice ages interspersed with warmer periods (the most recent ice age was at its height about 20,000 years ago).

Small mammals appeared (e.g., Crusafontia)

Dinosaurs became extinct

Global mountain building occurred

Multicellular soft-bodied animals appeared (e.g., worms and jellyfish)

Shelled invertebrates appeared (e.g., trilobites)

Marine plants flourished

Land plants appeared (e.g., Cooksonia)

Unicellular organisms appeared (e.g., blue-green algae)

Earth formed

Coral reefs appeared

Vertebrates appeared (e.g., Hemicyclaspis)

More complex types of algae appeared

Amphibians appeared (e.g., Ichthyostega)

CRETACEOUS

ORDOVICIAN

CAMBRIAN

PRECAMBRIAN TIME

SILURIAN

DEVONIAN

GEOLOGICAL TIMESCALE

MILLIONS OF YEARS AGO (MYA)

4,600		570	510	439	409	363	323	290
		CAMBRIAN	ORDOVICIAN	SILURIAN	DEVONIAN	MISSISSIPPIAN (NORTH AMERICA)	PENNSYLVANIAN (NORTH AMERICA)	
						CARBONIFEROUS		
PRECAMBRIAN TIME		PALEOZOIC						

EVOLUTION OF THE EARTH

Birds appeared
(e.g., Archaeopteryx)

Dinosaurs
flourished

Marine reptiles
appeared (e.g.,
Mixosaurus)

JURASSIC

TRIASSIC

Flowering plants
appeared (e.g.,
Magnolia)

Oil and gas
deposits formed

Himalayas
began to form

Coal-forming
forests flourished

Large mammals
appeared (e.g.,
Arsinoitherium)

Early
desertification
occurred

PERMIAN

Conifers
appeared

TERTIARY

Last glacial
period occurred

ARBONIFEROUS

Colorado River
began to cut out
the Grand Canyon

Modern humans
(Homo sapiens)
appeared

Uplift of the
Sierra Nevada
began

QUATERNARY

							65	56.5	35.5	23.5	5.2	1.64		0.01		0 MYA
							PALEOCENE	EOCENE	OLIGOCENE	MIOCENE	PLIOCENE		PLEISTOCENE		HOLOCENE	EPOCH
290		245		208				146								
PERMIAN		TRIASSIC		JURASSIC				CRETACEOUS				TERTIARY		QUATERNARY		PERIOD
					MESOZOIC								CENOZOIC			ERA

The Earth's crust

THE EARTH'S CRUST IS THE SOLID outer shell of the Earth. It includes continental crust (about 25 miles thick) and oceanic crust (about four miles thick). The crust and the topmost layer of the mantle form the lithosphere. The lithosphere consists of semi-rigid plates that move relative to each other on the underlying asthenosphere (a partly molten layer of the mantle). This movement is known as plate tectonics and helps explain continental drift. Where two plates move apart, there are rifts in the crust. In mid-ocean, this movement results in seafloor spreading and the formation of ocean ridges; on continents, crustal spreading can form rift valleys. When plates move toward each other, one may be subducted beneath (forced under) the other. In mid-ocean, this causes ocean trenches, seismic activity, and arcs of volcanic islands. Where oceanic crust is subducted beneath continental crust or where continents collide, land may be uplifted and mountains formed (see pp. 62–63). Plates may also slide past each other—along the San Andreas fault, for example. Crustal movement on continents may result in earthquakes, while movement under the seabed can lead to tidal waves.

ELEMENTS IN THE EARTH'S CRUST

Other elements 2%

Potassium 2.6%

Calcium 3.6%

Aluminum 8%

Magnesium 2%

Sodium 2.8%

Iron 5%

Silicon 28%

Oxygen 46%

FEATURES OF PLATE MOVEMENTS

Ridge where magma is rising to form new oceanic crust

Region of seafloor spreading

Ocean trench formed where oceanic crust is forced under continental crust

Subduction zone

Rift formed where two plates are moving apart

Magma rises to form a hot spot

Magma (molten rock) erupts at rift

Volcano develops over hot spot and builds up to form an island

Volcanic island that originally formed over hot spot

Oceanic crust melts

Magma rises to form a volcano

MAJOR PLATES OF THE EARTH'S CRUST

Hellenic plate

Eurasian plate

North American plate

Plates sliding past each other

Cocos plate

Caribbean plate

Nazca plate

Pacific plate

Philippine plate

Plates converging

South American plate

African plate

Indo-Australian plate

Plates moving apart

Boundary along which two plates slide past each other

Mountain range uplifted where subducting oceanic crust compresses and deforms edge of continental crust

Lithosphere (crust and topmost layer of mantle)

Asthenosphere (upper part of mantle)

MOVEMENT OF LAND ALONG OCEANIC RIDGES

Land moves apart at a constant rate, perpendicular to ridge

STRAIGHT OCEANIC RIDGE

Land moves apart at a constant rate, perpendicular to curve

CURVED OCEANIC RIDGE

Staggered parallel ridge sections take shape of curve

Transform fault

STRESSES RESOLVE INTO SECTIONS

Faults and folds

THE CONTINUOUS MOVEMENT of the Earth's crustal plates (see pp. 58–59) can squeeze, stretch, or break rock strata, deforming them and producing faults and folds. A fault is a fracture in a rock along which there is movement of one side relative to the other. The movement can be vertical, horizontal, or oblique (vertical and horizontal). Faults develop when rocks are subjected to compression or tension. They tend to occur in hard, rigid rocks, which are more likely to break than bend. The smallest faults occur in single mineral crystals and are microscopically small, while the largest —the Great Rift Valley in Africa, which formed between 5 million and 100,000 years ago—is more than 6,000 miles long. A fold is a bend in a rock layer caused by compression. Folds occur in elastic rocks, which tend to bend rather than break. The two main types of fold are anticlines (upfolds) and synclines (downfolds). Folds vary in size from a few millimeters long to folded mountain ranges hundreds of miles long, such as the Himalayas (see pp. 62–63) and the Alps, which are repeatedly folding. In addition to faults and folds, other features associated with rock deformations include boudins, mullions, and *en échelon* fractures.

STRUCTURE OF A FOLD

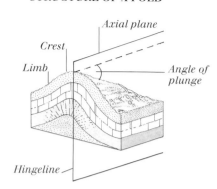

Axial plane

Crest

Limb

Angle of plunge

Hingeline

STRUCTURE OF A FAULT

Fault plane

Dip of fault plane (angle from horizontal)

Upthrow

Throw (vertical displacement of fault)

Downthrow

Hade of fault plane (angle from vertical)

STRUCTURE OF A SLOPE

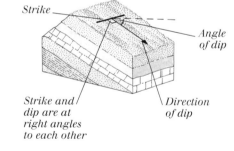

Strike

Angle of dip

Strike and dip are at right angles to each other

Direction of dip

FOLDED ROCK

Steeply dipping limbs

Crest of anticline

Plunge

SECTION THROUGH FOLDED ROCK STRATA THAT HAVE BEEN ERODED

Dipping bed

Anticlinal fold

Monoclinal fold

Mineral-filled fault

Upper Carboniferous Millstone Grit

Lower Carboniferous Limestone

EXAMPLES OF FOLDS

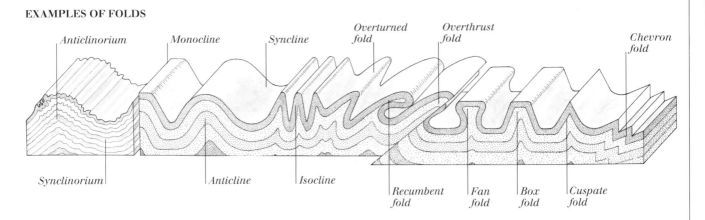

Anticlinorium
Monocline
Syncline
Overturned fold
Overthrust fold
Chevron fold
Synclinorium
Anticline
Isocline
Recumbent fold
Fan fold
Box fold
Cuspate fold

EXAMPLES OF FAULTS

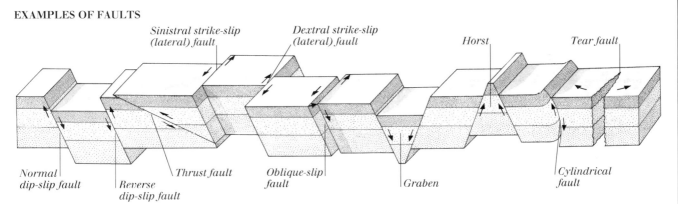

Sinistral strike-slip (lateral) fault
Dextral strike-slip (lateral) fault
Horst
Tear fault
Normal dip-slip fault
Reverse dip-slip fault
Thrust fault
Oblique-slip fault
Graben
Cylindrical fault

SMALL-SCALE ROCK DEFORMATIONS

Competent bed (rocks that break)
Tension
Tension
Incompetent bed
Tension
Tension
Tension
Masses of rock shear past each other
Tension
En échelon fracture
Tension
Incompetent bed (rocks that bend)
Competent bed breaks into sections
Competent bed
Competent bed splits into prisms
Tension
Joint opened by stress

BOUDIN
MULLION
EN ECHELON FRACTURE

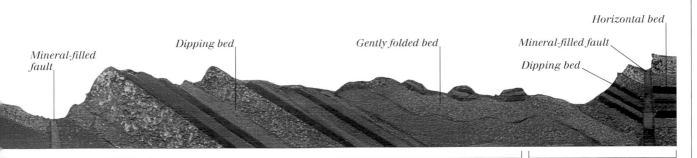

Horizontal bed
Mineral-filled fault
Dipping bed
Gently folded bed
Mineral-filled fault
Dipping bed
Mineral-filled fault

Upper Carboniferous Millstone Grit
Upper Carboniferous Coal Measures

Mountain building

THE PROCESSES INVOLVED in mountain building—termed orogenesis—occur
as a result of the movement of the Earth's crustal plates (see pp. 58-59).
There are three main types of mountains: volcanic mountains, fold mountains,
and block mountains. Most volcanic mountains have been formed along plate
boundaries where plates have come together or moved apart and
lava and other debris have been ejected onto the Earth's surface.
The lava and debris may have built up to form a dome around the
vent of a volcano. Fold mountains are formed where plates push
together and cause the rock to buckle
upward. Where oceanic crust meets
less dense continental crust, the oceanic
crust is forced under the continental
crust. The continental crust is buckled by the
impact. This is how folded mountain ranges,
such as the Appalachian Mountains in North
America, were formed. Fold mountains are also
formed where two areas of continental crust meet.
The Himalayas, for example, began to form when
India collided with Asia, buckling the sediments
and parts of the oceanic crust between them. Block mountains are formed
when a block of land is uplifted between two faults as a result of compression or tension
in the Earth's crust (see pp. 60-61). Often, the movement along faults has taken place
gradually over millions of years. However, two plates may cause an earthquake by
suddenly sliding past each other along a faultline.

Asia

*Himalayas
formed by
buckling of
sediment and
part of the
oceanic crust
between two
colliding
continents*

**BHAGIRATHI PARBAT,
HIMALAYAS**

*India moves
north*

*India collides
with Asia about 40
million years ago*

EXAMPLES OF MOUNTAINS

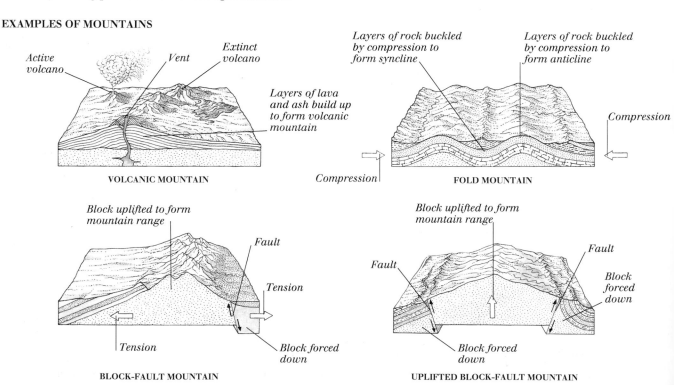

*Active
volcano*

Vent

*Extinct
volcano*

*Layers of lava
and ash build up
to form volcanic
mountain*

VOLCANIC MOUNTAIN

Compression

*Layers of rock buckled
by compression to
form syncline*

*Layers of rock buckled
by compression to
form anticline*

Compression

FOLD MOUNTAIN

*Block uplifted to form
mountain range*

Fault

Tension

Tension

*Block forced
down*

BLOCK-FAULT MOUNTAIN

*Block uplifted to form
mountain range*

Fault

Fault

*Block
forced
down*

*Block forced
down*

UPLIFTED BLOCK-FAULT MOUNTAIN

STAGES IN THE FORMATION OF THE HIMALAYAS

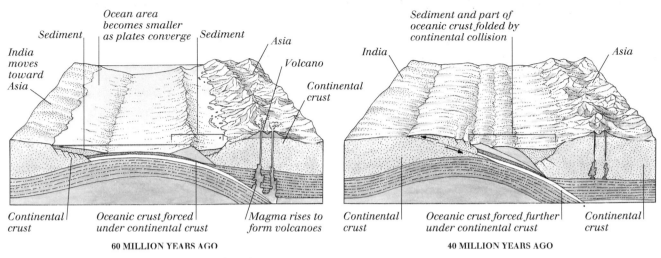

Sediment
Ocean area becomes smaller as plates converge
Sediment
Asia
India moves toward Asia
Volcano
Continental crust
Continental crust
Oceanic crust forced under continental crust
Magma rises to form volcanoes

60 MILLION YEARS AGO

Sediment and part of oceanic crust folded by continental collision
Asia
India
Continental crust
Oceanic crust forced further under continental crust
Continental crust

40 MILLION YEARS AGO

Ganges plain
Sediment and part of oceanic crust folded and uplifted
India
Asia
Continental crust
Continental crust

20 MILLION YEARS AGO

Sediment and part of oceanic crust further folded and uplifted to form Himalayas
Ripple effect of collision forms mountains and plateau of Tibet
Ganges plain
India
Asia
Continental crust
Continental crust

TODAY

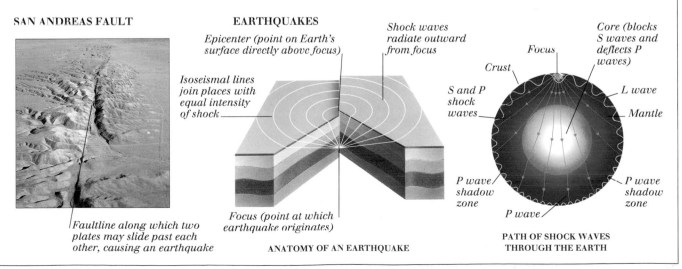

SAN ANDREAS FAULT

Faultline along which two plates may slide past each other, causing an earthquake

EARTHQUAKES

Epicenter (point on Earth's surface directly above focus)
Shock waves radiate outward from focus
Isoseismal lines join places with equal intensity of shock
Focus (point at which earthquake originates)

ANATOMY OF AN EARTHQUAKE

Focus
Core (blocks S waves and deflects P waves)
Crust
S and P shock waves
L wave
Mantle
P wave shadow zone
P wave shadow zone
P wave

PATH OF SHOCK WAVES THROUGH THE EARTH

Precambrian to Devonian periods

WHEN THE EARTH FORMED about 4,600 million years ago, its atmosphere consisted of volcanic gases with little oxygen, making it hostile to most forms of life. One large supercontinent, Gondwanaland, was situated over the southern polar region, while other smaller continents were spread over the rest of the world. Constant movement of the earth's crustal plates carried continents across the earth's surface. The first primitive life-forms emerged around 3,400 million years ago in shallow, warm seas. The build up of oxygen began to form a shield of ozone around the earth, protecting living organisms from the sun's harmful rays and helping to establish an atmosphere in which life could sustain itself. The first vertebrates appeared about 470 million years ago, during the Ordovician period (510–439 million years ago), the first land plants appeared around 400 million years ago during the Devonian period (409–363 million years ago), and the first land animals about 30 million years later.

MIDDLE ORDOVICIAN POSITIONS OF PRESENT-DAY LANDMASSES

North America
Greenland
China
South America
Australia
South Africa
Africa
Scandinavia
Europe
Siberia
India
North East Africa
Central Asia

EXAMPLES OF PRECAMBRIAN TO DEVONIAN PLANT GROUPS

A PRESENT-DAY CLUBMOSS
(*Lycopodium sp.*)

A PRESENT-DAY LAND PLANT
(*Asparagus setaceous*)

FOSSIL OF AN EXTINCT LAND PLANT
(*Cooksonia hemisphaerica*)

FOSSIL OF AN EXTINCT SWAMP PLANT
(*Zosterophyllum llanoveranum*)

EXAMPLES OF PRECAMBRIAN TO DEVONIAN TRILOBITES

ACADAGNOSTUS
Family: Agnostidae
Length: $^1/_3$ in (8 mm)

PHACOPS
Family: Phacopidae
Length: $1^3/_4$ in (4.5 cm)

OLENELLUS
Family: Olenellidae
Length: $2^1/_2$ in (6 cm)

ELRATHIA
Family: Ptychopariidae
Length: $^3/_4$ in (2 cm)

THE EARTH DURING THE MIDDLE ORDOVICIAN PERIOD

Siberia

Laurentia

China

Kazakstania

Gondwanaland

Baltica

EXAMPLES OF EARLY MARINE INVERTEBRATES

FOSSIL NAUTILOID
(*Estonioceras perforatum*)

FOSSIL BRACHIOPOD
(*Dicoelosia bilobata*)

TRACE FOSSIL
(*Mawsonites spriggi*)

FOSSIL GRAPTOLITE
(*Monograptus convolutus*)

EXAMPLES OF DEVONIAN FISH

RHAMPHODOPSIS
Family: Ptyctodontidae
Length: 6 in (15 cm)

PTERASPIS
Family: Pteraspidae
Length: 10 in (25 cm)

COCCOSTEUS
Family: Coccosteidae
Length: 14 in (35 cm)

BOTHRIOLEPIS
Family: Bothriolepidae
Length: 16 in (40 cm)

CHEIRACANTHUS
Family: Acanthodidae
Length: 12 in (30 cm)

PTERICHTHYODES
Family: Asterolepidae
Length: 6 in (15 cm)

CHEIROLEPIS
Family: Cheirolepidae
Length: 6 3/4 in (17 cm)

CEPHALASPIS
Family: Cephalaspidae
Length: 8 3/4 in (22 cm)

Carboniferous to Permian periods

THE CARBONIFEROUS PERIOD (363–290 million years ago) takes its name from the thick, carbon-rich layers—now coal—that were produced during this period when swampy tropical forests were repeatedly drowned by shallow seas. The humid climate across northern and equatorial continents throughout Carboniferous times produced the first dense plant cover on Earth. During the early part of this period, the first reptiles appeared. Their development of a waterproof egg with a protective internal structure ended animal life's dependence on an aquatic environment. Toward the end of Carboniferous times, the earth's continents Laurussia and Gondwanaland collided, resulting in the huge landmass of Pangaea. Glaciers smothered much of the southern hemisphere during the Permian period (290–245 million years ago), covering Antarctica, parts of Australia, and much of South America, Africa, and India. Ice locked up much of the world's water and large areas of the northern hemisphere experienced a drop in sea-level. Away from the poles, deserts and a hot dry climate predominated. As a result of these conditions, the Permian period ended with the greatest mass extinction of life on earth ever.

LATE CARBONIFEROUS POSITIONS OF PRESENT-DAY LANDMASSES

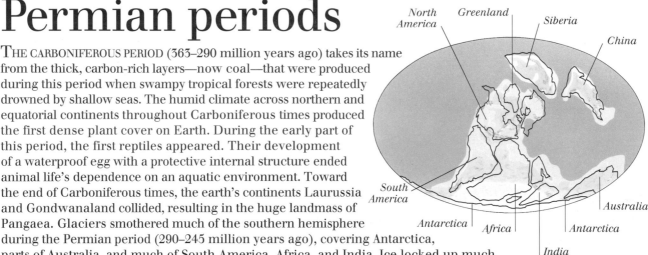

North America
Greenland
Siberia
China
South America
Antarctica
Africa
India
Australia
Antarctica

EXAMPLES OF CARBONIFEROUS AND PERMIAN PLANT GROUPS

A PRESENT-DAY FIR
(Abies concolor)

FOSSIL OF AN EXTINCT FERN
(Zeilleria frenzlii)

FOSSIL OF AN EXTINCT HORSETAIL
(Equisetites sp.)

FOSSIL OF AN EXTINCT CLUBMOSS
(Lepidodendron sp.)

EXAMPLES OF CARBONIFEROUS AND PERMIAN TREES

PECOPTERIS
Family: Marattiaceae
Height: 13 ft (4 m)

PARIPTERIS
Family: Medullosaceae
Height: 16 ft 6 in (5 m)

MARIOPTERIS
Family: Unclassified
Height: 16 ft 6 in (5 m)

MEDULLOSA
Family: Medullosaceae
Height: 16 ft 6 in (5 m)

THE EARTH DURING THE LATE CARBONIFEROUS PERIOD

Siberia

Laurussia

China

Ural Mountains

Caledonian Mountains

Appalachian Mountains

Gondwanaland

EXAMPLES OF CARBONIFEROUS AND PERMIAN ANIMALS

SKULL OF AN EXTINCT SYNAPSID REPTILE
(Dimetrodon loomisi)

FOSSIL TEETH OF AN EXTINCT SHARK
(Helicoprion bessonowi)

MODEL OF AN EXTINCT CARBONIFEROUS REPTILE
(Westlothiana lizziae)

LEPIDODENDRON
Family: Lepidodendraceae
Height: 100 ft (30 m)

CORDAITES
Family: Cordaitacca
Height: 33 ft (10 m)

GLOSSOPTERIS
Family: Glossopteridaceae
Height: 26 ft (8 m)

ALETHOPTERIS
Family Medullosaceae
Height: 16 ft 6 in (5 m)

Triassic period

THE TRIASSIC PERIOD (245–208 million years ago) marked the beginning of what is known as the Age of the Dinosaurs (the Mesozoic era). During this period, the present-day continents were massed together, forming one huge continent known as Pangaea. This landmass experienced extremes of climate, with lush green areas around the coast or by lakes and rivers, and arid deserts in the interior. The only forms of plant life were nonflowering plants, such as conifers, ferns, cycads, and ginkgos; flowering plants had not yet evolved. The principal forms of animal life included primitive amphibians, rhynchosaurs ("beaked lizards"), and primitive crocodilians. Dinosaurs first appeared about 230 million years ago, at the beginning of the Late Triassic period. The earliest known dinosaurs were the carnivorous (flesh-eating) herrerasaurids and staurikosaurids, such as *Herrerasaurus* and *Staurikosaurus*. Early herbivorous (plant-eating) dinosaurs first appeared in Late Triassic times and included *Plateosaurus* and *Technosaurus*. By the end of the Triassic period, dinosaurs dominated Pangaea, possibly contributing to the extinction of many other reptiles.

TRIASSIC POSITIONS OF PRESENT-DAY LANDMASSES

North America
Europe
Asia
South America
Africa
Antarctica
India
Australia

EXAMPLES OF TRIASSIC PLANT GROUPS

A PRESENT-DAY CYCAD
(*Cycas revoluta*)

A PRESENT-DAY GINKGO
(*Ginkgo biloba*)

A PRESENT-DAY CONIFER
(*Araucaria araucana*)

FOSSIL OF AN EXTINCT FERN
(*Pachypteris* sp.)

FOSSIL LEAF OF AN EXTINCT CYCAD
(*Cycas* sp.)

EXAMPLES OF TRIASSIC DINOSAURS

MELANOROSAURUS
A melanorosaurid
Length: 40 ft (12.2 m)

MUSSAURUS
A plateosaurid
Length: 6 ft 6 in–10 ft (2–3 m)

HERRERASAURUS
A herrerasaurid
Length: 10 ft (3 m)

PISANOSAURUS
A primitive ornithischian
Length: 3 ft (90 cm)

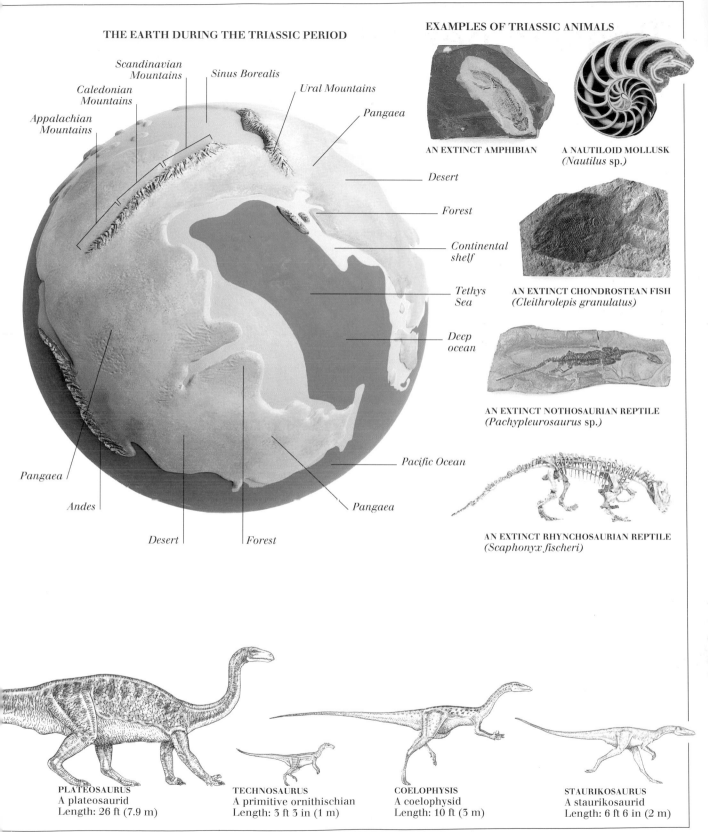

THE EARTH DURING THE TRIASSIC PERIOD

Scandinavian
Mountains

Sinus Borealis

Caledonian
Mountains

Ural Mountains

Appalachian
Mountains

Pangaea

Desert

Forest

Continental
shelf

Tethys
Sea

Deep
ocean

Pangaea

Andes

Pacific Ocean

Desert

Forest

Pangaea

EXAMPLES OF TRIASSIC ANIMALS

AN EXTINCT AMPHIBIAN

A NAUTILOID MOLLUSK
(*Nautilus* sp.)

AN EXTINCT CHONDROSTEAN FISH
(*Cleithrolepis granulatus*)

AN EXTINCT NOTHOSAURIAN REPTILE
(*Pachypleurosaurus* sp.)

AN EXTINCT RHYNCHOSAURIAN REPTILE
(*Scaphonyx fischeri*)

PLATEOSAURUS
A plateosaurid
Length: 26 ft (7.9 m)

TECHNOSAURUS
A primitive ornithischian
Length: 3 ft 3 in (1 m)

COELOPHYSIS
A coelophysid
Length: 10 ft (3 m)

STAURIKOSAURUS
A staurikosaurid
Length: 6 ft 6 in (2 m)

Jurassic period

THE JURASSIC PERIOD, the middle part of the Mesozoic era, lasted from 208 to 146 million years ago. During the Jurassic period, the landmass of Pangaea broke up into the continents of Gondwanaland and Laurasia, and sea-levels rose, flooding areas of lower land. The Jurassic climate was warm and moist. Plants such as ginkgos, horsetails, and conifers thrived, and giant redwood trees appeared, as did the first flowering plants. The abundance of plant food coincided with the proliferation of herbivorous (plant-eating) dinosaurs, such as the large sauropods (e.g., *Diplodocus*) and stegosaurs (e.g., *Stegosaurus*). Carnivorous (flesh-eating) dinosaurs, such as *Compsognathus* and *Allosaurus,* also flourished by hunting the many animals that existed—among them other dinosaurs. Further Jurassic animals included shrewlike mammals, and pterosaurs (flying reptiles), as well as plesiosaurs and ichthyosaurs (both marine reptiles).

JURASSIC POSITIONS OF PRESENT-DAY LANDMASSES

North America · Europe · Arabia · Asia · South America · Africa · Antarctica · India · Australia

EXAMPLES OF JURASSIC PLANT GROUPS

A PRESENT-DAY FERN
(Dicksonia antarctica)

A PRESENT-DAY HORSETAIL
(Equisetum arvense)

A PRESENT-DAY CONIFER
(Taxus baccata)

FOSSIL LEAF OF AN EXTINCT CONIFER
(Taxus sp.)

FOSSIL LEAF OF AN EXTINCT REDWOOD
(Sequoiadendron affinis)

EXAMPLES OF JURASSIC DINOSAURS

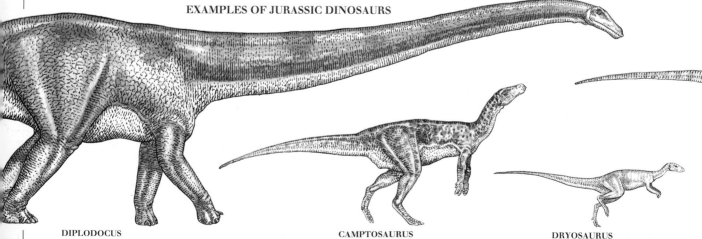

DIPLODOCUS
A diplodocid
Length: 88 ft (26.8 m)

CAMPTOSAURUS
A camptosaurid
Length: 16–23 ft (4.9–7 m)

DRYOSAURUS
A dryosaurid
Length: 10–13 ft (3–4 m)

THE EARTH DURING THE JURASSIC PERIOD

Laurasia

Laurasia

North Atlantic
Ocean

Ural Mountains

North
American
Cordillera

Turgai
Strait

Forest

Laurasia

Desert

Tethys Sea

Deep
ocean

Continental
shelf

Desert

Forest

Andes

Gondwanaland

Gondwanaland

Pacific Ocean

EXAMPLES OF JURASSIC ANIMALS

AN EXTINCT PTEROSAUR
(*Rhamphorhynchus* sp.)

**AN EXTINCT
BELEMNITE MOLLUSK**
(*Belemnoteuthis* sp.)

**AN EXTINCT
RHYNCHOSAURIAN REPTILE**
(*Homeosaurus pulchellus*)

AN EXTINCT PLESIOSAUR
(*Peloneustes philarcus*)

AN EXTINCT ICHTHYOSAUR
(*Ichthyosaurus megacephalus*)

ALLOSAURUS
An allosaurid
Length: 36 ft (11 m)

SCELIDOSAURUS
A scelidosaurid
Length: 13 ft (4 m)

STEGOSAURUS
A stegosaurid
Length: 30 ft (9.1 m)

Cretaceous period

THE MESOZOIC ERA ENDED WITH the Cretaceous period, which lasted from 146 to 65 million years ago. During this period, Gondwanaland and Laurasia were breaking up into smaller landmasses that more closely resembled those of the modern continents. The climate remained mild and moist, but the seasons became more marked. Flowering plants, including deciduous trees, replaced many cycads, seed ferns, and conifers. Animal species became more varied, with the evolution of new mammals, insects, fish, crustaceans, and turtles. Dinosaurs evolved into a wide variety of species during Cretaceous times; more than half of all known dinosaurs—including *Iguanodon*, *Deinonychus*, *Tyrannosaurus*, and *Hypsilophodon* —lived during this period. At the end of the Cretaceous period, however, large dinosaurs became extinct. The reason for this mass extinction is unknown but it is thought to have been caused by climatic changes due to either a catastrophic meteor impact with the Earth or extensive volcanic eruptions.

North America
Europe
Arabia
Asia
South America
Australia
Africa
India
Antarctica

EXAMPLES OF CRETACEOUS PLANT GROUPS

A PRESENT-DAY CONIFER
(*Pinus muricata*)

A PRESENT-DAY DECIDUOUS TREE
(*Magnolia* sp.)

FOSSIL OF AN EXTINCT FERN
(*Sphenopteris latiloba*)

FOSSIL OF AN EXTINCT GINKGO
(*Ginkgo pluripartita*)

FOSSIL LEAVES OF AN EXTINCT DECIDUOUS TREE
(*Cercidyphyllum* sp.)

EXAMPLES OF CRETACEOUS DINOSAURS

SALTASAURUS
A titanosaurid
Length: 40 ft (12.2 m)

TOROSAURUS
A ceratopsid
Length: 25 ft (7.6 m)

HYPSILOPHODON
A hypsilophodontid
Length: 4 ft 6 in–7 ft 6 in (1.4–2.3 m)

THE EARTH DURING THE CRETACEOUS PERIOD

West Africa

North America

Rocky Mountains

Greenland

Africa

Europe

Continental Sea

Ural Mountains

Desert

Tethys Sea

Asia

India

Indian Ocean

Australia

Forest

Antarctica

South Atlantic Ocean

South America

Andes

North Atlantic Ocean

Pacific Ocean

EXAMPLES OF CRETACEOUS ANIMALS

AN EXTINCT INSECT
(*Libellulium longialatum*)

AN EXTINCT MARINE TURTLE
(*Plesiochelys latiscutata*)

AN EXTINCT CRUSTACEAN
(*Homarus* sp.)

AN EXTINCT CROCODILIAN

AN EXTINCT HOLOSTEAN FISH
(*Lepidotes maximus*)

TYRANNOSAURUS
A tyrannosaurid
Length: 40 ft (12.2 m)

DEINONYCHUS
A dromaeosaurid
Length: 8–11 ft (2.4–3.4 m)

IGUANODON
An iguanodontid
Length: 30 ft (9.1 m)

Tertiary period

FOLLOWING THE DEMISE OF THE DINOSAURS at the end of the Cretaceous
period, the Tertiary period (65–1.6 million years ago), which formed the first
part of the Cenozoic era (65 million years ago–present), was characterized
by a huge expansion of mammal life. Placental mammals nourish and
maintain their young in the mother's uterus; only three orders of
placental mammals existed during Cretaceous times, compared
with 25 orders during the Tertiary period. One of these 25
included the first hominid (see pp.108–109), *Australopithecus*,
which appeared in Africa. By the beginning of the Tertiary
period, the continents had almost reached their present position.
The Tethys Sea, which had separated the northern continents
from Africa and India, began to close up, forming the Mediterranean
Sea and allowing the migration of terrestrial animals
between Africa and western Europe. India's collision with
Asia led to the formation of the Himalayas. During the middle
part of the Tertiary period, the forest-dwelling and browsing mammals
were replaced by mammals such as the horse, better suited to grazing the
open savannahs that began to dominate. Repeated cool periods throughout
the Tertiary period established the Antarctic as an icy island continent.

**TERTIARY POSITIONS OF
PRESENT-DAY LANDMASSES**

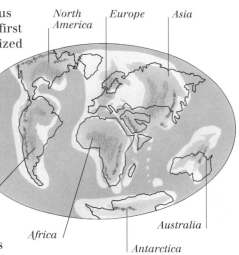

North
America

Europe

Asia

South
America

Africa

Australia

Antarctica

EXAMPLES OF TERTIARY PLANT GROUPS

A PRESENT-DAY OAK
(*Quercus palustris*)

A PRESENT-DAY BIRCH
(*Betula grossa*)

**FOSSIL LEAF OF AN
EXTINCT BIRCH**
(*Betulites sp.*)

**FOSSIL STEM OF AN
EXTINCT PALM**
(*Palmoxylon*)

EXAMPLES OF TERTIARY
ANIMAL GROUPS

HYAENODON
An hyaenodontid
Length: 6 ft 6 in (2 m)

TITANOHYRAX
A pliohyracid
Length: 6 ft 6 in (2 m)

PHORUSRHACUS
A phorusrhacid
Length: 5 ft (1.5 m)

SAMOTHERIUM
A giraffid
Length: 10 ft (3 m)

THE EARTH DURING THE TERTIARY PERIOD

North America
Rocky Mountains
Sierra Nevada
Appalachian Mountains
Pyrenees
Europe
Alps
Asia
Continental sea

Zagros Mountains

Himalayas

Tethys Sea

Australia

India

Andes
South America
Atlantic Ocean
Atlas Mountains
Africa
Antarctica
Vegetation
Indian Ocean

EXAMPLES OF TERTIARY ANIMALS

AN EXTINCT MAMMAL
(Arsinoitherium sp.)

AN EXTINCT MAMMAL
(Merycoidodon culbertsonii)

AN EXTINCT HOMINID
(Aegyptopithecus sp.)

AN EXTINCT GASTROPOD MOLLUSC
(Ecphora quadricostata)

MAMMUT
A mammutid
Length: 8 ft (2.5 m)

TETRALOPHODON
A gomphotheriid
Length: 8 ft (2.5 m)

Quaternary period

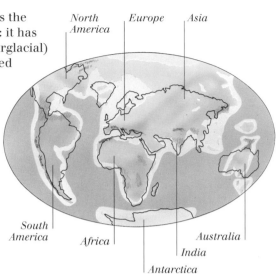

North
America

Europe

Asia

South
America

Africa

Australia

India

Antarctica

THE QUATERNARY PERIOD (1.6 million years ago–present) forms the second part of the Cenozoic era (65 million years ago–present): it has been characterized by alternating cold (glacial) and warm (interglacial) periods. During cold periods, ice sheets and glaciers have formed repeatedly on northern and southern continents. The cold environments in North America and Eurasia, and to a lesser extent in southern South America and parts of Australia, have caused the migration of many life forms toward the Equator. Only the specialized ice-age mammals such as *Mammuthus* and *Coelodonta*, with their thick wool and fat insulation, were suited to life in very cold climates. Humans developed throughout the Pleistocene period (1.6 million–10,000 years ago) in Africa and migrated northward into Europe and Asia. Modern humans, *Homo sapiens*, lived on the cold European continent 30,000 years ago and hunted mammals. The end of the last ice age and the climatic changes that occurred about 10,000 years ago brought extinction to many Pleistocene mammals, but enabled humans to flourish.

EXAMPLES OF QUATERNARY PLANT GROUPS

A PRESENT-DAY BIRCH
(Betula lenta)

A PRESENT-DAY SWEEETGUM
(Liquidambar styraciflua)

FOSSIL LEAF OF A SWEETGUM
(Liquidambar europeanum)

FOSSIL LEAF OF A BIRCH
(Betula sp.)

EXAMPLES OF QUATERNARY ANIMAL GROUPS

PROCOPTODON
A macropodid
Length: 10 ft (3 m)

DIPROTODON
A diprotodontid
Length: 10 ft (3 m)

TOXODON
A toxodontid
Length: 10 ft (3 m)

MAMMUTHUS
An elephantid
Length: 10 ft (3 m)

THE EARTH DURING THE QUATERNARY PERIOD

Pyrenees

Alps

Appalachian
Mountains

Ice sheet

Rocky
Mountains

Asia

Vegetation

North
America

Carpathian
Mountains

Taurus
Mountains

Himalayas

India

Australia

Desert

Andes

South
America

Indian
Ocean

Atlantic
Ocean

Ice cap

Atlas
Mountains

Africa

Antarctica

EXAMPLES OF QUATERNARY ANIMALS

A MAMMAL SKELETON
(*Hippopotamus
amphibius*)

**SKULL OF AN EXTINCT
CAVE BEAR**
(*Ursus spelaeus*)

**SKULL OF AN
EXTINCT TORTOISE**
(*Meiolania platyceps*)

A MAMMOTH TOOTH
(*Mammuthus
primigenius*)

DEINOTHERIUM
A deinotheriid
Length: 13 ft (4 m)

COELODONTA
A rhinocerotid
Length: 13 ft (4 m)

AUSTRALOPITHECUS
A hominid
Length: 4 ft (1.2 m)

Early signs of life

STROMATOLITIC LIMESTONE

FOR ALMOST A THOUSAND MILLION YEARS after its formation, there was no known life on Earth. The first simple, sea-dwelling organic structures appeared about 3,500 million years ago; they may have formed when certain chemical molecules joined together. Prokaryotes, single-celled micro-organisms such as blue-green algae, were able to photosynthesize (see pp. 138–139), and thus produce oxygen. A thousand million years later, sufficient oxygen had built up in the earth's atmosphere to allow multicellular organisms to proliferate in the Precambrian seas (before 570 million years ago). Soft-bodied jellyfish, corals, and seaworms flourished about 700 million years ago. Trilobites, the first animals with hard body frames, developed during the Cambrian period (570–510 million years ago). However, it was not until the beginning of the Devonian period (409–363 million years ago) that early land plants, such as *Asteroxylon*, formed a water-retaining cuticle, which ended their dependence on an aquatic environment. About 360 million years ago, the first amphibians (see pp. 80–81) crawled onto the land, although they still returned to the water to lay their soft eggs. Not until the emergence of the first reptiles would animals with backbones appear that were not dependent on water in this way.

Alternate layers of mud and sand

Layers bound by algae

Layered structure

Limestone

Long, beaklike snout

Growth line

Dorsal plate

Dorsal spine base

Fixed lateral plate

Bony dorsal shield

FOSSILIZED JAWLESS FISH

Glabella

Eye

Thoracic pleurae

Tail shield

Tail area

FOSSILIZED TRILOBITE

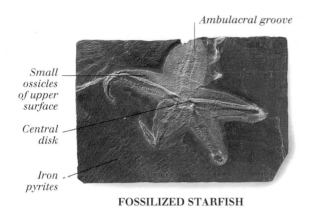

Ambulacral groove

Small ossicles of upper surface

Central disk

Iron pyrites

FOSSILIZED STARFISH

Row of ossicles

Broad disk

Row of ossicles

Short arm

UPPER SURFACE OF FOSSILIZED STARFISH

LOWER SURFACE OF FOSSILIZED STARFISH

Jointed leg

Chelicera (jointed pincer)

Jointed leg with oar-shaped paddle

Segmented abdomen

UNDERSIDE OF FOSSILIZED EURYPTERID

Telson (tail spine)

Abdominal segments

Shell contains eight somites (thoracic segments)

Hingeless, bivalved shell

FOSSIL OF AN EXTINCT SHRIMP

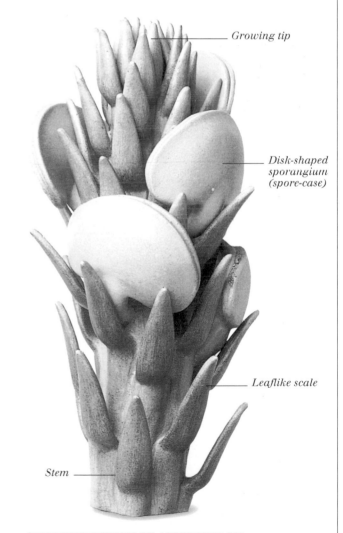

Growing tip

Disk-shaped sporangium (spore-case)

Leaflike scale

Stem

RECONSTRUCTION OF ASTEROXYLON

Amphibians and reptiles

THE EARLIEST KNOWN AMPHIBIANS, such as *Acanthostega* and *Ichthyostega*, lived about 363 million years ago at the end of the Devonian period (409–363 million years ago). Their limbs may have evolved from the muscular fins of lungfish-like creatures. These fish can use their fins to push themselves along the bottom of lakes and some can breathe at the water's surface. While amphibians (see pp. 182–183) can exist on land, they are dependent on a wet environment because their skin does not retain moisture and they must return to the water to lay their eggs. Evolving from amphibians, reptiles (see pp. 184–187) first appeared during the Carboniferous period (363–290 million years ago): *Westlothiana*, a possible early reptile, lived on land 338 million years ago. The development of the amniotic egg, with an embryo enclosed in its own wet environment (the amnion) and protected by a waterproof shell, freed reptiles from the amphibian's dependence on a wet habitat. A scaly skin protected the reptile from desiccation on land and enabled it to exploit ways of life closed to its amphibian ancestors. Reptiles include the dinosaurs, which came to dominate life on land during the Mesozoic era (245–65 million years ago).

Orbit
Pocket enclosing nostril
Sculpted or pitted bone surface
Spiracle to draw in water
Mandible
Small tooth

FOSSIL SKULL OF ACANTHOSTEGA

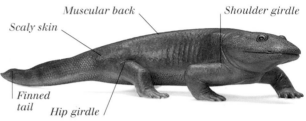

Muscular back
Shoulder girdle
Scaly skin
Finned tail
Hip girdle

MODEL OF ICHTHYOSTEGA

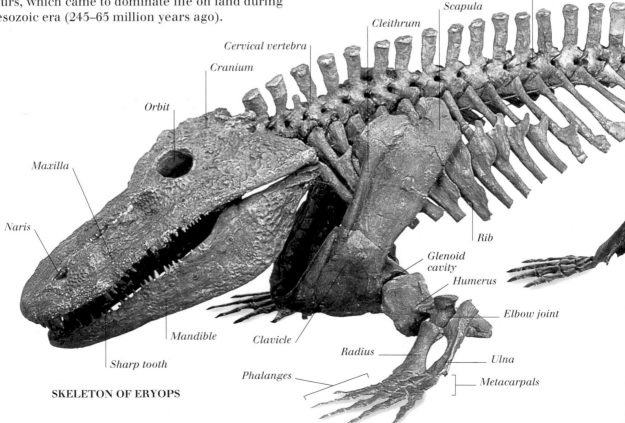

Dorsal vertebra
Scapula
Cleithrum
Cervical vertebra
Cranium
Orbit
Maxilla
Naris
Rib
Glenoid cavity
Humerus
Elbow joint
Mandible
Clavicle
Radius
Ulna
Sharp tooth
Phalanges
Metacarpals

SKELETON OF ERYOPS

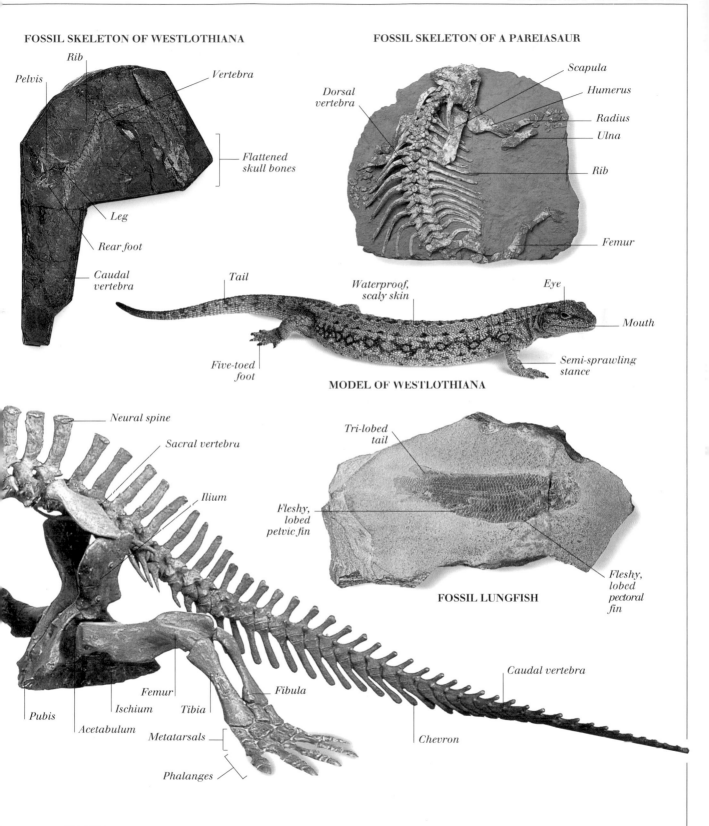

FOSSIL SKELETON OF WESTLOTHIANA

Rib

Pelvis

Vertebra

Flattened
skull bones

Leg

Rear foot

Caudal
vertebra

FOSSIL SKELETON OF A PAREIASAUR

Scapula

Humerus

Dorsal
vertebra

Radius

Ulna

Rib

Femur

Tail

Waterproof,
scaly skin

Eye

Mouth

Five-toed
foot

Semi-sprawling
stance

MODEL OF WESTLOTHIANA

Neural spine

Sacral vertebra

Ilium

Tri-lobed
tail

Fleshy,
lobed
pelvic fin

Fleshy,
lobed
pectoral
fin

FOSSIL LUNGFISH

Caudal vertebra

Pubis

Femur

Ischium

Tibia

Fibula

Acetabulum

Metatarsals

Chevron

Phalanges

The dinosaurs

THE DINOSAURS WERE A LARGE GROUP of reptiles that were the dominant land vertebrates (animals with backbones) for most of the Mesozoic era (245–65 million years ago). They appeared some 230 million years ago and were distinguished from other scaly, egg-laying reptiles by an important feature: dinosaurs had an erect limb stance. This enabled them to keep their bodies well above the ground, unlike the sprawling and semi-sprawling stance of other reptiles. The head of the dinosaur's femur (thighbone) fits into a socket in its pelvis (hipbone), producing efficient and mobile locomotion. Dinosaurs are categorized into two groups according to the structure of their pelvis: saurischian (lizard-hipped) and ornithischian (bird-hipped) dinosaurs. In the case of most saurischians, the pubis (part of the pelvis) jutted forward, while in ornithischians it slanted back, parallel to the ischium (another part of the pelvis). Dinosaurs ranged in size from smaller than a domestic cat to the biggest land animals ever known. The Dinosauria were the most successful land vertebrates ever, and survived for 165 million years, until their extinction 65 million years ago.

STRUCTURE OF SAURISCHIAN PELVIS

Ilium
Postacetabular process
Ilio-ischial joint
Ischium
Hook of preacetabular process
Ilio-pubic joint
Acetabulum
Pubis
Pubic foot

GALLIMIMUS
A saurischian dinosaur

POSITION OF PELVIS IN A SAURISCHIAN DINOSAUR

STRUCTURE OF ORNTHISCHIAN PELVIS

Ilium
Postacetabular process
Ilio-ischial joint
Pubis
Ischium
Preacetabular process
Ilio-pubic joint
Prepubis
Acetabulum

HYPSILOPHODON
An ornithischian dinosaur

POSITION OF PELVIS IN AN ORNITHISCHIAN DINOSAUR

BAROSAURUS
A saurischian dinosaur

COMPARISON OF ANIMAL STANCES

SPRAWLING STANCE
The thighs and upper arms project straight out from the body so that the knees and elbows are bent at right angles.

COMMON IGUANA
(Iguana iguana)
A present-day reptile

ERECT STANCE
The thighs and upper arms project straight down from the body so that the knees and elbows are straight.

SEMI-SPRAWLING STANCE
The thighs and upper arms project downward and outward so that the knees and elbows are slightly bent.

DWARF CROCODILE
(Osteolaemus tetraspis)
A present-day reptile

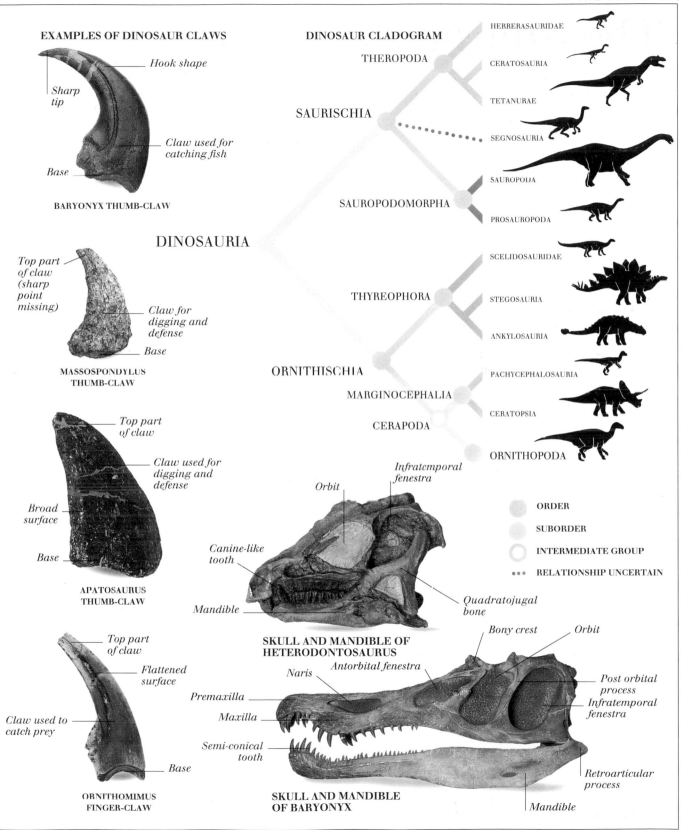

EXAMPLES OF DINOSAUR CLAWS

Hook shape

Sharp tip

Claw used for catching fish

Base

BARYONYX THUMB-CLAW

DINOSAURIA

Top part of claw (sharp point missing)

Claw for digging and defense

Base

MASSOSPONDYLUS THUMB-CLAW

Top part of claw

Claw used for digging and defense

Broad surface

Base

APATOSAURUS THUMB-CLAW

Top part of claw

Flattened surface

Claw used to catch prey

Base

ORNITHOMIMUS FINGER-CLAW

DINOSAUR CLADOGRAM

HERRERASAURIDAE

THEROPODA

CERATOSAURIA

SAURISCHIA

TETANURAE

SEGNOSAURIA

SAUROPODA

SAUROPODOMORPHA

PROSAUROPODA

SCELIDOSAURIDAE

THYREOPHORA

STEGOSAURIA

ANKYLOSAURIA

PACHYCEPHALOSAURIA

ORNITHISCHIA

MARGINOCEPHALIA

CERATOPSIA

CERAPODA

ORNITHOPODA

● ORDER

● SUBORDER

○ INTERMEDIATE GROUP

••• RELATIONSHIP UNCERTAIN

Orbit

Infratemporal fenestra

Canine-like tooth

Quadratojugal bone

Mandible

SKULL AND MANDIBLE OF HETERODONTOSAURUS

Bony crest

Orbit

Naris

Antorbital fenestra

Premaxilla

Post orbital process

Maxilla

Infratemporal fenestra

Semi-conical tooth

Retroarticular process

Mandible

SKULL AND MANDIBLE OF BARYONYX

Theropods 1

AN ENORMOUSLY SUCCESSFUL SUBORDER of the Saurischia, the bipedal (two-footed) theropods ("beast feet") emerged 230 million years ago in Late Triassic times; the oldest known example comes from South America. Theropods spanned the whole of the Age of the Dinosaurs (230–65 million years ago) and included most of the known predatory dinosaurs. The typical theropod had small arms with sharp, clawed fingers; powerful jaws lined with sharp teeth; an S-shaped neck; long, muscular hind limbs; and clawed, usually four-toed feet. Many theropods may have been warm-blooded; most were exclusively carnivorous. Theropods ranged from animals no larger than a chicken to huge creatures, such as Tyrannosaurus and Baryonyx. The group also included ostrich-like omnivores and herbivores with toothless beaks, such as Struthiomimus and Gallimimus. Many scientists believe that birds are the closest living relatives to the dinosaurs, and share a common ancestor with the theropods. Archaeopteryx, small and feathered, was the first known bird and lived alongside its dinosaur relatives.

INTERNAL ANATOMY OF ALBERTOSAURUS LEG

Ilio-tibial muscle
Ilio-femoral muscle
Femoro-tibial muscle
Internal tibial flexor muscle
Femur
Ilio-fibular muscle
Gastrocnemius muscle
Digital flexor muscle
Fibula
Tarsal
Metatarsal
Ambiens muscle
Femoro-tibial muscle
Anterior tibial muscle
Common digital extensor muscle
Toe
Claw

Cranium
Supraoccipital crest
Orbit
Naris
Cervical vertebrae
Dorsal vertebrae
Ilium
Cervical rib
Scapula
Shoulder joint
Ulna
Phalanges
Metacarpals
Wrist joint
Elbow joint
Coracoid
Rib
Humerus
Femur
Ischium
Hip joint
Pubis
Knee joint
Naris
Eye
Thigh
Scaly skin
Tail
Forelimb
Hand
Knee
Hind limb
Ankle
Toe
Foot
Claw
Phalanges
Metatarsals
Tibia
Fibula
Ankle joint
Hallux (first toe)

SKELETON OF TYRANNOSAURUS

Mandible
Serrated tooth

EXTERNAL FEATURES OF TYRANNOSAURUS

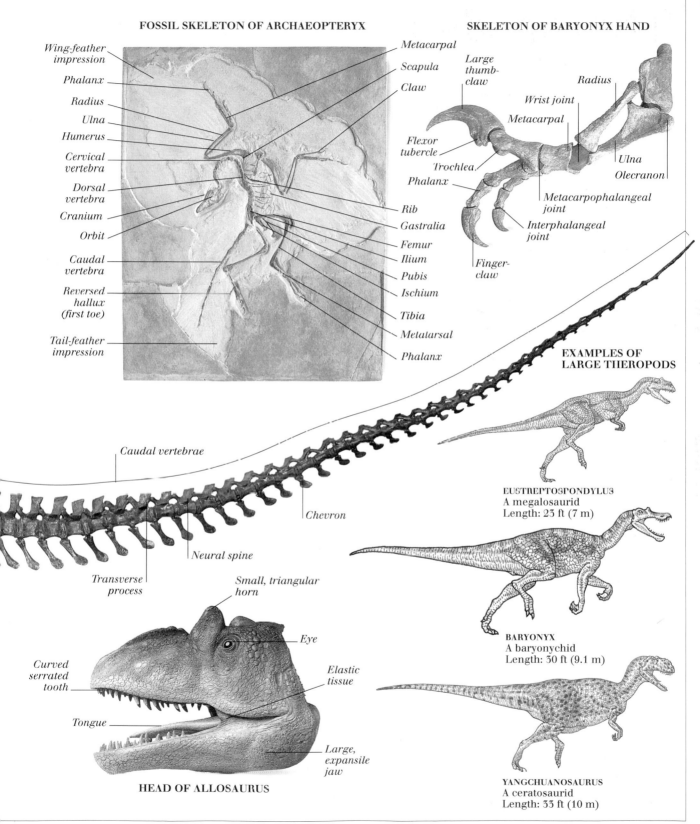

FOSSIL SKELETON OF ARCHAEOPTERYX

Wing-feather impression
Phalanx
Radius
Ulna
Humerus
Cervical vertebra
Dorsal vertebra
Cranium
Orbit
Caudal vertebra
Reversed hallux (first toe)
Tail-feather impression

Metacarpal
Scapula
Claw

Rib
Gastralia
Femur
Ilium
Pubis
Ischium
Tibia
Metatarsal
Phalanx

SKELETON OF BARYONYX HAND

Large thumb-claw
Flexor tubercle
Trochlea
Phalanx
Finger-claw

Wrist joint
Metacarpal
Radius
Ulna
Olecranon
Metacarpophalangeal joint
Interphalangeal joint

Caudal vertebrae
Chevron
Neural spine
Transverse process

EXAMPLES OF LARGE THEROPODS

EUSTREPTOSPONDYLUS
A megalosaurid
Length: 23 ft (7 m)

BARYONYX
A baryonychid
Length: 30 ft (9.1 m)

YANGCHUANOSAURUS
A ceratosaurid
Length: 33 ft (10 m)

Small, triangular horn
Eye
Elastic tissue
Curved serrated tooth
Tongue
Large, expansile jaw

HEAD OF ALLOSAURUS

Theropods 2

Eye

Toothless
beak

**EXAMPLES OF
ORNITHOMIMOSAURS**

DROMICEIOMIMUS
Length: 11 ft 6 in (3.5 m)

GARUDIMIMUS
Length: 11 ft 6 in (3.5 m)

Cervical
musculature

Scapula

Trachea

Lung

Rib

Gizzard

Dorsal
vertebra

Ovary

Kidney

Ilium

Hip joint

Femur

Shoulder joint

Coracoid

Heart

Posterior brachial
muscle

Anterior brachial
muscle

Humerus

Liver

Intestine

Anterior
antebrachial
muscle

Ulna

Posterior
antebrachial
muscle

Metacarpal

Pubis

Femoral
musculature

Tibia

Anterior
crural muscle

Eye

Snout

Short
forelimb

Grasping
claw

Long
shin

Hallux
(first toe)

Claw

Tail

Ankle

Foot

**EXTERNAL FEATURES OF AN EARLY
THEROPOD (HERRERASAURUS)**

**INTERNAL ANATOMY OF
FEMALE GALLIMIMUS**

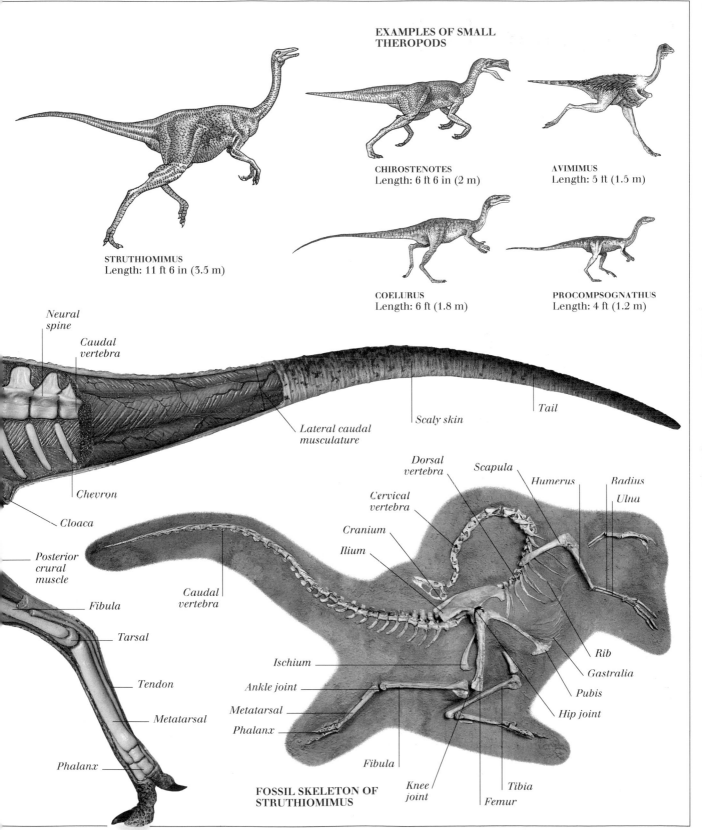

EXAMPLES OF SMALL THEROPODS

CHIROSTENOTES
Length: 6 ft 6 in (2 m)

AVIMIMUS
Length: 5 ft (1.5 m)

STRUTHIOMIMUS
Length: 11 ft 6 in (3.5 m)

COELURUS
Length: 6 ft (1.8 m)

PROCOMPSOGNATHUS
Length: 4 ft (1.2 m)

Neural spine

Caudal vertebra

Lateral caudal musculature

Scaly skin

Tail

Chevron

Cloaca

Posterior crural muscle

Fibula

Tarsal

Tendon

Metatarsal

Phalanx

Caudal vertebra

Dorsal vertebra

Scapula

Humerus

Radius

Ulna

Cervical vertebra

Cranium

Ilium

Rib

Gastralia

Pubis

Hip joint

Ischium

Ankle joint

Metatarsal

Phalanx

Fibula

Knee joint

Femur

Tibia

FOSSIL SKELETON OF STRUTHIOMIMUS

Sauropodomorphs 1

THE SAUROPODOMORPHA ("lizard-feet forms") were herbivorous, usually quadrupedal (four-footed) dinosaurs. A suborder of the Saurischia, they were characterized by small heads, bulky bodies, and long necks and tails. There were two infraorders: prosauropods and sauropods. Prosauropods lived from Late Triassic to Early Jurassic times (225–180 million years ago) and included beasts such as the small *Anchisaurus* and one of the first very large dinosaurs, *Plateosaurus*. By Middle Jurassic times (about 165 million years ago), sauropods had replaced prosauropods and spread worldwide. They included the heaviest and longest land animals ever, such as *Diplodocus* and *Brachiosaurus*. Sauropods persisted to the end of the Cretaceous period (65 million years ago). Many of these dinosaurs moved in herds, protected from predatory theropods by their huge bulk and powerful tails, which they could use to lash out at attackers. Sauropodomorphs were the most common large herbivores until Late Jurassic times (about 145 million years ago), and appear to have survived in southern continents long after they had disappeared from the north.

THECODONTOSAURUS

SKULL AND MANDIBLE OF PLATEOSAURUS

Naris

Antorbital fenestra

Orbit

Mandible

Infratemporal fenestra

Paroccipital process

Serrated, leaf-shaped tooth

Mandibular fenestra

SKELETON OF PLATEOSAURUS

Dorsal vertebrae

Sacral vertebrae

Ilium

Cervical vertebrae

Humerus

Scapula

Shoulder joint

Hip joint

Pubis

Femur

Ischium

Thumb claw

Rib

Elbow joint

Knee joint

Tail

Radius

Tibia

Wrist joint

Ulna

Fibula

Metacarpal

Ankle joint

Cranium

Metatarsals

Phalanx

Orbit

Mandible

Phalanges

Naris

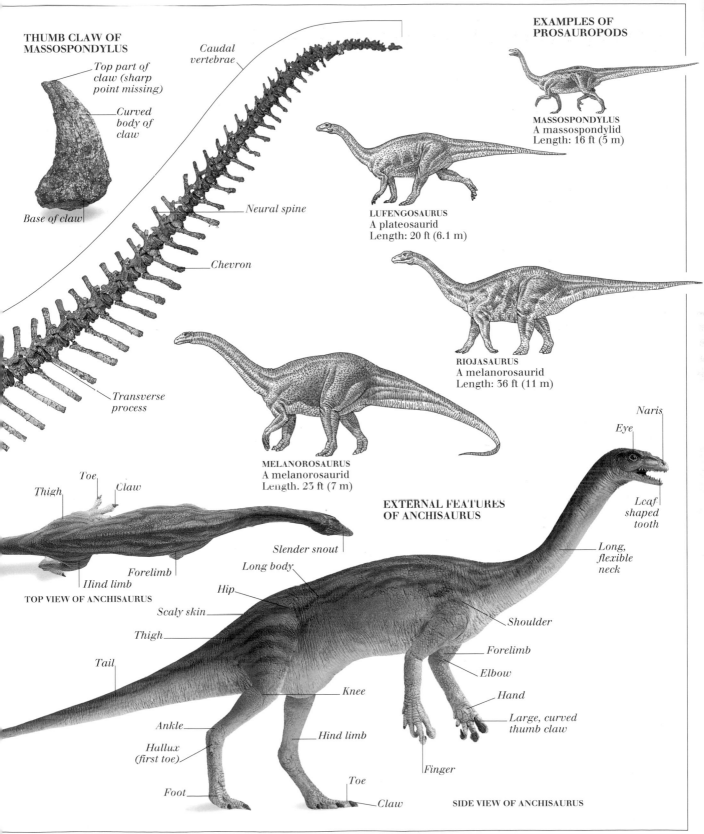

THUMB CLAW OF MASSOSPONDYLUS

Top part of claw (sharp point missing)

Curved body of claw

Base of claw

Caudal vertebrae

Neural spine

Chevron

Transverse process

EXAMPLES OF PROSAUROPODS

MASSOSPONDYLUS
A massospondylid
Length: 16 ft (5 m)

LUFENGOSAURUS
A plateosaurid
Length: 20 ft (6.1 m)

RIOJASAURUS
A melanorosaurid
Length: 36 ft (11 m)

MELANOROSAURUS
A melanorosaurid
Length. 23 ft (7 m)

Thigh

Toe

Claw

Forelimb

Hind limb

TOP VIEW OF ANCHISAURUS

EXTERNAL FEATURES OF ANCHISAURUS

Naris

Eye

Leaf shaped tooth

Long, flexible neck

Slender snout

Long body

Hip

Scaly skin

Thigh

Tail

Knee

Ankle

Hallux (first toe)

Hind limb

Foot

Toe

Claw

Shoulder

Forelimb

Elbow

Hand

Large, curved thumb claw

Finger

SIDE VIEW OF ANCHISAURUS

Sauropodomorphs 2

Orbit

Antorbital
fenestra

Cranium

Maxillary
fenestra

Maxilla

Sclerotic
ring

Peg-shaped
tooth

Infratemporal
fenestra

Mandible

**SKULL AND MANDIBLE
OF DIPLODOCUS**

FOREFOOT OF
ELEPHANT

FOREFOOT BONES
OF ELEPHANT

Radius

Ulna

Carpals

Metacarpals

Wrist

Phalanges

Nail

**COMPARISON OF
THE FOREFEET
OF AN ELEPHANT
AND DIPLODOCUS**

FOREFOOT BONES
OF DIPLODOCUS

Radius

Ulna

Carpals

Metacarpals

Caudal
vertebra

Phalanges

Coracoid

Dorsal
vertebra

Scapula

Sacral vertebra

Ilium

Neural
spine

Small
intestine

Dorsal vertebra

Ovary

Kidney

Rib

Large intestine

Hip joint

Ischium

Hip joint

Cecum

Pubis

Femur

Humerus

Rib

Knee joint

Femur

Oviduct

Elbow joint

Ankle joint

Cloaca

Ulna

Tibia

Radius

Fibula

Wrist joint

Phalanges

Metacarpals

MIDDLE SECTION OF DIPLODOCUS SKELETON

Thigh
musculature

Posterior crural
musculature

Caudal
musculature

Fibula

Ankle joint

Anterior
crural
muscle

Metatarsal

**FOSSIL EGG OF
TITANOSAURID**

*Fossil eggshell
fragment*

*Fossil
egg*

*Fossil eggshell
fragment*

Outer ear

Naris

Eye

Mouth

Orbit

Antorbital fenestra

Naris

Maxilla

Cranium

*Spoon-
shaped
tooth*

*Infratemporal
fenestra*

Mandible

**SKULL AND MANDIBLE
OF CAMARASAURUS**

**INTERNAL ANATOMY OF
FEMALE BRACHIOSAURUS**

Cervical vertebra
Scapula

Trachea

Esophagus

Intercostal muscle

Scapular muscle

Shoulder joint

Lung

Humerus

Gizzard

*Anterior brachial
muscle*

*Posterior brachial
musculature*

Elbow joint

Radius

Ulna

*Posterior antebrachial
musculature*

Wrist joint

Metacarpal

CETIOSAURUS
A cetiosaurid
Length: 59 ft (18 m)

SHUNOSAURUS
A cetiosaurid
Length: 33 ft (10 m)

SALTASAURUS
A titanosaurid
Length: 40 ft (12.2 m)

DIPLODOCUS
A diplodocid
Length: 90 ft (27.4 m)

Thyreophorans 1

THYREOPHORANS ("SHIELD BEARERS") were a group of quadrupedal armoured dinosaurs. A sub-order of the Ornithischia (bird-hipped dinosaurs), they were characterized by rows of bony studs, plates, or spikes along the back, which protected some from predators and may have helped others regulate body temperature. Up to 30ft (9m) long, with a small head and small cheek teeth, Thyreophorans had shorter forelimbs than hind limbs and probably browsed on low-level vegetation. The earliest thyreophorans were small and lived in Early Jurassic times (about 200 million years ago) in Europe, North America, and China. Stegosaurs, such as Stegosaurus and Kentrosaurus, replaced these older forms. The earliest stegosaur remains come mainly from China. Several genera of stegosaurs survived into the Early Cretaceous period (146–100 million years ago), but only in India did they persist into Late Cretaceous times (97–65 million years ago). Ankylosaurs, with their toothless beaks and cheek teeth adapted for cropping vegetation, appeared later than stegosaurs. They originated in the Late Jurassic period (155 million years ago) and in North America survived until 65 million years ago.

TUOJIANGOSAURUS
A stegosaurid
Length: 23 ft (7 m)

Dorsal plate

Hip

Thigh

Cervical plate

Eye

Naris

Beak

Cheek

Neck

Outer ear

Knee

Shoulder

Short forelimb

Long hind limb

Elbow

Ankle

Nail

Wrist

Hind foot

EXTERNAL FEATURES OF STEGOSAURUS

Nail

Forefoot

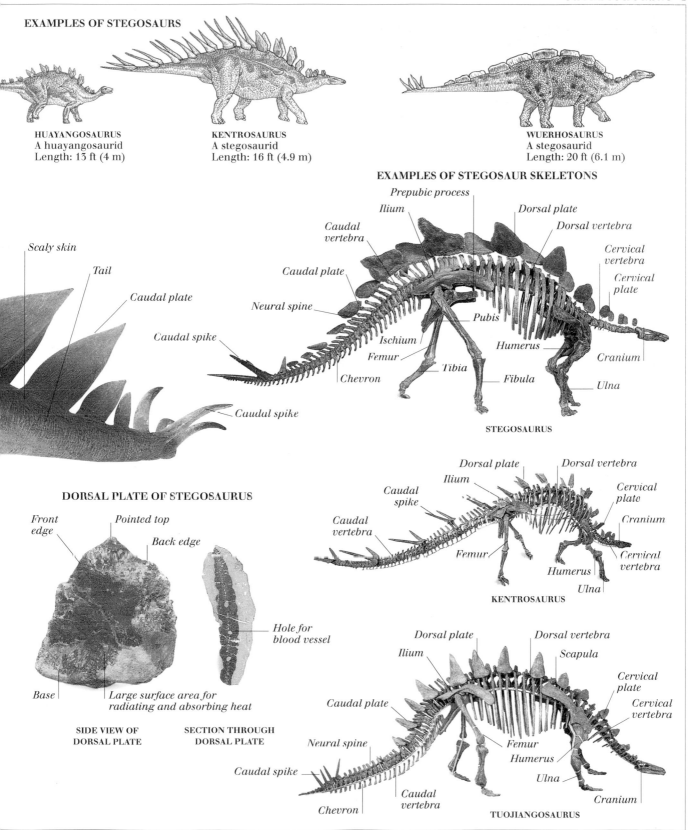

EXAMPLES OF STEGOSAURS

HUAYANGOSAURUS
A huayangosaurid
Length: 13 ft (4 m)

KENTROSAURUS
A stegosaurid
Length: 16 ft (4.9 m)

WUERHOSAURUS
A stegosaurid
Length: 20 ft (6.1 m)

EXAMPLES OF STEGOSAUR SKELETONS

Scaly skin

Tail

Caudal plate

Caudal spike

Caudal spike

Prepubic process
Ilium
Caudal vertebra
Caudal plate
Neural spine
Dorsal plate
Dorsal vertebra
Cervical vertebra
Cervical plate
Pubis
Ischium
Femur
Chevron
Tibia
Fibula
Humerus
Cranium
Ulna

STEGOSAURUS

DORSAL PLATE OF STEGOSAURUS

Front edge

Pointed top

Back edge

Hole for blood vessel

Base

Large surface area for radiating and absorbing heat

SIDE VIEW OF DORSAL PLATE

SECTION THROUGH DORSAL PLATE

Dorsal plate
Ilium
Caudal spike
Caudal vertebra
Dorsal vertebra
Cervical plate
Cranium
Femur
Humerus
Ulna
Cervical vertebra

KENTROSAURUS

Dorsal plate
Ilium
Caudal plate
Neural spine
Caudal spike
Chevron
Caudal vertebra
Dorsal vertebra
Scapula
Cervical plate
Cervical vertebra
Femur
Humerus
Ulna
Cranium

TUOJIANGOSAURUS

Thyreophorans 2

EXAMPLES OF ANKYLOSAUR SKULLS

Maxilla

Orbit

Posterolateral horn

Naris

Cranium

Beak

Tooth

Mandible

Jugal plate

SKULL AND MANDIBLE OF EUOPLOCEPHALUS

Posterolateral horn

Nasal bone

Maxilla

Cranium

Orbit

Naris

Beak

Tooth

Mandible

SKULL AND MANDIBLE OF ANKYLOSAURUS

Orbit

Beak

Nasal bone

Naris

Cranium

Infratemporal fenestra

Mandible

SKULL AND MANDIBLE OF PANOPLOSAURUS

Dorsal vertebra

Small intestine

Iliotibial muscle

Rib

Gizzard

Scapula

Lung

Ilium

Reproductive canal

Shoulder spike

Ischium

Coracoid

Cervical musculature

Head horn

Humerus

Radius

Wrist joint

Heart

Ilio-tibial muscle

Femur

Metacarpal

Liver

Knee joint

Fibula

Gastrocnemius muscle

Toothless beak

Elbow joint

Large intestine

Ankle joint

Ventral antebrachial muscle

Ulna

Digital extensor muscle

Metatarsal

INTERNAL ANATOMY OF FEMALE EUOPLOCEPHALUS

EXTERNAL FEATURES OF EDMONTONIA

EXAMPLES OF ANKYLOSAURS

Hind limb

Flank spike

Dorsal scute

Dermal armor

Scaly skin

Nuchal ring

Shoulder spike

Broad, flat snout

Naris

Ankle

Elbow

Forelimb

Forefoot

Blunt nail

Caudal vertebra

Neural spine

Ureter

Chevron

Cloaca

Lateral caudal musculature

PINACOSAURUS
An ankylosaurid
Length: 16 ft 6 in (5 m)

MINMI
A nodosaurid
Length: 8 ft (2.4 m)

POLACANTHUS
A nodosaurid
Length: 13 ft (4 m)

Terminal plate

Lateral plate

Ossified caudal vertebra

FOSSIL OF ANKYLOSAURUS TAIL CLUB

Tail club

Ornithopods 1

IGUANODON TOOTH

ORNITHOPODS ("BIRD FEET") were a group of ornithischian ("bird-hipped") dinosaurs. These bipedal and quadrupedal herbivores had a horny beak, plant-cutting or grinding cheek teeth, and a pelvic and tail region stiffened by bony tendons. They evolved teeth and jaws adapted to pulping vegetation and flourished from the Middle Jurassic to the Late Cretaceous period (165–65 million years ago) in North America, Europe, Africa, China, Australia, and Antarctica. Some ornithopods were no larger than a dog, while others were immense creatures up to 49 ft (15 m) long. Iguanodonts, an ornithopod group, had a broad, toothless beak at the end of a long snout, large jaws with long rows of ridged, closely packed teeth for grinding vegetation, a bulky body, and a heavy tail. *Iguanodon* and some other iguanodonts had large thumb-spikes that were strong enough to stab attackers. Another group, the hadrosaurs, such as *Gryposaurus* and *Hadrosaurus,* lived in Late Cretaceous times (97–65 million years ago) and with their broad beaks are sometimes known as "duckbills." They were characterized by their deep skulls and closely packed rows of teeth, while some, such as *Corythosaurus* and *Lambeosaurus,* had tall, hollow, bony head crests.

SKELETON OF IGUANODON

Orbit
Cranium
Naris
Mandible
Cervical vertebra
Cervical rib
Scapula
Dorsal vertebra
Humerus
Sternal bone
Radius
Sacral vertebra
Ulna
Caudal vertebra
Prepubic process
Neural spine
Femur
Pubis
Tibia
Ilium
Chevron
Fibula
Ischium
Metatarsal

Thigh
Heavy, stiff tail
Knee
Hind limb
Ankle
Toe
Foot
Hooflike nail

SKULL AND MANDIBLE OF YOUNG IGUANODON

Cheek tooth
Orbit
Cranium
Maxilla
Premaxilla
Paroccipital process
Jugal bone
Coronoid process
Predentary bone
Dentary bone
Mandible

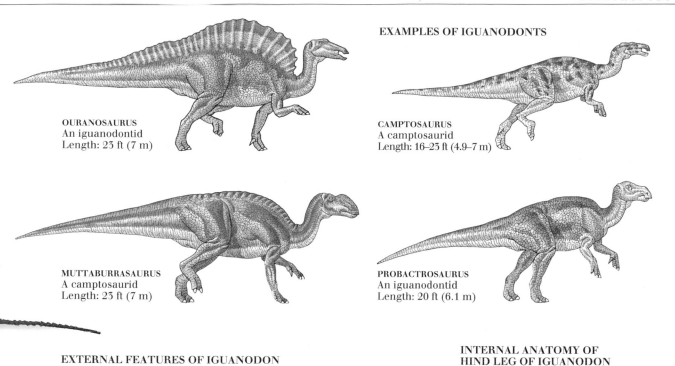

EXAMPLES OF IGUANODONTS

OURANOSAURUS
An iguanodontid
Length: 23 ft (7 m)

CAMPTOSAURUS
A camptosaurid
Length: 16–23 ft (4.9–7 m)

MUTTABURRASAURUS
A camptosaurid
Length: 23 ft (7 m)

PROBACTROSAURUS
An iguanodontid
Length: 20 ft (6.1 m)

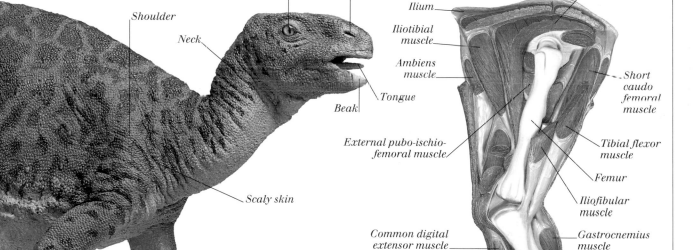

EXTERNAL FEATURES OF IGUANODON

Eye

Naris

Shoulder

Neck

Tongue

Beak

Scaly skin

Forelimb

Elbow

Wrist

Hand

Finger

Thumb-spike

Hooflike nail

**INTERNAL ANATOMY OF
HIND LEG OF IGUANODON**

Iliofemoral
muscle

Ilium

Iliotibial
muscle

Ambiens
muscle

Short
caudo
femoral
muscle

External pubo-ischio-
femoral muscle

Tibial flexor
muscle

Femur

Iliofibular
muscle

Common digital
extensor muscle

Gastrocnemius
muscle

Anterior tibial
muscle

Tibia

Fibula

Tarsal

Metatarsal

Toe

Hooflike nail

Ornithopods 2

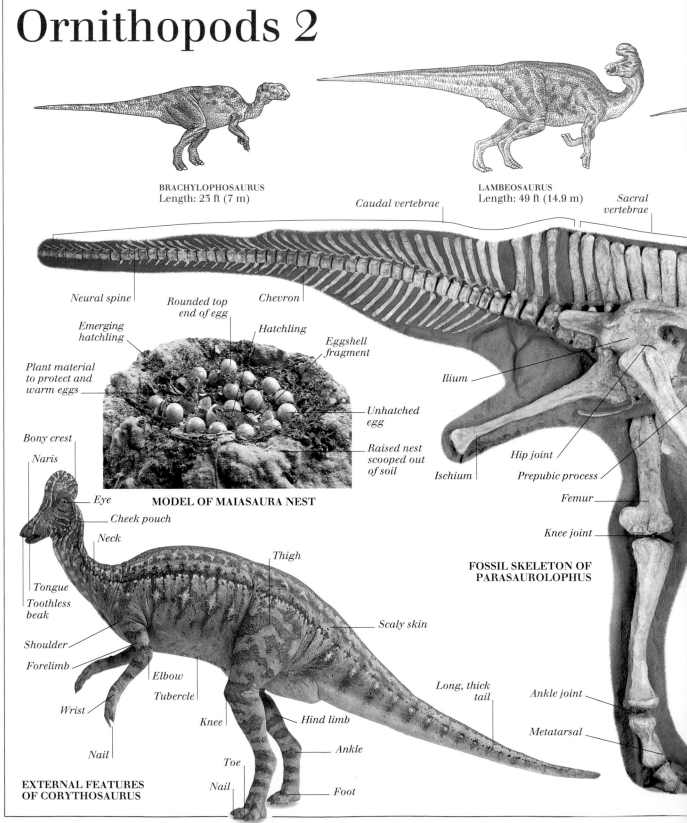

BRACHYLOPHOSAURUS
Length: 23 ft (7 m)

LAMBEOSAURUS
Length: 49 ft (14.9 m)

Caudal vertebrae

Sacral vertebrae

Neural spine

Rounded top end of egg

Chevron

Emerging hatchling

Hatchling

Eggshell fragment

Plant material to protect and warm eggs

Ilium

Unhatched egg

Bony crest

Raised nest scooped out of soil

Hip joint

Naris

Ischium

Prepubic process

Eye

MODEL OF MAIASAURA NEST

Femur

Cheek pouch

Neck

Thigh

Knee joint

Tongue

FOSSIL SKELETON OF PARASAUROLOPHUS

Toothless beak

Scaly skin

Shoulder

Forelimb

Elbow

Long, thick tail

Ankle joint

Tubercle

Wrist

Knee

Hind limb

Metatarsal

Nail

Ankle

Toe

EXTERNAL FEATURES OF CORYTHOSAURUS

Nail

Foot

EXAMPLES OF HADROSAURS

HYPACROSAURUS
Length: 30 ft (9.1 m)

HADROSAURUS
Length: 26–33 ft (7.9–10 m)

GRYPOSAURUS
Length: 26–33 ft (7.9–10 m)

Dorsal vertebrae

Bony crest

Air passage

Cranium

Infratemporal fenestra

Orbit

Cervical vertebrae

Mandible

Naris

Orbit

Infratemporal fenestra

Air passage

Naris

Mandible

Tooth

SKULL AND MANDIBLE OF JUVENILE LAMBEOSAURUS

Scapula

Shoulder joint

Tibia

Rib

Fibula

Humerus

Elbow joint

Radius

Wrist joint

Ulna

Phalanges

Metacarpal

Phalanges

Sclerotic ring

Cranium

Bony crest

Orbit

Naris

Infratemporal fenestra

Mandible

Premaxilla

SKULL AND MANDIBLE OF ADULT LAMBEOSAURUS

Marginocephalians 1

Thick, high-domed cranium
Supraorbital ridge
Orbit
Naris
Mandible
Neural spine

MARGINOCEPHALIA ("margined heads") were a group of bipedal and quadrupedal ornithischian dinosaurs with a narrow shelf or deep, bony frill at the back of the skull. Marginocephalians were probably descended from the same ancestor as the ornithopods and lived in what are now North America, Africa, Asia, and Europe during the Cretaceous period (146–65 million years ago). They were divided into two infraorders: Pachycephalosauria ("thick-headed lizards"), such as *Pachycephalosaurus* and *Stegoceras*, and Ceratopsia ("horned faces"), such as *Triceratops* and *Psittacosaurus*. The thick skulls of Pachycephalosauria protected their brains during head-butting contests fought to win territory and mates; their hips and spines were also strengthened to withstand the shock. The bony frill of Ceratopsia would have added to their frightening appearance when charging; the neck was strengthened for impact and to support the huge head, with its snipping beak and powerful slicing toothed jaws. A charging ceratops would have been a formidable opponent for even the largest predators. Ceratopsia were among the most abundant herbivorous dinosaurs of the Late Cretaceous period (97–65 million years ago).

HEAD-BUTTING PRENOCEPHALES

Cervical rib
Humerus
Ulna
Radius
Prepubis
Wrist joint
Metacarpal
Phalanx
Ilium
Ischium
Metatarsals
Phalanges

EXAMPLES OF SKULLS OF PACHYCEPHALOSAURS

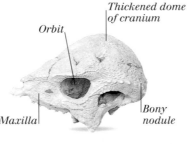

Orbit
Thickened dome of cranium
Maxilla
Bony ridge
Tooth
Mandible

SKULL AND MANDIBLE OF STEGOCERAS

Orbit
Thickened dome of cranium
Maxilla
Bony nodule

SKULL OF PRENOCEPHALE

Thickened dome of cranium
Bony spike
Maxilla
Orbit
Bony nodule

SKULL OF PACHYCEPHALOSAURUS

EXTERNAL FEATURES OF PACHYCEPHALOSAURUS

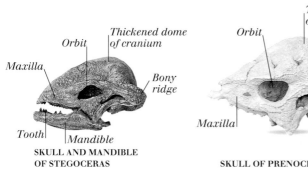

Scaly skin
Bony nodule
Domed head
Eye
Bony spike
Neck
Snout
Forelimb
Finger
Hand
Claw
Toe
Foot
Ankle
Hind limb
Knee
Tail

Thickened dome of cranium
Bony nodule
Buccal cavity
Brain cavity

SECTION THROUGH SKULL OF PACHYCEPHALOSAURUS

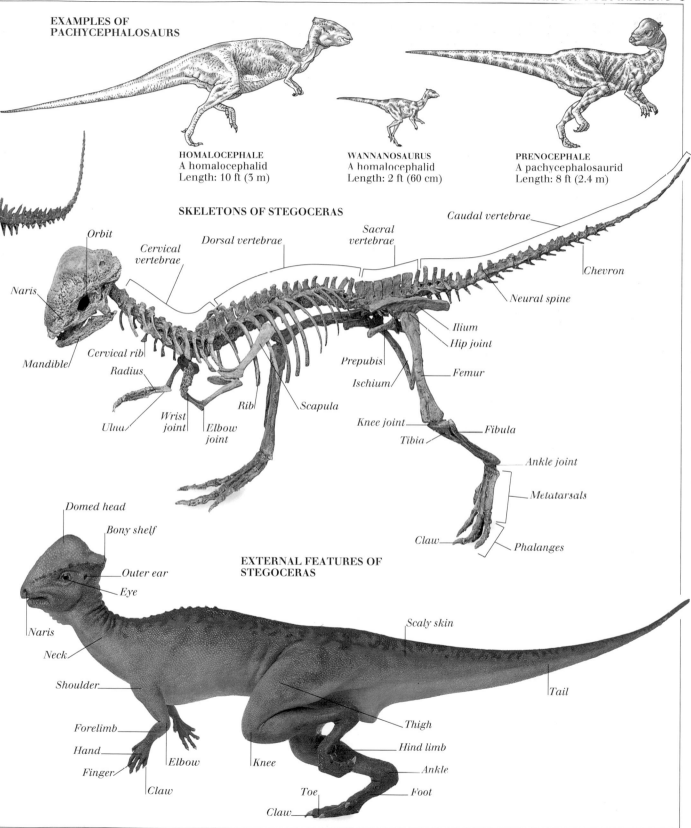

EXAMPLES OF PACHYCEPHALOSAURS

HOMALOCEPHALE
A homalocephalid
Length: 10 ft (3 m)

WANNANOSAURUS
A homalocephalid
Length: 2 ft (60 cm)

PRENOCEPHALE
A pachycephalosaurid
Length: 8 ft (2.4 m)

SKELETONS OF STEGOCERAS

Orbit

Cervical vertebrae

Dorsal vertebrae

Sacral vertebrae

Caudal vertebrae

Chevron

Neural spine

Naris

Ilium

Hip joint

Prepubis

Femur

Mandible

Cervical rib

Radius

Ischium

Rib

Scapula

Wrist joint

Elbow joint

Ulna

Knee joint

Tibia

Fibula

Ankle joint

Metatarsals

Claw

Phalanges

Domed head

Bony shelf

EXTERNAL FEATURES OF STEGOCERAS

Outer ear

Eye

Scaly skin

Naris

Neck

Shoulder

Tail

Forelimb

Hand

Thigh

Finger

Elbow

Knee

Hind limb

Claw

Ankle

Toe

Foot

Claw

Marginocephalians 2

Parietal fenestra

Epoccipital bone

Parietosquamosal frill

Nose-horn core

Supraorbital ridge

Naris

Orbit

Cranium

Mandible

SKULL AND MANDIBLE OF STYRACOSAURUS

Parietosquamosal frill

Epoccipital bone

Brow horn

Nose horn

Thick, scaly skin

Thigh

Tail

Ankle

Nail

Hind limb

Elbow

Forelimb

Wrist

Eye

Naris

Toothless beak

EXTERNAL FEATURES OF TRICERATOPS

Parietosquamosal frill

Cranium

Postorbital bone

Nasal bone

Orbit

Lacrimal bone

Naris

Beak

Rostral bone

Predentary bone

Dentary bone

Tooth

Mandible

Parietal fenestra

Infratemporal fenestra

Jugal bone

Surangular bone

Angular bone

SKULL AND MANDIBLE OF PROTOCERATOPS

Prepubis

Ilium

Hip joint

Dorsal vertebrae

Ischium

Femur

Knee joint

Fibula

Tibia

Ankle joint

Metatarsals

Phalanges

Caudal vertebra

Chevron

Neural spine

Rib

Scapula

Humerus

Elbow joint

Ulna

Sternal bone

Coracoid

Shoulder joint

Radius

SKELETON OF TRICERATOPS

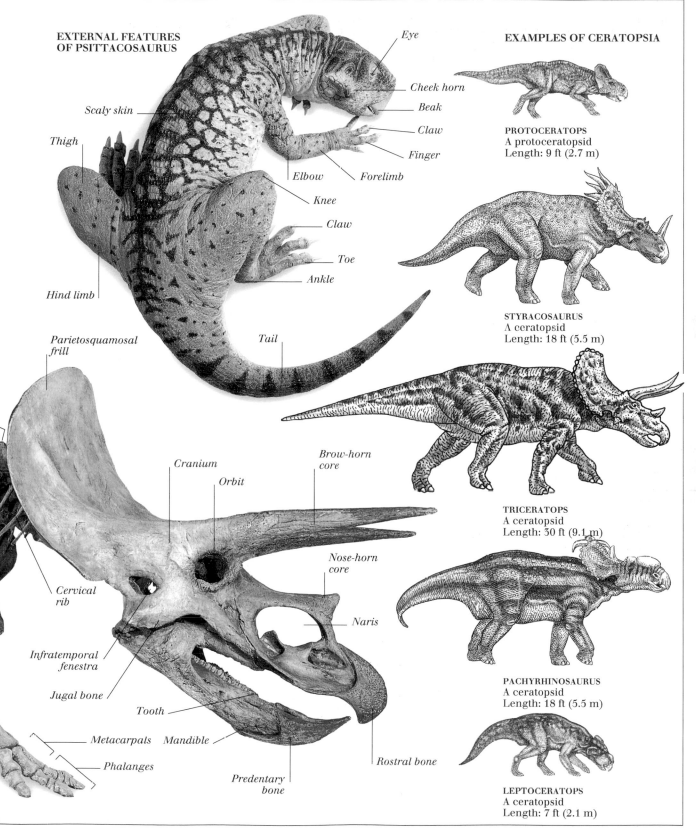

**EXTERNAL FEATURES
OF PSITTACOSAURUS**

Eye

Cheek horn

Beak

Claw

Finger

Scaly skin

Thigh

Elbow

Forelimb

Knee

Claw

Toe

Ankle

Hind limb

*Parietosquamosal
frill*

Tail

Cranium

Orbit

*Brow-horn
core*

*Nose-horn
core*

Naris

*Cervical
rib*

*Infratemporal
fenestra*

Jugal bone

Tooth

Metacarpals *Mandible*

Phalanges

*Predentary
bone*

Rostral bone

EXAMPLES OF CERATOPSIA

PROTOCERATOPS
A protoceratopsid
Length: 9 ft (2.7 m)

STYRACOSAURUS
A ceratopsid
Length: 18 ft (5.5 m)

TRICERATOPS
A ceratopsid
Length: 30 ft (9.1 m)

PACHYRHINOSAURUS
A ceratopsid
Length: 18 ft (5.5 m)

LEPTOCERATOPS
A ceratopsid
Length: 7 ft (2.1 m)

Mammals 1

TETRALOPHODON CHEEK TEETH

SINCE THE EXTINCTION of the dinosaurs 65 million years ago, mammals have been the dominant vertebrates on land. This class includes terrestrial, aerial, and aquatic forms. Having developed from the reptilian Therapsids, the first true mammals— small, nocturnal, shrewlike creatures, such as *Megazostrodon*— appeared over 200 million years ago during the Triassic period (245–208 million years ago). Mammals had several features that improved on those of their reptilian ancestors: an efficient four-chambered heart allowed these warm-blooded animals to sustain high levels of activity; a covering of hair helped them maintain a constant body temperature; an improved limb structure gave them more efficient locomotion; and the birth of live young and the immediate supply of food from the mother's milk aided their rapid growth. Since the end of the Mesozoic era (65 million years ago), the number of different mammal orders and the abundance of species in each order have varied dramatically. For example, the Perissodactyla (the order that includes *Coelodonta* and modern horses) was a common group during the Early Tertiary period (about 54 million years ago). Today, the mammalian orders with the most populous species are the Rodentia (rats and mice), the Chiroptera (bats), the Primates (monkeys and apes), the Carnivora (bears, cats, and dogs), and the Artiodactyla (cattle, deer, and pigs), while the Proboscidea order, which formerly included many genera, such as *Phiomia, Moeritherium, Tetralophodon,* and *Mammuthus,* now has only three species of elephant. In Australia and South America, millions of years of continental isolation led to increased diversity of the marsupials, a group of mammals distinct from the placentals (see p. 74) that existed elsewhere.

Long tail aids balance

Insulating hair

Neural spine

Scapula

Cervical vertebra

Humerus

Nasal horn

Naris

Orbit

Mandible

Predentary bone

Radius

Ulna

Chisel-edged molar

Metacarpal

Phalanx

UPPER JAWBONE (MAXILLA) OF A HORSE

Molars

Premolars

HOOFBONE (THIRD PHALANX) OF A HORSE

Articular surface

Tendon insertion

Cranium

Naris

Predentary bone

Molar tooth

SKULL AND MANDIBLE OF A MOERITHERIUM

Nasal tusk

Molar tooth

Shovel-shaped tusk

SKULL AND MANDIBLE OF A PHIOMIA

Trunk

Thick hide

Short tusk used for rooting up plants

MODEL OF A PHIOMIA

Dorsal vertebra

Ilium

Ball and socket joint

Pubis

Rib

Caudal vertebra

Femur

Tibia

Fibula

Metatarsal

Phalanx

SKELETON OF AN ARSINOITHERIUM

Cranium
Mandible
Teeth
Elongated digit

Humerus

Hind limb bone

FOSSIL SKELETON OF A BAT

Mammals 2

LOWER JAW OF A BEAR

Articulation with skull

Large canine

Diastema

Low cusp

Molar

Premolar

SKELETON OF A TOXODON

Scapula

Neural spine

Cervical vertebra

Coronoid process

Cranium

Zygomatic arch

Orbit

Maxilla

Nasal bone

Incisor

Canine

Mandible

Molar

Humerus

Radius

Ulna

Large breastbone

Metacarpals

SKULL OF AN OPOSSUM

Orbit

Cranium

Naris

Occipital region

Canine

Infraorbital foramen

Molar

**FOSSIL SKULL OF
AN HYAENODON**

Orbit

Naris

Sagittal crest

Cranium

Canine

Neck
insertion

Infraorbital
foramen

Mandible

Molar

**LOWER JAW OF AN
AUSTRALOPITHECUS**

Expanded
occlusal
surface

Premolar

Molar

SKULL OF A SMILODON

Orbit

Muscle scar

Naris

Sagittal crest

Infraorbital
foramen

Occipital
condyle

Canine

Dentary
bone

Slicing
tooth

Zygomatic
arch

Ilium

Rib

Femur

Knee
joint

Tibia

Fibula

Metatarsals

Phalanx

Thick,
insulating
coat

Ivory tusk

Woolly
underhair

Hairy trunk

RECONSTRUCTION OF A MAMMOTH

The first hominids

MODERN HUMANS BELONG TO THE MAMMALIAN order of primates
(see pp. 202–203), which originated about 55 million years ago; they
comprise the only extant hominid species. The earliest hominid was
Australopithecus ("southern ape"), a small-brained intermediate between
apes and humans that was capable of standing and walking upright. *Homo
habilis*, the first known human appeared at least 2 million years ago. This
larger-brained "handy man" began making tools for hunting. *Homo erectus*
first appeared in Africa about 1.8 million years ago and spread into Asia about
800,000 years later. Smaller toothed than *Homo habilis*, it developed fire as a
tool, which enabled it to cook food. Neanderthals, a near relative of modern
humans, originated about 200,000 years ago, and *Homo sapiens* (modern humans)
appeared in Africa about 100,000 years later. The two coexisted for thousands of
years, but by 30,000 years ago, *Homo sapiens* had become dominant and the
Neanderthals had died out. Classification of *Homo sapiens* in relation to its ancestors
is enormously problematic: modern humans must be classified not only by bone structure,
but also by specific behavior—the ability to plan future action; to follow traditions;
and to use symbolic communication, including complex language and the
ability to use and recognize symbols.

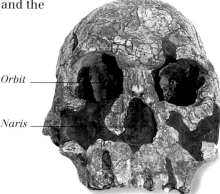

**JAWBONE OF AUSTRALOPITHECUS
(SOUTHERN APE)**

*Larger jawbone
than modern
human*

*Large back
tooth*

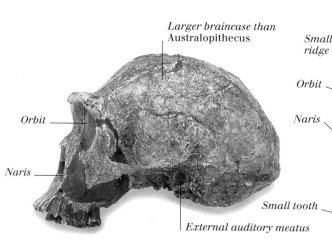

*Jutting brow
ridge*

Cranium

Orbit

Naris

*Jutting
jawbone*

**SKULL OF AUSTRALOPITHECUS
(SOUTHERN APE)**

Orbit

Naris

**SKULL OF HOMO HABILIS
(FIRST KNOWN HUMAN)**

Larger braincase than
Australopithecus

Orbit

Naris

External auditory meatus

SKULL OF HOMO ERECTUS (UPRIGHT MAN)

*Well-rounded
cranium*

*Small brow
ridge*

Orbit

Naris

Small tooth

*External
auditory meatus*

SKULL OF HOMO SAPIENS (MODERN HUMAN)

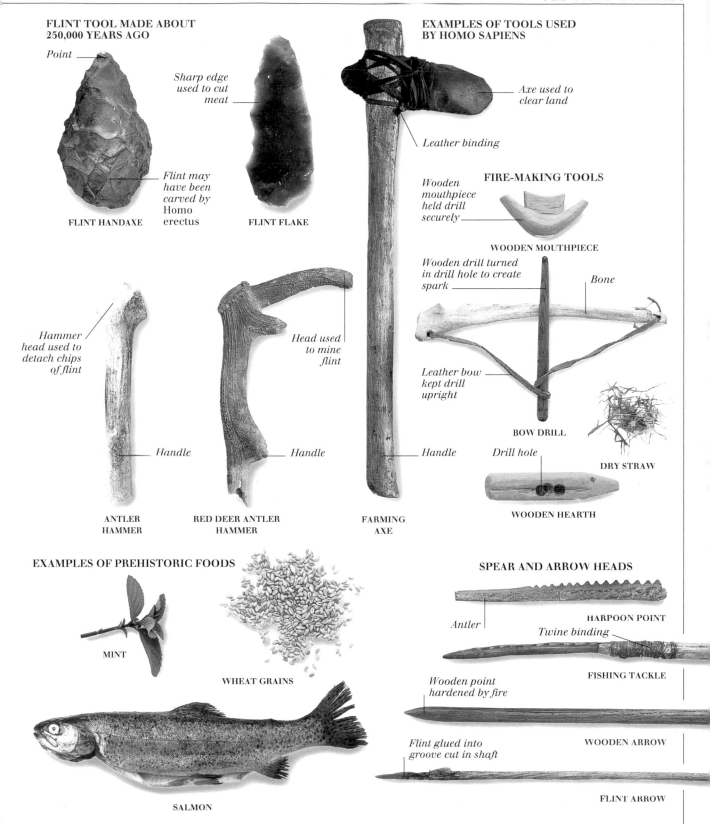

FLINT TOOL MADE ABOUT 250,000 YEARS AGO

Point

Sharp edge used to cut meat

Flint may have been carved by Homo erectus

FLINT HANDAXE

FLINT FLAKE

EXAMPLES OF TOOLS USED BY HOMO SAPIENS

Axe used to clear land

Leather binding

FIRE-MAKING TOOLS

Wooden mouthpiece held drill securely

WOODEN MOUTHPIECE

Wooden drill turned in drill hole to create spark

Bone

Leather bow kept drill upright

BOW DRILL

DRY STRAW

Drill hole

WOODEN HEARTH

Hammer head used to detach chips of flint

Handle

Head used to mine flint

Handle

Handle

ANTLER HAMMER

RED DEER ANTLER HAMMER

FARMING AXE

EXAMPLES OF PREHISTORIC FOODS

MINT

WHEAT GRAINS

SALMON

SPEAR AND ARROW HEADS

Antler

HARPOON POINT

Twine binding

FISHING TACKLE

Wooden point hardened by fire

WOODEN ARROW

Flint glued into groove cut in shaft

FLINT ARROW

PLANTS

Plant varieties

THERE ARE MORE THAN 300,000 SPECIES of plants. They
show a wide diversity of forms, ranging from delicate liverworts, adapted for life
in a damp habitat, to cacti, capable of surviving in the desert. The plant kingdom includes
herbaceous plants, such as corn, which completes its life cycle in one year, to the giant redwood tree, which
can live for thousands of years. This diversity reflects the adaptations of plants to survive in a wide range of
habitats. This is seen most clearly in the flowering plants (phylum Angiospermophyta), which are the most
numerous, with over 250,000 species. They are also the most widespread, being found from the tropics to the
arctic. Despite their diversity, plants share certain characteristics. Typically, plants are green, and make their
food by photosynthesis. Most plants live in or on a substrate, such as soil, and do not actively move. Algae
(kingdom Protista) and fungi (kingdom Fungi) have some plantlike characteristics and are
often studied alongside plants, although they are not true plants.

GREEN ALGA
Micrograph of desmid
(*Micrasterias sp.*)

*Pyrenoid
(small protein
body)*

Chloroplast

*Sinus
(division between
two halves of cell)*

Cell wall

FERN
Tree fern
(*Dicksonia antarctica*)

*Rachis
(main axis
of pinnate leaf)*

*Petiole
(leaf stalk)*

*Ramentum
(brown scale)*

*Base of dead
frond (leaf)*

Trunk

*Adventitious
root*

*Epiphytic
fern growing
at base*

BRYOPHYTE
Moss
(*Bryum sp.*)

*Seta
(stalk)*

Immature capsule

*Sporophyte
(spore-
producing
plant)*

*Capsule
(site of spore
production)*

"Leaf"

*Gametophyte
(gamete-producing
plant)*

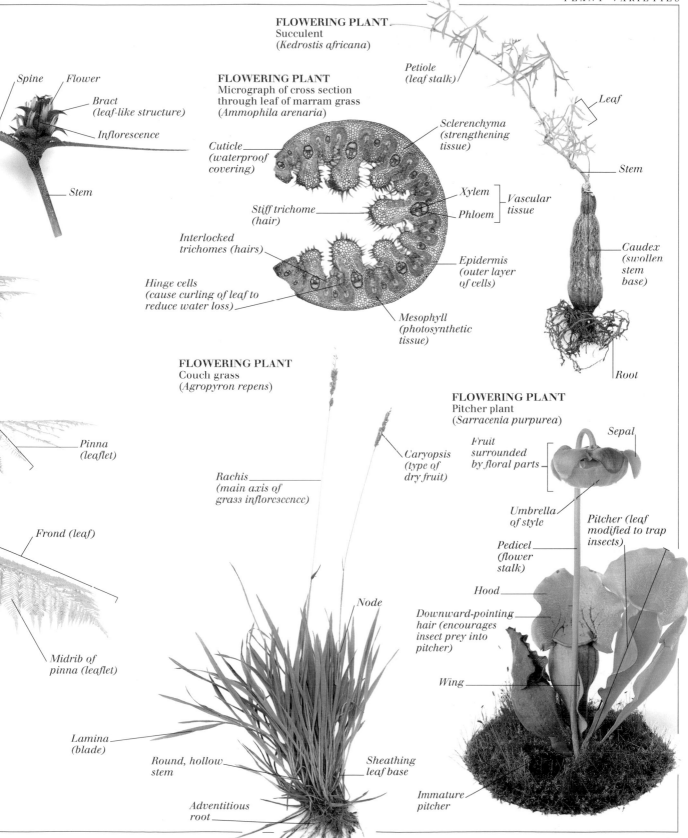

FLOWERING PLANT
Succulent
(*Kedrostis africana*)

*Petiole
(leaf stalk)*

Leaf

Stem

*Caudex
(swollen
stem
base)*

Root

FLOWERING PLANT
Micrograph of cross section
through leaf of marram grass
(*Ammophila arenaria*)

*Cuticle
(waterproof
covering)*

*Sclerenchyma
(strengthening
tissue)*

Xylem

Phloem

*Vascular
tissue*

*Stiff trichome
(hair)*

*Interlocked
trichomes (hairs)*

*Epidermis
(outer layer
of cells)*

*Hinge cells
(cause curling of leaf to
reduce water loss)*

*Mesophyll
(photosynthetic
tissue)*

Spine *Flower*

*Bract
(leaf-like structure)*

Inflorescence

Stem

FLOWERING PLANT
Couch grass
(*Agropyron repens*)

*Caryopsis
(type of
dry fruit)*

*Rachis
(main axis of
grass inflorescence)*

Node

*Pinna
(leaflet)*

Frond (leaf)

*Midrib of
pinna (leaflet)*

*Lamina
(blade)*

*Round, hollow
stem*

*Sheathing
leaf base*

*Adventitious
root*

FLOWERING PLANT
Pitcher plant
(*Sarracenia purpurea*)

*Fruit
surrounded
by floral parts*

Sepal

*Umbrella
of style*

*Pitcher (leaf
modified to trap
insects)*

*Pedicel
(flower
stalk)*

Hood

*Downward-pointing
hair (encourages
insect prey into
pitcher)*

Wing

*Immature
pitcher*

Fungi and lichens

FUNGI WERE ONCE THOUGHT OF AS PLANTS but are now classified as a separate kingdom. This kingdom includes not only the familiar mushrooms, puffballs, stinkhorns, and molds, but also yeasts, smuts, rusts, and lichens. Most fungi are multicellular, consisting of a mass of thread-like hyphae that together form a mycelium. However, the simpler fungi, like yeasts, are microscopic, single-celled organisms. Typically, fungi reproduce by means of spores. Most fungi feed on dead or decaying matter or on living organisms. A few fungi obtain their food from plants or algae, with which they have a symbiotic (mutually advantageous) relationship. Lichens are a symbiotic partnership between algae and fungi. Of the six types of lichens the three most common are crustose (flat and crusty), foliose (leafy), and fruticose (shrub-like). Some lichens (such as *Cladonia floerkeana*) are a combination of types. Lichens reproduce by means of spores or soredia (powdery vegetative fragments).

EXAMPLES OF FUNGI

Emerging sporophore (spore-bearing structure)

Pileus (cap) continuous with stipe (stalk)

Bark of dead beech tree

Inrolled margin of pileus (cap)

Gill (site of spore production)

Sporophore (spore-bearing structure)

Stipe (stalk)

Hyphae (fungal filaments)

OYSTER FUNGUS
(*Pleurotus pulmonarius*)

EXAMPLES OF LICHENS

Secondary fruticose thallus

Branched, hollow stem

Apothecium (spore-producing body)

FRUTICOSE
Cladonia portentosa

Soredia (powdery vegetative fragments) produced at end of lobe

Tree bark

Foliose thallus

FOLIOSE
Hypogymnia physodes

Gleba (spore-producing tissue found in this type of fungus)

Sporophore (spore-bearing structure)

Porous stipe (stalk)

Volva (remains of universal veil)

STINKHORN
(*Phallus impudicus*)

Toothed branchlet

Branch

Sporophore (spore-bearing structure)

Stipe (stalk)

RAMARIA FORMOSA

Soredia (powdery vegetative fragments) released onto surface of squamulose thallus

Moss

SQUAMULOSE (SCALY) AND FRUTICOSE THALLUS
Cladonia floerkeana

Apothecium (spore-producing body)

Basal scale of primary squamulose thallus

Podetium (granular stalk) of secondary fruticose thallus

SECTION THROUGH FOLIOSE LICHEN SHOWING REPRODUCTION BY SOREDIA

Algal cell

Soredium (powdery vegetative fragment involved in propagation) released from lichen

Fungal hypha

Upper cortex

Algal layer

Medulla of fungal hyphae (mycelium)

Lower cortex

Rhizine (bundle of absorptive hyphae)

Soralium (pore in upper surface of thallus)

Upper surface of thallus

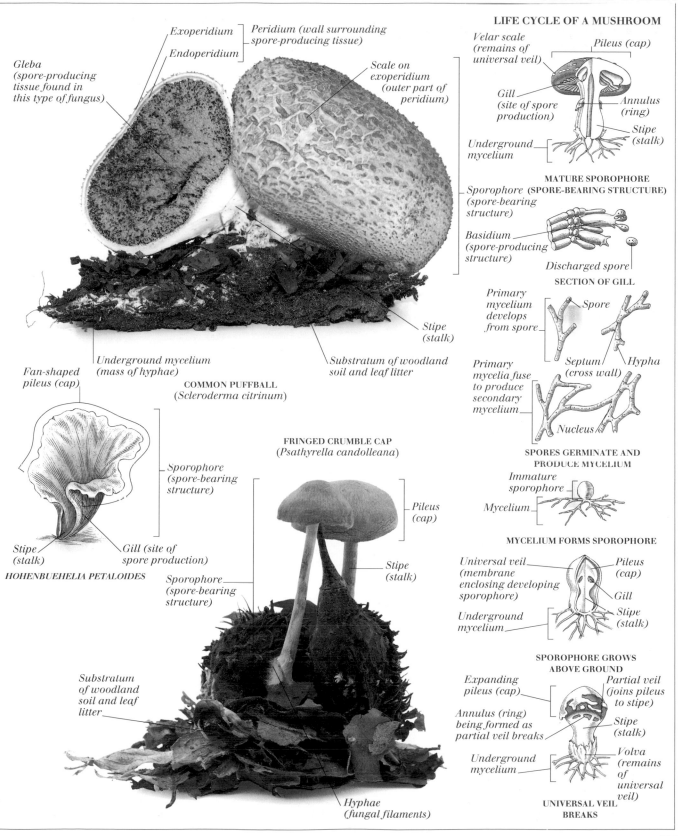

Exoperidium

Endoperidium

Peridium (wall surrounding spore-producing tissue)

Gleba (spore-producing tissue found in this type of fungus)

Scale on exoperidium (outer part of peridium)

Underground mycelium (mass of hyphae)

Stipe (stalk)

Substratum of woodland soil and leaf litter

COMMON PUFFBALL (Scleroderma citrinum)

Fan-shaped pileus (cap)

Sporophore (spore-bearing structure)

Stipe (stalk)

Gill (site of spore production)

HOHENBUEHELIA PETALOIDES

FRINGED CRUMBLE CAP (Psathyrella candolleana)

Sporophore (spore-bearing structure)

Pileus (cap)

Stipe (stalk)

Substratum of woodland soil and leaf litter

Hyphae (fungal filaments)

LIFE CYCLE OF A MUSHROOM

Velar scale (remains of universal veil)

Pileus (cap)

Gill (site of spore production)

Annulus (ring)

Stipe (stalk)

Underground mycelium

Sporophore (spore-bearing structure)

Basidium (spore-producing structure)

Discharged spore

MATURE SPOROPHORE (SPORE-BEARING STRUCTURE)

SECTION OF GILL

Primary mycelium develops from spore

Spore

Septum (cross wall)

Hypha

Primary mycelia fuse to produce secondary mycelium

Nucleus

SPORES GERMINATE AND PRODUCE MYCELIUM

Immature sporophore

Mycelium

MYCELIUM FORMS SPOROPHORE

Universal veil (membrane enclosing developing sporophore)

Pileus (cap)

Gill

Underground mycelium

Stipe (stalk)

SPOROPHORE GROWS ABOVE GROUND

Expanding pileus (cap)

Partial veil (joins pileus to stipe)

Annulus (ring) being formed as partial veil breaks

Stipe (stalk)

Underground mycelium

Volva (remains of universal veil)

UNIVERSAL VEIL BREAKS

Algae and seaweed

ALGAE ARE NOT TRUE PLANTS. They form a diverse group of plantlike organisms that belong to the kingdom Protista. Like plants, algae possess the green pigment chlorophyll and make their own food by photosynthesis (see pp. 138-139). Many algae also possess other pigments by which they can be classified. For example, the brown pigment fucoxanthin is found in brown algae. Some of the ten phyla of algae are exclusively unicellular (single-celled); others also contain aggregates of cells in filaments or colonies. Three phyla— the Chlorophyta (green algae), Rhodophyta (red algae), and Phaeophyta (brown algae)—contain larger, multicellular, thalloid (flat), marine organisms commonly known as seaweed. Most algae can reproduce sexually. For example, in brown seaweed *Fucus vesiculosus*, gametes (sex cells) are produced in conceptacles (chambers) in the receptacles (fertile tips of fronds); after their release into the sea, antherozoids (male gametes) and oospheres (female gametes) fuse. The resulting zygote settles on a rock and develops into a new seaweed.

BROWN SEAWEED
Channeled wrack
(*Pelvetia canaliculata*)

Thallus (plant body)

Receptacle (fertile tip of frond)

Margin of lamina (blade) rolled inwards to form channel

Apical notch

Hapteron (holdfast)

BROWN SEAWEED
Spiral wrack
(*Fucus spiralis*)

Apical notch

Conceptacle (chamber)

Receptacle (fertile tip of frond)

Lamina (blade)

Smooth margin

Midrib

Hapteron (holdfast)

Thallus (plant body)

EXAMPLES OF ALGAE

Reproductive chamber

Cap

Sterile whorl

Cell wall

Stalk

Rhizoid

GREEN ALGA
Acetabularia sp.

Flagellum

Eyespot

Contractile vacuole

Cytoplasm

Cell wall

Nucleus

Chloroplast

Starch grain

Pyrenoid (small protein body)

GREEN ALGA
Chlamydomonas sp.

Coenobium (colony of cells)

Daughter coenobium

Gelatinous sheath

Biflagellate cell

GREEN ALGA
Volvox sp.

Spine

Cytoplasm

Girdle

Vacuole

Nucleus

Plastid (photosynthetic organelle)

DIATOM
Thalassiosira sp.

Apical notch

Receptacle (fertile tip of frond)

Conceptacle (chamber) containing reproductive structures

Lamina (blade)

Midrib

RECEPTACLE
Spiral wrack
(*Fucus spiralis*)

BROWN SEAWEED
Oarweed
(*Laminaria digitata*)

Thallus (plant body)

Lamina (blade) palmately divided

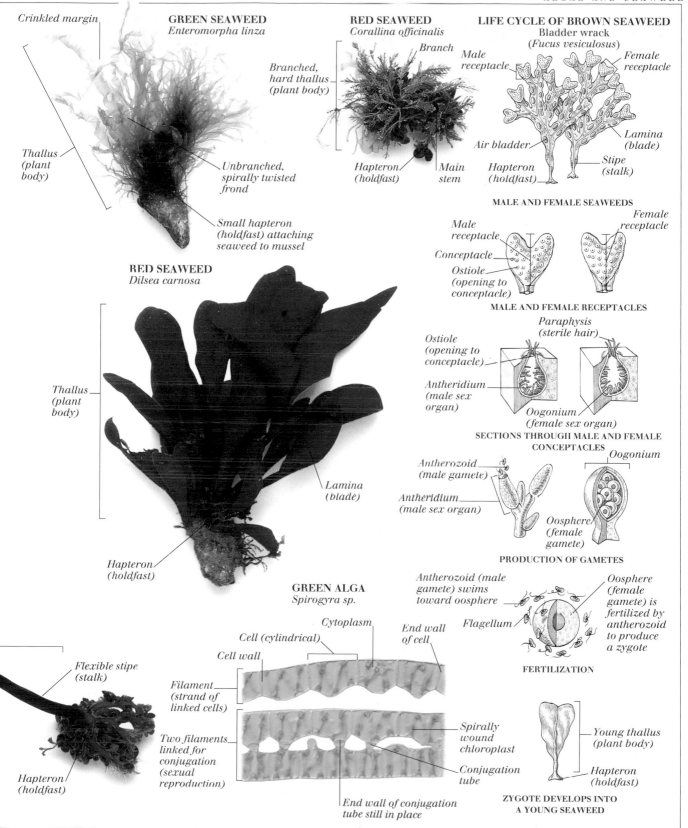

Crinkled margin

GREEN SEAWEED
Enteromorpha linza

RED SEAWEED
Corallina officinalis

LIFE CYCLE OF BROWN SEAWEED
Bladder wrack
(*Fucus vesiculosus*)

Branch

*Male
receptacle*

*Female
receptacle*

*Branched,
hard thallus
(plant body)*

*Thallus
(plant
body)*

*Unbranched,
spirally twisted
frond*

Air bladder

*Lamina
(blade)*

*Hapteron
(holdfast)*

*Main
stem*

*Hapteron
(holdfast)*

*Stipe
(stalk)*

*Small hapteron
(holdfast) attaching
seaweed to mussel*

MALE AND FEMALE SEAWEEDS

*Male
receptacle*

*Female
receptacle*

RED SEAWEED
Dilsea carnosa

Conceptacle

*Ostiole
(opening to
conceptacle)*

MALE AND FEMALE RECEPTACLES

*Paraphysis
(sterile hair)*

*Ostiole
(opening to
conceptacle)*

*Thallus
(plant
body)*

*Antheridium
(male sex
organ)*

*Oogonium
(female sex organ)*

**SECTIONS THROUGH MALE AND FEMALE
CONCEPTACLES**

*Antherozoid
(male gamete)*

Oogonium

*Lamina
(blade)*

*Antheridium
(male sex organ)*

*Oosphere
(female
gamete)*

PRODUCTION OF GAMETES

*Hapteron
(holdfast)*

*Antherozoid (male
gamete) swims
toward oosphere*

*Oosphere
(female
gamete) is
fertilized by
antherozoid
to produce
a zygote*

GREEN ALGA
Spirogyra sp.

Flagellum

Cytoplasm

Cell (cylindrical)

*End wall
of cell*

Cell wall

FERTILIZATION

*Flexible stipe
(stalk)*

*Filament
(strand of
linked cells)*

*Spirally
wound
chloroplast*

*Young thallus
(plant body)*

*Two filaments
linked for
conjugation
(sexual
reproduction)*

*Conjugation
tube*

*Hapteron
(holdfast)*

*Hapteron
(holdfast)*

*End wall of conjugation
tube still in place*

**ZYGOTE DEVELOPS INTO
A YOUNG SEAWEED**

Liverworts and mosses

LIVERWORTS AND MOSSES ARE SMALL, LOW-GROWING PLANTS that belong to the phylum Bryophyta. Bryophytes do not have true stems, leaves, or roots (they are anchored to the ground by rhizoids), nor do they have the vascular tissues (xylem and phloem) that transport water and nutrients in higher plants. With no outer, waterproof cuticle, bryophytes are susceptible to dehydration, and most grow in moist habitats. The bryophyte life cycle has two stages. In stage one, the green plant (gametophyte) produces male and female gametes (sex cells), which fuse to form a zygote. In stage two, the zygote develops into a sporophyte that remains attached to the gametophyte. The sporophyte produces spores, which are released and germinate into new green plants. Liverworts (class Hepaticae) grow horizontally and may be thalloid (flat and ribbon-like) or "leafy." Mosses (class Musci) typically have an upright "stem" with spirally arranged "leaves."

A LEAFY LIVERWORT
Scapania undulata

"Stem"

"Leaf"

Rhizoid

A THALLOID LIVERWORT
Marchantia polymorpha

Gemma cup

Gemma (detachable tissue that produces new plants)

Thallus (plant body)

Toothed margin of cup

DETAIL OF GEMMA CUP

Disk

Archegoniophore (stalked structure carrying archegonia)

Lobe

Stalk

Thallus (plant body)

Apical notch

Rhizoid

FEMALE GAMETOPHYTE

Disk

Lobe

Stalk

SIDE VIEW OF ARCHEGONIOPHORE

Lobe

Disk

Ray (radial groove)

Stalk

ARCHEGONIOPHORE FROM BELOW

Pore

Ray (radial groove)

MICROGRAPH OF LOBE

Gemma cup

Thallus (plant body)

Midrib

Archegoniophore (stalked structure carrying archegonia)

MICROGRAPH OF THALLUS
Conocephalum conicum

Position of air chamber

Pore for exchange of gases

Upper surface

Rhizoid

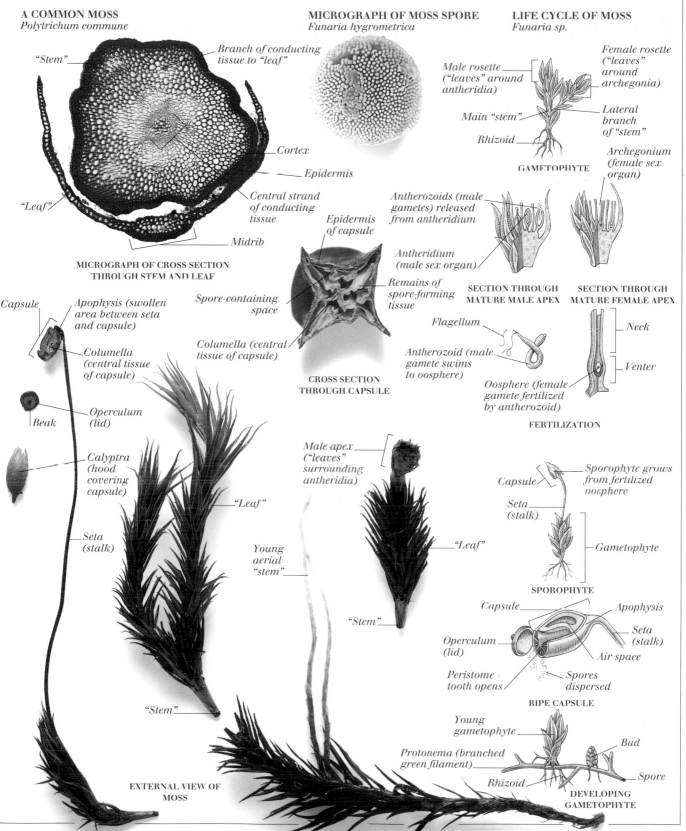

A COMMON MOSS
Polytrichum commune

"Stem"

Branch of conducting
tissue to "leaf"

Cortex

Epidermis

Central strand
of conducting
tissue

"Leaf"

Midrib

**MICROGRAPH OF CROSS SECTION
THROUGH STEM AND LEAF**

MICROGRAPH OF MOSS SPORE
Funaria hygrometrica

LIFE CYCLE OF MOSS
Funaria sp.

Female rosette
("leaves"
around
archegonia)

Male rosette
("leaves" around
antheridia)

Main "stem"

Lateral
branch
of "stem"

Rhizoid

GAMETOPHYTE

Archegonium
(female sex
organ)

Epidermis
of capsule

Spore-containing
space

Columella (central
tissue of capsule)

Remains of
spore-forming
tissue

**CROSS SECTION
THROUGH CAPSULE**

Antherozoids (male
gametes) released
from antheridium

Antheridium
(male sex organ)

**SECTION THROUGH
MATURE MALE APEX**

**SECTION THROUGH
MATURE FEMALE APEX**

Neck

Venter

Flagellum

Antherozoid (male
gamete swims
to oosphere)

Oosphere (female
gamete fertilized
by antherozoid)

FERTILIZATION

Capsule

Apophysis (swollen
area between seta
and capsule)

Columella
(central tissue
of capsule)

Operculum
(lid)

Beak

Calyptra
(hood
covering
capsule)

Seta
(stalk)

"Leaf"

Young
aerial
"stem"

"Stem"

Male apex
("leaves"
surrounding
antheridia)

"Leaf"

"Stem"

Capsule

Seta
(stalk)

Sporophyte grows
from fertilized
oosphere

Gametophyte

SPOROPHYTE

Capsule

Operculum
(lid)

Peristome
tooth opens

Apophysis

Seta
(stalk)

Air space

Spores
dispersed

RIPE CAPSULE

Young
gametophyte

Protonema (branched
green filament)

Rhizoid

Bud

Spore

**DEVELOPING
GAMETOPHYTE**

**EXTERNAL VIEW OF
MOSS**

Horsetails, club mosses, and ferns

HORSETAILS, CLUB MOSSES, AND FERNS are primitive land plants, which, like higher plants, have stems, roots, leaves, and vascular systems that transport water, minerals, and food. Unlike higher plants, however, they do not produce seeds when reproducing. Their life cycles involve two stages. In stage one, the sporophyte (green plant) produces spores in sporangia. In stage two, the spores germinate, developing into small, short-lived gametophyte plants that produce male and female gametes (sex cells). The gametes fuse to form a zygote from which a new sporophyte plant develops. Horsetails (phylum Sphenophyta) have erect green stems with branches arranged in whorls. Some stems are fertile and have a single spore-producing strobilus (group of sporangia) at the tip. Club mosses (phylum Lycopodophyta) typically have small leaves arranged spirally around the stem, with spore-producing strobili at the tip of some stems. Ferns (phylum Filicinophyta) usually have large, pinnate leaves called fronds. Sporangia, grouped together in sori, develop on the underside of fertile fronds.

FROND
Male fern
(*Dryopteris filix-mas*)

CLUB MOSS
Lycopodium sp.

Stem with spirally arranged leaves

Branch

Strobilus (group of sporangia)

CLUB MOSS
Selaginella sp.

Epidermis (outer layer of cells)

Cortex (layer between epidermis and vascular tissue)

Vascular tissue — Phloem / Xylem

Lacuna (air space)

Root

Shoot apex

Branch

Rhizophore (leafless branch)

Creeping stem with spirally arranged leaves

MICROGRAPH OF CROSS SECTION THROUGH CLUB MOSS STEM

HORSETAIL
Common horsetail
(*Equisetum arvense*)

Apex of sterile shoot

Sporangiophore (structure carrying sporangia)

Strobilus (group of sporangia)

Non-photosynthetic fertile stem

Collar of small brown leaves

Young shoot

Lateral branch

Photosynthetic sterile stem

Node

Internode

Node

Tuber

Rhizome

Adventitious root

Endodermis (inner layer of cortex)

Vascular tissue

Sclerenchyma (strengthening tissue)

Chlorenchyma (photosynthetic tissue)

Epidermis (outer layer of cells)

Parenchyma (packing tissue)

Cortex (layer between epidermis and vascular tissue)

Hollow pith cavity

Vallecular canal (longitudinal channel)

Carinal canal (longitudinal channel)

MICROGRAPH OF CROSS SECTION THROUGH HORSETAIL STEM

SPORE PRODUCTION IN FERN
Bracken
(*Pteridium aquilinum*)

Apex of pinnule

Pinnule (leaflet of pinna)

Sporangium (spore-producing structure)

Spore inside dehisced (split open) sporangium

Abaxial (lower) surface of pinnule

Midrib of pinnule

Sorus (group of sporangia)

MICROGRAPH OF LOWER SURFACE OF FERTILE PINNULE

Sporangium (spore-producing structure)

Annulus (ring of cells around sporangium)

Spore

Midrib of pinnule

MICROGRAPH OF SPORANGIA ON LOWER SURFACE OF FERTILE PINNULE

LIFE CYCLE OF FERN

Pinna (leaflet)

Pinnule (leaflet of pinna)

Frond (leaf)

Rolled immature frond

SPOROPHYTE

Rhizome

Pinnule (leaflet of pinna)

Placenta

Indusium (flap protecting sorus)

Sorus (group of sporangia)

Sporangium (spore-producing structure)

SECTION THROUGH MATURE PINNULE

Annulus ruptures at weak point

Sporangium splits and releases spores

Spore

RELEASE OF SPORES FROM SPORANGIUM

Spore

Rhizoid

Filament develops into prothallus

GERMINATION OF SPORE

Antheridium (male sex organ)

Archegonium (female sex organ)

Prothallus (free-living gametophyte)

Rhizoid

GAMETOPHYTE PRODUCES GAMETES

Antheridium (male sex organ)

Oosphere (female gamete)

Antherozoid (male gamete) swims to oosphere

Archegonium (female sex organ)

FERTILIZATION

Primary leaf of growing sporophyte

Remains of gametophyte

FERTILIZED OOSPHERE GROWS INTO NEW SPOROPHYTE PLANT

FERN
Male fern
(*Dryopteris filix-mas*)

Midrib of pinna (leaflet)

Apex of frond (leaf)

Pinna (leaflet)

Pinnule (leaflet of pinna)

Frond (leaf)

Young frond (leaf)

Rachis (main axis of pinnate leaf)

Base of old dead frond (leaf)

Young frond (leaf) rolled and covered by ramenta

Ramentum (brown scale)

Rhizome

Vascular bundle

Sclerenchyma (strengthening tissue)

Phloem

Xylem

Vascular tissue

Epidermis (outer layer of cells)

Parenchyma (packing tissue)

MICROGRAPH OF CROSS SECTION THROUGH FERN RACHIS

Adventitious root

Gymnosperms 1

THE GYMNOSPERMS ARE FOUR RELATED PHYLA of seed-producing plants: Their seeds, however, lack the protective outer covering which surrounds the seeds of flowering plants. Typically, gymnosperms are woody, perennial shrubs or trees, with stems, leaves, roots, and a well-developed vascular (transport) system. The reproductive structures in most gymnosperms are cones. Male cones produce microspores in which male gametes (sex cells) develop; female cones produce megaspores in which female gametes develop. Microspores are blown by the wind to female cones, male and female gametes fuse during fertilization, and a seed develops. The four gymnosperm phyla are the conifers (phylum Coniferophyta), mostly tall trees; cycads (phylum Cycadophyta), small palm-like trees; the ginkgo or maidenhair tree (phylum Ginkgophyta), a tall tree with bilobed leaves; and gnetophytes (phylum Gnetophyta), a diverse group of plants, mainly shrubs, but also including the horizontally growing welwitschia.

LIFE CYCLE OF SCOTS PINE
(*Pinus sylvestris*)

Needle (*foliage leaf*)

Cone

Ovuliferous scale (*ovule-/seed-bearing structure*)

MALE CONES   **YOUNG FEMALE CONE**

Pollen grain in micropyle (*entrance to ovule*)

Ovuliferous scale

Pollen grain

Nucleus

Air sac

Ovule (*contains female gamete*)

POLLINATION

Integument (*outer part of ovule*)

Archegonium (*containing female gamete*)

Pollen tube (*carries male gamete from pollen grain to ovum*)

FERTILIZATION

SCALE AND SEEDS
Pine
(*Pinus sp.*)

Ovuliferous scale (*ovule-/seed-bearing structure*)

Wing scar

Wing of seed derived from ovuliferous scale

Seed

Seed

Seed scar

Point of attachment to axis of cone

OVULIFEROUS SCALE FROM THIRD-YEAR FEMALE CONE

Seed

Ovuliferous scale (*ovule-/seed-bearing structure*)

Seed

Wing

MATURE FEMALE CONE AND WINGED SEED

Plumule (*embryonic shoot*)

Cotyledon (*seed leaf*)

Root

GERMINATION OF PINE SEEDLING

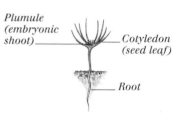

Microsporangium (*structure in which pollen grains are formed*)

Microsporophyll (*modified leaf carrying microsporangia*)

Ovule (*contains female gametes*)

Bract scale

Scale leaf

Axis of cone

Ovuliferous scale (*ovule-/seed-bearing structure*)

Axis of cone

MICROGRAPH OF LONGITUDINAL SECTION THROUGH YOUNG MALE CONE

MICROGRAPH OF LONGITUDINAL SECTION THROUGH SECOND-YEAR FEMALE CONE

WELWITSCHIA
(*Welwitschia mirabilis*)

Frayed end of leaf

SMOOTH CYPRESS
(*Cupressus glabra*)

Immature female cone

Ovuliferous scale (ovule-/seed-bearing structure)

Mature female cone

Scalelike leaf

Immature male cone

Ovuliferous scale

Ovule (contains female gamete)

CROSS SECTION THROUGH IMMATURE CONE

Seed

Ovuliferous scale (ovule-/seed-bearing structure)

CROSS SECTION THROUGH MATURE CONE

Woody scale

Opening between woody scales through which seeds are released

DISCARDED CONE

YEW
(*Taxus baccata*)

Single ovule (contains female gamete)

Scale

Female "cone"

Scale

Developing seed

Scale

Seed

Aril (fleshy outgrowth from seed)

Stem

Needle (foliage leaf)

FEMALE "CONES" AT VARIOUS STAGES OF DEVELOPMENT

CYCAD
Sago palm
(*Cycas revoluta*)

Pinna (leaflet)

Pinnate leaf

Scale leaf

Old leaf base

Stem covered by scale leaves

GINKGO
(*Ginkgo biloba*)

Girdle scar

Stem

Petiole (leaf stalk)

Bilobed leaf

Continuously growing leaf

Site of cone growth

Adaxial (upper) surface of leaf

Abaxial (lower) surface of leaf

Frayed end of leaf

Immature cone

Stalk scar

Woody stem

Gymnosperms 2

BRANCH OF BISHOP PINE
(*Pinus muricata*)

Second-year female cone

*Ovuliferous scale
(ovule-/seed-bearing
structure)*

*Needle
(foliage leaf)*

*Ovuliferous scale
(ovule-/seed-bearing
structure)*

*Bud
scale*

Cone

Apical bud

Cone stalk

Stem

Dwarf shoot

Scale leaf scar

FEMALE CONE (FIRST YEAR)

Stem

Needle (foliage leaf)

Dwarf shoot

Male cone

*Upper surface
of needle
(foliage leaf)*

*Margin
of needle
(foliage leaf)*

*Needle
(foliage leaf)*

Apical bud

*Scar of
dwarf shoot*

Stem

Dwarf shoot

TERMINAL ZONE OF BRANCH

*Stoma
(pore)*

*Female
cone*

Vascular tissue

*Mesophyll
(photosynthetic tissue)*

Phloem

Xylem

*Epidermis
(outer
layer of
cells)*

*Stoma
(pore)*

*Woody ovuliferous
scale (ovule-/seed-
bearing structure)*

*Endodermis
(inner layer
of cortex)*

Resin canal

*Cuticle
(waterproof
covering)*

FEMALE CONE (THIRD YEAR)

**MICROGRAPH OF CROSS SECTION
THROUGH NEEDLE (FOLIAGE LEAF)**

**MICROGRAPH OF NEEDLE
(FOLIAGE LEAF) OF PINE
(*Pinus sp.*)**

Apical bud scale

Apical bud

Shoot apex

Needle (foliage leaf) bud

Bud scale

Scale leaf

CROSS SECTION THROUGH MATURE STEM OF BISHOP PINE
(*Pinus muricata*)

Annual ring

Immature needle (foliage leaf)

MICROGRAPH OF LONGITUDINAL SECTION THROUGH SHOOT APEX OF PINE
(*Pinus sp.*)

Heartwood (supportive, inactive secondary xylem)

Branch trace (vascular bundle supplying branch)

Pith

Medullary ray (extension of pith)

Hypodermis (cell layer below epidermis)

Cortex (layer between epidermis and vascular tissue)

Base of dwarf shoot

Dwarf shoot trace (vascular bundle supplying dwarf shoot)

Secondary xylem

Vascular tissue

Phloem

Primary xylem

Epidermis (outer layer of cells)

Resin canal

Pith

Sapwood (active secondary xylem)

Phloem

Bark

Periderm (outer layer of bark)

MICROGRAPH OF CROSS SECTION THROUGH YOUNG STEM OF PINE
(*Pinus sp.*)

Cortex (layer between phellem and vascular tissue)

Resin canal

Cortex (layer between phellem and vascular tissue)

Secondary xylem

Primary xylem

Endodermis (inner layer of cortex)

Phellem (protective outer layer)

Phloem

Secondary xylem

Phellem (protective outer layer)

Primary xylem

Phloem

Resin canal

MICROGRAPH OF CROSS SECTION THROUGH YOUNG ROOT OF PINE
(*Pinus sp.*)

MICROGRAPH OF CROSS SECTION THROUGH MATURE ROOT OF PINE
(*Pinus sp.*)

Monocotyledons and dicotyledons

FLOWERING PLANTS (PHYLUM ANGIOSPERMOPHYTA) are divided into two classes: monocotyledons (class Monocotyledoneae) and dicotyledons (class Dicotyledoneae). Typically, monocotyledons have seeds with one cotyledon (seed leaf); their foliage leaves are narrow with parallel veins; the flower components occur in multiples of three; sepals and petals are indistinguishable and are known as tepals; vascular (transport) tissues are scattered in random bundles throughout the stem; and, because they lack stem cambium (actively dividing cells that produce wood), most monocotyledons are herbaceous (see pp. 128-129). Dicotyledons have seeds with two cotyledons; leaves are broad with a central midrib and branched veins; flower parts occur in multiples of four or five; sepals are generally small and green; petals are large and colorful; vascular bundles are arranged in a ring around the edge of the stem; and, because many dicotyledons possess wood-producing stem cambium, there are woody forms (see pp. 130-131) as well as herbaceous ones.

CROSS SECTION THROUGH MONOCOTYLEDONOUS LEAF BASES

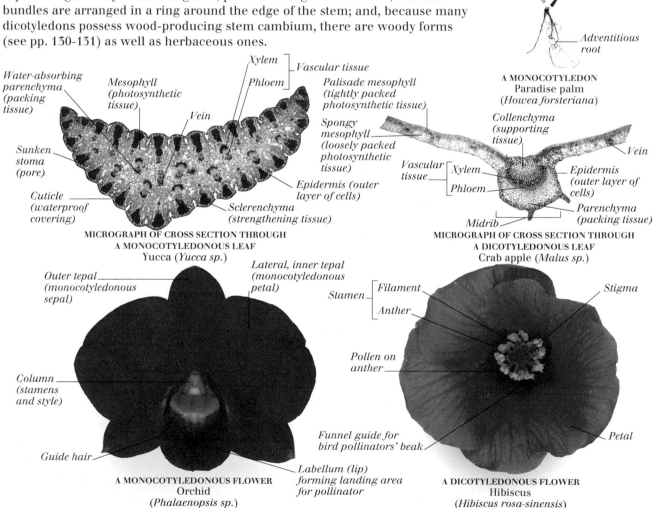

Vein (parallel venation)

Leaflet

Petiole (leaf stalk)

Emerging leaf

Leaf base

Adventitious root

A MONOCOTYLEDON
Paradise palm
(*Howea forsteriana*)

Water-absorbing parenchyma (packing tissue)

Mesophyll (photosynthetic tissue)

Vein

Sunken stoma (pore)

Cuticle (waterproof covering)

Xylem

Phloem

Vascular tissue

Epidermis (outer layer of cells)

Sclerenchyma (strengthening tissue)

MICROGRAPH OF CROSS SECTION THROUGH
A MONOCOTYLEDONOUS LEAF
Yucca (*Yucca sp.*)

Palisade mesophyll (tightly packed photosynthetic tissue)

Spongy mesophyll (loosely packed photosynthetic tissue)

Vascular tissue

Xylem

Phloem

Midrib

Collenchyma (supporting tissue)

Vein

Epidermis (outer layer of cells)

Parenchyma (packing tissue)

MICROGRAPH OF CROSS SECTION THROUGH
A DICOTYLEDONOUS LEAF
Crab apple (*Malus sp.*)

Outer tepal (monocotyledonous sepal)

Lateral, inner tepal (monocotyledonous petal)

Column (stamens and style)

Guide hair

Labellum (lip) forming landing area for pollinator

A MONOCOTYLEDONOUS FLOWER
Orchid
(*Phalaenopsis sp.*)

Stamen

Filament

Anther

Pollen on anther

Funnel guide for bird pollinators' beak

Stigma

Petal

A DICOTYLEDONOUS FLOWER
Hibiscus
(*Hibiscus rosa-sinensis*)

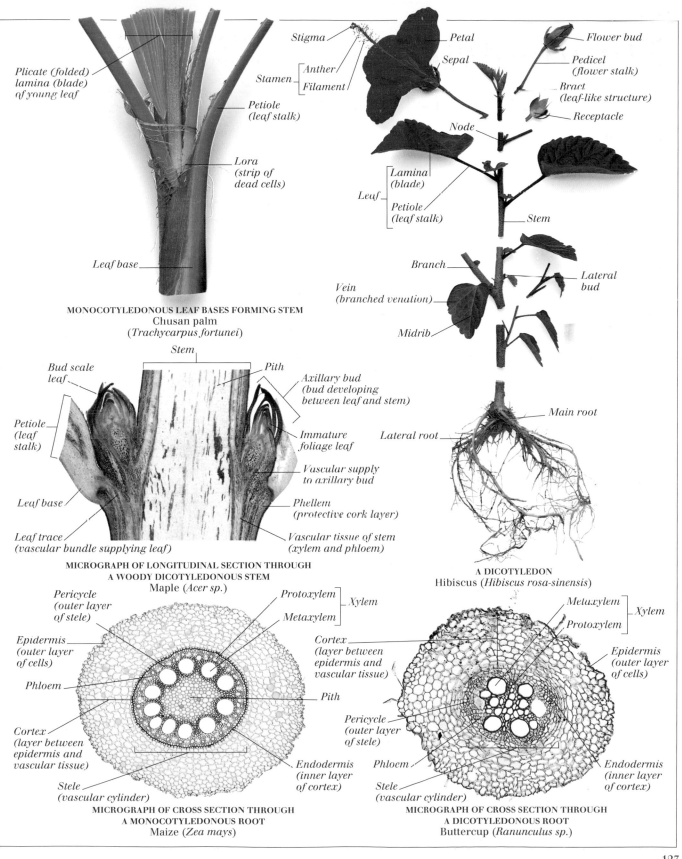

Plicate (folded) lamina (blade) of young leaf

Petiole (leaf stalk)

Lora (strip of dead cells)

Leaf base

MONOCOTYLEDONOUS LEAF BASES FORMING STEM
Chusan palm
(*Trachycarpus fortunei*)

Stigma

Stamen { **Anther** / **Filament** }

Petal

Sepal

Flower bud

Pedicel (flower stalk)

Bract (leaf-like structure)

Receptacle

Node

Leaf { **Lamina (blade)** / **Petiole (leaf stalk)** }

Stem

Branch

Vein (branched venation)

Midrib

Lateral bud

Lateral root

Main root

A DICOTYLEDON
Hibiscus (*Hibiscus rosa-sinensis*)

Bud scale leaf

Petiole (leaf stalk)

Leaf base

Leaf trace (vascular bundle supplying leaf)

Stem

Pith

Axillary bud (bud developing between leaf and stem)

Immature foliage leaf

Vascular supply to axillary bud

Phellem (protective cork layer)

Vascular tissue of stem (xylem and phloem)

MICROGRAPH OF LONGITUDINAL SECTION THROUGH A WOODY DICOTYLEDONOUS STEM
Maple (*Acer sp.*)

Pericycle (outer layer of stele)

Epidermis (outer layer of cells)

Phloem

Cortex (layer between epidermis and vascular tissue)

Stele (vascular cylinder)

Protoxylem } **Xylem**
Metaxylem

Pith

Endodermis (inner layer of cortex)

MICROGRAPH OF CROSS SECTION THROUGH A MONOCOTYLEDONOUS ROOT
Maize (*Zea mays*)

Cortex (layer between epidermis and vascular tissue)

Metaxylem } **Xylem**
Protoxylem

Epidermis (outer layer of cells)

Pericycle (outer layer of stele)

Phloem

Stele (vascular cylinder)

Endodermis (inner layer of cortex)

MICROGRAPH OF CROSS SECTION THROUGH A DICOTYLEDONOUS ROOT
Buttercup (*Ranunculus sp.*)

Herbaceous flowering plants

HERBACEOUS FLOWERING PLANTS TYPICALLY HAVE GREEN NON-WOODY STEMS, and tend to be relatively short-lived. Many herbaceous plants live for only one or two years. Annuals (such as sweet peas) grow from seed, produce flowers and then seeds, and die within a single year. Biennials (like carrots) have a two-year life cycle. In the first year, seeds grow into plants, which produce leaves and store food in underground storage organs; the stems and foliage then die in winter. In the second year, new stems grow from the storage organs, produce leaves, flowers, and seeds, and then die. Some herbaceous plants (such as potatoes) are perennial. They grow back year after year, producing shoots and flowers in spring, storing food in underground tubers or rhizomes during summer, dying in autumn, and surviving underground during winter.

Young plant forming

Petiole (stalk) of young leaf

Stipule (structure at base of leaf)

Trifoliate leaf

Node

Simple ovate leaflet

Lateral root

Root nodule

Main root

SWEET PEA
(*Lathyrus odoratus*)

STRAWBERRY
(*Fragaria x ananassa*)

Runner (creeping stem)

Leaf scar

Stem

Rib

Lateral root scar

Remains of leaves

Lateral root

Tap root

CARROT
(*Daucus carota*)

Leaf scar

Petiole (leaf stalk)

Leaf base

Spine (modified leaf)

Slender rhizome

Stem tuber

Adventitious root

Stem

Narrow, succulent leaf

Simple deltoid leaf

ROCK STONECROP
(*Sedum rupestre*)

POTATO
(*Solanum tuberosum*)

Adventitious root

PARTS OF HERBACEOUS FLOWERING PLANTS

Bract
(leaf-like
structure)

Bracteole
(small bract)

Midrib

Succulent,
simple ovate
leaf

Cyme (type of
inflorescence)

Inner, tubular
disk floret

Outer, ligulate
ray floret

Node

Flower bud

Dentate
margin

Peduncle
(inflorescence stalk)

Internode

SHOWY STONECROP
(*Sedum spectabile*)

Capitulum (type
of inflorescence)

Leaf

Simple lobed
leaf

Peduncle
(inflorescence
stalk)

Flower
bud

Petiole
(leaf stalk)

Petiole
(leaf
stalk)

Leaf base

Stem

FLORISTS' CHRYSANTHEMUM
(*Chrysanthemum morifolium*)

Succulent
stem

Leaf
scar

Lateral
bud

Prickle

Linear
leaf

**CEREOID
CACTUS**

BEGONIA
(*Begonia* x
tuberhybrida)

Bract
(leaf-like
structure)

Capitulum (type
of inflorescence)

Hollow
stem

Sheath formed
from leaf base

TOADFLAX
(*Linuria sp.*)

Spinose dentate
margin

Dentate
margin

Unwinged rachis
(main axis of
pinnate leaf)

Rachis (main
axis of pinnate
leaf)

SLENDER THISTLE
(*Carduus tenuiflorus*)

Peduncle
(inflorescence
stalk)

Winged
stem

Stipule
(structure at
base of leaf)

Tendril

Stem
segment

Winged
rachis
(main
axis of
pinnate
leaf)

Flower bud

Pinna
(leaflet)

HOGWEED
(*Heracleum sphondylium*)

Bract
(leaflike
structure)

Tepal

Petiole
(leaf stalk)

Margin of
cladode

Toothed
notch

PERUVIAN LILY
(*Alstroemeria aurea*)

Peduncle
(inflorescence
stalk)

Cladode
(flattened stem)

Stem
branch

Raceme (type
of inflorescence)

Petal

Sepal

EVERLASTING PEA
(*Lathyrus latifolius*)

CRAB CACTUS
(*Schlumbergera truncata*)

Woody flowering plants

WOODY FLOWERING PLANTS ARE PERENNIAL: They continue to grow and reproduce for many years. They have one or more permanent stems above ground and numerous smaller branches. The stems and branches have a strong woody core that supports the plant and contains vascular tissue for transporting water and nutrients. Outside the woody core is a layer of tough, protective bark, which has lenticels (tiny pores) to allow gases to pass through. Woody flowering plants may be shrubs, which have several stems rising from the soil; bushes, which are shrubs with dense branching and foliage; or trees, which typically have a single upright stem (the trunk) that bears branches. Deciduous woody plants (like roses) shed all their leaves once a year and remain leafless during winter. Evergreen woody plants (such as holly) shed their leaves gradually, so they retain full leaf cover throughout the year.

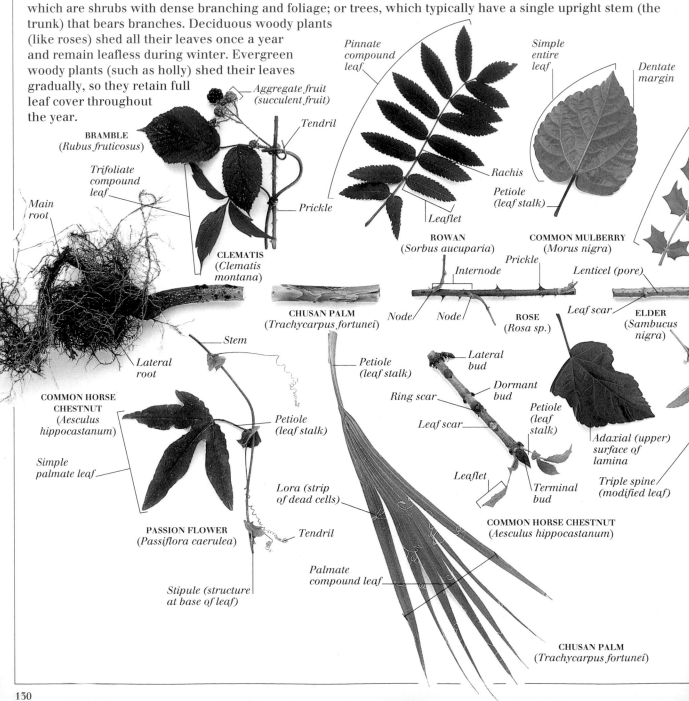

BRAMBLE
(*Rubus fruticosus*)

Aggregate fruit (succulent fruit)

Trifoliate compound leaf

Tendril

Prickle

CLEMATIS
(*Clematis montana*)

Main root

Lateral root

Pinnate compound leaf

Rachis

Leaflet

Petiole (leaf stalk)

ROWAN
(*Sorbus aucuparia*)

Simple entire leaf

Dentate margin

Petiole (leaf stalk)

COMMON MULBERRY
(*Morus nigra*)

Internode

Prickle

Node

Node

ROSE
(*Rosa sp.*)

Lenticel (pore)

Leaf scar

ELDER
(*Sambucus nigra*)

CHUSAN PALM
(*Trachycarpus fortunei*)

COMMON HORSE CHESTNUT
(*Aesculus hippocastanum*)

Simple palmate leaf

Stem

Petiole (leaf stalk)

Lateral bud

Ring scar

Dormant bud

Leaf scar

Petiole (leaf stalk)

Leaflet

Terminal bud

Adaxial (upper) surface of lamina

Triple spine (modified leaf)

COMMON HORSE CHESTNUT
(*Aesculus hippocastanum*)

PASSION FLOWER
(*Passiflora caerulea*)

Tendril

Lora (strip of dead cells)

Palmate compound leaf

Stipule (structure at base of leaf)

CHUSAN PALM
(*Trachycarpus fortunei*)

PARTS OF WOODY FLOWERING PLANTS

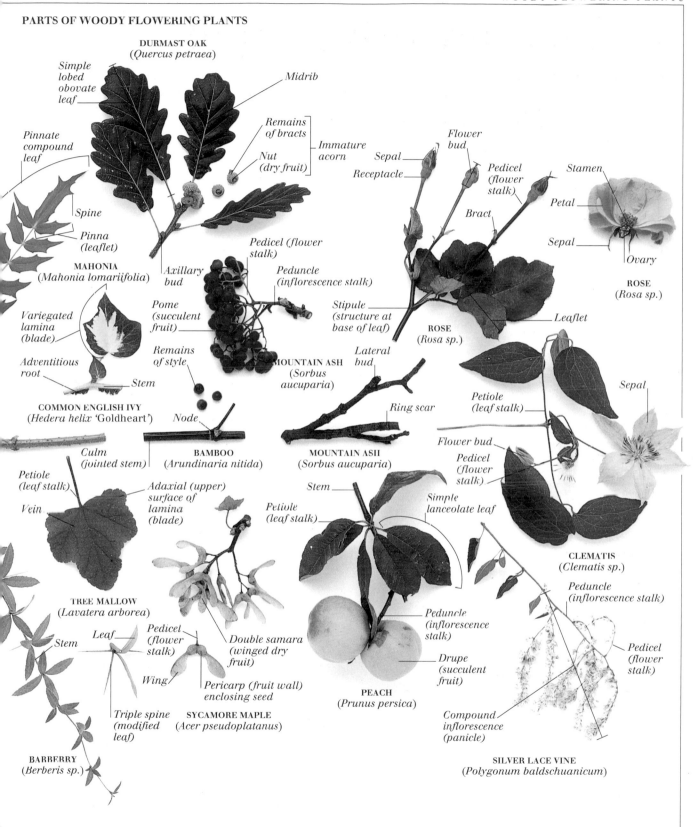

DURMAST OAK
(*Quercus petraea*)

Simple lobed obovate leaf

Midrib

Pinnate compound leaf

Remains of bracts

Nut (dry fruit)

Immature acorn

Spine

Pinna (leaflet)

MAHONIA
(*Mahonia lomariifolia*)

Axillary bud

Pedicel (flower stalk)

Pome (succulent fruit)

Peduncle (inflorescence stalk)

Variegated lamina (blade)

Adventitious root

Remains of style

Stem

COMMON ENGLISH IVY
(*Hedera helix* 'Goldheart')

Node

BAMBOO
(*Arundinaria nitida*)

Culm (jointed stem)

MOUNTAIN ASH
(*Sorbus aucuparia*)

Lateral bud

MOUNTAIN ASH
(*Sorbus aucuparia*)

Ring scar

Stipule (structure at base of leaf)

ROSE
(*Rosa sp.*)

Leaflet

Flower bud

Sepal

Receptacle

Pedicel (flower stalk)

Bract

Stamen

Petal

Sepal

Ovary

ROSE
(*Rosa sp.*)

Sepal

Petiole (leaf stalk)

Flower bud

Pedicel (flower stalk)

Simple lanceolate leaf

CLEMATIS
(*Clematis sp.*)

Petiole (leaf stalk)

Vein

Adaxial (upper) surface of lamina (blade)

Stem

Petiole (leaf stalk)

Peduncle (inflorescence stalk)

Drupe (succulent fruit)

TREE MALLOW
(*Lavatera arborea*)

Leaf

Pedicel (flower stalk)

Double samara (winged dry fruit)

Wing

Pericarp (fruit wall) enclosing seed

Stem

Triple spine (modified leaf)

SYCAMORE MAPLE
(*Acer pseudoplatanus*)

BARBERRY
(*Berberis sp.*)

PEACH
(*Prunus persica*)

Peduncle (inflorescence stalk)

Pedicel (flower stalk)

Compound inflorescence (panicle)

SILVER LACE VINE
(*Polygonum baldschuanicum*)

Roots

ROOTS ARE THE UNDERGROUND PARTS OF PLANTS. They have three main functions. First, they anchor the plant in the soil. Second, they absorb water and minerals from the spaces between soil particles. The roots' absorptive properties are increased by root hairs, which grow behind the root tip, allowing maximum absorption of vital substances. Third, the root is part of the plant's transport system. Xylem carries water and minerals from the roots to the stem and leaves, and phloem carries nutrients from the leaves to all parts of the root system. In addition, some roots (like carrots) are food stores. Roots have an outer epidermis covering a cortex of parenchyma (packing tissue), and a central cylinder of vascular tissue. This arrangement helps the roots resist the forces of compression as they grow through the soil.

CARROT
(Daucus carota)

MICROGRAPH OF PRIMARY ROOT DEVELOPMENT
Cabbage *(Brassica sp.)*

Split in testa
as seed
germinates

*Cotyledon
(seed leaf)*

Primary root

*Testa
(seed coat)*

Root hair

*Root tip
(region of
cell division)*

FEATURES OF A TYPICAL ROOT
Buttercup
(Ranunculus sp.)

*Stele
(vascular cylinder)*

*Phloem sieve tube
(through which
nutrients are
transported)*

*Pericycle
(outer layer
of stele)*

Root hair

*Air space
(allowing gas
diffusion in
the root)*

*Companion cell
(cell associated
with phloem
sieve tube)*

*Cortex
(layer between
epidermis and
vascular tissue)*

Root hair

*Epidermis
(outer layer
of cells)*

*Xylem vessel
(through which water
and minerals are transported)*

*Endodermis
(inner layer
of cortex)*

Cell wall

Nucleus

Cytoplasm

*Parenchyma
(packing) cell*

PRIMARY ROOT AND MICROGRAPHS OF SECTIONS THROUGH ROOTS

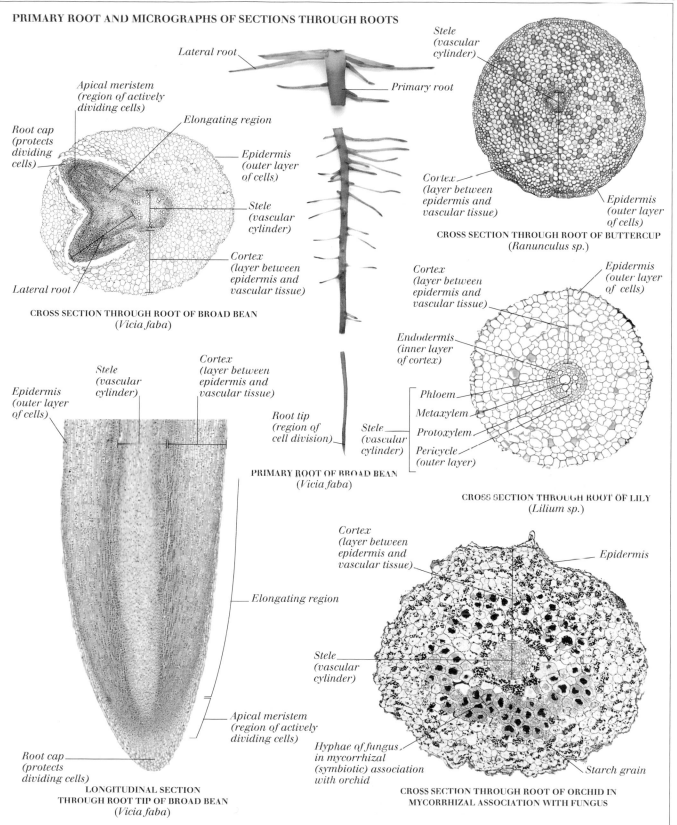

Lateral root

Primary root

*Stele
(vascular
cylinder)*

*Apical meristem
(region of actively
dividing cells)*

Elongating region

*Root cap
(protects
dividing
cells)*

*Epidermis
(outer layer
of cells)*

*Stele
(vascular
cylinder)*

*Cortex
(layer between
epidermis and
vascular tissue)*

*Epidermis
(outer layer
of cells)*

Lateral root

CROSS SECTION THROUGH ROOT OF BROAD BEAN
(*Vicia faba*)

CROSS SECTION THROUGH ROOT OF BUTTERCUP
(*Ranunculus sp.*)

*Stele
(vascular
cylinder)*

*Cortex
(layer between
epidermis and
vascular tissue)*

*Epidermis
(outer layer
of cells)*

*Cortex
(layer between
epidermis and
vascular tissue)*

*Epidermis
(outer layer
of cells)*

*Endodermis
(inner layer
of cortex)*

*Root tip
(region of
cell division)*

Phloem

Metaxylem

Protoxylem

*Stele
(vascular
cylinder)*

*Pericycle
(outer layer)*

PRIMARY ROOT OF BROAD BEAN
(*Vicia faba*)

CROSS SECTION THROUGH ROOT OF LILY
(*Lilium sp.*)

Elongating region

*Cortex
(layer between
epidermis and
vascular tissue)*

Epidermis

*Stele
(vascular
cylinder)*

*Apical meristem
(region of actively
dividing cells)*

*Root cap
(protects
dividing cells)*

*Hyphae of fungus
in mycorrhizal
(symbiotic) association
with orchid*

Starch grain

**LONGITUDINAL SECTION
THROUGH ROOT TIP OF BROAD BEAN**
(*Vicia faba*)

**CROSS SECTION THROUGH ROOT OF ORCHID IN
MYCORRHIZAL ASSOCIATION WITH FUNGUS**

Stems

THE STEM IS THE MAIN SUPPORTIVE PART OF A PLANT that grows above ground. Stems bear leaves (organs of photosynthesis), which grow at nodes; buds (shoots covered by protective scales), which grow at the stem tip (apical or terminal buds) and in the angle between a leaf and the stem (axillary or lateral buds); and flowers (reproductive structures). The stem forms part of the plant's transport system. Xylem tissue in the stem transports water and minerals from the roots to the aerial parts of the plant, and phloem tissue transports nutrients manufactured in the leaves to other parts of the plant. Stem tissues are also used for storing water and food. Herbaceous (nonwoody) stems have an outer protective epidermis covering a cortex that consists mainly of parenchyma (packing tissue) but also has some collenchyma (supporting tissue). The vascular tissue of such stems is arranged in bundles, each of which consists of xylem, phloem, and sclerenchyma (strengthening tissue). Woody stems have an outer protective layer of tough bark, which is perforated with lenticels (pores) to allow gas exchange. Inside the bark is a ring of secondary phloem, which surrounds an inner core of secondary xylem.

MICROGRAPH OF LONGITUDINAL SECTION THROUGH APEX OF STEM
Coleus sp.

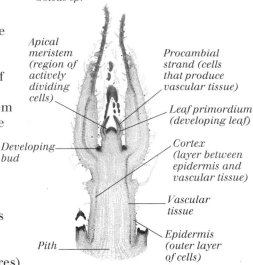

Apical meristem (region of actively dividing cells)

Procambial strand (cells that produce vascular tissue)

Leaf primordium (developing leaf)

Developing bud

Cortex (layer between epidermis and vascular tissue)

Vascular tissue

Epidermis (outer layer of cells)

Pith

YOUNG WOODY STEM
Linden
(*Tilia sp.*)

EMERGENT BUDS
Maple
(*Acer*)

Secondary phloem

Pith

Phellem (protective cork layer)

Cortex (layer between phellem and vascular tissue)

Xylem vessel (through which water and minerals are transported)

Xylem fiber (supporting tissue)

Ray (parenchyma cells)

Phloem sieve tube (through which nutrients are transported)

Phloem fiber (supporting tissue)

Lenticel (pore)

Vascular cambium (actively dividing cells that produce xylem and phloem)

Summer wood

Spring wood

Companion cell (cell associated with phloem sieve tube)

Young leaves emerging

Terminal bud

Lateral bud

Node

Internode

Inner bud scale

Secondary xylem

Outer bud scale

Node

Leaf scar

Lenticel (pore)

Woody stem

MICROGRAPHS OF CROSS SECTIONS THROUGH VARIOUS STEMS

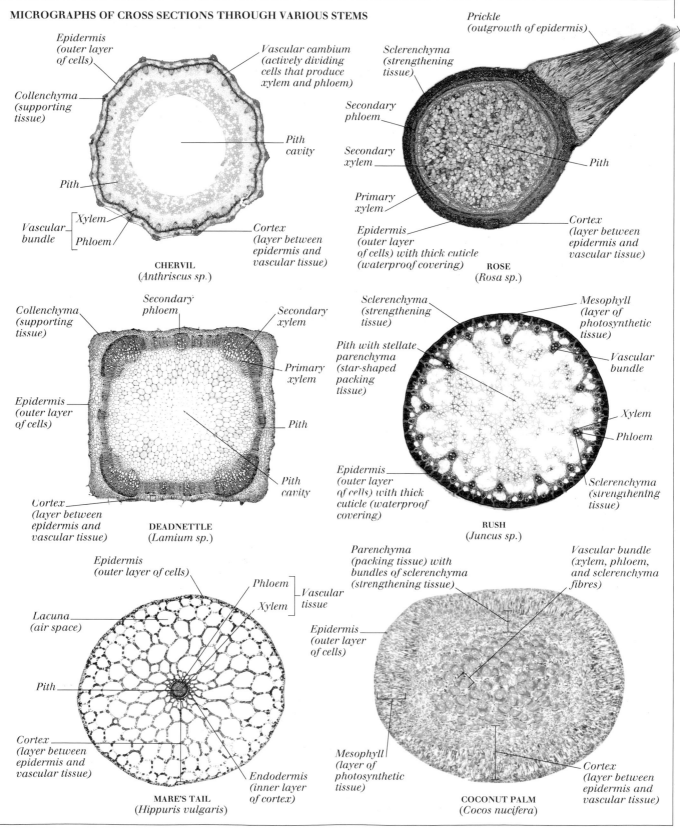

Epidermis (outer layer of cells)

Collenchyma (supporting tissue)

Pith

Vascular bundle — *Xylem* / *Phloem*

Vascular cambium (actively dividing cells that produce xylem and phloem)

Pith cavity

Cortex (layer between epidermis and vascular tissue)

CHERVIL
(Anthriscus sp.)

Prickle (outgrowth of epidermis)

Sclerenchyma (strengthening tissue)

Secondary phloem

Secondary xylem

Primary xylem

Epidermis (outer layer of cells) with thick cuticle (waterproof covering)

Pith

Cortex (layer between epidermis and vascular tissue)

ROSE
(Rosa sp.)

Collenchyma (supporting tissue)

Secondary phloem

Secondary xylem

Epidermis (outer layer of cells)

Primary xylem

Pith

Pith cavity

Cortex (layer between epidermis and vascular tissue)

DEADNETTLE
(Lamium sp.)

Sclerenchyma (strengthening tissue)

Pith with stellate parenchyma (star-shaped packing tissue)

Mesophyll (layer of photosynthetic tissue)

Vascular bundle

Xylem

Phloem

Epidermis (outer layer of cells) with thick cuticle (waterproof covering)

Sclerenchyma (strengthening tissue)

RUSH
(Juncus sp.)

Epidermis (outer layer of cells)

Phloem / *Xylem* — *Vascular tissue*

Lacuna (air space)

Pith

Cortex (layer between epidermis and vascular tissue)

Endodermis (inner layer of cortex)

MARE'S TAIL
(Hippuris vulgaris)

Parenchyma (packing tissue) with bundles of sclerenchyma (strengthening tissue)

Vascular bundle (xylem, phloem, and sclerenchyma fibres)

Epidermis (outer layer of cells)

Mesophyll (layer of photosynthetic tissue)

Cortex (layer between epidermis and vascular tissue)

COCONUT PALM
(Cocos nucifera)

Leaves

LEAVES ARE THE MAIN SITES OF PHOTOSYNTHESIS (see pp. 138-139) and transpiration (water loss by evaporation) in plants. A typical leaf consists of a thin, flat lamina (blade) supported by a network of veins; a petiole (leaf stalk); and a leaf base, where the petiole joins the stem. Leaves can be classified as simple, in which the lamina is a single unit, or compound, in which the lamina is divided into separate leaflets. Compound leaves may be pinnate, with pinnae (leaflets) on both sides of a rachis (main axis), or palmate, with leaflets arising from a single point at the tip of the petiole. Leaves can be classified further by the overall shape of the lamina, and by the shape of the lamina's apex, margin, and base.

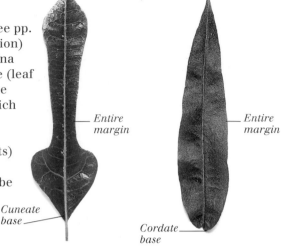

SIMPLE LEAF SHAPES

Subacute apex

Acuminate apex

Entire margin

Entire margin

Cuneate base

Cordate base

PANDURIFORM
Croton
(*Codiaeum variegatum*)

LANCEOLATE
Sea buckthorn
(*Hippophae rhamnoides*)

CHECKERBLOOM
(*Sidalcea malviflora*)

GENERAL LEAF FEATURES

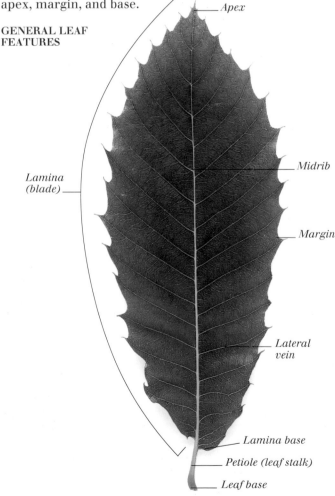

Apex

Midrib

Margin

Lateral vein

Lamina (blade)

Lamina base

Petiole (leaf stalk)

Leaf base

Spanish chestnut
(*Castanea sativa*)

COMPOUND LEAF SHAPES

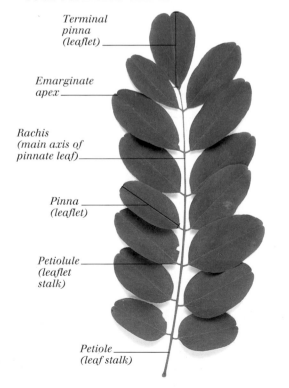

Terminal pinna (leaflet)

Emarginate apex

Rachis (main axis of pinnate leaf)

Pinna (leaflet)

Petiolule (leaflet stalk)

Petiole (leaf stalk)

ODD PINNATE
Black locust
(*Robinia pseudoacacia*)

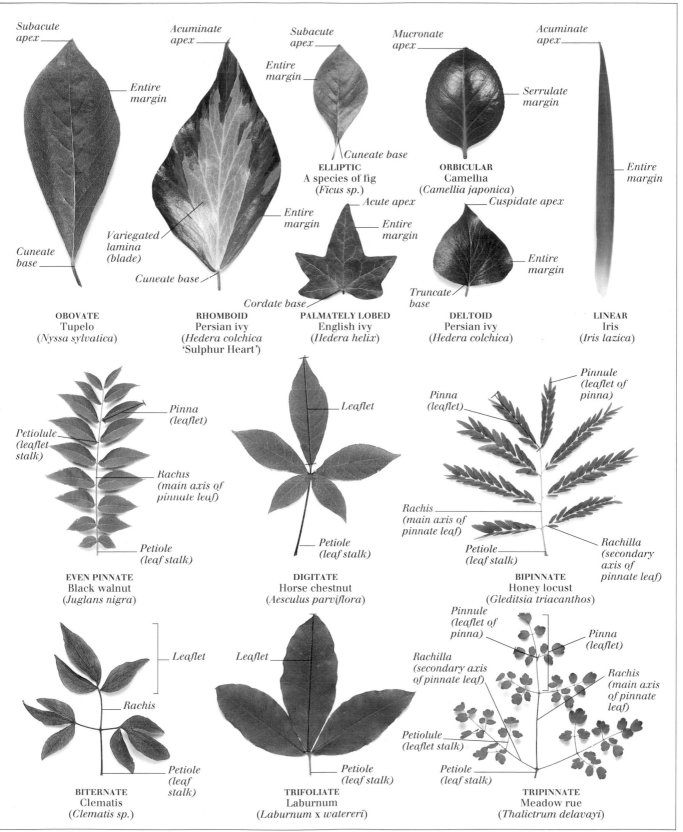

Subacute apex

Entire margin

Cuneate base

OBOVATE
Tupelo
(*Nyssa sylvatica*)

Acuminate apex

Variegated lamina (blade)

Cuneate base

RHOMBOID
Persian ivy
(*Hedera colchica* 'Sulphur Heart')

Subacute apex

Entire margin

Cuneate base

ELLIPTIC
A species of fig
(*Ficus sp.*)

Acute apex

Entire margin

Entire margin

Cordate base

PALMATELY LOBED
English ivy
(*Hedera helix*)

Mucronate apex

Serrulate margin

ORBICULAR
Camellia
(*Camellia japonica*)

Cuspidate apex

Entire margin

Truncate base

DELTOID
Persian ivy
(*Hedera colchica*)

Acuminate apex

Entire margin

LINEAR
Iris
(*Iris lazica*)

Pinna (leaflet)

Petiolule (leaflet stalk)

Rachis (main axis of pinnate leaf)

Petiole (leaf stalk)

EVEN PINNATE
Black walnut
(*Juglans nigra*)

Leaflet

Petiole (leaf stalk)

DIGITATE
Horse chestnut
(*Aesculus parviflora*)

Pinnule (leaflet of pinna)

Pinna (leaflet)

Rachis (main axis of pinnate leaf)

Petiole (leaf stalk)

Rachilla (secondary axis of pinnate leaf)

BIPINNATE
Honey locust
(*Gleditsia triacanthos*)

Leaflet

Rachis

Petiole (leaf stalk)

BITERNATE
Clematis
(*Clematis sp.*)

Leaflet

Petiole (leaf stalk)

TRIFOLIATE
Laburnum
(*Laburnum* x *watereri*)

Pinnule (leaflet of pinna)

Pinna (leaflet)

Rachilla (secondary axis of pinnate leaf)

Rachis (main axis of pinnate leaf)

Petiolule (leaflet stalk)

Petiole (leaf stalk)

TRIPINNATE
Meadow rue
(*Thalictrum delavayi*)

Photosynthesis

PHOTOSYNTHESIS IS THE PROCESS by which plants make their food using sunlight, water, and carbon dioxide. It takes place inside special structures in leaf cells called chloroplasts. The chloroplasts contain chlorophyll, a green pigment that absorbs energy from sunlight. During photosynthesis, the absorbed energy is used to join together carbon dioxide and water to form the sugar glucose, which is the energy source for the whole plant. Oxygen, a waste product, is released into the air. Leaves are the main sites of photosynthesis and have various adaptations for that purpose. Flat laminae (blades) provide a large surface for absorbing sunlight; stomata (pores) in the lower surface of the laminae allow gases (carbon dioxide and oxygen) to pass into and out of the leaves; and an extensive network of veins brings water into the leaves and transports the glucose produced by photosynthesis to the rest of the plant.

MICROGRAPH OF LEAF
Lily (*Lilium sp.*)

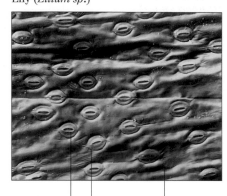

Stoma (pore)

Guard cell (controls opening and closing of stoma)

Lower surface of lamina (blade)

THE PROCESS OF PHOTOSYNTHESIS

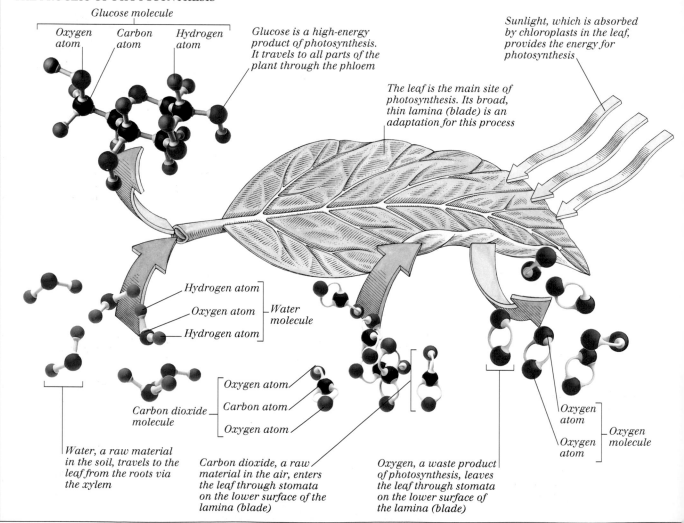

Glucose molecule

Oxygen atom

Carbon atom

Hydrogen atom

Glucose is a high-energy product of photosynthesis. It travels to all parts of the plant through the phloem

Sunlight, which is absorbed by chloroplasts in the leaf, provides the energy for photosynthesis

The leaf is the main site of photosynthesis. Its broad, thin lamina (blade) is an adaptation for this process

Hydrogen atom

Oxygen atom — Water molecule

Hydrogen atom

Carbon dioxide molecule

Oxygen atom

Carbon atom

Oxygen atom

Oxygen atom

Oxygen atom — Oxygen molecule

Water, a raw material in the soil, travels to the leaf from the roots via the xylem

Carbon dioxide, a raw material in the air, enters the leaf through stomata on the lower surface of the lamina (blade)

Oxygen, a waste product of photosynthesis, leaves the leaf through stomata on the lower surface of the lamina (blade)

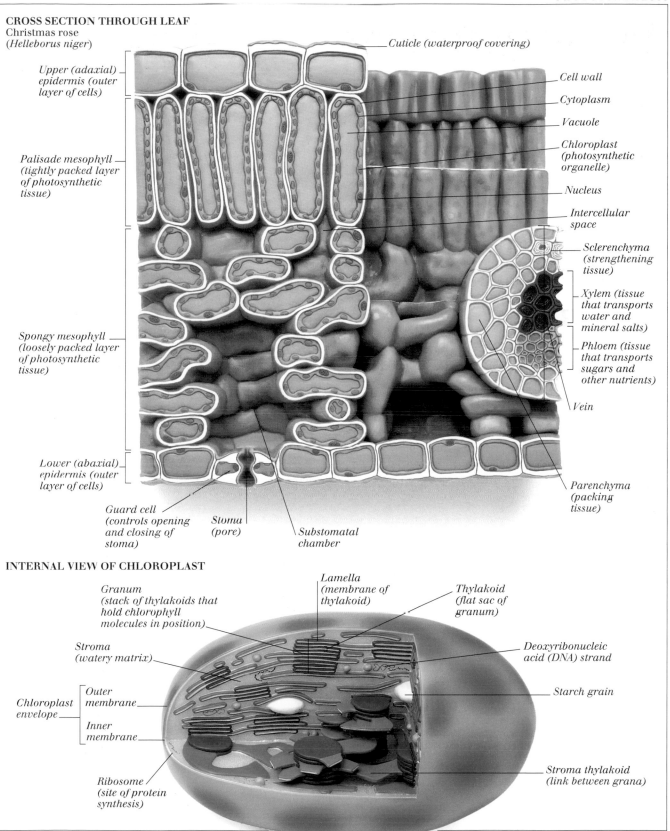

CROSS SECTION THROUGH LEAF
Christmas rose
(*Helleborus niger*)

Cuticle (waterproof covering)

Upper (adaxial) epidermis (outer layer of cells)

Cell wall

Cytoplasm

Vacuole

Chloroplast (photosynthetic organelle)

Palisade mesophyll (tightly packed layer of photosynthetic tissue)

Nucleus

Intercellular space

Sclerenchyma (strengthening tissue)

Xylem (tissue that transports water and mineral salts)

Phloem (tissue that transports sugars and other nutrients)

Spongy mesophyll (loosely packed layer of photosynthetic tissue)

Vein

Lower (abaxial) epidermis (outer layer of cells)

Parenchyma (packing tissue)

Guard cell (controls opening and closing of stoma)

Stoma (pore)

Substomatal chamber

INTERNAL VIEW OF CHLOROPLAST

Granum (stack of thylakoids that hold chlorophyll molecules in position)

Lamella (membrane of thylakoid)

Thylakoid (flat sac of granum)

Stroma (watery matrix)

Deoxyribonucleic acid (DNA) strand

Chloroplast envelope

Outer membrane

Inner membrane

Starch grain

Ribosome (site of protein synthesis)

Stroma thylakoid (link between grana)

Flowers 1

FLOWERS ARE THE SITES OF SEXUAL REPRODUCTION in flowering plants. Their component parts are arranged in whorls around the receptacle (tip of the flower stalk). The sepals (collectively called the calyx) are outermost; typically small and green, they protect the developing flower. The petals (collectively called the corolla) are typically large and brightly colored; they are found inside the sepals. In monocotyledonous flowers (see pp. 126-127), sepals and petals are indistinguishable; individually they are called tepals (collectively called the perianth). The petals surround the male and female reproductive structures (androecium and gynoecium). The androecium consists of stamens (male organs); each stamen is made up of a filament (stalk) and anther. The gynoecium has one or more carpels (female organs); each carpel consists of an ovary, style, and stigma. Some flowers (like the lily) occur singly on a pedicel (flower stalk); others (such as elder, sunflower) are arranged in a group (inflorescence) on a peduncle (inflorescence stalk).

A MONOCOTYLEDONOUS FLOWER
Lily
(*Lilium sp.*)

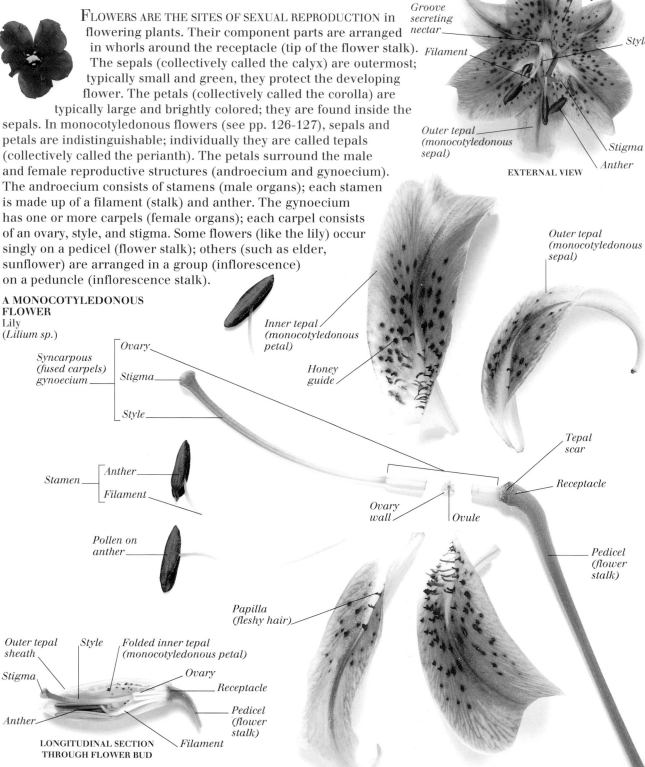

EXTERNAL VIEW

Inner tepal (monocotyledonous petal)
Honey guide
Groove secreting nectar
Filament
Style
Outer tepal (monocotyledonous sepal)
Stigma
Anther

Outer tepal (monocotyledonous sepal)

Inner tepal (monocotyledonous petal)
Honey guide

Syncarpous (fused carpels) gynoecium
Ovary
Stigma
Style

Tepal scar
Receptacle

Stamen
Anther
Filament

Ovary wall
Ovule

Pollen on anther

Pedicel (flower stalk)

Papilla (fleshy hair)

Outer tepal sheath
Style
Folded inner tepal (monocotyledonous petal)
Ovary
Receptacle
Stigma
Pedicel (flower stalk)
Anther
Filament

LONGITUDINAL SECTION THROUGH FLOWER BUD

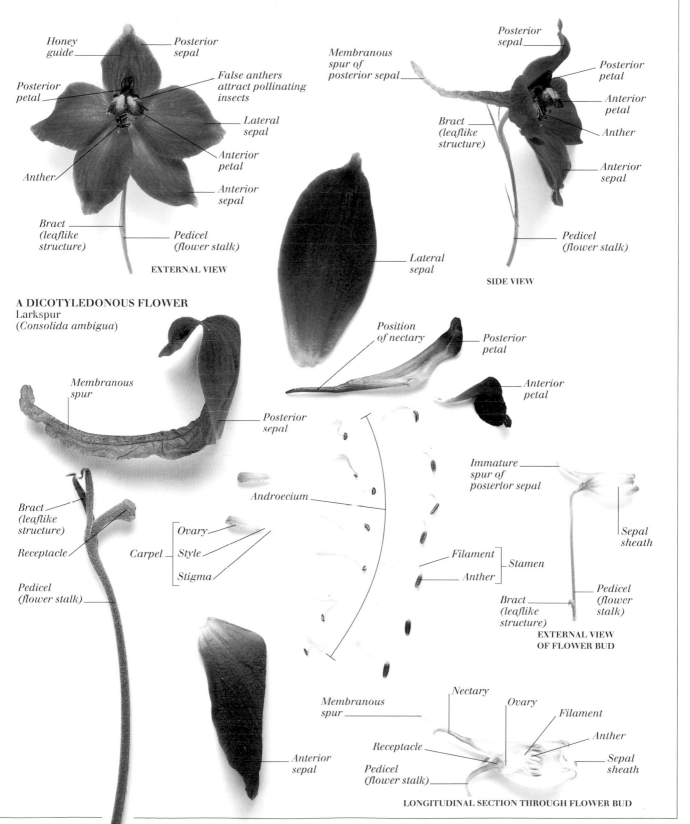

Honey guide

Posterior sepal

Posterior petal

False anthers attract pollinating insects

Lateral sepal

Anterior petal

Anterior sepal

Anther

Bract (leaflike structure)

Pedicel (flower stalk)

EXTERNAL VIEW

A DICOTYLEDONOUS FLOWER
Larkspur
(*Consolida ambigua*)

Membranous spur

Posterior sepal

Bract (leaflike structure)

Receptacle

Pedicel (flower stalk)

Carpel — Ovary / Style / Stigma

Androecium

Membranous spur

Anterior sepal

Membranous spur of posterior sepal

Posterior sepal

Posterior petal

Anterior petal

Anther

Anterior sepal

Bract (leaflike structure)

Pedicel (flower stalk)

SIDE VIEW

Lateral sepal

Position of nectary

Posterior petal

Anterior petal

Immature spur of posterior sepal

Sepal sheath

Filament

Anther

Stamen

Bract (leaflike structure)

Pedicel (flower stalk)

EXTERNAL VIEW OF FLOWER BUD

Nectary

Ovary

Filament

Anther

Receptacle

Sepal sheath

Pedicel (flower stalk)

LONGITUDINAL SECTION THROUGH FLOWER BUD

Flowers 2

COMPOUND INFLORESCENCE (CAPITULUM)
Sunflower
(*Helianthus annuus*)

Disk florets

Ray floret

Florets (small flowers) are grouped together to resemble a single large flower

Sterile ray floret to attract pollinating insects

Outer fertilized floret

Two-lobed stigma

Florets with anthers ready to shed pollen

Style

Pollen

Anther

Inner, immature florets

Corolla tube (fused petals)

Pappus (modified sepal)

Ovary

Corolla tube (fused petals)

Ovary

FLORETS FROM SUNFLOWER

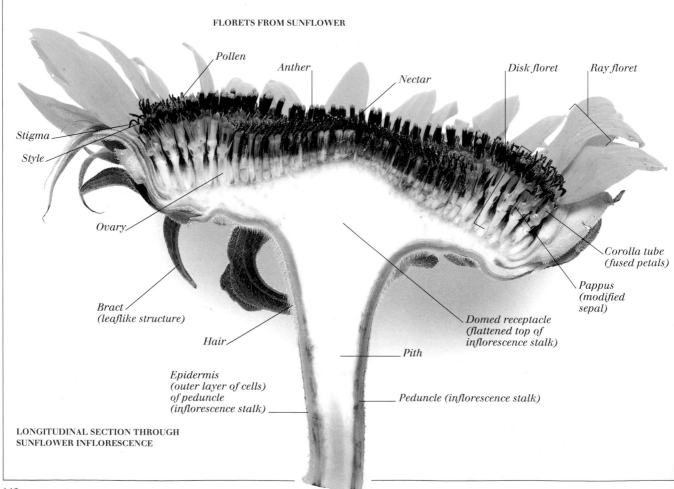

Pollen

Anther

Nectar

Disk floret

Ray floret

Stigma

Style

Ovary

Corolla tube (fused petals)

Pappus (modified sepal)

Bract (leaflike structure)

Hair

Domed receptacle (flattened top of inflorescence stalk)

Pith

Epidermis (outer layer of cells) of peduncle (inflorescence stalk)

Peduncle (inflorescence stalk)

LONGITUDINAL SECTION THROUGH SUNFLOWER INFLORESCENCE

ARRANGEMENT OF FLOWERS ON STEM

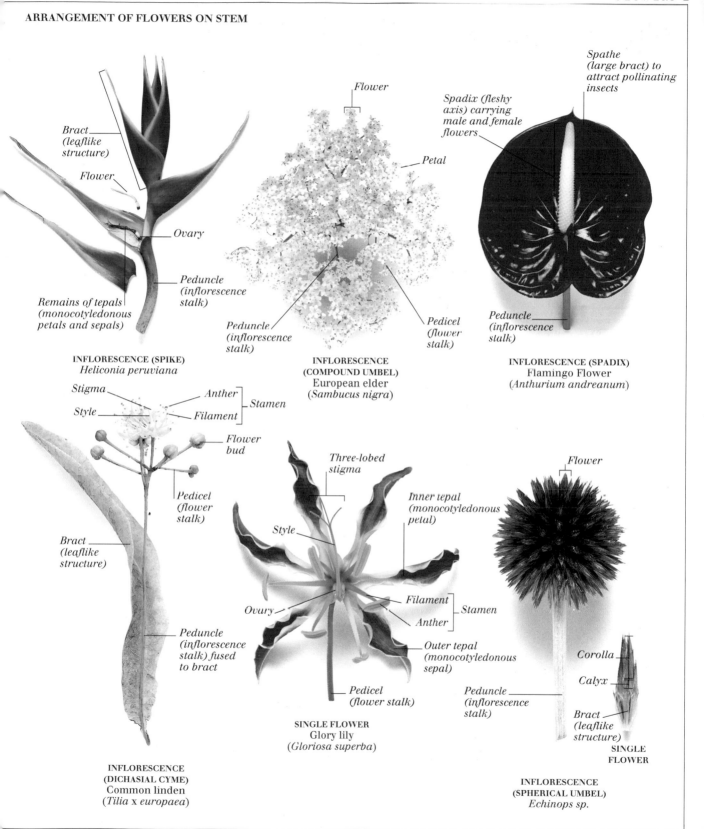

Bract
(leaflike
structure)

Flower

Ovary

Peduncle
(inflorescence
stalk)

Remains of tepals
(monocotyledonous
petals and sepals)

INFLORESCENCE (SPIKE)
Heliconia peruviana

Flower

Petal

Peduncle
(inflorescence
stalk)

Pedicel
(flower
stalk)

**INFLORESCENCE
(COMPOUND UMBEL)**
European elder
(*Sambucus nigra*)

Spathe
(large bract) to
attract pollinating
insects

Spadix (fleshy
axis) carrying
male and female
flowers

Peduncle
(inflorescence
stalk)

INFLORESCENCE (SPADIX)
Flamingo Flower
(*Anthurium andreanum*)

Stigma

Style

Anther

Filament

Stamen

Flower
bud

Pedicel
(flower
stalk)

Bract
(leaflike
structure)

Peduncle
(inflorescence
stalk) fused
to bract

**INFLORESCENCE
(DICHASIAL CYME)**
Common linden
(*Tilia x europaea*)

Three-lobed
stigma

Style

Ovary

Inner tepal
(monocotyledonous
petal)

Filament

Stamen

Anther

Outer tepal
(monocotyledonous
sepal)

Pedicel
(flower stalk)

SINGLE FLOWER
Glory lily
(*Gloriosa superba*)

Flower

Peduncle
(inflorescence
stalk)

Corolla

Calyx

Bract
(leaflike
structure)

**SINGLE
FLOWER**

**INFLORESCENCE
(SPHERICAL UMBEL)**
Echinops sp.

Pollination

POLLINATION IS THE TRANSFER OF POLLEN (which contains the male sex cells) from an anther (part of the male reproductive organ) to a stigma (part of the female reproductive organ). This process precedes fertilization (see pp. 146-147). Pollination may occur within the same flower (self-pollination), or between flowers on separate plants of the same species (cross-pollination). In most plants, pollination is carried out either by insects (entomophilous pollination) or by the wind (anemophilous pollination). Less commonly, birds, bats, or water are the agents of pollination. Insect-pollinated flowers are typically scented and brightly colored. They also produce nectar, on which insects feed. Such flowers also tend to have patterns that are visible only in ultraviolet light, which many insects can see but which humans cannot. These features attract insects, which become covered with the sticky pollen grains when they visit one flower, and then transfer the pollen to the next flower they visit. Wind-pollinated flowers are generally small, relatively inconspicuous, and unscented. They produce large quantities of light pollen grains that are easily blown by the wind to other flowers.

REPRODUCTIVE STRUCTURES IN WIND-POLLINATED PLANT
Sweet chestnut
(*Castanea sativa*)

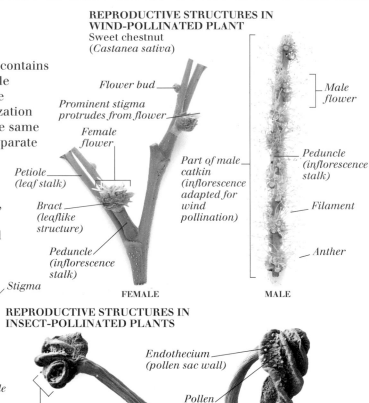

Flower bud

Prominent stigma protrudes from flower

Female flower

Petiole (leaf stalk)

Bract (leaflike structure)

Peduncle (inflorescence stalk)

FEMALE

Male flower

Peduncle (inflorescence stalk)

Part of male catkin (inflorescence adapted for wind pollination)

Filament

Anther

MALE

REPRODUCTIVE STRUCTURES IN INSECT-POLLINATED PLANTS

Stigma

Style

Dehisced (split open) pollen sac

Boundary between two fused carpels (each carpel consists of a stigma, style, and ovary)

Ovary

Endothecium (pollen sac wall)

Pollen grain

Anther

Stamen

Filament

Calyx (whorl of sepals)

MICROGRAPHS OF POLLEN GRAINS

Exine (outer coat of pollen grain)

Pore

EUROPEAN FIELD ELM
(*Ulmus minor*)

Colpus (furrow-shaped aperture)

Exine (outer coat of pollen grain)

JUSTICIA AUREA

MICROGRAPH OF CARPELS (FEMALE ORGANS)
Yellow-wort
(*Blackstonia perfoliata*)

Exine (outer coat of pollen grain)

Pore

Baculum (rod-shaped structure)

MEADOW CRANESBILL
(*Geranium pratense*)

MICROGRAPH OF STAMENS (MALE ORGANS)
Common centaury
(*Centaurium erythraea*)

Colpus (furrow-shaped aperture)

Exine (outer coat of pollen grain)

Equatorial furrow

BOX-LEAVED MILKWORT
(*Polygala chamaebuxus*)

INSECT POLLINATION OF MEADOW SAGE

Immature, unreceptive stigma

Sepal

Anther pushed on to bee's hairy abdomen

Labellum (lip) forming landing area for bee

Pollen grains from anther stick to bee's abdomen

1. BEE VISITS FLOWER WITH MATURE ANTHERS BUT IMMATURE STIGMA

Pollen grains attached to hairy abdomen

2. BEE FLIES TO OTHER FLOWERS

Long style curves downward when bee enters flower

Sepal

Mature, receptive stigma touches bee's abdomen, picking up pollen

Labellum (lip) forming landing area for bee

3. BEE VISITS FLOWER WHERE THE ANTHERS HAVE WITHERED AND THE STIGMA IS MATURE

SUNFLOWER UNDER NORMAL AND ULTRAVIOLET LIGHT

Central area of disc florets

Ray floret

NORMAL LIGHT

Petal

Ovary

Stamen — **Filament**, **Anther**

Stigma

NORMAL LIGHT

ST JOHN'S WORT UNDER NORMAL AND ULTRAVIOLET LIGHT

Honey guide directs insects to dark, central part of flower

Lighter, outer part of ray floret

Darker, inner part of ray floret

Insects attracted to darkest, central part of flower, which contains nectaries, anthers, and stigmas

ULTRAVIOLET LIGHT

Dark central area containing nectaries, anthers, and stigmas

ULTRAVIOLET LIGHT

Colpus (furrow-shaped aperture)

Exine (outer coat of pollen grain)

Columella (small column-shaped structure)

Trilete mark (development scar)

Pore

Exine (outer coat of pollen grain)

Exine (outer coat of pollen grain)

Exine (outer coat of pollen grain)

Tricolpate (three colpae) pollen grain

MIMULOPSIS SOLMSII

THESIUM ALPINIUM

RUELLIA GRANDIFLORA

CROSSANDRA NILOTICA

Fertilization

FERTILIZATION IS THE FUSION of male and female gametes (sex cells) to produce a zygote (embryo). Following pollination (see pp. 144-145), the pollen grains that contain the male gametes are on the stigma, some distance from the female gamete (ovum) inside the ovule. To enable the gametes to meet, the pollen grain germinates and produces a pollen tube, which grows down and enters the embryo sac (the inner part of the ovule that contains the ovum). Two male gametes, traveling at the tip of the pollen tube, enter the embryo sac. One gamete fuses with the ovum to produce a zygote that will develop into an embryo plant. The other male gamete fuses with two polar nuclei to produce the endosperm, which acts as a food supply for the developing embryo. Fertilization also initiates other changes: the integument (outer part of ovule) forms a testa (seed coat) around the embryo and endosperm; the petals fall off; the stigma and style wither; and the ovary wall forms a layer (called the pericarp) around the seed. Together, the pericarp and seed form the fruit, which may be succulent (see pp. 148-149) or dry (see pp. 150-151). In some species (such as blackberry), apomixis can occur: The seed develops without fertilization of the ovum by a male gamete, but endosperm formation and fruit development take place as in other species.

BANANA
(*Musa 'Lacatan'*)

DEVELOPMENT OF A SUCCULENT FRUIT
Blackberry
(*Rubus fruticosus*)

Petal

Stamen {
Filament
Anther
}

Carpel {
Ovary
Stigma
Style
}

**1. FLOWER IN FULL BLOOM
ATTRACTS POLLINATORS**

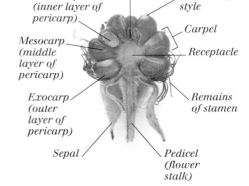

Endocarp (inner layer of pericarp)

Mesocarp (middle layer of pericarp)

Exocarp (outer layer of pericarp)

Sepal

Abortive seed

Remains of style

Carpel

Receptacle

Remains of stamen

Pedicel (flower stalk)

**4. PERICARP FORMS
FLESH, SKIN, AND A HARD INNER
LAYER (SHOWN IN CROSS SECTION)**

Exocarp (outer layer of pericarp)

Carpel

Remains of style

Remains of stamen

Remains of sepal

Pedicel (flower stalk)

**7. MESOCARP (FLESHY PART OF PERICARP)
OF EACH CARPEL STARTS TO
CHANGE COLOR**

Exocarp (outer layer of pericarp)

Drupelet

Remains of style

Remains of stamen

Remains of sepal

Pedicel (flower stalk)

**8. CARPELS MATURE INTO DRUPELETS
(SMALL FLESHY FRUITS WITH SINGLE SEEDS
SURROUNDED BY HARD ENDOCARP)**

Exocarp (outer layer of pericarp)

Drupelet

Remains of style

Remains of stamen

Remains of sepal

Pedicel (flower stalk)

**9. MESOCARP OF DRUPELET BECOMES
DARKER AND SWEETER**

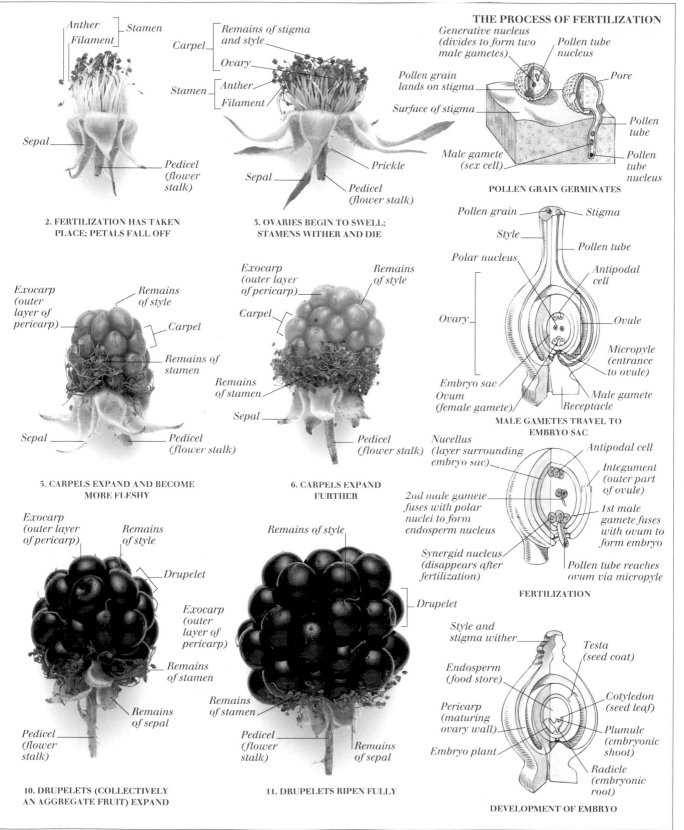

2. FERTILIZATION HAS TAKEN PLACE; PETALS FALL OFF

Anther — Stamen
Filament —
Sepal
Pedicel (flower stalk)

5. OVARIES BEGIN TO SWELL; STAMENS WITHER AND DIE

Carpel
Remains of stigma and style
Ovary
Stamen — Anther
Filament
Sepal
Prickle
Pedicel (flower stalk)

THE PROCESS OF FERTILIZATION

Generative nucleus (divides to form two male gametes)
Pollen tube nucleus
Pollen grain lands on stigma
Pore
Surface of stigma
Pollen tube
Male gamete (sex cell)
Pollen tube nucleus

POLLEN GRAIN GERMINATES

5. CARPELS EXPAND AND BECOME MORE FLESHY

Exocarp (outer layer of pericarp)
Remains of style
Carpel
Remains of stamen
Sepal
Pedicel (flower stalk)

6. CARPELS EXPAND FURTHER

Exocarp (outer layer of pericarp)
Remains of style
Carpel
Remains of stamen
Sepal
Pedicel (flower stalk)

Pollen grain
Stigma
Style
Pollen tube
Polar nucleus
Antipodal cell
Ovary
Ovule
Micropyle (entrance to ovule)
Embryo sac
Ovum (female gamete)
Male gamete
Receptacle

MALE GAMETES TRAVEL TO EMBRYO SAC

Nucellus (layer surrounding embryo sac)
Antipodal cell
Integument (outer part of ovule)
2nd male gamete fuses with polar nuclei to form endosperm nucleus
1st male gamete fuses with ovum to form embryo
Synergid nucleus (disappears after fertilization)
Pollen tube reaches ovum via micropyle

FERTILIZATION

10. DRUPELETS (COLLECTIVELY AN AGGREGATE FRUIT) EXPAND

Exocarp (outer layer of pericarp)
Remains of style
Drupelet
Remains of stamen
Pedicel (flower stalk)
Remains of sepal

11. DRUPELETS RIPEN FULLY

Remains of style
Drupelet
Exocarp (outer layer of pericarp)
Remains of stamen
Pedicel (flower stalk)
Remains of sepal

Style and stigma wither
Testa (seed coat)
Endosperm (food store)
Cotyledon (seed leaf)
Pericarp (maturing ovary wall)
Plumule (embryonic shoot)
Embryo plant
Radicle (embryonic root)

DEVELOPMENT OF EMBRYO

147

Succulent fruits

A FRUIT IS A FULLY DEVELOPED and ripened ovary—the seed-producing part of a plant's female reproductive organs. Fruits may be succulent or dry (see pp. 150-151). Succulent fruits are fleshy and brightly colored, making them attractive to animals, which eat them and disperse the seeds away from the parent plant. The wall (pericarp) of a succulent fruit has three layers: an outer exocarp, a middle mesocarp, and an inner endocarp. These three layers vary in thickness and texture in different types of fruits and may blend into each other. Succulent fruits can be classed as simple (derived from one ovary) or compound (derived from several ovaries). Simple succulent fruits include berries, which typically have many seeds, and drupes, which typically have a single stone or pit (such as cherry and peach). Compound succulent fruits include aggregate fruits, which are formed from many ovaries in one flower, and multiple fruits, which develop from the ovaries of many flowers. Some fruits, known as false fruits or pseudocarps, develop from parts of the flower in addition to the ovaries. For example, the flesh of the apple is formed from the receptacle (the upper end of the flower stalk).

BERRY
Cocoa
(*Theobroma cacao*)

HESPERIDIUM (A TYPE OF BERRY)
Lemon
(*Citrus limon*)

Pedicel (flower stalk)
Endocarp
Mesocarp
Pedicel (flower stalk)
Exocarp
Leathery exocarp
Seed
Vesicle (juice sac)
Oil gland
Remains of style
Remains of style
Placenta

EXTERNAL VIEW OF FRUIT

LONGITUDINAL SECTION THROUGH FRUIT

Embryo
Seed
Carpel wall
Hilum (point of attachment to ovary)
Carpel
Testa (seed coat)
Cotyledon (seed leaf)
Placenta

EXTERNAL VIEW AND SECTION THROUGH SEED

CROSS SECTION THROUGH FRUIT

SYCONIUM (A TYPE OF FALSE FRUIT)
Fig
(*Ficus carica*)

Remains of female flowers
Fleshy infolded receptacle
Remains of male flowers
Peduncle (inflorescence stalk)
Pit (seed surrounded by endocarp)
Skin
Pore closed by scales

EXTERNAL VIEW OF FRUIT

LONGITUDINAL SECTION THROUGH FRUIT

FRUIT WITH FLESHY ARIL
Lychee
(*Litchi chinensis*)

Pedicel (flower stalk)
Pedicel (flower stalk)
Seed
Aril (fleshy outgrowth from seed stalk)
Pericarp (fruit wall)
Pericarp (fruit wall)

Remains of style
Endocarp
EXTERNAL VIEW AND SECTION THROUGH PIT
Drupelet
Pit
Pedicel (flower stalk)
Endocarp
Embryo
Testa (seed coat)
Cotyledon (seed leaf)

EXTERNAL VIEW OF FRUIT

LONGITUDINAL SECTION THROUGH FRUIT

REMAINS OF A SINGLE FEMALE FLOWER

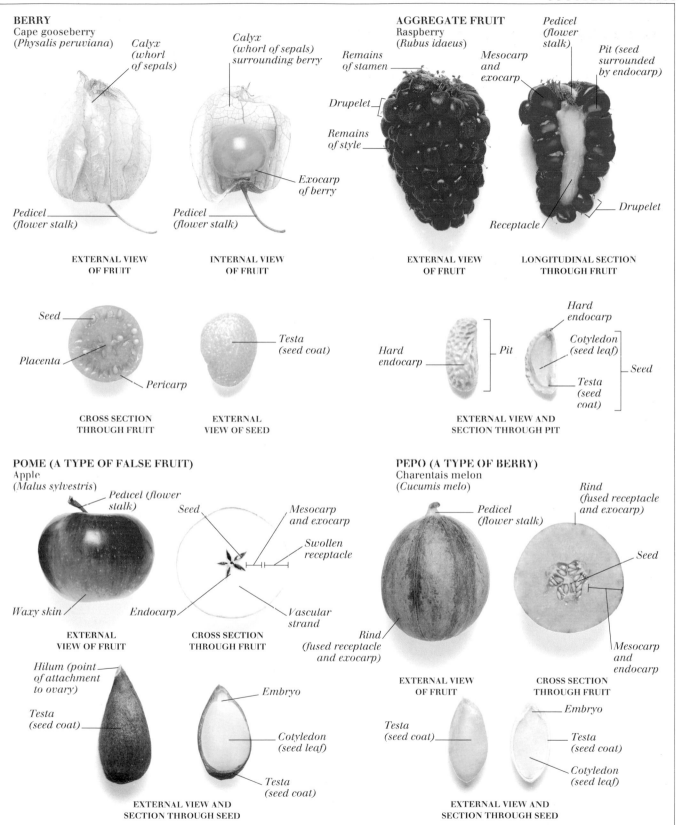

BERRY
Cape gooseberry
(*Physalis peruviana*)

Calyx (whorl of sepals)

Calyx (whorl of sepals) surrounding berry

Pedicel (flower stalk)

Exocarp of berry

Pedicel (flower stalk)

EXTERNAL VIEW
OF FRUIT

INTERNAL VIEW
OF FRUIT

Seed

Placenta

Pericarp

Testa (seed coat)

CROSS SECTION
THROUGH FRUIT

EXTERNAL
VIEW OF SEED

AGGREGATE FRUIT
Raspberry
(*Rubus idaeus*)

Remains of stamen

Drupelet

Remains of style

Pedicel (flower stalk)

Mesocarp and exocarp

Pit (seed surrounded by endocarp)

Receptacle

Drupelet

EXTERNAL VIEW
OF FRUIT

LONGITUDINAL SECTION
THROUGH FRUIT

Hard endocarp

Hard endocarp

Pit

Cotyledon (seed leaf)

Testa (seed coat)

Seed

EXTERNAL VIEW AND
SECTION THROUGH PIT

POME (A TYPE OF FALSE FRUIT)
Apple
(*Malus sylvestris*)

Pedicel (flower stalk)

Seed

Mesocarp and exocarp

Swollen receptacle

Waxy skin

Endocarp

Vascular strand

EXTERNAL
VIEW OF FRUIT

CROSS SECTION
THROUGH FRUIT

Hilum (point of attachment to ovary)

Testa (seed coat)

Embryo

Cotyledon (seed leaf)

Testa (seed coat)

EXTERNAL VIEW AND
SECTION THROUGH SEED

PEPO (A TYPE OF BERRY)
Charentais melon
(*Cucumis melo*)

Pedicel (flower stalk)

Rind (fused receptacle and exocarp)

Seed

Rind (fused receptacle and exocarp)

Mesocarp and endocarp

EXTERNAL VIEW
OF FRUIT

CROSS SECTION
THROUGH FRUIT

Testa (seed coat)

Embryo

Testa (seed coat)

Cotyledon (seed leaf)

EXTERNAL VIEW AND
SECTION THROUGH SEED

Dry fruits

DRY FRUITS HAVE A HARD, DRY PERICARP (fruit wall) around their seeds, unlike succulent fruits, which have fleshy pericarps (see pp. 148-149). Dry fruits are divided into three types: dehiscent, in which the pericarp splits open to release the seeds; indehiscent, which do not split open; and schizocarpic, in which the fruit splits but the seeds are not exposed. Dehiscent dry fruits include capsules (for example, love-in-a-mist), follicles (delphinium), legumes (pea), and silicles (honesty). Typically, the seeds of dehiscent fruits are dispersed by the wind. Indehiscent dry fruits include nuts (sweet chestnut), nutlets (goose grass), achenes (strawberry), caryopses (wheat), samaras (elm), and cypselas (dandelion). Some indehiscent dry fruits are dispersed by the wind, assisted by "wings" (elm) or "parachutes" (dandelion); others (goose grass) have hooked pericarps to aid dispersal on animals' fur. Schizocarpic dry fruits include cremocarps (hogweed), and double samaras (sycamore maple); these are dispersed by the wind.

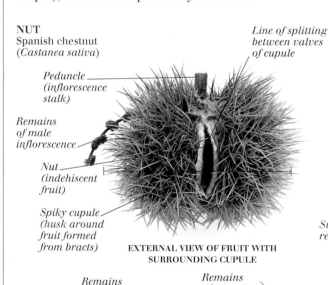

NUTLET
Goose grass
(*Galium aparine*)

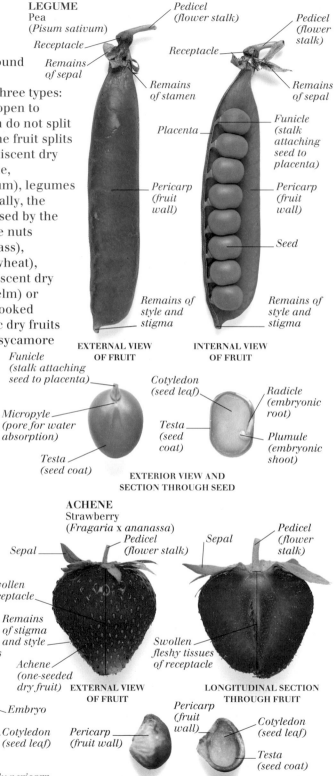

LEGUME
Pea
(*Pisum sativum*)

Pedicel (flower stalk)
Receptacle
Remains of sepal
Remains of stamen
Placenta
Pericarp (fruit wall)
Remains of style and stigma

Pedicel (flower stalk)
Receptacle
Remains of sepal
Funicle (stalk attaching seed to placenta)
Pericarp (fruit wall)
Seed
Remains of style and stigma

EXTERNAL VIEW OF FRUIT

INTERNAL VIEW OF FRUIT

Funicle (stalk attaching seed to placenta)
Micropyle (pore for water absorption)
Testa (seed coat)

Cotyledon (seed leaf)
Radicle (embryonic root)
Testa (seed coat)
Plumule (embryonic shoot)

EXTERIOR VIEW AND SECTION THROUGH SEED

NUT
Spanish chestnut
(*Castanea sativa*)

Line of splitting between valves of cupule

Peduncle (inflorescence stalk)
Remains of male inflorescence
Nut (indehiscent fruit)
Spiky cupule (husk around fruit formed from bracts)

EXTERNAL VIEW OF FRUIT WITH SURROUNDING CUPULE

Remains of stigma
Remains of style

Remains of stigma
Remains of style

Nut (indehiscent fruit)
Woody pericarp (fruit wall)

EXTERNAL VIEW AND SECTION THROUGH FRUIT

Embryo
Cotyledon (seed leaf)
Testa (seed coat)
Woody pericarp (fruit wall)

ACHENE
Strawberry
(*Fragaria x ananassa*)

Sepal
Pedicel (flower stalk)
Swollen receptacle
Remains of stigma and style
Achene (one-seeded dry fruit)

EXTERNAL VIEW OF FRUIT

Sepal
Pedicel (flower stalk)
Swollen fleshy tissues of receptacle

LONGITUDINAL SECTION THROUGH FRUIT

Pericarp (fruit wall)
Cotyledon (seed leaf)
Testa (seed coat)

EXTERNAL VIEW AND SECTION THROUGH SEED

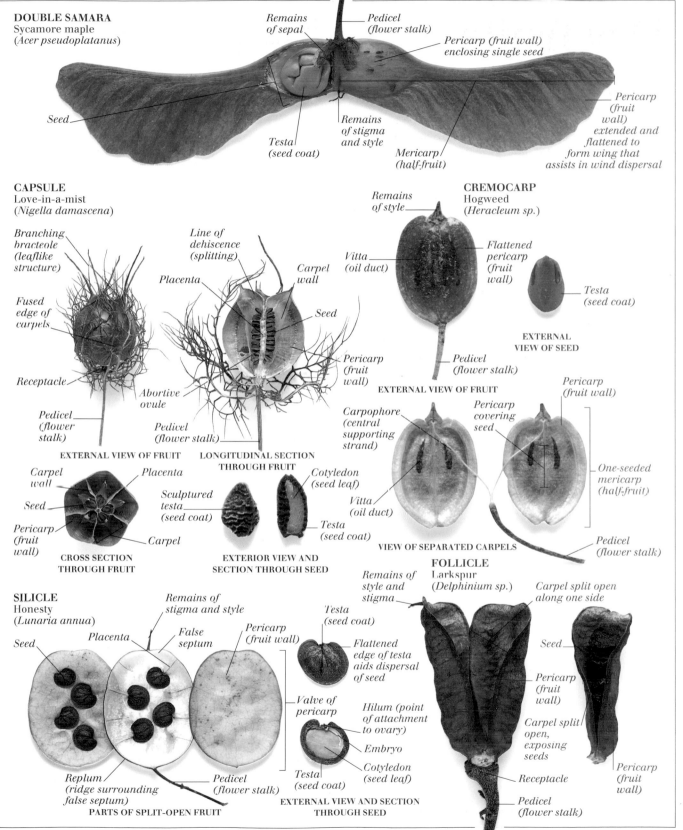

DOUBLE SAMARA
Sycamore maple
(*Acer pseudoplatanus*)

Remains of sepal

Pedicel (flower stalk)

Pericarp (fruit wall) enclosing single seed

Seed

Testa (seed coat)

Remains of stigma and style

Mericarp (half-fruit)

Pericarp (fruit wall) extended and flattened to form wing that assists in wind dispersal

CAPSULE
Love-in-a-mist
(*Nigella damascena*)

Branching bracteole (leaflike structure)

Fused edge of carpels

Receptacle

Pedicel (flower stalk)

EXTERNAL VIEW OF FRUIT

Line of dehiscence (splitting)

Placenta

Carpel wall

Seed

Pericarp (fruit wall)

Abortive ovule

Pedicel (flower stalk)

LONGITUDINAL SECTION THROUGH FRUIT

Carpel wall

Placenta

Seed

Pericarp (fruit wall)

Carpel

CROSS SECTION THROUGH FRUIT

Sculptured testa (seed coat)

Cotyledon (seed leaf)

Testa (seed coat)

EXTERIOR VIEW AND SECTION THROUGH SEED

CREMOCARP
Hogweed
(*Heracleum sp.*)

Remains of style

Vitta (oil duct)

Flattened pericarp (fruit wall)

Testa (seed coat)

EXTERNAL VIEW OF SEED

Pedicel (flower stalk)

EXTERNAL VIEW OF FRUIT

Carpophore (central supporting strand)

Pericarp covering seed

Pericarp (fruit wall)

Vitta (oil duct)

One-seeded mericarp (half-fruit)

VIEW OF SEPARATED CARPELS

Pedicel (flower stalk)

SILICLE
Honesty
(*Lunaria annua*)

Seed

Placenta

Remains of stigma and style

False septum

Pericarp (fruit wall)

Replum (ridge surrounding false septum)

Pedicel (flower stalk)

PARTS OF SPLIT-OPEN FRUIT

Testa (seed coat)

Flattened edge of testa aids dispersal of seed

Valve of pericarp

Hilum (point of attachment to ovary)

Embryo

Cotyledon (seed leaf)

Testa (seed coat)

EXTERNAL VIEW AND SECTION THROUGH SEED

FOLLICLE
Larkspur
(*Delphinium sp.*)

Remains of style and stigma

Carpel split open along one side

Seed

Pericarp (fruit wall)

Carpel split open, exposing seeds

Receptacle

Pedicel (flower stalk)

Pericarp (fruit wall)

Germination

GERMINATION IS THE GROWTH OF SEEDS INTO SEEDLINGS. It starts when seeds become active below ground, and ends when the first foliage leaves appear above ground. A seed consists of an embryo and its food supply, surrounded by a testa (seed coat). The embryo is made up of one or two cotyledons (seed leaves) attached to a central axis. The upper part of the axis consists of an epicotyl, which has a plumule (embryonic shoot) at its tip. The lower part of the axis consists of a hypocotyl and a radicle (embryonic root). After dispersal from the parent plant, the seeds dehydrate and enter a period of dormancy. Germination begins, following this dormant period, as long as the seeds have enough water, oxygen, warmth, and, in some cases, light. In the first stages of germination, the seed takes in water; the embryo starts to use its food store; and the radicle swells, breaks through the testa, and grows downward. Germination then proceeds in one of two ways, depending on the type of seed. In epigeal germination, the hypocotyl lengthens, pulling the plumule and its protective cotyledons out of the soil. In hypogeal germination, the cotyledons remain below ground and the epicotyl lengthens, pushing the plumule upward.

HYPOGEAL GERMINATION
Broad bean
(*Vicia faba*)

Cotyledon
(seed leaf)

Cotyledon
(seed leaf)

Plumule
(embryonic
shoot)

Testa
(seed
coat)

Epicotyl
(upper part
of axis)

Hypocotyl
(region
between
epicotyl and
radicle)

Radicle
(embryonic
root)

**SEED AT START OF
GERMINATION**

Cotyledon
(seed leaf)

Foliage leaf

Cotyledon
(seed leaf)

Stipule
(structure at
base of leaf)

Epicotyl
increases in
length and
turns green

Cataphyll
(scale leaf
of plumule)

Epicotyl
(upper part
of axis)

Hypocotyl (region
between epicotyl and
radicle)

**FOLIAGE LEAVES
APPEAR**

Cotyledons (seed leaves)
remain food source for
the seedling

Primary
root

Radicle
(embryonic
root)

Lateral
root
system

Split in testa
(seed coat) due
to expanding
cotyledons

Young
shoot

Cataphyll
(scale leaf of
plumule)

Cotyledons
(seed leaves)
remain within
testa (seed
coat) below
soil's surface

**SHOOT APPEARS
ABOVE SOIL**

Epicotyl
(upper part
of axis)
lengthens

Testa
(seed coat)

Plumule
(embryonic
shoot)

Primary
root

Lateral root

Hilum (point of
attachment to ovary)

Cortex

Vascular tissue
(xylem and
phloem)

Epidermis

**RADICLE BREAKS
THROUGH TESTA**

Root tip
(region of
cell division)

EPIGEAL GERMINATION
Black bean
(*Phaseolus sp.*)

*Epicotyl
(upper part
of axis)*

*Plumule
(embryonic
shoot)*

*Hypocotyl
(region between
epicotyl and
radicle)*

*Radicle
(embryonic
root)*

*Hilum
(point of
attachment
to ovary)*

*Testa
(seed coat)*

*Cotyledon
(seed leaf)*

**LONGITUDINAL SECTION
THROUGH SEED AT START
OF GERMINATION**

*Epicotyl
(upper part
of axis)*

*Testa
(seed coat)*

*Plumule
(embryonic
shoot)*

*Cotyledon
(seed leaf)*

*Hypocotyl
(region between
epicotyl and
radicle)*

*Testa
(seed coat)*

*Raphe
(ridge)*

*Hilum (point
of attachment
to ovary)*

*Micropyle
(pore for
water
absorption)*

**EXTERNAL VIEW OF SEED AT
START OF GERMINATION**

*First foliage
leaf fully
grown*

*Petiole
(leaf stalk)*

*Growing
point*

Lateral root

*Cotyledon (seed
leaf) withers*

*Primary root
(elongated
radicle)*

*Cotyledon
(seed leaf)*

*First foliage leaf
protected by cotyledons
(seed leaves)*

*Hypocotyl
"hook" pushes
out of soil*

*Testa
(seed
coat)
splits*

*Hypocotyl (region
between epicotyl and
radicle) elongates*

*Hypocotyl (region
between epicotyl
and radicle)
straightens
and lengthens*

**RADICLE BREAKS THROUGH
TESTA AND LENGTHENS**

*Testa (seed
coat) shed*

*Testa (seed
coat) begins to
disintegrate*

*Lateral
root*

Root

Root

*Primary
root*

**HYPOCOTYL
"HOOK" APPEARS
ABOVE SOIL**

**HYPOCOTYL
STRAIGHTENS,
PULLING LEAVES
AND COTYLEDONS
OUT OF SOIL**

**FIRST FOLIAGE
LEAVES FULLY
DEVELOPED**

*Root cap
(protective
covering for
root tip)*

Vegetative reproduction

MANY PLANTS CAN PROPAGATE THEMSELVES by vegetative reproduction. In this process, part of a plant separates, takes root, and grows into a new plant. Vegetative reproduction is a type of asexual reproduction; it involves only one parent and there is no fusion of gametes (sex cells). Plants use various structures to reproduce vegetatively. Some plants use underground storage organs. Such organs include rhizomes (horizontal, underground stems), the branches of which produce new plants; bulbs (swollen leaf bases) and corms (swollen stems), which produce daughter bulbs or corms that separate from the parent; and stem tubers (thickened underground stems) and root tubers (swollen adventitious roots), which also separate from the parent. Other propagative structures include runners and stolons, creeping horizontal stems that take root and produce new plants; bulbils, small bulbs that develop on the stem or in the place of flowers, and then drop off and grow into new plants; and adventitious buds, miniature plants that form on leaf margins before dropping to the ground and growing into mature plants.

CORM
Gladiolus
(*Gladiolus sp.*)

ADVENTITIOUS BUD
Mexican hat plant
(*Kalanchoe daigremontiana*)

Apex of leaf

Lamina (blade) of leaf

Leaf margin

Notch in leaf margin containing meristematic (actively dividing) cells

Adventitious bud (detachable bud with adventitious roots) drops from leaf

Petiole (leaf stalk)

BULBIL IN PLACE OF FLOWER
Orange lily
(*Lilium bulbiferum*)

Scar left by flower

Leaf

Pedicel (flower stalk)

Detachable bulbil formed in place of flower

Peduncle (inflorescence stalk)

STOLON
Ground ivy
(*Glechoma hederacea*)

Terminal bud

Internode

Node

Node

Parent plant

Stolon (creeping stem)

Adventitious root of daughter plant

Daughter plant developed from lateral bud

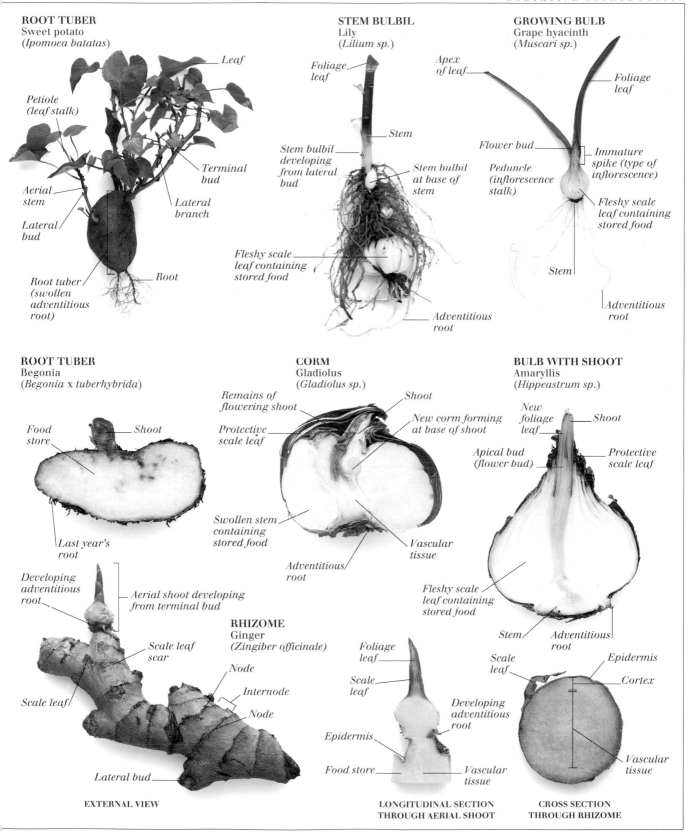

ROOT TUBER
Sweet potato
(*Ipomoea batatas*)

Leaf

Petiole
(leaf stalk)

Terminal
bud

Aerial
stem

Lateral
branch

Lateral
bud

Root tuber
(swollen
adventitious
root)

Root

STEM BULBIL
Lily
(*Lilium sp.*)

Foliage
leaf

Stem

Stem bulbil
developing
from lateral
bud

Stem bulbil
at base of
stem

Fleshy scale
leaf containing
stored food

Adventitious
root

GROWING BULB
Grape hyacinth
(*Muscari sp.*)

Apex
of leaf

Foliage
leaf

Flower bud

Immature
spike (type of
inflorescence)

Peduncle
(inflorescence
stalk)

Fleshy scale
leaf containing
stored food

Stem

Adventitious
root

ROOT TUBER
Begonia
(*Begonia* x *tuberhybrida*)

Food
store

Shoot

Last year's
root

Developing
adventitious
root

Aerial shoot developing
from terminal bud

Scale leaf
scar

RHIZOME
Ginger
(*Zingiber officinale*)

Node

Internode

Node

Scale leaf

Lateral bud

EXTERNAL VIEW

CORM
Gladiolus
(*Gladiolus sp.*)

Remains of
flowering shoot

Shoot

Protective
scale leaf

New corm forming
at base of shoot

Swollen stem
containing
stored food

Adventitious
root

Vascular
tissue

Foliage
leaf

Scale
leaf

Developing
adventitious
root

Epidermis

Food store

Vascular
tissue

**LONGITUDINAL SECTION
THROUGH AERIAL SHOOT**

BULB WITH SHOOT
Amaryllis
(*Hippeastrum sp.*)

New
foliage
leaf

Shoot

Apical bud
(flower bud)

Protective
scale leaf

Fleshy scale
leaf containing
stored food

Stem

Adventitious
root

Scale
leaf

Epidermis

Cortex

Vascular
tissue

**CROSS SECTION
THROUGH RHIZOME**

155

Dryland plants

LEAF SUCCULENT
Lithops sp.

DRYLAND PLANTS (XEROPHYTES) are able to survive in unfavorable habitats. All are found in places where little water is available; some live in high temperatures that cause excessive loss of water from the leaves. Xerophytes show a number of adaptations to dry conditions. These include reduced leaf area, rolled leaves, sunken stomata, hairs, spines, and thick cuticles. One group, succulent plants, stores water in specially enlarged spongy tissues found in leaves, roots, or stems. Leaf succulents have enlarged, fleshy, water-storing leaves. Root succulents have a large underground water-storage organ with short-lived stems and leaves above ground. Stem succulents are represented by the cacti (family Cactaceae). Cacti stems are fleshy, green, and photosynthetic. They are typically ribbed or covered by tubercles in rows, with leaves being reduced to spines or entirely absent.

STEM SUCCULENT
Golden barrel cactus
(*Echinocactus grusonii*)

Areole (modified lateral shoot)

Trichome (hair)

Spine (modified leaf)

Tubercle (projection from stem surface)

Vascular cylinder (transport tissue)

Root

LONGITUDINAL SECTION THROUGH STEM

Spine (modified leaf)

Tubercle (projection from stem surface)

Root

EXTERNAL VIEW

Waxy cuticle (waterproof covering)

Water-storing parenchyma (packing tissue)

Sinuous (wavy) cell wall

Stoma (pore) controlling exchange of gases

MICROGRAPH OF STEM SURFACE

Spine (modified leaf)

Areole (modified lateral shoot)

Tubercle (projection from stem surface)

Waxy cuticle (waterproof covering)

DETAIL OF STEM SURFACE

LEAF SUCCULENT
Haworthia truncata

Translucent "window" allows light to reach base of leaf

Succulent leaf

Root tuber

Root

Translucent "window" allows light to reach base of leaf

Waxy cuticle (waterproof covering)

Water-storing parenchyma (packing tissue)

Photosynthetic region

LONGITUDINAL SECTION THROUGH LEAF

LEAF SUCCULENT
Lithops bromfieldii

Leaf

Fissure

Mottled surface of leaf

Dead, withered leaf

Dead flower in old fissure

Unified leaf pair

Translucent "window" allows light to reach center of leaf

Fissure

Waxy cuticle (waterproof covering)

Photosynthetic region

Water-storing parenchyma (packing tissue)

LONGITUDINAL SECTION THROUGH LEAF PAIR

Raised cell surface

Stoma (pore)

Cup surrounding sunken stoma (pore)

MICROGRAPH OF LEAF SURFACE

ROOT SUCCULENT
Oxalis sp.

Petiole (leaf stalk)

Flower bud

Pedicel (flower stalk)

Stem

Trifoliate leaf

Root tuber

Root

STEM AND ROOT SUCCULENT
String of hearts
(*Ceropegia woodii*)

Stem

Root tuber

Root

EXTERNAL VIEW

Petiole (leaf stalk)

Succulent trailing stem

Succulent leaf

Root tuber

Water-storing parenchyma

Root

LONGITUDINAL SECTION THROUGH ROOT TUBER

Wetland plants

WETLAND PLANTS GROW SUBMERGED IN WATER, either partially, like the water hyacinth, or completely, like the pondweeds, and show various adaptations to this habitat. Typically, there are numerous air spaces inside the stems, leaves, and roots; these aid gas exchange and buoyancy. Submerged parts generally have no cuticle (waterproof covering), allowing the plants to absorb minerals and gases directly from the water. Also, because they are supported by the water, wetland plants need little of the supportive tissue found in land plants. Stomata, the gas exchange pores, are absent from plants that are completely submerged. In partially submerged plants with floating leaves, such as water lilies, stomata are found on the upper leaf surfaces, where they cannot be flooded.

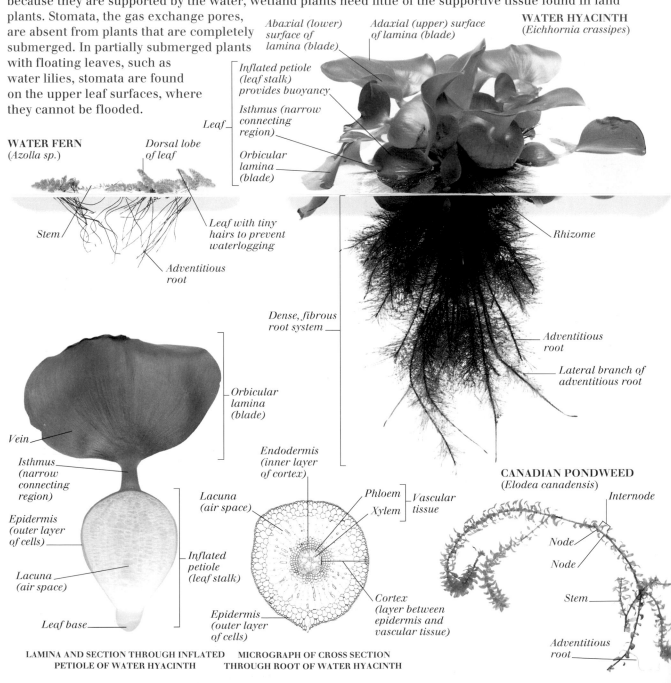

Abaxial (lower) surface of lamina (blade)

Adaxial (upper) surface of lamina (blade)

WATER HYACINTH
(*Eichhornia crassipes*)

Inflated petiole (leaf stalk) provides buoyancy

Isthmus (narrow connecting region)

Leaf

Orbicular lamina (blade)

WATER FERN
(*Azolla sp.*)

Dorsal lobe of leaf

Stem

Leaf with tiny hairs to prevent waterlogging

Adventitious root

Rhizome

Dense, fibrous root system

Adventitious root

Lateral branch of adventitious root

Vein

Isthmus (narrow connecting region)

Epidermis (outer layer of cells)

Lacuna (air space)

Leaf base

Orbicular lamina (blade)

Endodermis (inner layer of cortex)

Lacuna (air space)

Phloem | *Vascular tissue*
Xylem |

Inflated petiole (leaf stalk)

Epidermis (outer layer of cells)

Cortex (layer between epidermis and vascular tissue)

CANADIAN PONDWEED
(*Elodea canadensis*)

Internode

Node

Node

Stem

Adventitious root

LAMINA AND SECTION THROUGH INFLATED PETIOLE OF WATER HYACINTH

MICROGRAPH OF CROSS SECTION THROUGH ROOT OF WATER HYACINTH

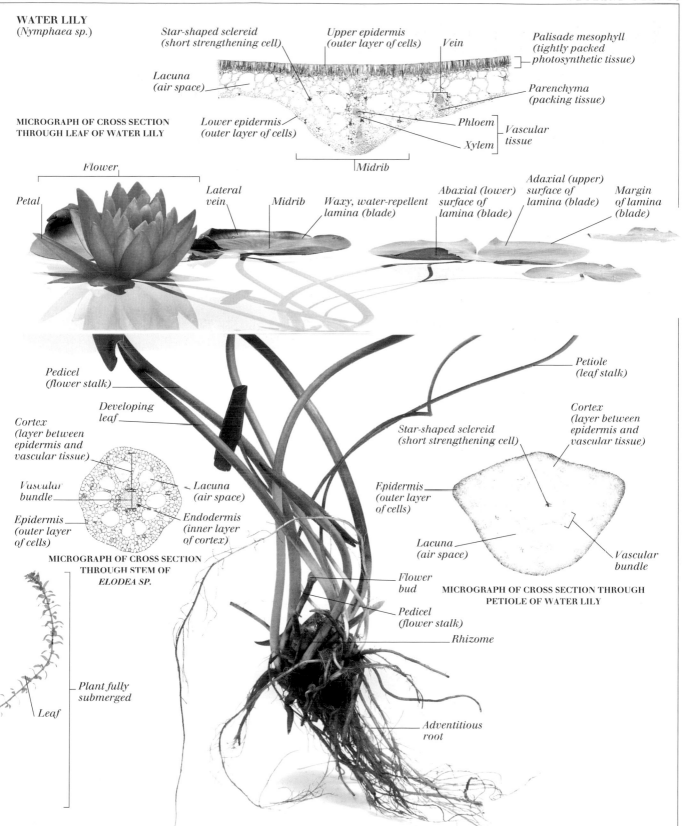

WATER LILY
(*Nymphaea sp.*)

Star-shaped sclereid
(short strengthening cell)

Upper epidermis
(outer layer of cells)

Vein

Palisade mesophyll
(tightly packed
photosynthetic tissue)

Lacuna
(air space)

Parenchyma
(packing tissue)

**MICROGRAPH OF CROSS SECTION
THROUGH LEAF OF WATER LILY**

Lower epidermis
(outer layer of cells)

Phloem

Xylem

Vascular
tissue

Midrib

Flower

Petal

Lateral
vein

Midrib

Waxy, water-repellent
lamina (blade)

Abaxial (lower)
surface of
lamina (blade)

Adaxial (upper)
surface of
lamina (blade)

Margin
of lamina
(blade)

Pedicel
(flower stalk)

Petiole
(leaf stalk)

Developing
leaf

Cortex
(layer between
epidermis and
vascular tissue)

Star-shaped sclereid
(short strengthening cell)

Cortex
(layer between
epidermis and
vascular tissue)

Vascular
bundle

Lacuna
(air space)

Epidermis
(outer layer
of cells)

Epidermis
(outer layer
of cells)

Endodermis
(inner layer
of cortex)

Lacuna
(air space)

Vascular
bundle

**MICROGRAPH OF CROSS SECTION
THROUGH STEM OF
ELODEA SP.**

**MICROGRAPH OF CROSS SECTION THROUGH
PETIOLE OF WATER LILY**

Flower
bud

Pedicel
(flower stalk)

Rhizome

Plant fully
submerged

Leaf

Adventitious
root

Carnivorous plants

CARNIVOROUS (INSECTIVOROUS) PLANTS FEED ON INSECTS and other small animals in addition to producing food in their leaves by photosynthesis. The nutrients absorbed from trapped insects allow carnivorous plants to thrive in acid, boggy soils that lack essential minerals, especially nitrates, where most other plants could not survive.

All carnivorous plants have some leaves modified as traps. Many use bright colors and scented nectar to attract prey, and most use enzymes to digest the prey. There are three types of traps. Pitcher plants, such as the monkey cup and cobra lily, have leaves modified as pitcher-shaped pitfall traps, half-filled with water. Once lured inside the mouth of the trap, insects lose their footing on the slippery surface, fall into the liquid, and either decompose or are digested. Venus fly-traps use a spring-trap mechanism; when an insect touches trigger hairs on the inner surfaces of the leaves, the two lobes of the trap snap shut. Butterworts and sundews entangle prey by sticky droplets on the leaf surface, while the edges of the leaves slowly curl over to envelop and digest the prey.

A PITCHER PLANT
Cobra lily (*Darlingtonia californica*)

Areola ("window" of transparent tissue)

Fishtail nectary

Wing

Hood

Pitcher

Tubular petiole (leaf stalk)

Areola ("window" of transparent tissue)

Dome-shaped hood develops

Smooth surface

Nectar roll

Fishtail nectary appears

Mouth

Immature pitcher

Wing

Downward-pointing hair

DEVELOPMENT OF MODIFIED LEAF IN COBRA LILY

Immature trap

Interlocked teeth

Closed trap

VENUS FLYTRAP
(*Dionaea muscipula*)

Red color of trap attracts insects

Phyllode (flattened petiole)

Summer petiole (leaf stalk)

Nectary zone (glands secrete nectar)

Digestive zone (glands secrete digestive enzymes)

Tooth

Lobe of trap

Midrib (hinge of trap)

Trigger hair

Spring petiole (leaf stalk)

Trap (twin-lobed leaf blade)

Sensory hinge

Trigger hair

Inner surface of trap

Digestive gland

MICROGRAPH OF LOBE OF VENUS FLYTRAP

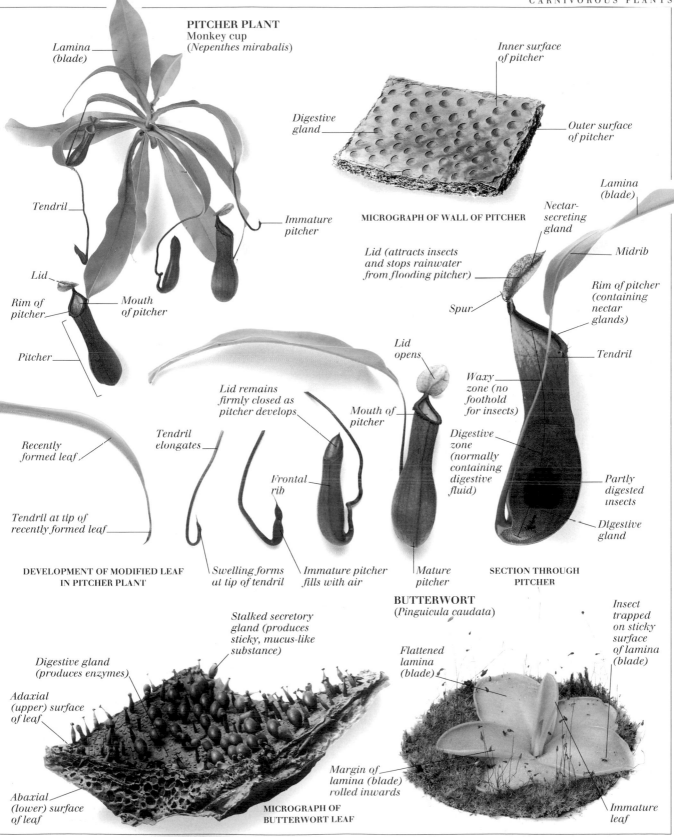

PITCHER PLANT
Monkey cup
(*Nepenthes mirabalis*)

Lamina
(blade)

Tendril

Immature
pitcher

Lid

Rim of
pitcher

Mouth
of pitcher

Pitcher

*Inner surface
of pitcher*

*Digestive
gland*

*Outer surface
of pitcher*

MICROGRAPH OF WALL OF PITCHER

*Nectar-
secreting
gland*

Lamina
(blade)

Midrib

Lid (attracts insects
and stops rainwater
from flooding pitcher)

Rim of pitcher
(containing
nectar
glands)

Spur

Tendril

Waxy
zone (no
foothold
for insects)

Digestive
zone
(normally
containing
digestive
fluid)

Partly
digested
insects

Digestive
gland

**SECTION THROUGH
PITCHER**

Lid
opens

Mouth of
pitcher

Recently
formed leaf

Tendril
elongates

Lid remains
firmly closed as
pitcher develops

Frontal
rib

Tendril at tip of
recently formed leaf

Swelling forms
at tip of tendril

Immature pitcher
fills with air

Mature
pitcher

**DEVELOPMENT OF MODIFIED LEAF
IN PITCHER PLANT**

BUTTERWORT
(*Pinguicula caudata*)

Stalked secretory
gland (produces
sticky, mucus-like
substance)

Insect
trapped
on sticky
surface
of lamina
(blade)

Digestive gland
(produces enzymes)

Flattened
lamina
(blade)

Adaxial
(upper) surface
of leaf

Abaxial
(lower) surface
of leaf

Margin of
lamina (blade)
rolled inwards

Immature
leaf

**MICROGRAPH OF
BUTTERWORT LEAF**

161

Epiphytic and parasitic plants

EPIPHYTIC AND PARASITIC PLANTS GROW ON OTHER LIVING PLANTS. Typically, epiphytic plants are not rooted in the soil. Instead, they live above ground level on the stems and branches of other plants. Epiphytes obtain water from trapped rainwater and from moisture in the air. They obtain minerals from organic matter that has accumulated on the surface of the plant on which they are growing. Like other green plants, epiphytes produce their food by photosynthesis. Epiphytes include tropical orchids and bromeliads (air plants) and some mosses that live in temperate regions. Parasitic plants obtain all their nutrient requirements from the host plants on which they grow. The parasites produce haustoria, root-like organs that penetrate the stem or roots of the host and grow inward to merge with the host's vascular tissue. These extract water, minerals, and manufactured nutrients. Because they have no need to produce their own food, parasitic plants lack chlorophyll, the green photosynthetic pigment, and they have no foliage leaves. Partial parasitic plants, like mistletoe, obtain water and minerals from the host plant but have green leaves and stems and are therefore able to produce their own food by photosynthesis.

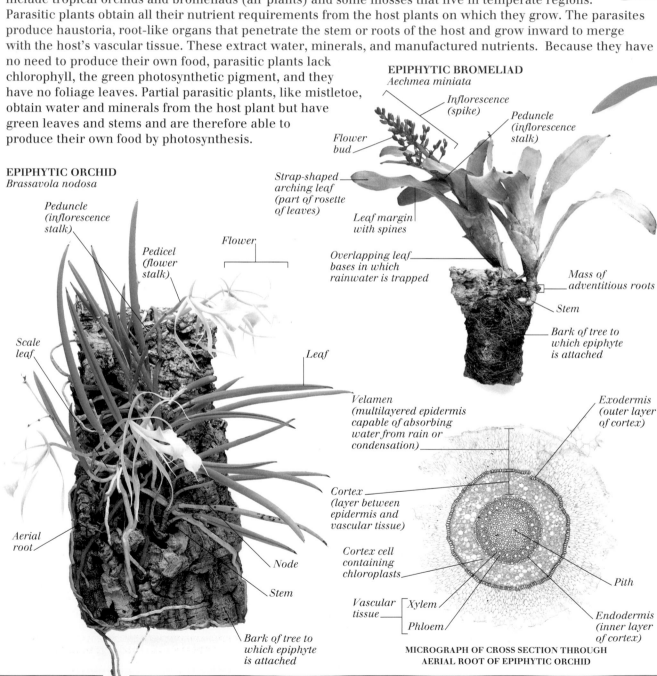

EPIPHYTIC BROMELIAD
Aechmea miniata

Inflorescence (spike)

Peduncle (inflorescence stalk)

Flower bud

Strap-shaped arching leaf (part of rosette of leaves)

Leaf margin with spines

Overlapping leaf bases in which rainwater is trapped

Mass of adventitious roots

Stem

Bark of tree to which epiphyte is attached

EPIPHYTIC ORCHID
Brassavola nodosa

Peduncle (inflorescence stalk)

Pedicel (flower stalk)

Flower

Scale leaf

Leaf

Velamen (multilayered epidermis capable of absorbing water from rain or condensation)

Exodermis (outer layer of cortex)

Cortex (layer between epidermis and vascular tissue)

Cortex cell containing chloroplasts

Pith

Aerial root

Node

Stem

Vascular tissue

Xylem

Phloem

Endodermis (inner layer of cortex)

Bark of tree to which epiphyte is attached

MICROGRAPH OF CROSS SECTION THROUGH AERIAL ROOT OF EPIPHYTIC ORCHID

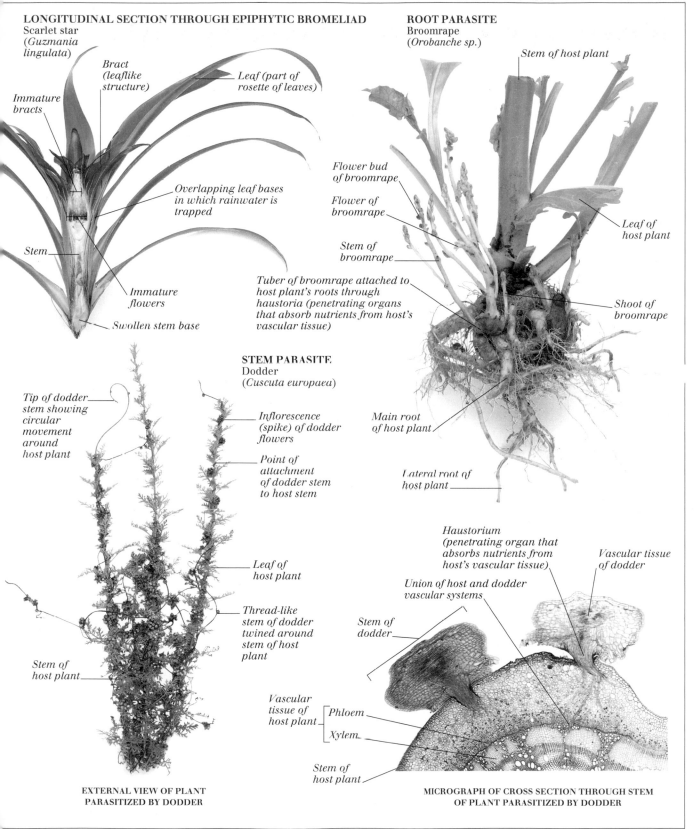

LONGITUDINAL SECTION THROUGH EPIPHYTIC BROMELIAD
Scarlet star
(*Guzmania
lingulata*)

*Bract
(leaflike
structure)*

*Leaf (part of
rosette of leaves)*

*Immature
bracts*

*Overlapping leaf bases
in which rainwater is
trapped*

Stem

*Immature
flowers*

Swollen stem base

ROOT PARASITE
Broomrape
(*Orobanche sp.*)

Stem of host plant

*Flower bud
of broomrape*

*Flower of
broomrape*

*Stem of
broomrape*

*Tuber of broomrape attached to
host plant's roots through
haustoria (penetrating organs
that absorb nutrients from host's
vascular tissue)*

*Leaf of
host plant*

*Shoot of
broomrape*

*Main root
of host plant*

*Lateral root of
host plant*

STEM PARASITE
Dodder
(*Cuscuta europaea*)

*Tip of dodder
stem showing
circular
movement
around
host plant*

*Inflorescence
(spike) of dodder
flowers*

*Point of
attachment
of dodder stem
to host stem*

*Leaf of
host plant*

*Thread-like
stem of dodder
twined around
stem of host
plant*

*Stem of
host plant*

*Haustorium
(penetrating organ that
absorbs nutrients from
host's vascular tissue)*

*Vascular tissue
of dodder*

*Union of host and dodder
vascular systems*

*Stem of
dodder*

*Vascular
tissue of
host plant*

[*Phloem*]
[*Xylem*]

*Stem of
host plant*

**EXTERNAL VIEW OF PLANT
PARASITIZED BY DODDER**

**MICROGRAPH OF CROSS SECTION THROUGH STEM
OF PLANT PARASITIZED BY DODDER**

ANIMALS

Sponges, jellyfish, and sea anemones

SPONGES ARE MAINLY MARINE animals that make up the phylum Porifera. They are among the simplest of all animals, having no tissues or organs. Their bodies consist of two layers of cells separated by a jelly-like layer (mesohyal) that is strengthened by mineral spicules or protein fibers. The body is perforated by a system of pores and water channels called the aquiferous system. Special cells (choanocytes) with whip-like structures (flagella) draw water through the aquiferous system, thereby bringing tiny food particles to the sponge's cells. Jellyfish (class Scyphozoa), sea anemones (class Anthozoa), and corals (also class Anthozoa) belong to the phylum Cnidaria, also known as Coelenterata. More complex than sponges, coelenterates have simple tissues, such as nervous tissue; a radially symmetrical body; and a mouth surrounded by tentacles with unique stinging cells (cnidocytes).

INTERNAL ANATOMY OF A SPONGE

Amebocyte

Osculum (excurrent pore)

Choanocyte (collar cell)

Ostium (incurrent pore)

Porocyte (pore cell)

Mesohyal

Spongocoel (atrium; paragaster)

Spicule

Pinacocyte (epidermal cell)

Ostium (incurrent pore)

SKELETON OF A SPONGE

Protein matrix

Pore

EXTERNAL FEATURES OF A SEA ANEMONE

Tentacle

EXAMPLES OF SEA ANEMONES

JEWEL ANEMONE
(*Corynactis viridis*)

PARASITIC ANEMONE
(*Calliactis parasitica*)

PLUMOSE ANEMONE
(*Metridium senile*)

MEDITERRANEAN SEA ANEMONE
(*Condylactis sp.*)

GREEN SNAKELOCK
ANEMONE
(*Anemonia viridis*)

BEADLET ANEMONE
(*Actinia equina*)

GHOST ANEMONE
(*Actinothoe sphyrodeta*)

Sagartia elegans

**EXTERNAL APPEARANCE
OF A JELLYFISH**

INTERNAL ANATOMY OF A JELLYFISH

Stomach

Filament

Ectoderm

Endoderm

Radial canal

Hood

Rhopalium

Mouth

Gonad

Mesoglea

Tentacle

Subgenital pit

Oral arm

**EXAMPLES OF
CORALS**

HONEYCOMB CORAL
(*Goniastrea aspera*)

MUSHROOM CORAL
(*Fungia fungites*)

STAR CORAL
(*Balanophyllia regia*)

STRUCTURE OF A CNIDOCYTE

Cnidocil (trigger)

Operculum

Barb (stylet)

Thread

Nucleus

BEFORE DISCHARGE

Thread

Spine

Cnidocil
(trigger)

Barb (stylet)

Operculum

Nucleus

AFTER DISCHARGE

**INTERNAL ANATOMY OF A
SEA ANEMONE**

Oral disk

Mouth

Ostium (mesenteric
perforation)

Sphincter
muscle

Mesenteric
filament

Incomplete
mesentery

Gonad

Tentacle

Collar

Siphonoglyph

Complete
mesentery

Retractor
muscle

Basal disk
(pedal disk)

Pharynx

Gastrovascular
cavity

Oral disk

Mouth

Insects

PUPA
(CHRYSALIS)

THE WORD INSECT REFERS to small invertebrate creatures, especially those with bodies divided into sections. Insects, including beetles, ants, bees, butterflies, and moths, belong to various orders in the class Insecta, which is a division of the phylum Arthropoda. Features common to all insects are an exoskeleton (external skeleton); three pairs of jointed legs; three body sections (head, thorax, and abdomen); and one pair of sensory antennae. Beetles (order Coleoptera) are the biggest group of insects, with about 300,000 species (about 30 percent of all known insects). They have a pair of hard elytra (wing cases), which are modified front wings. The principal function of the elytra is to protect the hind wings, which are used for flying. Ants, together with bees and wasps, form the order Hymenoptera, which contains about 200,000 species. This group is characterized by a marked narrowing between the thorax and abdomen. Butterflies and moths form the order Lepidoptera, which has about 150,000 species. They have wings covered with tiny scales, hence the name of their order (Lepidoptera means "scale wings"). The separation of lepidopterans into butterflies and moths is largely artificial as there are no features that categorically distinguish one group from the other. In general, however, most butterflies fly by day, whereas most moths are night flyers. Some insects, including butterflies and moths, undergo complete metamorphosis (transformation) during their life cycle. A butterfly metamorphoses from an egg to a larva (caterpillar), then to a pupa (chrysalis), and finally to an imago (adult).

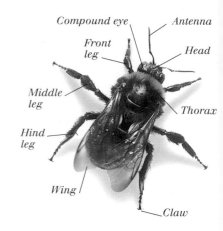

EXAMPLES OF INSECTS

Compound eye

Antenna

Front leg

Head

Middle leg

Thorax

Hind leg

Wing

Claw

BUMBLEBEE

Compound eye

Stigma (spot)

Vein

Abdomen

DAMSELFLY

**EXTERNAL FEATURES
OF A BEETLE**

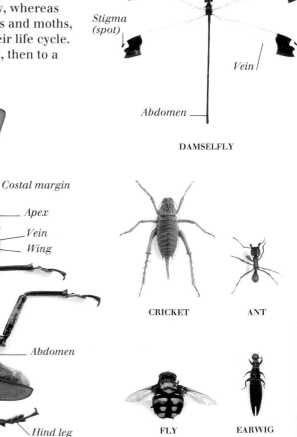

Elytron

Tarsus

Claw

Tibia

Costal margin

Apex

Pedicel

Vein

Femur

Wing

Flagellum

Trochanter

Mandible

Scape

Coxa

Labrum

Labial palpus

Abdomen

Compound eye

Head

Prothorax

Mesothorax

Front leg

Scutellum

Hind leg

Metathorax

Middle leg

CRICKET

ANT

FLY

EARWIG

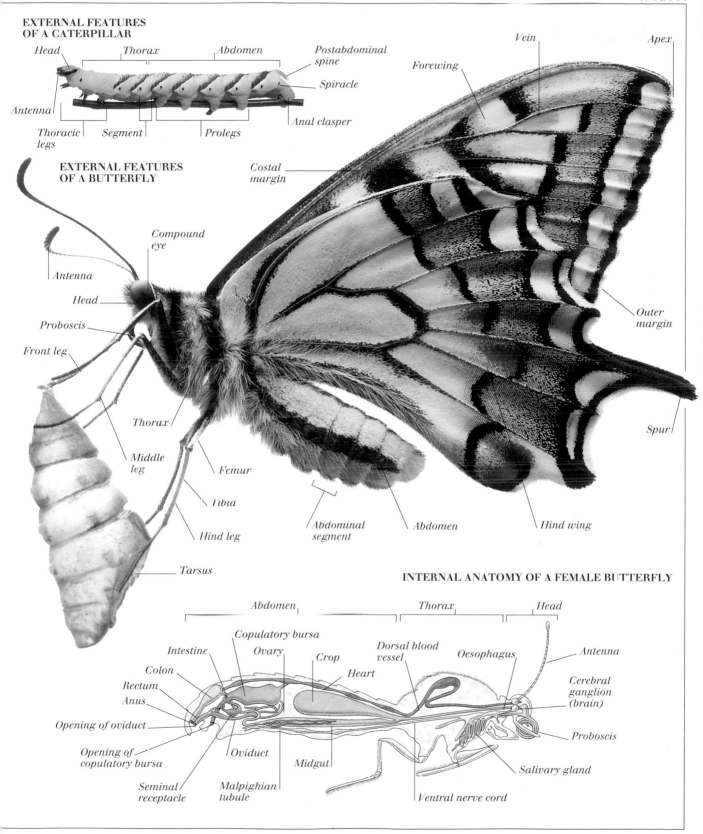

**EXTERNAL FEATURES
OF A CATERPILLAR**

Head

Thorax

Abdomen

Postabdominal
spine

Spiracle

Antenna

Thoracic
legs

Segment

Prolegs

Anal clasper

Vein

Forewing

Apex

**EXTERNAL FEATURES
OF A BUTTERFLY**

Costal
margin

Compound
eye

Antenna

Head

Proboscis

Front leg

Thorax

Middle
leg

Femur

Tibia

Hind leg

Tarsus

Abdominal
segment

Abdomen

Outer
margin

Spur

Hind wing

INTERNAL ANATOMY OF A FEMALE BUTTERFLY

Abdomen

Thorax

Head

Intestine

Copulatory bursa

Ovary

Crop

Dorsal blood
vessel

Heart

Oesophagus

Antenna

Colon

Rectum

Anus

Opening of oviduct

Opening of
copulatory bursa

Seminal
receptacle

Oviduct

Malpighian
tubule

Midgut

Ventral nerve cord

Cerebral
ganglion
(brain)

Proboscis

Salivary gland

Arachnids

THE CLASS ARACHNIDA INCLUDES SPIDERS (order Araneae) and scorpions (order Scorpiones). The class is part of the phylum Arthropoda, which also includes insects and crustaceans.

Spiders and scorpions are characterized by having four pairs of walking legs; a pair of pincer-like mouthparts called chelicerae; another pair of frontal appendages called pedipalps, which are sensory in spiders but used for grasping in scorpions; and a body divided into two sections (a combined head and thorax called a cephalothorax, or prosoma, and an abdomen, or opisthosoma). Unlike other arthropods, spiders and scorpions lack antennae. Spiders and scorpions are carnivorous. Spiders poison prey by biting with the fanged chelicerae, scorpions by stinging with the end of the metasoma (tail).

MEXICAN TRUE RED-LEGGED TARANTULA
(Euathlus emilia)

INTERNAL ANATOMY OF A FEMALE SPIDER

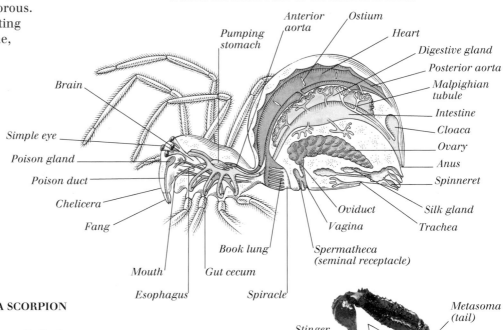

Brain
Simple eye
Poison gland
Poison duct
Chelicera
Fang
Mouth
Esophagus
Gut cecum
Book lung
Spiracle
Spermatheca (seminal receptacle)
Vagina
Oviduct
Pumping stomach
Anterior aorta
Ostium
Heart
Digestive gland
Posterior aorta
Malpighian tubule
Intestine
Cloaca
Ovary
Anus
Spinneret
Silk gland
Trachea

EXTERNAL FEATURES OF A SCORPION

Chela (claw of pedipalp)
Pedipalp
Prosoma (cephalothorax)
Opisthosoma (abdomen)
Stinger
Metasoma (tail)
Chelicera
Median eye
Coxa
1st walking leg
Trochanter
2nd walking leg
Claw
3rd walking leg
Femur
Metatarsus
4th walking leg
Tarsus
Tibia
Patella

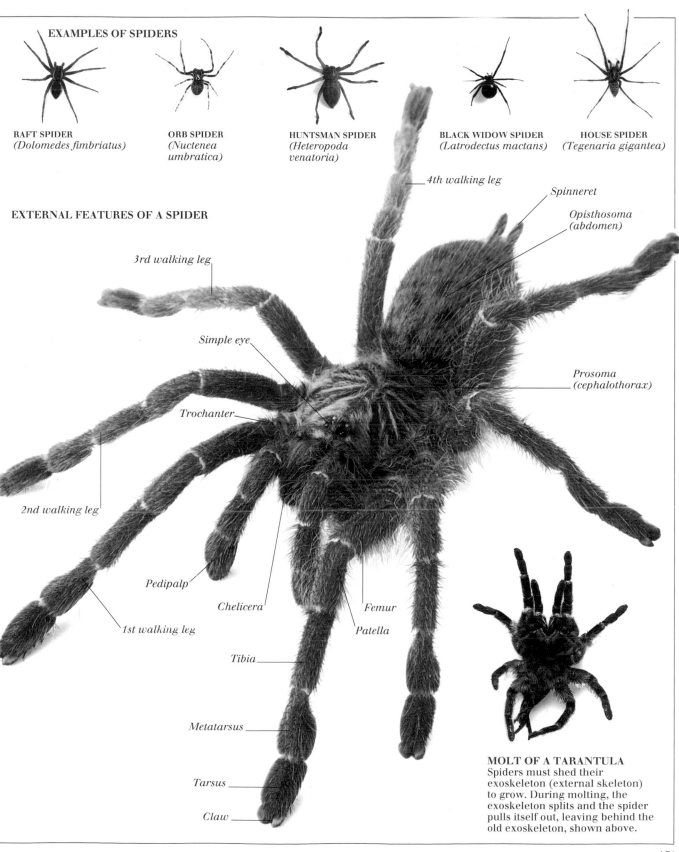

EXAMPLES OF SPIDERS

RAFT SPIDER
(Dolomedes fimbriatus)

ORB SPIDER
(Nuctenea umbratica)

HUNTSMAN SPIDER
(Heteropoda venatoria)

BLACK WIDOW SPIDER
(Latrodectus mactans)

HOUSE SPIDER
(Tegenaria gigantea)

EXTERNAL FEATURES OF A SPIDER

4th walking leg

Spinneret

Opisthosoma (abdomen)

3rd walking leg

Simple eye

Prosoma (cephalothorax)

Trochanter

2nd walking leg

Pedipalp

Chelicera

Femur

Patella

1st walking leg

Tibia

Metatarsus

Tarsus

Claw

MOLT OF A TARANTULA
Spiders must shed their
exoskeleton (external skeleton)
to grow. During molting, the
exoskeleton splits and the spider
pulls itself out, leaving behind the
old exoskeleton, shown above.

Crustaceans

THE SUBPHYLUM CRUSTACEA is one of the largest groups in the phylum Arthropoda. The subphylum is divided into several classes, the most important of which are Malacostraca and Cirripedia. The class Malacostraca includes crayfish, crabs, lobsters, and shrimps. Typical features of malacostracans include a body divided into two sections (a combined head and thorax called a cephalothorax, and an abdomen); an exoskeleton (external skeleton) with a large plate (carapace) covering the cephalothorax; stalked, compound eyes; and two pairs of antennae. The class Cirripedia includes barnacles, which, unlike other crustaceans, spend their adult lives attached to a surface, such as a rock. Other characteristics of cirripedes include an exoskeleton of overlapping calcareous plates; a body consisting almost entirely of thorax (the abdomen and head are minute); and six pairs of thoracic appendages (cirri) used for filter feeding.

1st swimmeret (1st pleopod)

2nd swimmeret (2nd pleopod)

3rd swimmeret (3rd pleopod)

4th swimmeret (4th pleopod)

5th swimmeret (5th pleopod)

Telson

Abdomen

Endopod
Exopod
Uropod

Abdominal segment

3rd leg (3rd pereopod)

5th leg (5th pereopod)

4th leg (4th pereopod)

2nd leg (2nd pereopod)

EXTERNAL FEATURES OF A CRAB

Propodus

Carpus

Dactylus

Compound eye

Antenna

Cheliped (chela; claw; 1st leg; 1st pereopod)

Carapace (shell)

Merus

Abdomen

2nd leg (2nd pereopod)

5th leg (5th pereopod)

3rd leg (3rd pereopod)

4th leg (4th pereopod)

EXTERNAL FEATURES OF A SHRIMP

Compound eye

Cephalothorax

Abdomen

Antenna

Leg (pereopod)

Swimmeret (pleopod)

Uropod
Exopod
Endopod

Telson

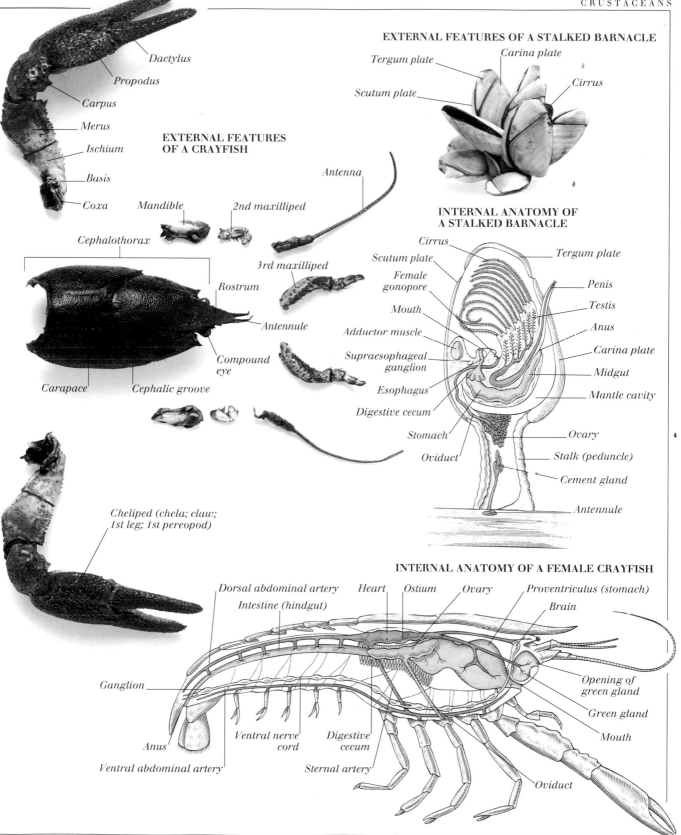

EXTERNAL FEATURES OF A STALKED BARNACLE

Tergum plate
Carina plate
Scutum plate
Cirrus

Dactylus
Propodus
Carpus
Merus
Ischium
Basis
Coxa

**EXTERNAL FEATURES
OF A CRAYFISH**

Mandible
2nd maxilliped
Antenna
Cephalothorax
3rd maxilliped
Rostrum
Antennule
Compound eye
Carapace
Cephalic groove

**INTERNAL ANATOMY OF
A STALKED BARNACLE**

Cirrus
Scutum plate
Female gonopore
Mouth
Adductor muscle
Supraesophageal ganglion
Esophagus
Digestive cecum
Stomach
Oviduct

Tergum plate
Penis
Testis
Anus
Carina plate
Midgut
Mantle cavity
Ovary
Stalk (peduncle)
Cement gland
Antennule

Cheliped (chela; claw;
1st leg; 1st pereopod)

INTERNAL ANATOMY OF A FEMALE CRAYFISH

Dorsal abdominal artery
Intestine (hindgut)
Heart
Ostium
Ovary
Proventriculus (stomach)
Brain

Ganglion
Anus
Ventral nerve cord
Digestive cecum
Ventral abdominal artery
Sternal artery
Oviduct
Opening of green gland
Green gland
Mouth

173

Starfish and sea urchins

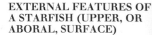

STARFISH, SEA URCHINS, AND THEIR relatives (including feather stars, brittle stars, basket stars, sea daisies, sea lilies, and sea cucumbers) make up the phylum Echinodermata. A unique feature of echinoderms is the water vascular system, which consists of a series of water-filled canals from which protrude thousands of tiny tube feet. The tube feet may be used for movement, feeding, or respiration. Other features include pentaradiate symmetry (that is, the body can be divided into five parts radiating from the center); no head; a diffuse, decentralized nervous system that lacks a brain; and no excretory organs. Typically, echinoderms also have an endoskeleton (internal skeleton) consisting of hard calcite ossicles embedded in the body wall and often bearing protruding spines or tubercles. The ossicles may fit together to form a test (as in sea urchins) or remain separate (as in sea cucumbers).

EXTERNAL FEATURES OF A STARFISH (UPPER, OR ABORAL, SURFACE)

Disk

Madreporite

Spine

Arm

INTERNAL ANATOMY OF A STARFISH

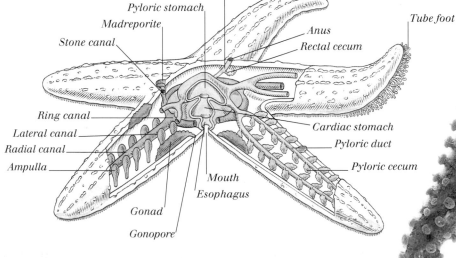

Rectum

Pyloric stomach

Madreporite

Stone canal

Anus

Rectal cecum

Tube foot

Ring canal

Lateral canal

Radial canal

Ampulla

Cardiac stomach

Pyloric duct

Pyloric cecum

Mouth

Esophagus

Gonad

Gonopore

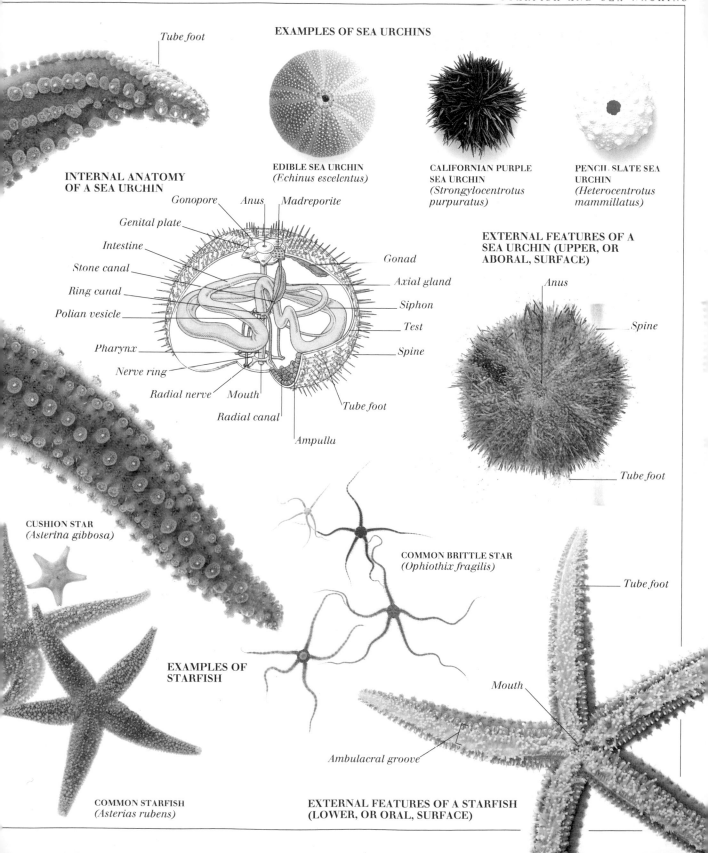

Tube foot

EXAMPLES OF SEA URCHINS

EDIBLE SEA URCHIN
(Echinus esclentus)

CALIFORNIAN PURPLE SEA URCHIN
(Strongylocentrotus purpuratus)

PENCIL SLATE SEA URCHIN
(Heterocentrotus mammillatus)

INTERNAL ANATOMY OF A SEA URCHIN

Gonopore
Anus
Madreporite
Genital plate
Intestine
Stone canal
Ring canal
Polian vesicle
Pharynx
Nerve ring
Radial nerve
Mouth
Radial canal
Ampulla
Gonad
Axial gland
Siphon
Test
Spine
Tube foot

EXTERNAL FEATURES OF A SEA URCHIN (UPPER, OR ABORAL, SURFACE)

Anus
Spine
Tube foot

CUSHION STAR
(Asterina gibbosa)

COMMON BRITTLE STAR
(Ophiothix fragilis)

Tube foot

Mouth

EXAMPLES OF STARFISH

Ambulacral groove

COMMON STARFISH
(Asterias rubens)

EXTERNAL FEATURES OF A STARFISH (LOWER, OR ORAL, SURFACE)

Mollusks

THE PHYLUM MOLLUSCA (MOLLUSKS) is a large group of animals that includes octopuses, snails, and scallops. Octopuses and their relatives —including squid and cuttlefish—form the class Cephalopoda. Cephalopods typically have a head with a radula (a file-like feeding organ) and beak; a well-developed nervous system; sucker-bearing tentacles; a muscular mantle (part of the body wall) that can expel water through the siphon, enabling movement by jet propulsion; and a small shell or no shell. Snails and their relatives—including slugs, limpets, and abalones—make up the class Gastropoda. Gastropods typically have a coiled external shell, although some, such as slugs, have a small internal shell or no shell; a flat foot; and a head with tentacles and a radula. Scallops and their relatives—including clams, mussels, and oysters—make up the class Bivalvia (also called Pelecypoda). Features of bivalves include a shell with two halves (valves); large gills that are used for breathing and filter feeding; and no radula.

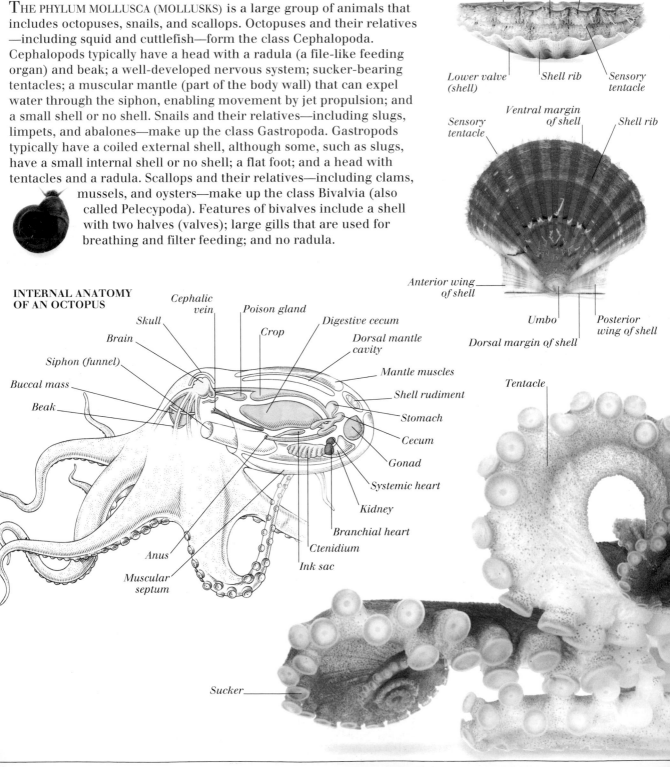

EXTERNAL FEATURES OF A SCALLOP

Upper valve (shell) Mantle Ocellus (eye)

Lower valve (shell) Shell rib Sensory tentacle

Ventral margin of shell
Sensory tentacle Shell rib

Anterior wing of shell

Umbo Posterior wing of shell

Dorsal margin of shell

INTERNAL ANATOMY OF AN OCTOPUS

Cephalic vein Poison gland Digestive cecum
Skull Crop Dorsal mantle cavity
Brain
Siphon (funnel) Mantle muscles
Buccal mass Shell rudiment
Beak Stomach
Cecum
Gonad
Systemic heart
Kidney
Branchial heart
Ctenidium
Anus Ink sac
Muscular septum

Tentacle

Sucker

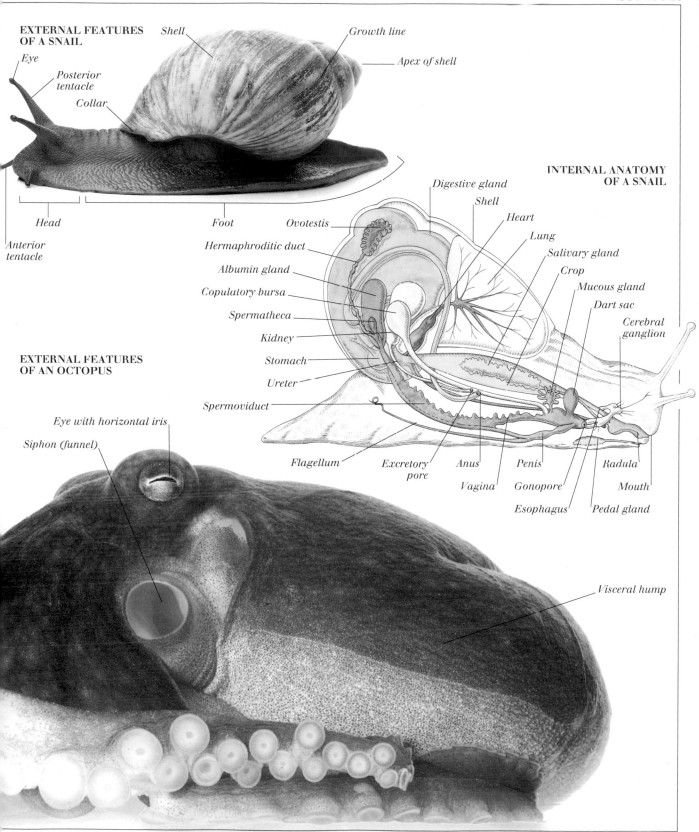

EXTERNAL FEATURES OF A SNAIL

Shell

Growth line

Apex of shell

Eye

Posterior tentacle

Collar

Head

Foot

Anterior tentacle

INTERNAL ANATOMY OF A SNAIL

Digestive gland

Shell

Heart

Lung

Salivary gland

Crop

Mucous gland

Dart sac

Cerebral ganglion

Ovotestis

Hermaphroditic duct

Albumin gland

Copulatory bursa

Spermatheca

Kidney

Stomach

Ureter

Spermoviduct

Flagellum

Excretory pore

Anus

Penis

Radula

Vagina

Gonopore

Mouth

Esophagus

Pedal gland

EXTERNAL FEATURES OF AN OCTOPUS

Eye with horizontal iris

Siphon (funnel)

Visceral hump

Sharks and jawless fish

SHARKS, DOGFISH (WHICH ARE actually small sharks), skates, and rays belong to a class of fish called Chondrichthyes, which is a division of the superclass Gnathostomata (meaning "jawed mouths"). Also sometimes known as elasmobranchs, sharks and their relatives have a skeleton made of cartilage (hence their common name, cartilaginous fish), a characteristic that distinguishes them from bony fish (see pp. 180-181). Other important features of cartilaginous fish are extremely tough, tooth-like scales, and lack of a swim bladder. Jawless fish—lampreys and hagfish—are primitive, eel-like fish that make up the order Cyclostomata (meaning "round mouths"), a division of the superclass Agnatha (meaning "without jaws"). In addition to their characteristic round, sucker-like mouths and lack of jaws, cyclostomes also have smooth, slimy skin without scales, and unpaired fins.

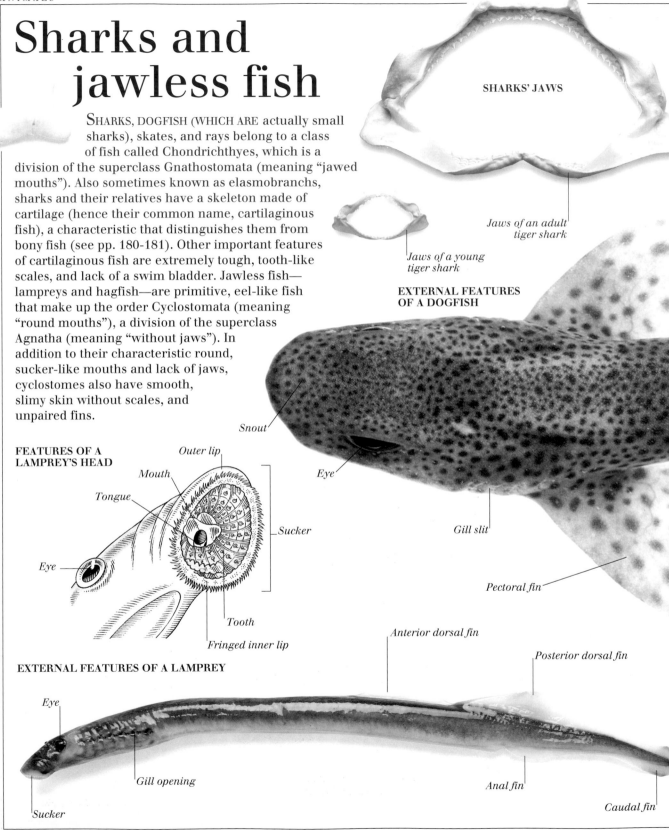

SHARKS' JAWS

Jaws of an adult tiger shark

Jaws of a young tiger shark

EXTERNAL FEATURES OF A DOGFISH

Snout

Eye

Gill slit

Pectoral fin

Anterior dorsal fin

Posterior dorsal fin

FEATURES OF A LAMPREY'S HEAD

Outer lip

Mouth

Tongue

Sucker

Eye

Tooth

Fringed inner lip

EXTERNAL FEATURES OF A LAMPREY

Eye

Gill opening

Anal fin

Caudal fin

Sucker

EXAMPLES OF CARTILAGINOUS FISH

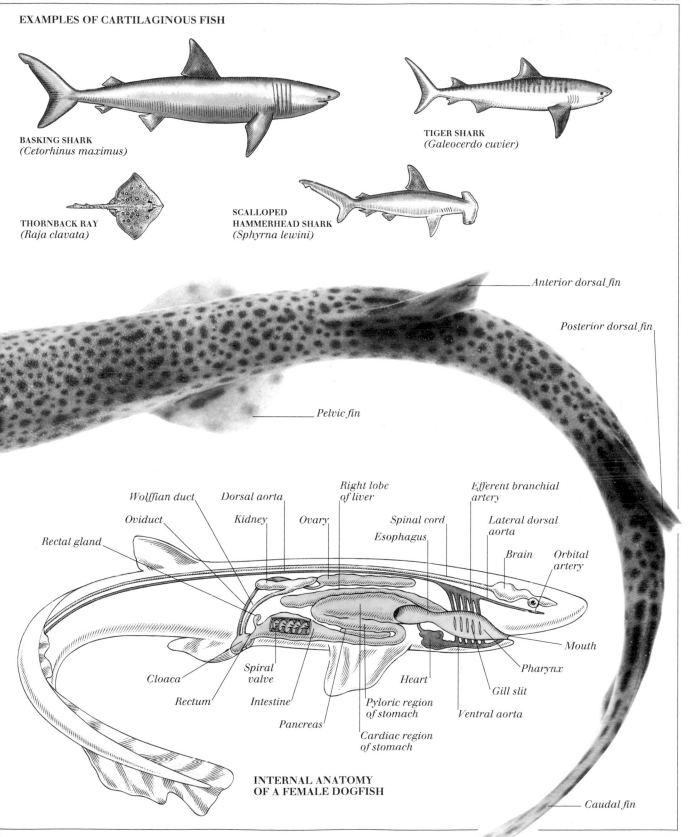

BASKING SHARK
(Cetorhinus maximus)

TIGER SHARK
(Galeocerdo cuvier)

THORNBACK RAY
(Raja clavata)

**SCALLOPED
HAMMERHEAD SHARK**
(Sphyrna lewini)

Anterior dorsal fin

Posterior dorsal fin

Pelvic fin

Wolffian duct

Dorsal aorta

*Right lobe
of liver*

*Efferent branchial
artery*

Oviduct

Kidney

Ovary

Spinal cord

*Lateral dorsal
aorta*

Esophagus

Rectal gland

Brain

*Orbital
artery*

Cloaca

*Spiral
valve*

Heart

Mouth

Pharynx

Rectum

Intestine

Gill slit

Pancreas

*Pyloric region
of stomach*

Ventral aorta

*Cardiac region
of stomach*

**INTERNAL ANATOMY
OF A FEMALE DOGFISH**

Caudal fin

Bony fish

BONY FISH, SUCH AS CARP, TROUT, SALMON, perch, and cod, are by far the best known and largest group of fish, with more than 20,000 species (over 95 percent of all known fish). As their name suggests, bony fish have skeletons made of bone, in contrast to the cartilaginous skeletons of sharks, jawless fish, and their relatives (see pp. 178-179). Other typical features of bony fish include a swim bladder, which functions as a variable-buoyancy organ, enabling a fish to remain effortlessly at whatever depth it is swimming; relatively thin, bone-like scales; a flap (called an operculum) covering the gills; and paired pelvic and pectoral fins. Scientifically, bony fish belong to the class Osteichthyes, which is a division of the superclass Gnathostomata (meaning "jawed mouths").

HOW FISH BREATHE

Fish "breathe" by extracting oxygen from water through their gills. Water is sucked in through the mouth; simultaneously, the opercula close to prevent the water from escaping. The mouth is then closed, and muscles in the walls of the mouth, pharynx, and opercular cavity contract to pump the water inside over the gills and out through the opercula. Some fish rely on swimming with their mouths open to keep water flowing over the gills.

Pharynx

Gill raker

Water out

Gill slit

Mouth

Water in

Gill filament

Operculum

EXAMPLES OF BONY FISH

MANDARINFISH
(*Synchiropus splendidus*)

ANGLERFISH
(*Caulophryne jordani*)

OCEANIC SEAHORSE
(*Hippocampus kuda*)

LIONFISH
(*Pterois volitans*)

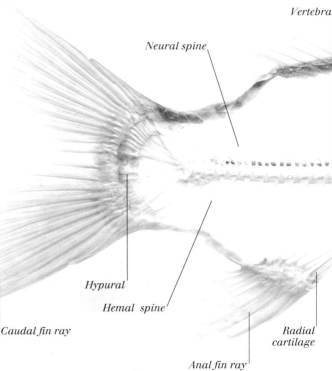

Vertebra

Neural spine

Hypural

Hemal spine

Caudal fin ray

Anal fin ray

Radial cartilage

STURGEON
(*Acipenser sturio*)

SNOWFLAKE MORAY EEL
(*Echidna nebulosa*)

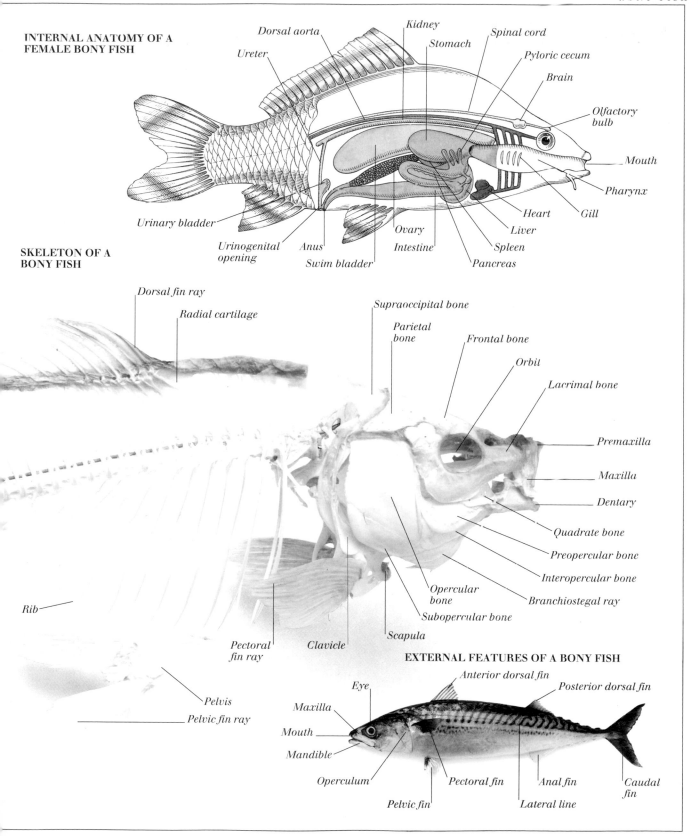

INTERNAL ANATOMY OF A FEMALE BONY FISH

Dorsal aorta

Ureter

Kidney

Stomach

Spinal cord

Pyloric cecum

Brain

Olfactory bulb

Mouth

Pharynx

Gill

Heart

Liver

Spleen

Pancreas

Ovary

Intestine

Swim bladder

Anus

Urinogenital opening

Urinary bladder

SKELETON OF A BONY FISH

Dorsal fin ray

Radial cartilage

Supraoccipital bone

Parietal bone

Frontal bone

Orbit

Lacrimal bone

Premaxilla

Maxilla

Dentary

Quadrate bone

Preopercular bone

Interopercular bone

Branchiostegal ray

Opercular bone

Subopercular bone

Scapula

Clavicle

Pectoral fin ray

Rib

Pelvis

Pelvic fin ray

EXTERNAL FEATURES OF A BONY FISH

Eye

Anterior dorsal fin

Posterior dorsal fin

Maxilla

Mouth

Mandible

Operculum

Pelvic fin

Pectoral fin

Anal fin

Lateral line

Caudal fin

Amphibians

THE CLASS AMPHIBIA INCLUDES FROGS and toads (which make up the order Anura) and newts and salamanders (which make up the order Urodela). Amphibians typically have moist, scaleless, hairless skin; lungs; and are cold-blooded. They also undergo complete metamorphosis, from eggs laid in water through various water-living larval stages (such as the tadpole stage) to land-living adults. Typical features of adult frogs and toads include a squat body with no tail; long, powerful hind legs; and large, often bulging, eyes. Adult newts and salamanders typically have a long body with a well-developed tail; and relatively short legs of equal size. However, newts and salamanders show considerable variation; for example, in some species the adults have minute legs, external gills rather than lungs, and spend their entire lives in water.

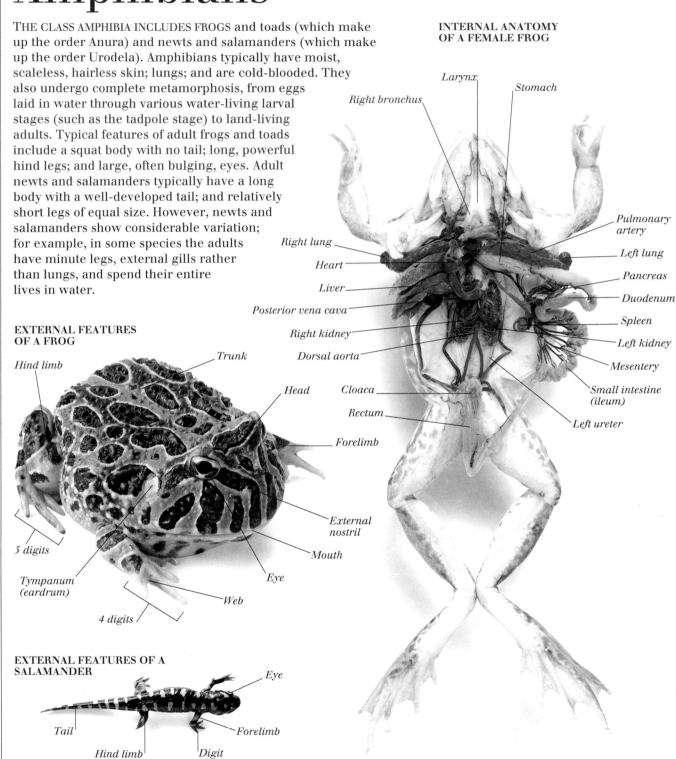

INTERNAL ANATOMY OF A FEMALE FROG

Larynx
Right bronchus
Stomach
Pulmonary artery
Right lung
Left lung
Heart
Pancreas
Liver
Duodenum
Posterior vena cava
Spleen
Right kidney
Left kidney
Dorsal aorta
Mesentery
Cloaca
Small intestine (ileum)
Rectum
Left ureter

EXTERNAL FEATURES OF A FROG

Hind limb
Trunk
Head
Forelimb
5 digits
External nostril
Mouth
Tympanum (eardrum)
Eye
Web
4 digits

EXTERNAL FEATURES OF A SALAMANDER

Eye
Forelimb
Tail
Hind limb
Digit

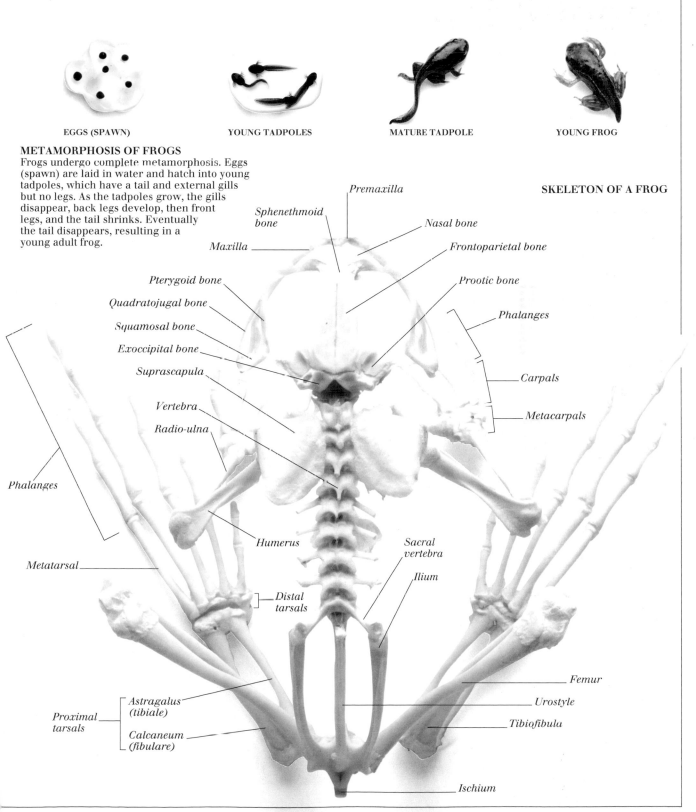

EGGS (SPAWN) **YOUNG TADPOLES** **MATURE TADPOLE** **YOUNG FROG**

METAMORPHOSIS OF FROGS

Frogs undergo complete metamorphosis. Eggs (spawn) are laid in water and hatch into young tadpoles, which have a tail and external gills but no legs. As the tadpoles grow, the gills disappear, back legs develop, then front legs, and the tail shrinks. Eventually the tail disappears, resulting in a young adult frog.

SKELETON OF A FROG

Premaxilla

Sphenethmoid bone

Nasal bone

Frontoparietal bone

Maxilla

Prootic bone

Pterygoid bone

Phalanges

Quadratojugal bone

Squamosal bone

Exoccipital bone

Carpals

Suprascapula

Metacarpals

Vertebra

Radio-ulna

Phalanges

Humerus

Sacral vertebra

Ilium

Metatarsal

Distal tarsals

Femur

Astragalus (tibiale)

Urostyle

Proximal tarsals

Calcaneum (fibulare)

Tibiofibula

Ischium

Lizards and snakes

LIZARDS AND SNAKES BELONG to the order Squamata, a division of the class Reptilia. Characteristic reptilian features include scaly skin, lungs, and cold-bloodedness. Most reptiles lay leathery-shelled eggs, although some hatch the eggs inside their bodies and give birth to live young. Lizards belong to the suborder Lacertilia. Typically, they have long tails, and shed their skin in several pieces. Many lizards can regenerate a tail if it is lost; some can change color; and some are limbless. Snakes make up the suborder Ophidia (also called Serpentes). All snakes have long, limbless bodies; can dislocate their lower jaw to swallow large prey; and have eyelids that are joined together to form a single transparent covering over the front of the eye. Most snakes shed their skin in a single piece. Constrictor snakes kill their prey by squeezing; venomous snakes poison their prey.

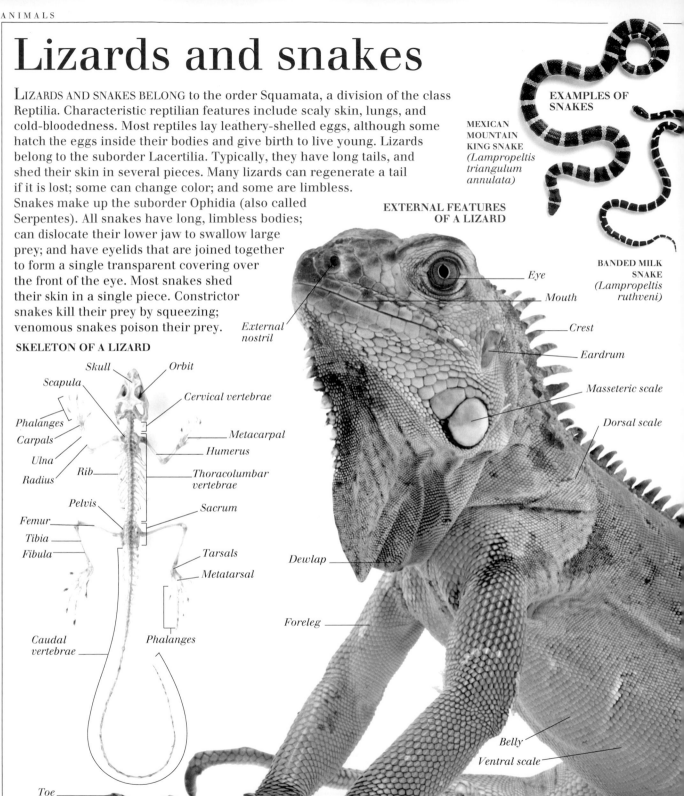

EXAMPLES OF SNAKES

MEXICAN MOUNTAIN KING SNAKE
(*Lampropeltis triangulum annulata*)

BANDED MILK SNAKE
(*Lampropeltis ruthveni*)

EXTERNAL FEATURES OF A LIZARD

Eye
Mouth
Crest
Eardrum
Masseteric scale
Dorsal scale
External nostril
Dewlap
Foreleg
Belly
Ventral scale

SKELETON OF A LIZARD

Skull
Orbit
Scapula
Cervical vertebrae
Phalanges
Carpals
Metacarpal
Humerus
Ulna
Radius
Rib
Thoracolumbar vertebrae
Pelvis
Sacrum
Femur
Tibia
Fibula
Tarsals
Metatarsal
Caudal vertebrae
Phalanges
Toe
Claw

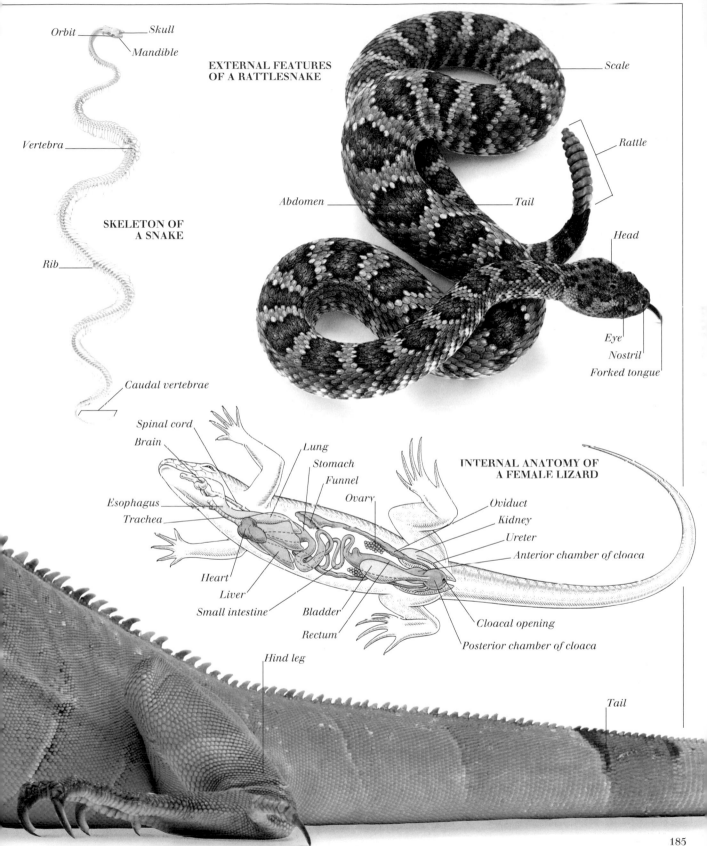

Orbit — *Skull*

Mandible

EXTERNAL FEATURES OF A RATTLESNAKE

Scale

Vertebra

Rattle

SKELETON OF A SNAKE

Abdomen — *Tail*

Head

Rib

Eye

Nostril

Forked tongue

Caudal vertebrae

Spinal cord

Brain

Lung

Stomach

Funnel

INTERNAL ANATOMY OF A FEMALE LIZARD

Ovary

Esophagus

Oviduct

Trachea

Kidney

Ureter

Anterior chamber of cloaca

Heart

Liver

Bladder

Small intestine

Rectum

Cloacal opening

Posterior chamber of cloaca

Hind leg

Tail

Crocodilians and turtles

CROCODILIANS AND TURTLES BELONG to different orders in the class Reptilia. The order Crocodilia includes crocodiles, alligators, caimans, and gharials. Typically, crocodilians are carnivores (flesh-eaters), and have a long snout, sharp teeth for gripping prey, and hard, square scales. All crocodilians are adapted to living on land and in water: they have four strong legs for moving on land; a powerful tail for swimming; and their eyes and nostrils are high on the head so that they stay above water while the rest of the body is submerged. The order Chelonia includes marine turtles, freshwater turtles (terrapins), and land turtles (tortoises). Characteristically, chelonians have a short, broad body encased in a bony shell with an outer horny covering, into which the head and limbs can be withdrawn; and a horny beak instead of teeth.

SKULLS OF CROCODILIANS

GHARIAL
(Gavialis gangeticus)

NILE CROCODILE
(Crocodylus niloticus)

MISSISSIPPI ALLIGATOR
(Alligator mississippiensis)

SKELETON OF A CROCODILE

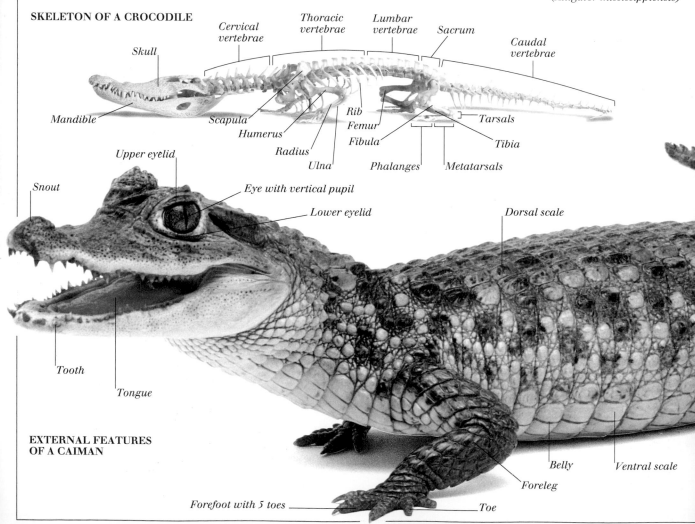

Skull

Mandible

Cervical vertebrae

Thoracic vertebrae

Lumbar vertebrae

Sacrum

Caudal vertebrae

Scapula

Humerus

Radius

Ulna

Rib

Femur

Fibula

Phalanges

Metatarsals

Tarsals

Tibia

Upper eyelid

Eye with vertical pupil

Lower eyelid

Dorsal scale

Snout

Tooth

Tongue

EXTERNAL FEATURES OF A CAIMAN

Belly

Ventral scale

Foreleg

Forefoot with 5 toes

Toe

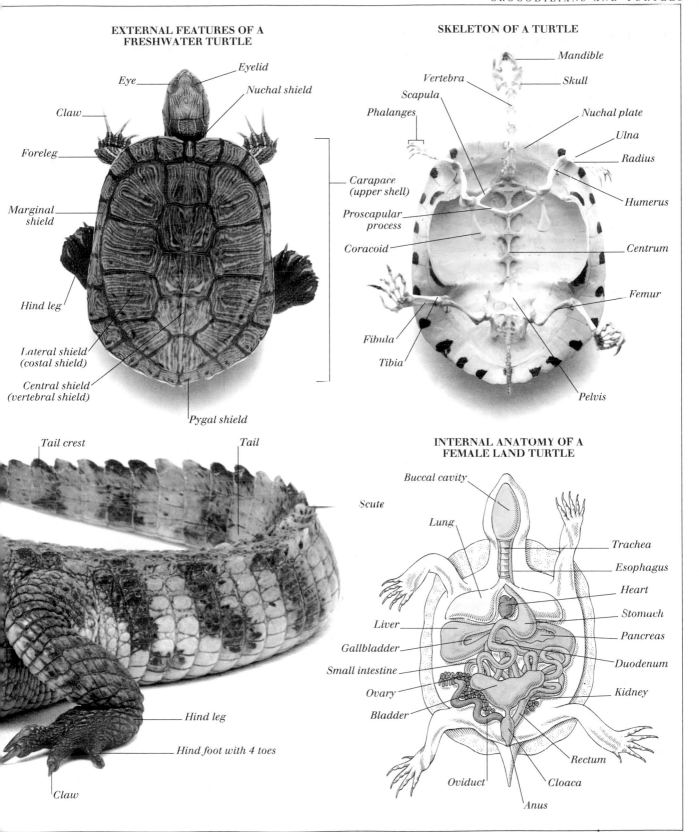

EXTERNAL FEATURES OF A FRESHWATER TURTLE

Eye

Eyelid

Nuchal shield

Claw

Foreleg

Marginal shield

Hind leg

Lateral shield (costal shield)

Central shield (vertebral shield)

Pygal shield

Carapace (upper shell)

SKELETON OF A TURTLE

Mandible

Vertebra

Skull

Scapula

Phalanges

Nuchal plate

Ulna

Radius

Humerus

Proscapular process

Coracoid

Centrum

Femur

Fibula

Tibia

Pelvis

Tail crest

Tail

Scute

Hind leg

Hind foot with 4 toes

Claw

INTERNAL ANATOMY OF A FEMALE LAND TURTLE

Buccal cavity

Lung

Trachea

Esophagus

Heart

Liver

Stomach

Pancreas

Gallbladder

Duodenum

Small intestine

Kidney

Ovary

Bladder

Rectum

Oviduct

Cloaca

Anus

Birds 1

BIRDS MAKE UP THE CLASS AVES. There are more than 9,000 species, almost all of which can fly (the only flightless birds are penguins, ostriches, rheas, cassowaries, and kiwis). The ability to fly is reflected in the typical bird features: forelimbs modified as wings, a streamlined body, and hollow bones to reduce weight. All birds lay hard-shelled eggs, which the parents incubate. Birds' beaks and feet vary according to diet and way of life. Beaks range from general purpose types suitable for a mixed diet (those of thrushes, for example), to types specialized for particular foods (such as the large, curved, sieving beaks of flamingos). Feet range from the webbed "paddles" of ducks, to the talons of birds of prey. Plumage also varies widely, and in many species the male is brightly colored for courtship display whereas the female is drab.

EXTERNAL FEATURES OF A BIRD

Forehead
Eye
Crown
Nostril
Nape
Upper mandible
Beak
Lower mandible
Chin
Throat
Breast
Belly
Flank
Thigh
Claw
Tarsus
Toe

EXAMPLES OF BIRDS

MALE TUFTED DUCK
(*Aythya fuligula*)

WHITE STORK
(*Ciconia ciconia*)

MALE OSTRICH
(*Struthio camelus*)

Minor coverts
Lesser wing coverts
Median wing coverts

Greater wing coverts
(major coverts)

Secondary flight feathers
(secondary remiges)

Primary flight feathers
(primary remiges)

Under tail coverts

Tail feathers (retrices)

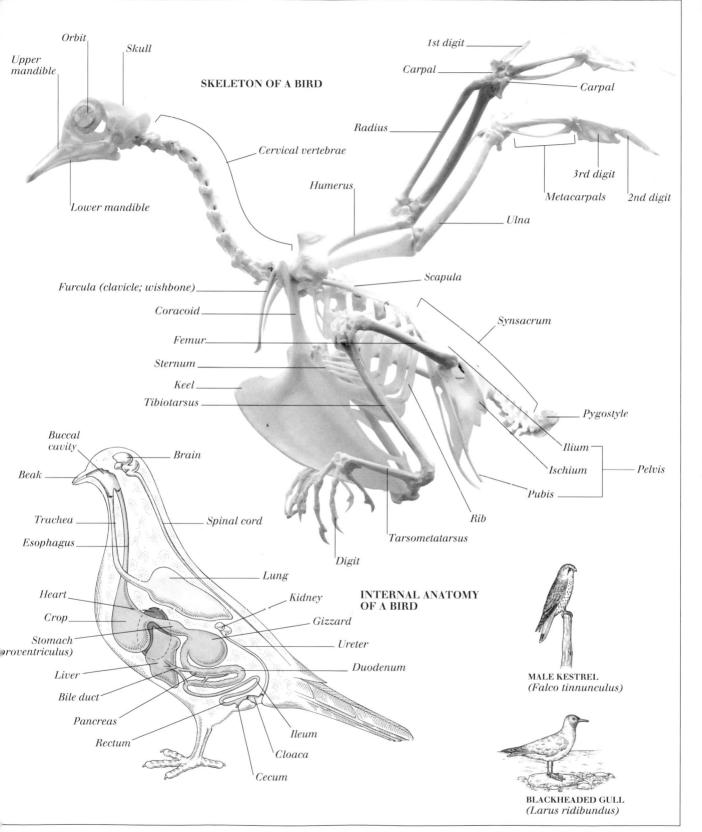

SKELETON OF A BIRD

Orbit

Skull

Upper mandible

1st digit

Carpal

Carpal

Radius

3rd digit

Metacarpals

2nd digit

Humerus

Ulna

Cervical vertebrae

Lower mandible

Scapula

Furcula (clavicle; wishbone)

Synsacrum

Coracoid

Femur

Sternum

Keel

Tibiotarsus

Pygostyle

Ilium

Ischium

Pelvis

Pubis

Rib

Tarsometatarsus

Digit

INTERNAL ANATOMY OF A BIRD

Buccal cavity

Brain

Beak

Spinal cord

Trachea

Esophagus

Lung

Heart

Kidney

Crop

Gizzard

Stomach (proventriculus)

Ureter

Liver

Duodenum

Bile duct

Pancreas

Ileum

Rectum

Cloaca

Cecum

MALE KESTREL
(Falco tinnunculus)

BLACKHEADED GULL
(Larus ridibundus)

Birds 2

EXAMPLES OF BIRDS' FEET

KITTIWAKE
(Rissa tridactyla)
The webbed feet are
adapted for paddling
through water.

LITTLE GREBE
(Tachybaptus ruficollis)
The lobed, flattened feet
are adapted for swimming
underwater.

TAWNY OWL
(Strix aluco)
The clawed feet are adapted
for gripping prey.

EXAMPLES OF BIRDS' BEAKS

KING VULTURE
(Sarcorhamphus papa)
The hooked beak is adapted
for pulling apart flesh.

GREATER FLAMINGO
(Phoenicopterus ruber)
In the living bird, the large,
curved beak contains a
cartilaginous "sieve" for
filtering food particles
from water.

MAVIS, OR MISTLE THRUSH
(Turdus viscivorus)
The all-purpose beak is suitable
for gathering a wide range of
animal and plant foods.

BLUE-AND-YELLOW MACAW
(Ara ararauna)
The broad, powerful, hooked beak
is adapted for crushing seeds and
eating fruit.

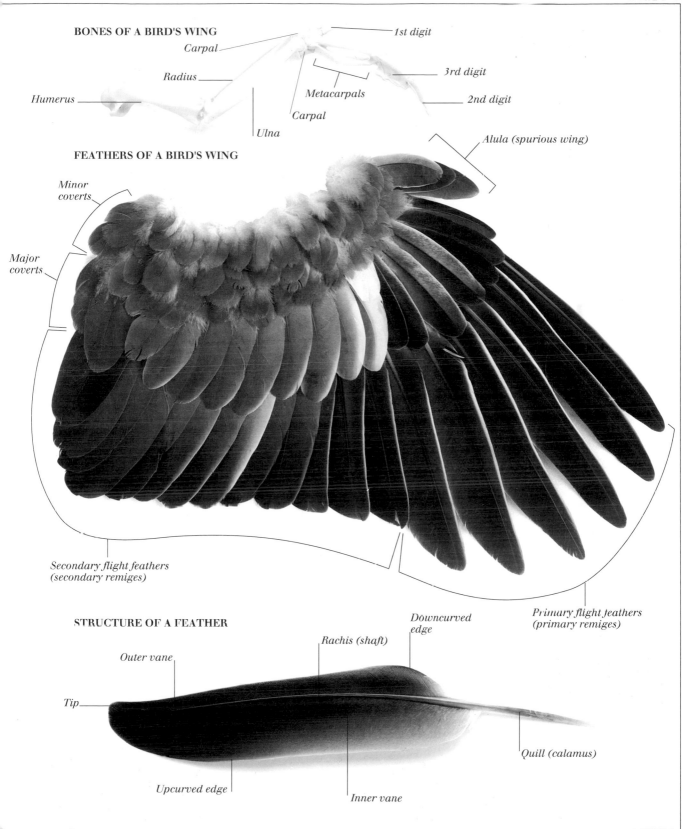

BONES OF A BIRD'S WING

1st digit

Carpal

Radius

3rd digit

Humerus

Metacarpals

2nd digit

Carpal

Alula (spurious wing)

Ulna

FEATHERS OF A BIRD'S WING

Minor coverts

Major coverts

Secondary flight feathers (secondary remiges)

Primary flight feathers (primary remiges)

STRUCTURE OF A FEATHER

Downcurved edge

Rachis (shaft)

Outer vane

Tip

Quill (calamus)

Upcurved edge

Inner vane

Eggs

AN EGG IS A SINGLE CELL, produced by the female, with the capacity to develop into a new individual. Development may take place inside the mother's body (as in most mammals) or outside, in which case the egg has a protective covering such as a shell. Egg yolk nourishes the growing young. Eggs developing inside the mother generally have little yolk, because the young are nourished from her body. Eggs developing outside may also have little yolk if they are produced by animals whose young go through a larval stage (such as a caterpillar) that feeds itself while developing into the adult form. The shelled eggs of birds and reptiles contain enough yolk to sustain the young until it hatches into a juvenile version of the adult.

SECTION THROUGH A CHICKEN'S EGG

Yolk
Yolk sac
Shell
Allantoic fluid
Allantois
Chorioallantoic membrane
Air sac
Albumen (egg white)
Amnion
Amniotic fluid
Developing chick
Developing wing
Shell membrane

VARIETY OF EGGS

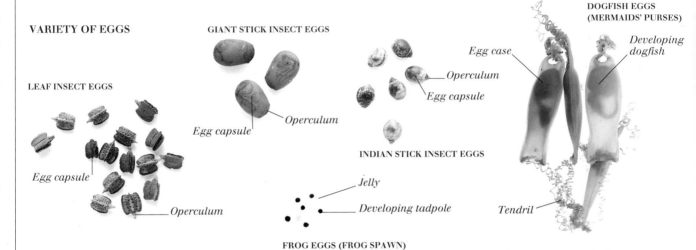

LEAF INSECT EGGS

Egg capsule
Operculum

GIANT STICK INSECT EGGS

Egg capsule
Operculum

INDIAN STICK INSECT EGGS

Operculum
Egg capsule

FROG EGGS (FROG SPAWN)

Jelly
Developing tadpole

DOGFISH EGGS (MERMAIDS' PURSES)

Egg case
Developing dogfish
Tendril

HATCHING OF A QUAIL'S EGG

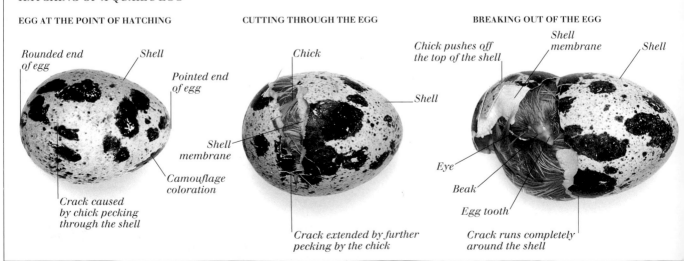

EGG AT THE POINT OF HATCHING

Rounded end of egg
Shell
Pointed end of egg
Shell membrane
Camouflage coloration
Crack caused by chick pecking through the shell

CUTTING THROUGH THE EGG

Chick
Shell
Crack extended by further pecking by the chick

BREAKING OUT OF THE EGG

Chick pushes off the top of the shell
Shell membrane
Shell
Eye
Beak
Egg tooth
Crack runs completely around the shell

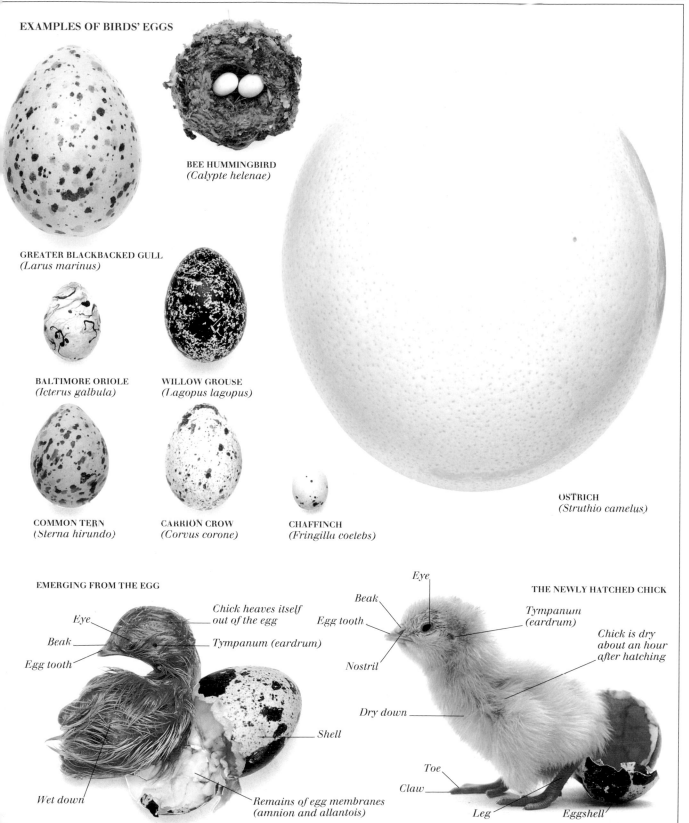

EXAMPLES OF BIRDS' EGGS

BEE HUMMINGBIRD
(Calypte helenae)

GREATER BLACKBACKED GULL
(Larus marinus)

BALTIMORE ORIOLE
(Icterus galbula)

WILLOW GROUSE
(Lagopus lagopus)

COMMON TERN
(Sterna hirundo)

CARRION CROW
(Corvus corone)

CHAFFINCH
(Fringilla coelebs)

OSTRICH
(Struthio camelus)

EMERGING FROM THE EGG

Eye

Beak

Egg tooth

Chick heaves itself
out of the egg

Tympanum (eardrum)

Shell

Wet down

Remains of egg membranes
(amnion and allantois)

THE NEWLY HATCHED CHICK

Eye

Beak

Egg tooth

Nostril

Tympanum
(eardrum)

Chick is dry
about an hour
after hatching

Dry down

Toe

Claw

Leg

Eggshell

Carnivores

THE MAMMALIAN ORDER CARNIVORA includes cats, dogs, bears, raccoons, pandas, weasels, badgers, skunks, otters, civets, mongooses, and hyenas. The order's name is derived from the fact that most of its members are carnivores (flesh-eaters). Typical carnivore features therefore reflect a hunting lifestyle: speed and agility; sharp claws and well-developed canine teeth for holding and killing prey; carnassial teeth (cheek teeth) for cutting flesh; and forward-facing eyes for good distance judgment. However, some members of the order—bears, badgers, and foxes, for example—have a more mixed diet, and a few are entirely herbivorous (plant-eating), notably pandas. Such animals have no carnassial teeth and tend to be slower-moving than pure flesh-eaters.

EXTERNAL FEATURES OF A MALE LION

Nose
Eye
Mane
Nostril
Vibrissa (whisker)
Tongue
Canine tooth
Incisor tooth
Chest
Elbow
Lower arm
Toe

SKULL OF A LION

Zygomatic arch
Coronoid process
Nasal bone
Orbit
Maxilla
Sagittal crest
Upper premolars
Upper canine
Lower canine
Mandible
Lower premolars
Occipital condyle
Condyle
Upper carnassial tooth (4th upper premolar)
Tympanic bulla
Angular process

SKULL OF A BEAR

Sagittal crest
Zygomatic arch
Upper molars
Occipital condyle
Orbit
Nasal bone
Upper premolars
Maxilla
Upper canine
Upper incisor
Lower incisor
Lower canine
Mandible
Tympanic bulla
Angular process
Condyle
Lower molars
Lower premolars

EXAMPLES OF CARNIVORES

GERMAN SHEPHERD DOG
(Canis familiaris)

MANED WOLF
(Chrysocyon brachyurus)

RACCOON
(Procyon lotor)

AMERICAN BLACK BEAR
(Ursus americanus)

SKELETON OF A DOMESTIC CAT

INTERNAL ANATOMY OF A MALE DOMESTIC CAT

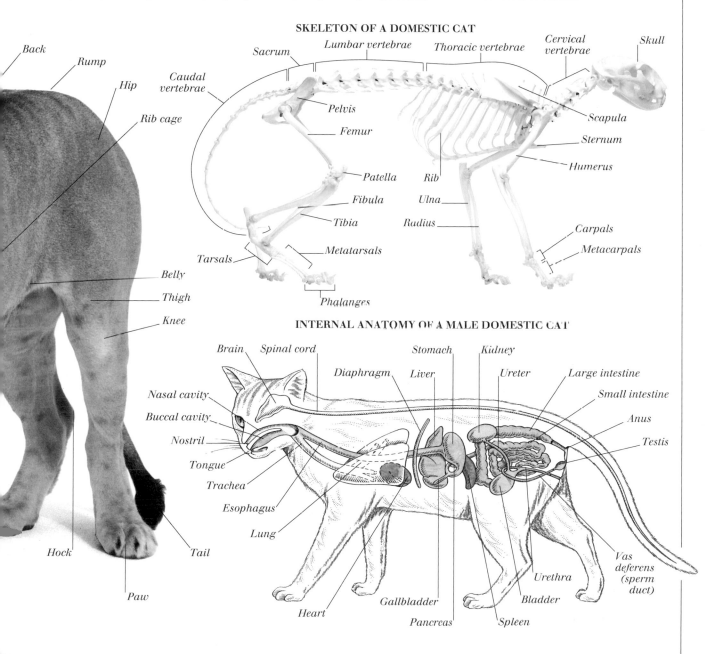

Back
Rump
Hip
Rib cage
Belly
Thigh
Knee
Hock
Paw
Tail

Sacrum
Lumbar vertebrae
Thoracic vertebrae
Cervical vertebrae
Skull
Caudal vertebrae
Pelvis
Femur
Scapula
Sternum
Humerus
Patella
Rib
Fibula
Ulna
Tibia
Rudius
Carpals
Metacarpals
Tarsals
Metatarsals
Phalanges

Brain
Spinal cord
Stomach
Kidney
Diaphragm
Liver
Ureter
Large intestine
Nasal cavity
Small intestine
Buccal cavity
Anus
Nostril
Testis
Tongue
Trachea
Esophagus
Lung
Heart
Gallbladder
Pancreas
Spleen
Bladder
Urethra
Vas deferens (sperm duct)

Rabbits and rodents

ALTHOUGH RABBITS AND RODENTS belong to different orders of mammals, they have some features in common. These features include chisel-shaped incisor teeth that grow continually, and eating their feces to extract more nutrients from their plant diet. Rabbits and hares belong to the order Lagomorpha. Characteristically, they have four incisors in the upper jaw and two in the lower jaw; powerful hind legs for jumping; forelimbs adapted for burrowing; long ears; and a small tail. Rodents make up the order Rodentia. This is the largest order of mammals, with more than 1,700 species, including squirrels, beavers, chipmunks, gophers, rats, mice, lemmings, gerbils, porcupines, cavies, and the capybara. Typical rodent features include two incisors in each jaw; short forelimbs for manipulating food; and cheek pouches for storing food.

EXTERNAL FEATURES OF A RAT

Snout
Eye
Ear
Nose
Pinna (ear flap)
Nostril
Vibrissa (whisker)
Neck
Mouth
Tail
Forelimb
Hind limb
5 digits
5 digits

EXTERNAL FEATURES OF A RABBIT

Pinna (ear flap)
Ear
Shoulder
Eye
Nose
Nostril
Vibrissa (whisker)
Forelimb
5 digits

INTERNAL ANATOMY OF A MALE RABBIT

Brain
Gallbladder
Liver
Stomach
Kidney
Spinal cord
Colon
Ileum
Ureter
Rectum
Bladder
Anus
Urethra
Testis
Vas deferens
Appendix
Cecum
Duodenum
Heart
Pancreas
Diaphragm
Lung
Trachea
Esophagus
Tongue
Buccal cavity
Mouth
Nasal cavity

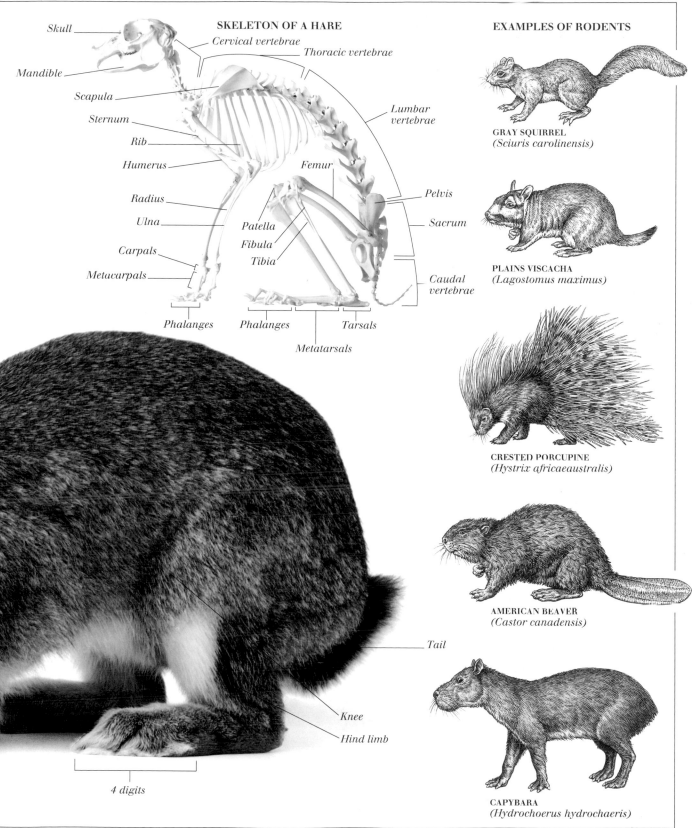

SKELETON OF A HARE

Skull

Cervical vertebrae

Thoracic vertebrae

Mandible

Scapula

Lumbar vertebrae

Sternum

Rib

Humerus

Femur

Radius

Pelvis

Ulna

Sacrum

Patella

Carpals

Fibula

Metacarpals

Tibia

Caudal vertebrae

Phalanges

Phalanges

Tarsals

Metatarsals

Tail

Knee

Hind limb

4 digits

EXAMPLES OF RODENTS

GRAY SQUIRREL
(Sciuris carolinensis)

PLAINS VISCACHA
(Lagostomus maximus)

CRESTED PORCUPINE
(Hystrix africaeaustralis)

AMERICAN BEAVER
(Castor canadensis)

CAPYBARA
(Hydrochoerus hydrochaeris)

Ungulates

UNGULATES IS A GENERAL TERM FOR a large, varied group of mammals that includes horses, cattle, and their relatives. The ungulates are divided into two orders on the basis of the number of toes. Members of the order Perissodactyla (odd-toed ungulates) have one or three toes. Perissodactyls include horses, asses, and zebras (all of which are one-toed), and rhinoceroses and tapirs (which are three-toed). Members of the order Artiodactyla (even-toed ungulates) have two or four toes. Most artiodactyls have two toes, which are typically encased in hooves to give the so-called cloven hoof. Two-toed, cloven-hoofed artiodactyls include cows and other cattle, sheep, goats, antelopes, deer, and giraffes. The other main two-toed artiodactyls are camels and llamas. Most two-toed artiodactyls are ruminants; that is, they have a four-chambered stomach and chew the cud. The principal four-toed artiodactyls are hogs and hippopotamuses.

DIGESTIVE SYSTEM OF A COW

COMPARISON OF THE FRONT FEET OF A HORSE AND A COW

SKELETON OF THE LEFT FRONT FOOT OF A HORSE

SKELETON OF THE RIGHT FRONT FOOT OF A COW

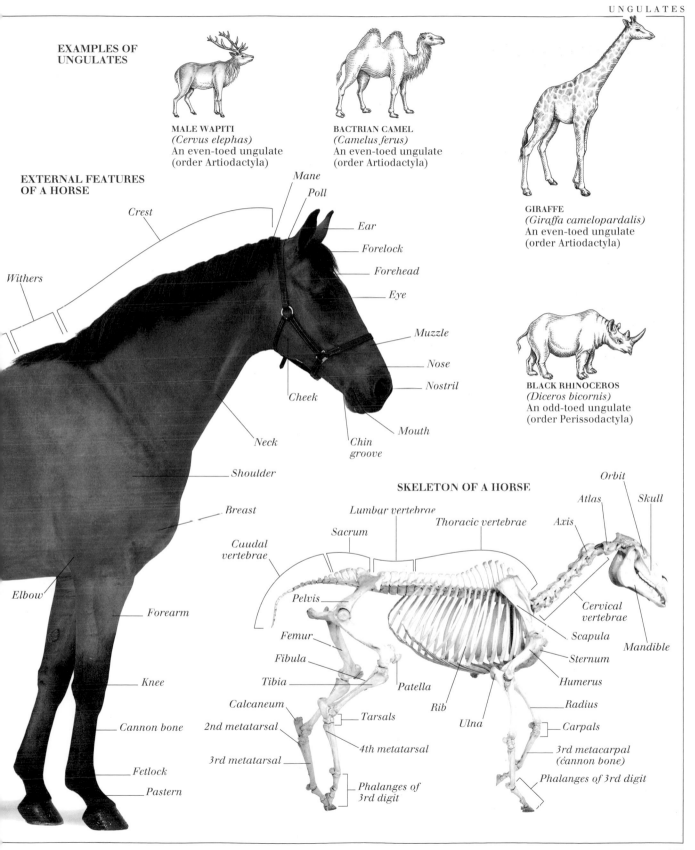

EXAMPLES OF UNGULATES

MALE WAPITI
(*Cervus elephas*)
An even-toed ungulate
(order Artiodactyla)

BACTRIAN CAMEL
(*Camelus ferus*)
An even-toed ungulate
(order Artiodactyla)

GIRAFFE
(*Giraffa camelopardalis*)
An even-toed ungulate
(order Artiodactyla)

BLACK RHINOCEROS
(*Diceros bicornis*)
An odd-toed ungulate
(order Perissodactyla)

EXTERNAL FEATURES OF A HORSE

Mane
Poll
Crest
Ear
Forelock
Forehead
Eye
Withers
Muzzle
Nose
Nostril
Cheek
Mouth
Chin groove
Neck
Shoulder
Breast
Elbow
Forearm
Knee
Cannon bone
Fetlock
Pastern

SKELETON OF A HORSE

Lumbar vertebrae
Thoracic vertebrae
Orbit
Atlas
Skull
Axis
Sacrum
Caudal vertebrae
Cervical vertebrae
Pelvis
Scapula
Mandible
Femur
Sternum
Fibula
Humerus
Tibia
Patella
Calcaneum
Radius
Tarsals
Rib
2nd metatarsal
4th metatarsal
Ulna
Carpals
3rd metatarsal
3rd metacarpal (cannon bone)
Phalanges of 3rd digit
Phalanges of 3rd digit

199

Elephants

THE TWO SPECIES OF elephants—African
and Asian—are the only members of the
mammalian order Proboscidea. The
bigger African elephant is the largest
land animal: a fully grown male may
be up to 13 ft (4m) tall and weigh as
much as 7.7 tons (7 tonnes). A fully
grown male Asian elephant may be
11 ft (3.3 m) tall and weigh 6 tons
(5.4 tonnes). The muscular trunk—an
extension of the nose and upper lip—is
the elephant's most obvious feature.
It is used for manipulating and lifting,
feeding, drinking and spraying water,
smelling, touching, and producing
trumpeting sounds. Other characteristic
features of this mighty plant-eater
include a pair of ivory tusks, used for
defense and for crushing vegetation;
thick, pillar-like legs and broad feet to
support the massive body; and large ear
flaps that act as radiators to keep the
elephant cool.

**DIFFERENCES BETWEEN
AFRICAN AND ASIAN ELEPHANTS**

Flat forehead

Very large ears

2 "lips" at the end of the trunk

4 toenails

AFRICAN ELEPHANT
(*Loxodonta africana*)

Concave back

3 toenails

Twin-domed forehead

Smaller ears

1 "lip" at the end of the trunk

5 toenails

Arched back

4 toenails

ASIAN ELEPHANT
(*Elephas maximus*)

Rump

Hind leg

Toenail

**INTERNAL ANATOMY OF A
FEMALE ELEPHANT**

Spinal cord

Heart

Stomach

Duodenum

Kidney

Ureter

Uterus

Rectum

Bladder

Anal flap

Anus

Vagina

Brain

Nasal cavity

Buccal cavity

Mouth

Tongue

Tusk

Epiglottis

Esophagus

Trachea

Lung

Diaphragm

Nasal passage

Nostril

Spleen

Vulva

Small intestine

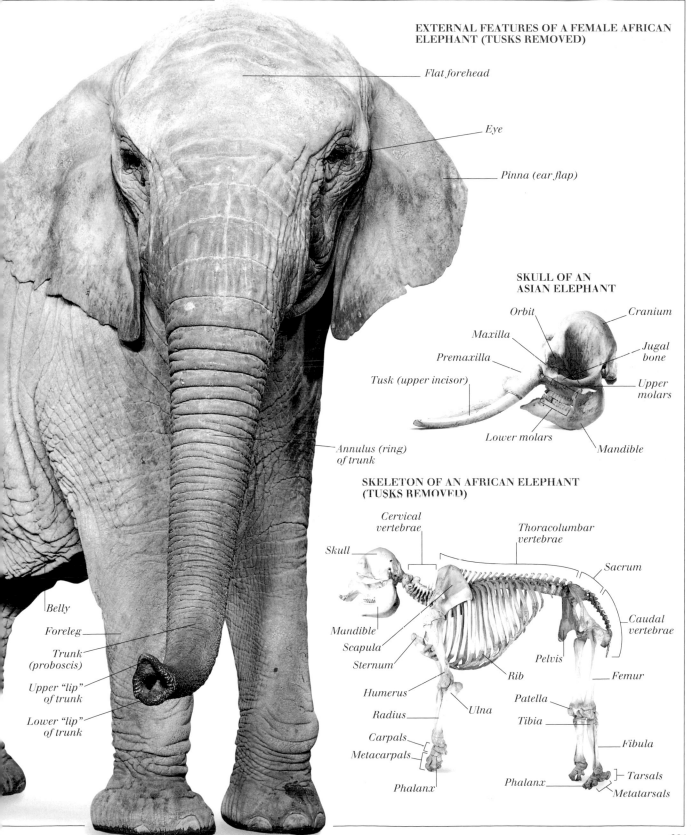

EXTERNAL FEATURES OF A FEMALE AFRICAN ELEPHANT (TUSKS REMOVED)

Flat forehead

Eye

Pinna (ear flap)

SKULL OF AN ASIAN ELEPHANT

Orbit

Cranium

Maxilla

Jugal bone

Premaxilla

Tusk (upper incisor)

Upper molars

Lower molars

Mandible

Annulus (ring) of trunk

SKELETON OF AN AFRICAN ELEPHANT (TUSKS REMOVED)

Cervical vertebrae

Thoracolumbar vertebrae

Skull

Sacrum

Mandible

Scapula

Pelvis

Caudal vertebrae

Sternum

Femur

Rib

Belly

Foreleg

Trunk (proboscis)

Humerus

Patella

Upper "lip" of trunk

Radius

Ulna

Tibia

Lower "lip" of trunk

Carpals

Fibula

Metacarpals

Phalanx

Tarsals

Phalanx

Metatarsals

Primates

THE MAMMALIAN ORDER PRIMATES consists of monkeys, apes, and their relatives (including humans). There are two suborders of primates: Prosimii, the primitive primates, which include lemurs, tarsiers, and lorises; and Anthropoidea, the advanced primates, which include monkeys, apes, and humans. The anthropoids are divided into New World monkeys, Old World monkeys, and hominids. New World monkeys typically have widespread nostrils that open to the side; and long tails, which are prehensile (grasping) in some species. This group of monkeys lives in South America, and includes marmosets, tamarins, and howler monkeys. Old World monkeys typically have close-set nostrils that open forward or downward and nonprehensile tails. This group of monkeys lives in Africa and Asia, and includes langurs, mandrills, macaques, and baboons. Hominids typically have large brains and no tail. This group includes the apes—chimpanzees, gibbons, gorillas, and orangutans—and humans.

INTERNAL ANATOMY OF A FEMALE CHIMPANZEE

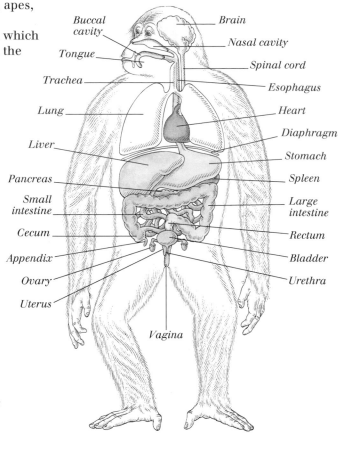

Buccal cavity, Tongue, Trachea, Lung, Liver, Pancreas, Small intestine, Cecum, Appendix, Ovary, Uterus, Brain, Nasal cavity, Spinal cord, Esophagus, Heart, Diaphragm, Stomach, Spleen, Large intestine, Rectum, Bladder, Urethra, Vagina

SKELETON OF A RHESUS MONKEY

Skull, Orbit, Cervical vertebrae, Thoracic vertebrae, Mandible, Clavicle, Scapula, Rib, Humerus, Lumbar vertebrae, Radius, Ulna, Sacrum, Femur, Patella, Tibia, Fibula, Pelvis, Carpals, Metacarpals, Phalanges, Tarsals, Metatarsals, Phalanges, Caudal vertebrae

SKULL OF A CHIMPANZEE

Temporal bone, Suture, Parietal bone, Frontal bone, Supraorbital ridge, Orbit, Occipital bone, Maxilla, Premaxilla, Auditory meatus, Zygomatic arch, Incisor tooth, Canine tooth, Mandible, Molar tooth, Premolar tooth

EXAMPLES OF PRIMATES

RING-TAILED LEMUR
(*Lemur catta*)
A prosimian

MALE RED HOWLER MONKEY
(*Alouatta seniculus*)
A New World monkey

MALE MANDRILL
(*Mandrillus sphinx*)
An Old World monkey

CHIMPANZEE
(*Pan troglodytes*)
An ape

EXTERNAL FEATURES OF A YOUNG GORILLA

GOLDEN LION TAMARIN
(*Leontopithecus rosalia*)
A New World monkey

Pinna (ear flap)

Shoulder

Brow ridge

Eye

Nostril

Mouth

Upper arm

Thigh

Forearm

Chest

Knee

Elbow

Lower leg

Hand

Foot

Toe

Finger

Toenail

Dolphins, whales, and seals

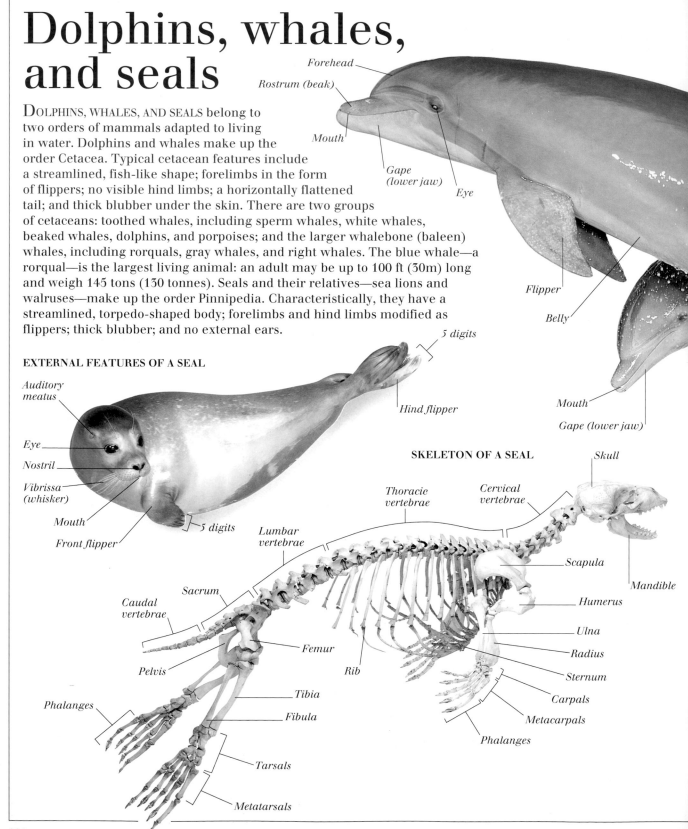

DOLPHINS, WHALES, AND SEALS belong to two orders of mammals adapted to living in water. Dolphins and whales make up the order Cetacea. Typical cetacean features include a streamlined, fish-like shape; forelimbs in the form of flippers; no visible hind limbs; a horizontally flattened tail; and thick blubber under the skin. There are two groups of cetaceans: toothed whales, including sperm whales, white whales, beaked whales, dolphins, and porpoises; and the larger whalebone (baleen) whales, including rorquals, gray whales, and right whales. The blue whale—a rorqual—is the largest living animal: an adult may be up to 100 ft (30m) long and weigh 145 tons (130 tonnes). Seals and their relatives—sea lions and walruses—make up the order Pinnipedia. Characteristically, they have a streamlined, torpedo-shaped body; forelimbs and hind limbs modified as flippers; thick blubber; and no external ears.

Forehead

Rostrum (beak)

Mouth

Gape (lower jaw)

Eye

Flipper

Belly

Mouth

Gape (lower jaw)

EXTERNAL FEATURES OF A SEAL

5 digits

Hind flipper

Auditory meatus

Eye

Nostril

Vibrissa (whisker)

Mouth

Front flipper

5 digits

SKELETON OF A SEAL

Skull

Thoracic vertebrae

Cervical vertebrae

Lumbar vertebrae

Scapula

Mandible

Sacrum

Humerus

Caudal vertebrae

Ulna

Femur

Radius

Pelvis

Rib

Sternum

Tibia

Carpals

Phalanges

Fibula

Metacarpals

Phalanges

Tarsals

Metatarsals

EXAMPLES OF CETACEANS

**EXTERNAL FEATURES
OF A DOLPHIN**

Dorsal fin

BLUE WHALE
(*Balaenoptera musculus*)

SPERM WHALE
(*Physeter catodon*)

Tail

MALE BAIRD'S BEAKED WHALE
(*Berardius bairdi*)

MALE KILLER WHALE
(*Orcinus orca*)

Tail fluke

MALE NARWHAL
(*Monodon monoceros*)

**INTERNAL ANATOMY OF
A MALE DOLPHIN**

Spinal cord

Stomach

Kidney

Blowhole (nostril)

Brain

Aorta

Intestine

Nasal plug

Bladder

Buccal cavity

Anus

Rectum

Tongue

Penis

Esophagus

Testis

Trachea

Liver

Urinogenital opening

Heart

Lung

Marsupials and Monotremes

MARSUPIALS AND MONOTREMES are two orders of mammals that differ from other mammalian groups in the ways that their young develop. The order Marsupalia, the pouched mammals, is made up of kangaroos and their relatives. Typically, marsupials give birth to their young at a very early stage of development. The young then crawls to the mother's pouch (which is on the outside of her abdomen), where it attaches itself to a nipple and remains until fully developed. Most marsupials live in Australia, although the opossums—which are classified as marsupials despite not having a pouch—live in the Americas. The order Monotremata is made up of the platypus and its relatives (the echidnas, or spiny anteaters). The monotremes are primitive mammals that lay eggs, which the mother incubates. The monotremes are found only in Australia and New Guinea.

SKELETON OF A KANGAROO

Skull

Mandible

Cervical vertebrae

Scapula

Clavicle

Humerus

Sternum

Radius

Ulna

Thoracic vertebrae

Carpals

Metacarpals

Phalanges

Rib

Lumbar vertebrae

Femur

Sacrum

Caudal vertebrae

Fibula

Pelvis

Tibia

Tarsals

Metatarsals

Phalanges

Tail

SKELETON OF A PLATYPUS

Skull

Orbit

1st cervical vertebra

Scapula

Phalanges

Metacarpals

Carpals

Ulna

Radius

Humerus

1st thoracic vertebra

Rib

Femur

1st lumbar vertebra

Tarsals

Metatarsals

Phalanges

Fibula

Tibia

Patella

Pelvis

1st caudal vertebra

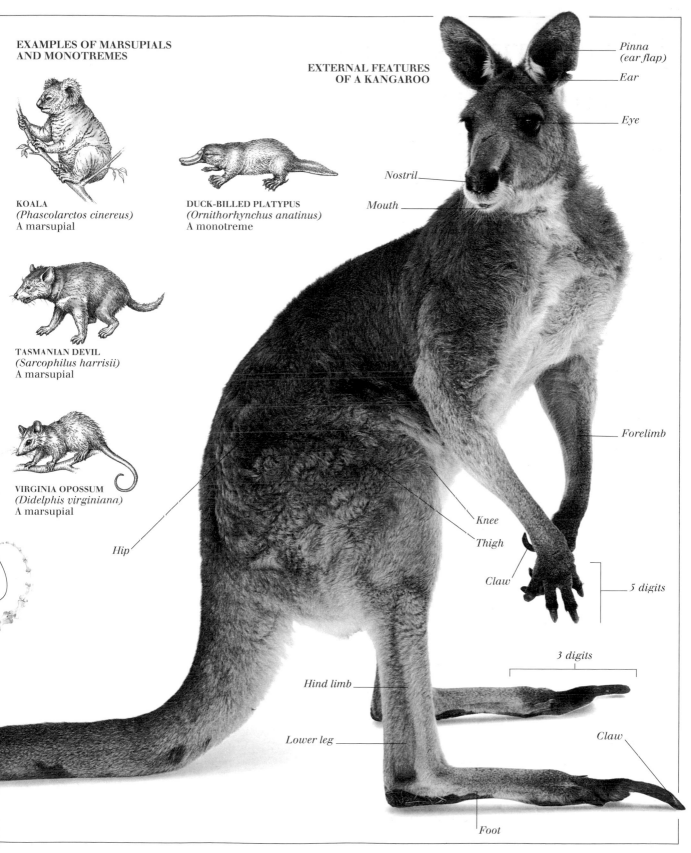

**EXAMPLES OF MARSUPIALS
AND MONOTREMES**

**EXTERNAL FEATURES
OF A KANGAROO**

KOALA
(*Phascolarctos cinereus*)
A marsupial

DUCK-BILLED PLATYPUS
(*Ornithorhynchus anatinus*)
A monotreme

TASMANIAN DEVIL
(*Sarcophilus harrisii*)
A marsupial

VIRGINIA OPOSSUM
(*Didelphis virginiana*)
A marsupial

Pinna
(ear flap)

Ear

Eye

Nostril

Mouth

Forelimb

Knee

Thigh

Claw

5 digits

Hip

3 digits

Hind limb

Lower leg

Claw

Foot

THE HUMAN BODY

Body features

ALTHOUGH THERE IS enormous variation between the external appearances of humans, all bodies contain the same basic features. The outward form of the human body depends on the size of the skeleton, the shape of the muscles, the thickness of the fat layer beneath the skin, the elasticity or sagginess of the skin, and the person's age and gender. Males tend to be taller than females, with broader shoulders, more body hair, and a different pattern of fat deposits under the skin; the female body tends to be less muscular and has a shallower and wider pelvis to allow for childbirth.

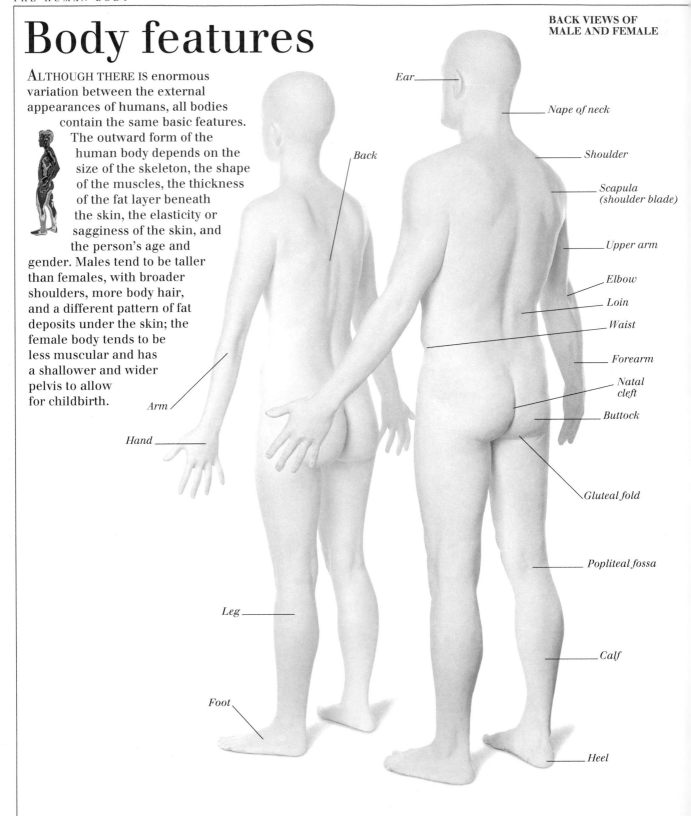

Ear

Nape of neck

Shoulder

Scapula
(shoulder blade)

Upper arm

Elbow

Loin

Waist

Forearm

Natal
cleft

Buttock

Gluteal fold

Popliteal fossa

Calf

Heel

Back

Arm

Hand

Leg

Foot

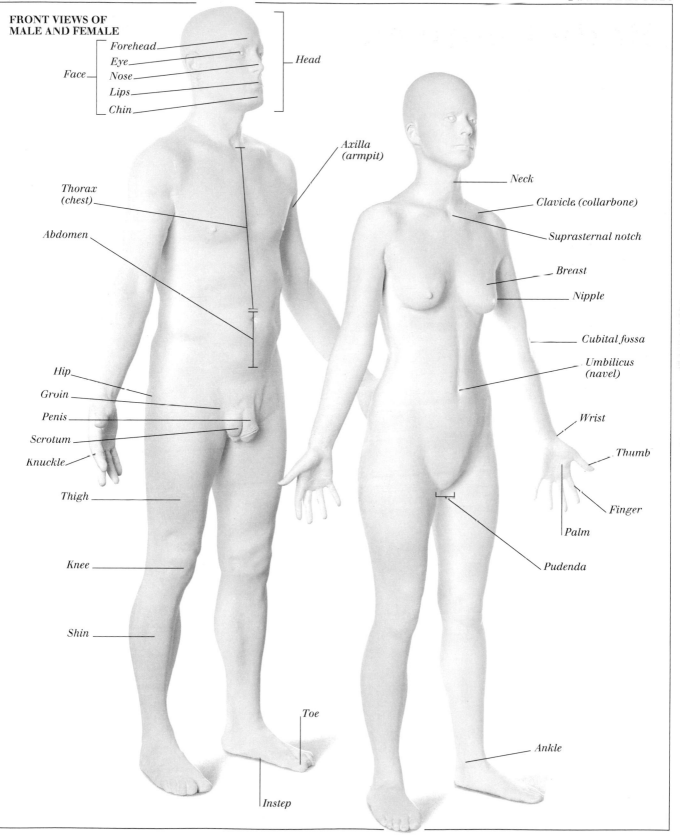

**FRONT VIEWS OF
MALE AND FEMALE**

Forehead

Eye

Face — Nose

Lips

Chin

— Head

Axilla
(armpit)

Thorax
(chest)

Neck

Clavicle (collarbone)

Suprasternal notch

Abdomen

Breast

Nipple

Cubital fossa

Umbilicus
(navel)

Hip

Groin

Penis

Scrotum

Knuckle

Wrist

Thumb

Finger

Thigh

Knee

Palm

Pudenda

Shin

Toe

Ankle

Instep

Head

IN A NEWBORN BABY, the head accounts for one quarter of the total body length; by adulthood, the proportion has reduced to one eighth. Contained in the head are the body's main sense organs: eyes, ears, olfactory nerves that detect smells, and the taste buds of the tongue. Signals from these organs pass to the body's great coordination center: the brain, housed in the protective, bony dome of the skull. Hair on the head insulates against heat loss, and adult males also grow thick facial hair. The face has three important openings: two nostrils through which air passes, and the mouth, which takes in nourishment and helps form speech. Although all heads are basically similar, differences in the size, shape, and color of features produce an infinite variety of appearances.

SIDE VIEW OF EXTERNAL FEATURES OF HEAD

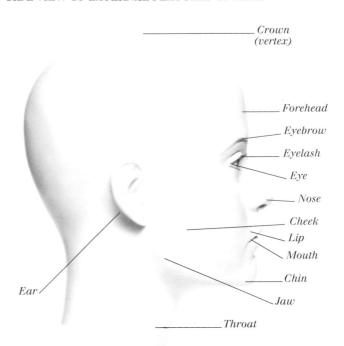

Crown
(vertex)

Forehead

Eyebrow

Eyelash

Eye

Nose

Cheek

Lip

Mouth

Chin

Jaw

Throat

Ear

SECTION THROUGH HEAD

Skull

Pineal body

Pituitary gland

Cerebellum

Pons

Medulla oblongata

Pharynx

Cervical vertebra

Spinal cord

Intervertebral disk

Superior sagittal sinus

Cerebrum

Frontal sinus

Sphenoidal sinus

Superior concha

Middle concha

Inferior concha

Vestibule

Maxilla (upper jaw)

Hard palate

Soft palate

Tongue

Uvula

Mandible (lower jaw)

Palatine tonsil

Epiglottis

Trachea

Esophagus

**FRONT VIEW OF EXTERNAL
FEATURES OF HEAD**

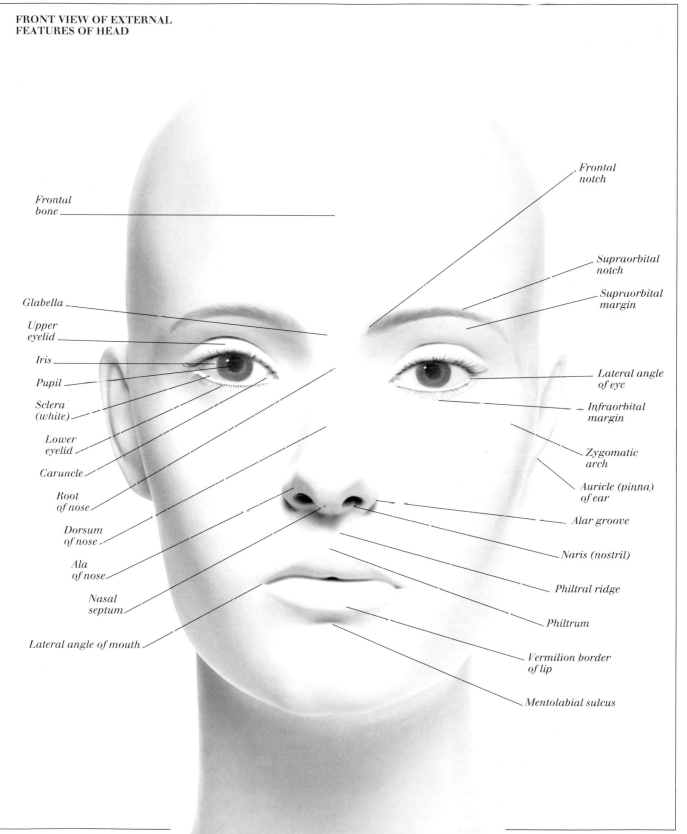

Frontal
notch

Supraorbital
notch

Supraorbital
margin

Frontal
bone

Glabella

Upper
eyelid

Iris

Pupil

Sclera
(white)

Lower
eyelid

Caruncle

Root
of nose

Dorsum
of nose

Ala
of nose

Nasal
septum

Lateral angle of mouth

Lateral angle
of eye

Infraorbital
margin

Zygomatic
arch

Auricle (pinna)
of ear

Alar groove

Naris (nostril)

Philtral ridge

Philtrum

Vermilion border
of lip

Mentolabial sulcus

Body organs

ALL THE VITAL BODY ORGANS except for the brain are enclosed within the trunk or torso (the body apart from the head and limbs). The trunk contains two large cavities separated by a muscular sheet called the diaphragm. The upper cavity, known as the thorax or chest cavity, contains the heart and lungs. The lower cavity, called the abdominal cavity, contains the stomach, intestines, liver, and pancreas, which all play a role in digesting food. Also within the trunk are the kidneys and bladder, which are part of the urinary system, and the reproductive organs, which hold the seeds of new human life. Modern imaging techniques, such as contrast X-rays and different types of scans, make it possible to see and study body organs without the need to cut through their protective coverings of skin, fat, muscle, and bone.

MAJOR INTERNAL STRUCTURES

Thyroid gland

Larynx

Heart

Right lung

Left lung

Diaphragm

Liver

Stomach

Large intestine

Small intestine

Greater omentum

IMAGING THE BODY

SCINTIGRAM OF HEART CHAMBERS

ANGIOGRAM OF RIGHT LUNG

CONTRAST X-RAY OF GALLBLADDER

SCINTIGRAM OF NERVOUS SYSTEM

DOUBLE CONTRAST X-RAY OF COLON

ULTRASOUND SCAN OF TWINS IN UTERUS

ANGIOGRAM OF KIDNEYS

ANGIOGRAM OF ARTERIES OF HEAD

CT SCAN THROUGH FEMALE CHEST

THERMOGRAM OF CHEST REGION

ANGIOGRAM OF ARTERIES OF HEART

MRI SCAN THROUGH HEAD AT EYE LEVEL

**CHEST AND ABDOMINAL
CAVITIES WITH SOME
ORGANS REMOVED**

Right common carotid artery

Right jugular vein

Right
subclavian
artery

Right
lung

Upper
lobe

Middle
lobe

Lower
lobe

Heart

Left atrium

Right atrium

Left ventricle

Right ventricle

Right adrenal gland

Right kidney

Duodenum

Right ureter

Inferior vena cava

Common iliac vein

Rectum

External iliac vein

Larynx

Thyroid gland

Trachea

Superior vena cava

Aorta

Left lung

Primary bronchus

Secondary bronchus

Tertiary bronchus

Diaphragm

Esophagus

Spleen

Left adrenal gland

Pancreas

Left kidney

Left ureter

Abdominal aorta

Common iliac artery

Internal iliac artery

External iliac artery

Colon

Bladder

Adipose
(fat) tissue

Body cells

EVERYONE IS MADE UP OF BILLIONS OF CELLS, which are the basic structural units of the body. Bones, muscles, nerves, skin, blood, and all other body tissues are formed from different types of cells. Each cell has a specific function but works with other types of cells to perform the enormous number of tasks needed to sustain life. Most body cells have a similar basic structure. Each cell has an outer layer (called the cell membrane) and contains a fluid material (cytoplasm). Within the cytoplasm are many specialized structures (organelles). The most important organelle is the nucleus, which contains vital genetic material and acts as the cell's control center.

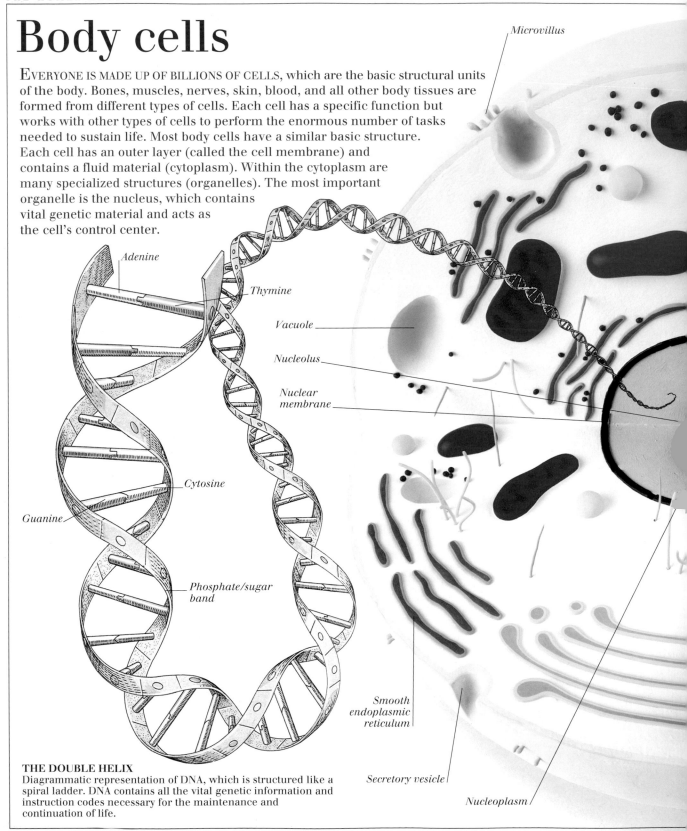

Microvillus

Adenine

Thymine

Vacuole

Nucleolus

Nuclear membrane

Cytosine

Guanine

Phosphate/sugar band

Smooth endoplasmic reticulum

Secretory vesicle

Nucleoplasm

THE DOUBLE HELIX
Diagrammatic representation of DNA, which is structured like a spiral ladder. DNA contains all the vital genetic information and instruction codes necessary for the maintenance and continuation of life.

GENERALIZED HUMAN CELL

Cytoplasm

Lysosome

Cell membrane

Mitochondrial crista

Nucleus

Rough endoplasmic reticulum

Microfilament

Pore of nuclear membrane

Ribosome

Centriole

Mitochondrion

Microtubule

Peroxisome

Pinocytotic vesicle

Golgi complex (Golgi apparatus; Golgi body)

TYPES OF CELLS

BONE-FORMING CELL

NERVE CELLS IN SPINAL CORD

SPERM CELLS IN SEMEN

SECRETORY THYROID GLAND CELLS

ACID-SECRETING STOMACH CELLS

CONNECTIVE TISSUE CELLS

MUCUS-SECRETING DUODENAL CELLS

RED AND TWO WHITE BLOOD CELLS

FAT CELLS IN ADIPOSE TISSUE

EPITHELIAL CELLS IN CHEEK

Skeleton

THE SKELETON IS A MOBILE FRAMEWORK made up of 206 bones, approximately half of which are in the hands and feet. Although individual bones are rigid, the skeleton as a whole is remarkably flexible and allows the human body a huge range of movement. The skeleton serves as an anchorage for the skeletal muscles, and as a protective cage for the body's internal organs. Female bones are usually smaller and lighter than male bones, and the female pelvis is shallower and has a wider cavity.

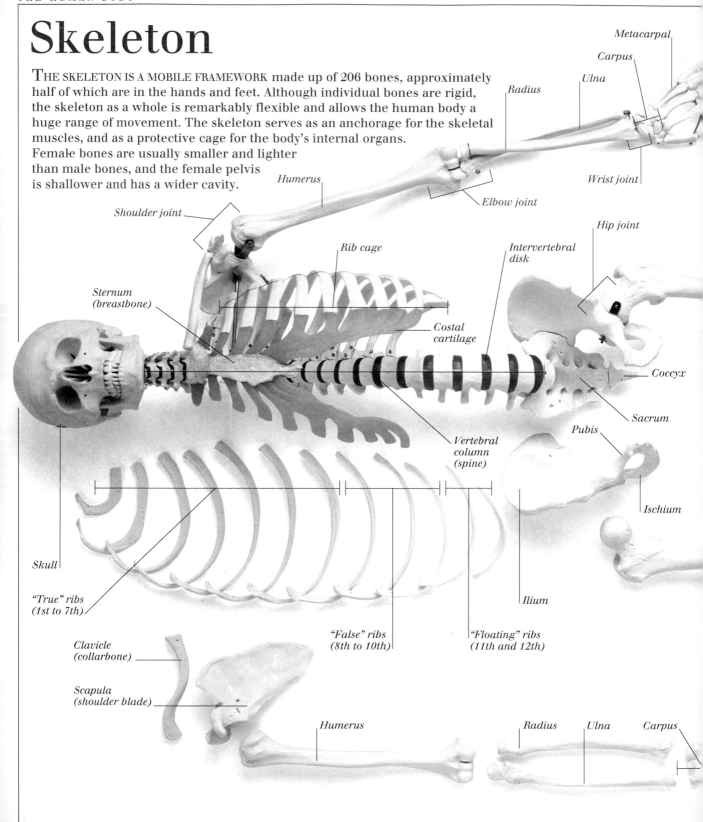

Metacarpal

Carpus

Ulna

Radius

Humerus

Shoulder joint

Elbow joint

Wrist joint

Hip joint

Intervertebral disk

Rib cage

Sternum (breastbone)

Costal cartilage

Coccyx

Sacrum

Pubis

Vertebral column (spine)

Ischium

Skull

Ilium

"True" ribs (1st to 7th)

"False" ribs (8th to 10th)

"Floating" ribs (11th and 12th)

Clavicle (collarbone)

Scapula (shoulder blade)

Humerus

Radius

Ulna

Carpus

Distal phalanx

Middle phalanx

Proximal phalanx

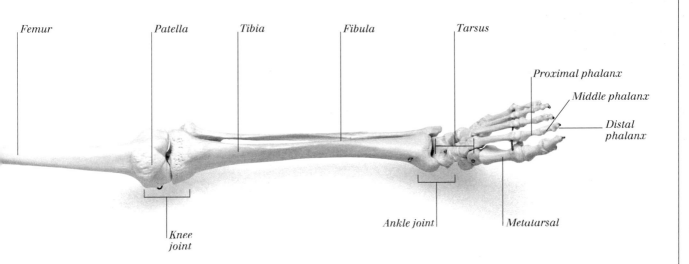

Femur   *Patella*   *Tibia*   *Fibula*   *Tarsus*

Proximal phalanx

Middle phalanx

Distal phalanx

Knee joint

Ankle joint   *Metatarsal*

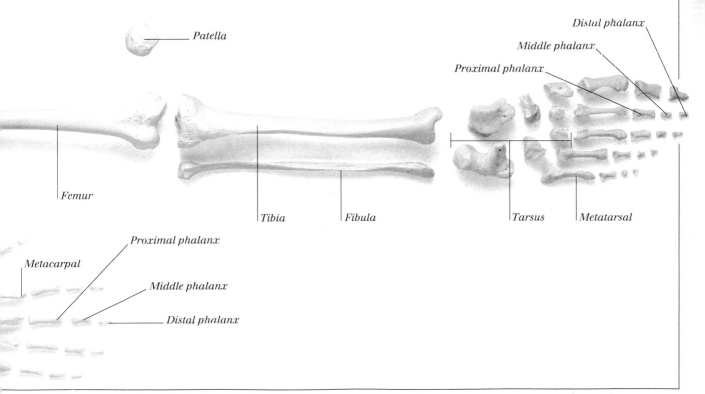

Patella

Distal phalanx

Middle phalanx

Proximal phalanx

Femur

Tibia   *Fibula*

Tarsus   *Metatarsal*

Metacarpal

Proximal phalanx

Middle phalanx

Distal phalanx

Skull

THE SKULL is the most complicated bony structure of the body—but every feature serves a purpose. Internally, the main hollow chamber of the skull has three levels that support the brain, with every bump and hollow corresponding to the shape of the brain. Underneath and toward the back of the skull is a large round hole, called the foramen magnum, through which the spinal cord passes. To the front of this are many smaller openings through which nerves, arteries, and veins pass to and from the brain. The roof of the skull is formed from four thin, curved bones that are firmly fixed together from the age of about two years. At the front of the skull are two orbits, which contain the eyeballs, and a central hole for the airway of the nose. The jawbone hinges on either side of the skull at ear level.

RIGHT SIDE VIEW OF A FETAL SKULL

Anterior fontanelle

Parietal bone

Coronal suture

Frontal bone

Nasal bone

Mental symphysis

Lambdoid suture

Occipital bone

Mastoid fontanelle

External auditory meatus

Sphenoidal fontanelle

RIGHT SIDE VIEW OF SKULL

Greater wing of sphenoid bone

Coronal suture

Frontal bone

Frontozygomatic suture

Parietal bone

Squamous suture

Supraorbital margin

Orbital cavity

Nasal bone

Anterior nasal spine

Maxilla (upper jaw)

Mandible (lower jaw)

Lambdoid suture

Occipital bone

Temporal bone

External auditory meatus

Mastoid process

Condyle

Coronoid process

Zygomatic bone

Mental foramen

Styloid process

Zygomatic arch

Posterior border of vomer

Concha

Mandible (lower jaw)

VIEW OF SKULL FROM BELOW

External occipital crest

Foramen magnum

Occipital condyle

Carotid canal

Mastoid process

Pharyngeal tubercle

Pterygoid plate

Pterygoid hamulus

Greater palatine foramen

Posterior nasal aperture

FRONT VIEW OF SKULL

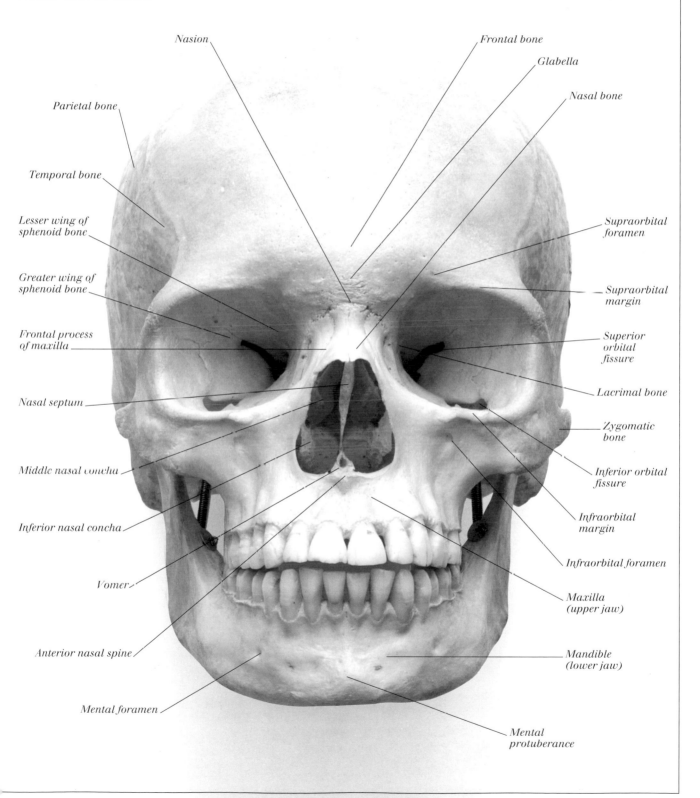

Nasion

Frontal bone

Glabella

Nasal bone

Parietal bone

Temporal bone

Lesser wing of
sphenoid bone

Greater wing of
sphenoid bone

Frontal process
of maxilla

Nasal septum

Middle nasal concha

Inferior nasal concha

Vomer

Anterior nasal spine

Mental foramen

Supraorbital
foramen

Supraorbital
margin

Superior
orbital
fissure

Lacrimal bone

Zygomatic
bone

Inferior orbital
fissure

Infraorbital
margin

Infraorbital foramen

Maxilla
(upper jaw)

Mandible
(lower jaw)

Mental
protuberance

Spine

THE SPINE (OR VERTEBRAL COLUMN) has two main functions: it serves as a protective surrounding for the delicate spinal cord and forms the supporting back bone of the skeleton. The spine consists of 24 separate differently shaped bones (vertebrae) with a curved, triangular bone (the sacrum) at the bottom. The sacrum is made up of fused vertebrae; at its lower end is a small tail-like structure made up of tiny bones collectively called the coccyx. Between each pair of vertebrae is a disc of cartilage that cushions the bones during movement. The top two vertebrae differ in appearance from the others and work as a pair: the first, called the atlas, rotates around a stout vertical peg on the second, the axis. This arrangement allows the skull to move freely up and down, and from side to side.

SPINE DIVIDED INTO VERTEBRAL SECTIONS
FRONT

- Cervical vertebrae
- Thoracic vertebrae
- Lumbar vertebrae
- Sacral vertebrae
- Coccygeal vertebrae

TYPES OF VERTEBRAE (VIEWED FROM ABOVE)

ATLAS

- Anterior arch
- Anterior tubercle
- Vertebral foramen
- Transverse process
- Lateral mass with superior articular facet
- Posterior arch
- Posterior tubercle
- Transverse foramen

AXIS

- Facet
- Dens
- Vertebral foramen
- Spinous process
- Lamina
- Transverse process and foramen

CERVICAL VERTEBRA

- Body
- Anterior tubercle
- Posterior tubercle
- Superior articular process
- Spinous process
- Vertebral foramen
- Transverse foramen

SKULL AND SPINE

- Skull
- Cervical vertebrae
- 1st 2nd 3rd 4th 5th 6th 7th
- Thoracic vertebrae
- 1st 2nd 3rd 4th 5th 6th 7th
- Atlas
- Axis

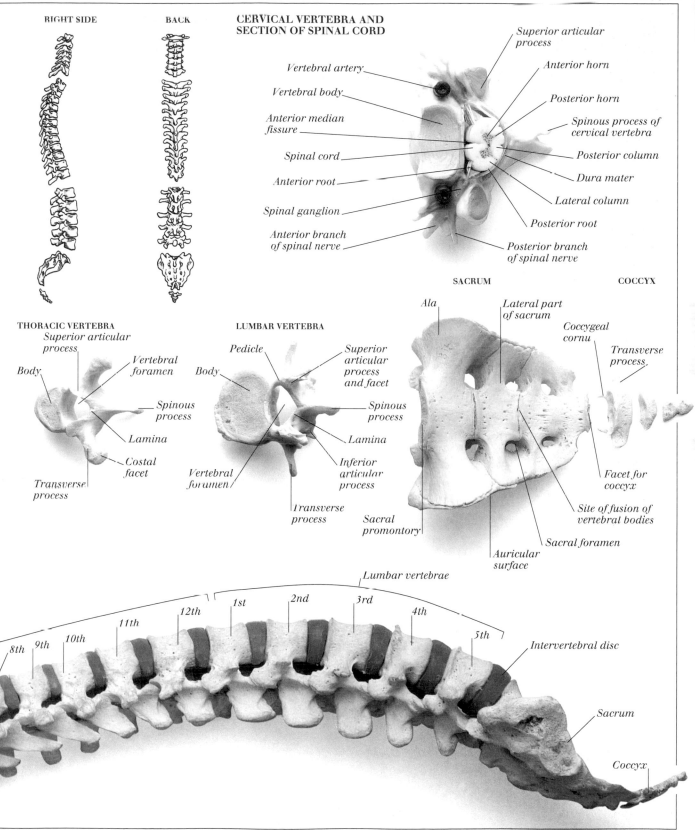

RIGHT SIDE

BACK

**CERVICAL VERTEBRA AND
SECTION OF SPINAL CORD**

Superior articular
process

Vertebral artery

Anterior horn

Vertebral body

Posterior horn

Anterior median
fissure

Spinous process of
cervical vertebra

Spinal cord

Posterior column

Anterior root

Dura mater

Spinal ganglion

Lateral column

Posterior root

Anterior branch
of spinal nerve

Posterior branch
of spinal nerve

SACRUM

COCCYX

Ala

Lateral part
of sacrum

Coccygeal
cornu

Transverse
process

THORACIC VERTEBRA

Superior articular
process

Vertebral
foramen

Body

Spinous
process

Lamina

Costal
facet

Transverse
process

LUMBAR VERTEBRA

Pedicle

Body

Superior
articular
process
and facet

Spinous
process

Lamina

Inferior
articular
process

Vertebral
foramen

Transverse
process

Sacral
promontory

Auricular
surface

Sacral foramen

Site of fusion of
vertebral bodies

Facet for
coccyx

Lumbar vertebrae

8th 9th 10th 11th 12th 1st 2nd 3rd 4th 5th

Intervertebral disc

Sacrum

Coccyx

Bones and joints

BONES FORM the body's hard, strong skeletal framework. Each bone has a hard, compact exterior surrounding a spongy, lighter interior. The long bones of the arms and legs, such as the femur (thigh bone), have a central cavity containing bone marrow. Bones are composed chiefly of calcium, phosphorus, and a fibrous substance known as collagen. Bones meet at joints, which are of several different types. For example, the hip is a ball-and-socket joint that allows the femur a wide range of movement, whereas finger joints are simple hinge joints that allow only bending and straightening. Joints are held in place by bands of tissue called ligaments. Movement of joints is facilitated by the smooth hyaline cartilage that covers the bone ends and by the synovial membrane that lines and lubricates the joint.

LIGAMENTS SURROUNDING HIP JOINT

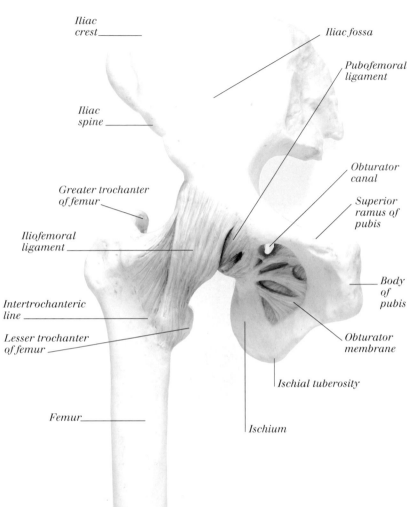

Iliac crest

Iliac fossa

Pubofemoral ligament

Iliac spine

Obturator canal

Superior ramus of pubis

Greater trochanter of femur

Iliofemoral ligament

Body of pubis

Intertrochanteric line

Obturator membrane

Lesser trochanter of femur

Ischial tuberosity

Femur

Ischium

SECTION THROUGH LEFT FEMUR

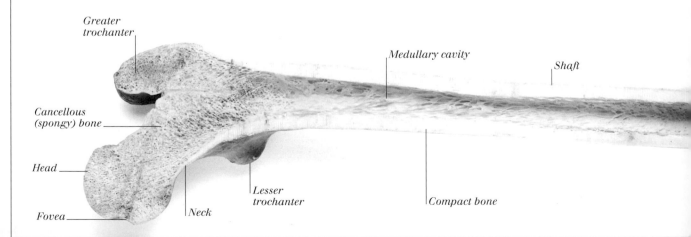

Greater trochanter

Medullary cavity

Shaft

Cancellous (spongy) bone

Head

Fovea

Neck

Lesser trochanter

Compact bone

SECTION THROUGH HIP JOINT

Psoas major muscle

Iliacus muscle

External iliac artery

Iliac crest

Hyaline cartilage of acetabulum

Hyaline cartilage of head of femur

Ligament of head of femur

Gluteus minimus muscle

Gluteus medius muscle

Acetabular labrum

Femoral artery

Articular cavity

Head of femur

Greater trochanter of femur

Neck of femur

Vastus lateralis muscle

Pectineus muscle

Shaft of femur

Adductor longus muscle

Iliacus muscle

Vastus medialis muscle

SECTION OF COMPACT BONE

Parallel rows of concentric bony layers make up this strong material.

BONE MARROW CELLS

Composed mainly of red and white blood cells, marrow fills the cavities of bones.

Lateral epicondyle

Patellar surface

Medial epicondyle

Adductor tubercle

SECTION THROUGH LONG BONE

Osteon (haversian system)

Haversian lamella

Outer lamella

Osteocyte (bone cell)

Sharpey's fiber

Intermediate lamella

Endosteum

Periosteum

Haversian canal

Volkmann's vessel

Lacuna

225

Muscles 1

THERE ARE THREE MAIN TYPES OF MUSCLE: skeletal muscle (also called voluntary muscle because it can be consciously controlled); smooth muscle (also called involuntary muscle because it is not under voluntary control); and the specialized muscle tissue of the heart. Humans have more than 600 skeletal muscles, which differ in size and shape according to the jobs they do. Skeletal muscles are attached either directly or indirectly (via tendons) to bones, and work in opposing pairs (one muscle in the pair contracts while the other relaxes) to produce body movements as diverse as walking, threading a needle, and an array of facial expressions. Smooth muscles occur in the walls of internal body organs and perform actions such as forcing food through the intestines, contracting the uterus (womb) in childbirth, and pumping blood through the blood vessels.

SOME OTHER MUSCLES IN THE BODY

- Iris
- Pupil

IRIS
The muscle fibers contract and dilate (expand) to alter pupil size.

TONGUE
Interlacing layers of muscle allow great mobility.

ILEUM
Opposing muscle layers transport semidigested food.

SUPERFICIAL SKELETAL MUSCLES

FRONT VIEW

- Brachioradialis
- Flexors of forearm
- Brachialis
- Frontalis
- Orbicularis oculi
- Temporalis
- Sternocleidomastoid
- Trapezius
- Pectoralis major
- Deltoid
- Serratus anterior
- Biceps brachii
- Rectus abdominis
- Linea alba
- External oblique
- Tensor fasciae latae
- Iliopsoas
- Pectineus
- Adductor longus
- Rectus femoris
- Sartorius
- Vastus lateralis
- Gracilis
- Vastus medialis
- Gastrocnemius
- Tibialis anterior

BACK VIEW

Extensors
of hand

Flexors
of hand

Temporalis

Sternocleidomastoid

Trapezius

Deltoid

Triceps
brachii

Teres minor

Teres major

Infraspinatus

Rhomboideus major

Latissimus dorsi

Gluteus
maximus

Adductor
magnus

Gracilis

Biceps femoris

Semitendinosus

Gastrocnemius

Soleus

Peroneus
brevis

MOVEMENT OF THE FOREARM
Controlled movement of the limbs relies
on coordinated relaxation and contraction
of opposing muscles. To raise the forearm,
the biceps (two-rooted muscle) contracts
and shortens while the triceps (three-
rooted muscle) relaxes; the reverse occurs
when the forearm is lowered.

Triceps in
resting phase

Biceps in
resting phase

Forearm
at rest

Triceps
relaxes

Biceps
contracts

Forearm
half raised

Triceps fully
relaxed

Biceps fully
contracted

Forearm
fully raised

Triceps
contracts

Biceps
relaxes

Forearm
half lowered

Triceps back in
resting phase

Biceps back in
resting phase

Forearm
back at rest

Muscles 2

SKELETAL MUSCLE FIBER

Myofibril

Sarcomere

Motor end plate

Nucleus

Synaptic knob

Sarcoplasmic reticulum

Sarcolemma

Schwann cell

Endomysium

Motor neuron

Node of Ranvier

MUSCLES OF FACIAL EXPRESSION

A single expression is the result of movement of many muscles; the main muscles of expression are shown in action below.

FRONTALIS

CORRUGATOR SUPERCILII

ORBICULARIS ORIS

ZYGOMATICUS MAJOR

DEPRESSOR ANGULI ORIS

TYPES OF MUSCLE

CARDIAC MUSCLE

SKELETAL MUSCLE

SMOOTH MUSCLE

CONTRACTION OF SKELETAL MUSCLE

RELAXED STATE

CONTRACTED STATE

**MUSCLES OF
HEAD AND NECK**

Frontalis

Procerus

Temporalis

*Corrugator
supercilii*

*Orbicularis
oculi*

*Levator labii
superioris*

Nasalis

*Zygomaticus
major*

Orbicularis oris

Buccinator

Masseter

Risorius

*Depressor labii
inferioris*

Levator anguli oris

Platysma

Mentalis

Depressor anguli oris

Thyrohyoid

Scalenus medius

Sternocleidomastoid

Sternohyoid

Omohyoid

Cricothyroid

Trapezius

Hands

THE HUMAN HAND is an extremely versatile tool, capable of delicate manipulation as well as powerful gripping actions. The arrangement of its 27 small bones, moved by 37 skeletal muscles that are connected to the bones by tendons, allows a wide range of movements. Our ability to bring the tips of our thumbs and fingers together, combined with the extraordinary sensitivity of our fingertips due to their rich supply of nerve endings, makes our hands uniquely dextrous.

X-RAY OF LEFT HAND OF A YOUNG CHILD

Area of ossification in phalanx

Area of ossification in metacarpal

Area of ossification in wrist

Epiphysis of ulna

Epiphysis of radius

Areas of cartilage in the wrist and at the ends of the finger bones are the sites of growth and have still to ossify.

BONES OF HAND

Ring finger

Middle finger

Index finger

Little finger

Distal phalanx

Middle phalanx

Proximal phalanx

2nd metacarpal

3rd metacarpal

4th metacarpal

5th metacarpal

Hamate

Pisiform

Capitate

Triquetral

Lunate

Ulna

Head

Shaft

Base

Trapezium

Trapezoid

Scaphoid

Radius

Distal phalanx of thumb

Proximal phalanx of thumb

1st metacarpal

**STRUCTURES UNDERLYING SKIN
OF PALM OF HAND**

*Flexor pollicis
brevis muscle*

*Opponens
pollicis
muscle*

*Abductor
pollicis
brevis
muscle*

Adductor pollicis muscle

2nd lumbrical muscle

*Flexor
retinaculum*

*Radial
artery*

Digital artery

Digital nerve

Flexor digitorum tendon

*Opponens
digiti
minimi
muscle*

*Abductor
digiti
minimi
muscle*

*Ulnar
nerve*

*Palmaris
longus
tendon*

*Ulnar
artery*

EXTERNAL FEATURES OF BACK OF HAND

Little finger

*Distal
interphalangeal joint*

*Proximal
interphalangeal joint*

*Extensor digitorum
tendon*

Head of ulna

Ring finger

*Middle
finger*

Cuticle

Lunule

*Index
finger*

Nail

*Metacarpophalangeal
joint*

Wrist

*Distal end
of radius*

Thumb

Feet

THE FEET AND TOES are essential elements in body movement. They bear and propel the weight of the body during walking and running, and also help to maintain balance during changes of body position. Each foot has 26 bones, more than 100 ligaments, and 33 muscles, some of which are attached to the lower leg. The heel pad and the arch of the foot act as shock absorbers, providing a cushion against the jolts that occur with every step.

BONES OF FOOT

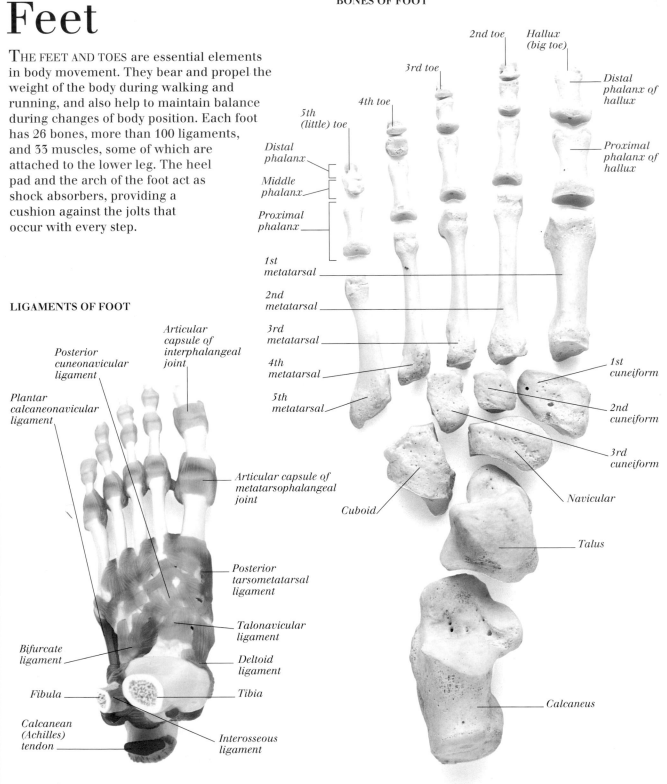

2nd toe

Hallux (big toe)

3rd toe

Distal phalanx of hallux

4th toe

Proximal phalanx of hallux

5th (little) toe

Distal phalanx

Middle phalanx

Proximal phalanx

1st metatarsal

2nd metatarsal

3rd metatarsal

4th metatarsal

5th metatarsal

1st cuneiform

2nd cuneiform

3rd cuneiform

Navicular

Cuboid

Talus

Calcaneus

LIGAMENTS OF FOOT

Posterior cuneonavicular ligament

Articular capsule of interphalangeal joint

Plantar calcaneonavicular ligament

Articular capsule of metatarsophalangeal joint

Posterior tarsometatarsal ligament

Talonavicular ligament

Bifurcate ligament

Deltoid ligament

Fibula

Tibia

Calcanean (Achilles) tendon

Interosseous ligament

STRUCTURES UNDERLYING SKIN OF FOOT

Extensor hallucis longus tendon

1st dorsal interosseous muscle

Inferior extensor retinaculum

Medial malleolus

Tibialis anterior muscle

Tibia

Flexor hallucis longus muscle

Flexor digitorum longus muscle

Calcanean (Achilles) tendon

Soleus muscle

Extensor digitorum longus tendon

Abductor digiti minimi muscle

Extensor hallucis brevis muscle

Extensor digitorum brevis muscle

Peroneus brevis tendon

Lateral malleolus

Tibialis posterior muscle

Peroneus brevis muscle

Fibula

Peroneus longus muscle

EXTERNAL FEATURES OF FOOT

Toenail

Hallux (big toe)

Interphalangeal joint

Extensor hallucis longus tendon

Extensor digitorum longus tendon

Medial malleolus

2nd toe

3rd toe

4th toe

5th (little) toe

Lateral malleolus

Skin and hair

SKIN IS THE BODY'S LARGEST ORGAN, a waterproof barrier that protects the internal organs against infection, injury, and harmful sun rays. The skin is also an important sensory organ and helps to control body temperature. The outer layer of the skin, known as the epidermis, is coated with keratin, a tough, horny protein that is also the chief constituent of hair and nails. Dead cells are shed from the skin's surface and are replaced by new cells from the base of the epidermis, the region that also produces the skin pigment, melanin. The dermis contains most of the skin's living structures, and includes nerve endings, blood vessels, elastic fibers, sweat glands that cool the skin, and sebaceous glands that produce oil to keep the skin supple. Beneath the dermis lies the subcutaneous tissue (hypodermis), which is rich in fat and blood vessels. Hair shafts grow from hair follicles situated in the dermis and subcutaneous tissue. Hair grows on every part of the skin apart from the palms of the hands and soles of the feet.

SECTION OF HAIR

Medulla

Cortex

Melanin granule

Cell nucleus residue

Macrofibril

Cuticle

SECTIONS OF DIFFERENT TYPES OF SKIN

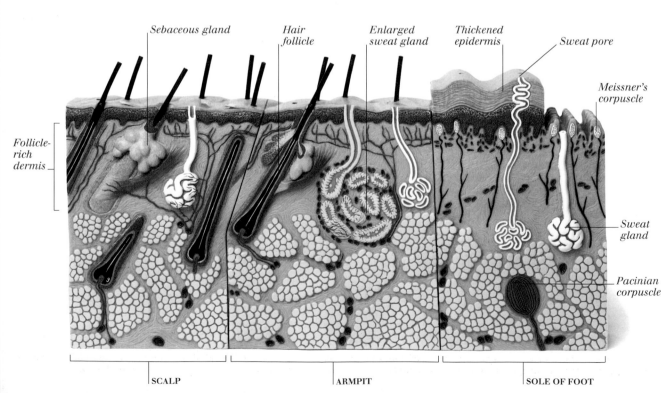

Sebaceous gland

Hair follicle

Enlarged sweat gland

Thickened epidermis

Sweat pore

Meissner's corpuscle

Follicle-rich dermis

Sweat gland

Pacinian corpuscle

SCALP

ARMPIT

SOLE OF FOOT

SECTION OF SKIN

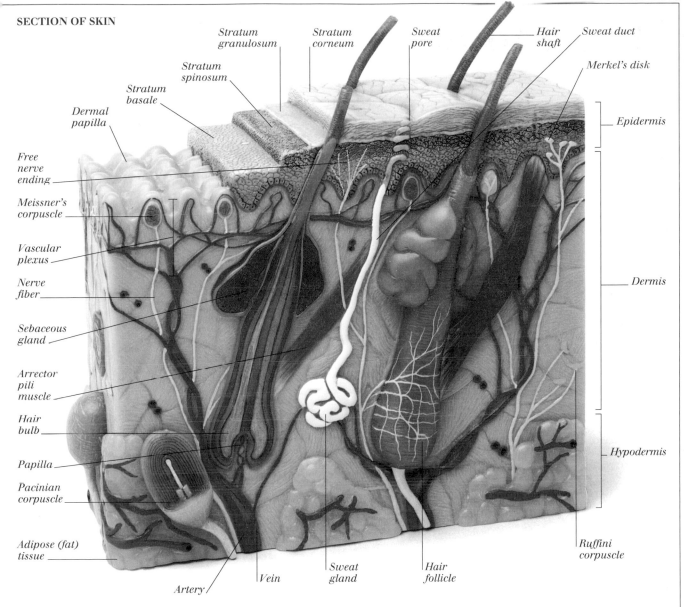

Stratum
granulosum

Stratum
spinosum

Stratum
basale

Stratum
corneum

Sweat
pore

Hair
shaft

Sweat duct

Merkel's disk

Dermal
papilla

Epidermis

Free
nerve
ending

Meissner's
corpuscle

Vascular
plexus

Nerve
fiber

Sebaceous
gland

Arrector
pili
muscle

Hair
bulb

Papilla

Pacinian
corpuscle

Adipose (fat)
tissue

Dermis

Hypodermis

Ruffini
corpuscle

Artery

Vein

Sweat
gland

Hair
follicle

PHOTOMICROGRAPHS OF SKIN AND HAIR

SECTION OF SKIN
The flaky cells at the skin's
surface are shed continuously.

SWEAT PORE
This allows loss of fluid as part
of temperature control.

SKIN HAIR
Two hairs pushing through the
outer layer of skin.

HEAD HAIR
The root and part of the shaft of
a hair from the scalp.

Brain

THE BRAIN IS THE MAJOR ORGAN of the central nervous system and the control center for all the body's voluntary and involuntary activities. It is also responsible for the complexities of thought, memory, emotion, and language. In adults, this complex organ is a mere 3 lb (1.4 kg) in weight, containing over 10 thousand million nerve cells. Three distinct regions can easily be seen—the brainstem, the cerebellum, and the large cerebrum. The brainstem controls vital body functions, such as breathing and digestion. The cerebellum's main functions are the maintenance of posture and the coordination of body movements. The cerebrum, which consists of the right and left cerebral hemispheres joined by the corpus callosum, is the site of most conscious and intelligent activities.

MRI SCAN OF TRANSVERSE SECTION THROUGH BRAIN

White matter

Gray matter

Skull

Scalp

Lateral ventricle

Longitudinal fissure

Coronal section

Sagittal section

SAGITTAL SECTION THROUGH BRAIN

Central sulcus

Fornix

Cerebrum

Parietal lobe

Corpus callosum

Parieto-occipital sulcus

Thalamus

Pineal body

Occipital lobe

Frontal lobe

Aqueduct

Hypothalamus

Cerebellum

Optic chiasma

4th ventricle

Pituitary gland

Mesencephalon (midbrain)

Pons

Brainstem

Spinal cord

Medulla oblongata

SECTION THROUGH SKULL AND BRAIN

Scalp
Epicranial aponeurosis
Arachnoid granulation
Pericranium
Skull
Lateral lacuna
Dura mater
Superior sagittal sinus
Arachnoid mater
Falx cerebri
Pia mater
Subarachnoid space
Cerebral vessel
Cerebrum
Gray matter
White matter

EXTERNAL ANATOMY OF BRAIN

Parietal lobe
Parieto-occipital sulcus
Precentral gyrus
Postcentral gyrus
Central sulcus
Frontal lobe
Lateral sulcus
Occipital lobe
Temporal lobe
Cerebellum

SPECIFIC ROLES OF AREAS OF CEREBRUM

Skilled movements
Basic movements
Sensation
Visual recognition
Behavior and emotion
Speech
Vision
Hearing
Balance and muscle coordination

CORONAL SECTION THROUGH BRAIN

Corpus callosum
Longitudinal fissure
Gray matter
White matter
Cerebrum
Caudate nucleus
Lateral ventricle
Fornix
Lentiform nucleus
Internal capsule
Thalamus
Crus cerebri of midbrain
3rd ventricle
Pons
Medulla oblongata
Cerebellum

NERVE CELLS IN BRAIN

The dark cells are Purkinje cells, which are among the largest nerve cells in the body.

237

Nervous system

THE NERVOUS SYSTEM IS THE BODY'S internal, electrochemical, communications network. Its main parts are the brain, spinal cord, and nerves. The brain and spinal cord form the central nervous system (CNS), the body's chief controlling and coordinating centers. Billions of long neurons, many grouped as nerves, make up the peripheral nervous system, transmitting nerve impulses between the CNS and other regions of the body. Each neuron has three parts: a cell body, branching dendrites that receive chemical signals from other neurons, and a tube-like axon that conveys these signals as electrical impulses.

CENTRAL AND PERIPHERAL NERVOUS SYSTEMS

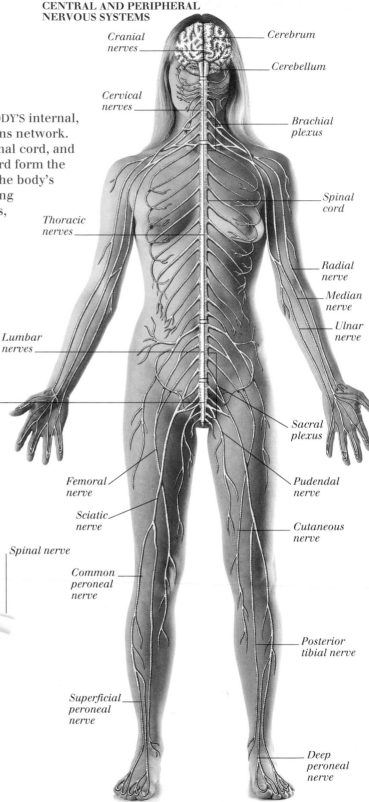

Cranial nerves

Cerebrum

Cerebellum

Cervical nerves

Brachial plexus

Spinal cord

Thoracic nerves

Radial nerve

Median nerve

Ulnar nerve

Lumbar nerves

Sacral nerves

Sacral plexus

Femoral nerve

Pudendal nerve

Sciatic nerve

Cutaneous nerve

Common peroneal nerve

Posterior tibial nerve

Superficial peroneal nerve

Deep peroneal nerve

SECTION THROUGH SPINAL CORD

Spinal ganglion

Gray matter

Central canal

Posterior root of spinal nerve

Spinal nerve

White matter

Anterior median fissure

Anterior root of spinal nerve

STRUCTURE OF A MOTOR NEURON

Cell body

Nucleus

Synaptic knob

Axon hillock

Axon

Dendrite

Nucleolus

Nissl body

Schwann cell

Node of Ranvier

Myelin sheath

Mitochondrion

TYPES OF NERVE ENDING

FREE NERVE ENDING

MEISSNER'S CORPUSCLE

MERKEL'S DISK

RUFFINI CORPUSCLE

PACINIAN CORPUSCLE

TYPES OF NEURON

MULTIPOLAR

UNIPOLAR

BIPOLAR

Motor end plate

Dendrite

Dendrite

Axon

Aron

Node of Ranvier

Schwann cell

Cell body

Nucleus

Myelin sheath

Axon

Nucleus

Dendrite

Cell body

Nucleus

Dendrite

Receptor

Cell body

Nucleus

Dendrite

STRUCTURE OF A SYNAPTIC KNOB

Presynaptic axon

Microtubule

Neurofilament

Endoplasmic reticulum

Mitochondrion

Synaptic vesicle

Neurotransmitter

Presynaptic membrane

Eye

THE EYE IS THE ORGAN OF SIGHT. The two eyeballs, protected within bony sockets called orbits and on the outside by the eyelids, eyebrows, and tear film, are directly connected to the brain by the optic nerves. Each eye is moved by six muscles, which are attached around the eyeball. Light rays entering the eye through the pupil are focused by the cornea and lens to form an image on the retina. The retina contains millions of light-sensitive cells, called rods and cones, which convert the image into a pattern of nerve impulses. These impulses are transmitted along the optic nerve to the brain. Information from the two optic nerves is processed in the brain to produce a single coordinated image.

Lateral rectus muscle

Vitreous humor

Macula

Central retinal vein

Central retinal artery

Pia mater

Arachnoid mater

Dura mater

Optic nerve

Area of optic disk

Retina

Choroid

Sclera

Retinal blood vessel

Medial rectus muscle

SECTION THROUGH LEFT EYE

LACRIMAL (TEAR-PRODUCING) APPARATUS

Lacrimal sac   Lacrimal canaliculus   Lacrimal gland

Middle meatus

Middle nasal concha

Nasal septum   Inferior nasal concha   Nasolacrimal duct   Lacrimal punctum

Iris

Anterior chamber
Posterior chamber   } Aqueous humor

Conjunctiva

Pupil

Cornea

Lens

Sphincter muscle

Dilator muscle

Zonular ligament

Sinus venosus sclerae

Iridocorneal angle

Ciliary body

Ora serrata

OPHTHALMOSCOPIC VIEW OF RETINA

Retinal blood vessel

Macula   Optic disk

The blind spot, where the optic nerve leaves the eye, can be clearly seen as a light circular area toward the center of the image.

MUSCLES SURROUNDING RIGHT EYE

Medial rectus   Superior oblique   Trochlea

Levator palpebrae superioris   Superior rectus

Annular tendon

Inferior rectus   Lateral rectus

Inferior oblique

Ear

THE EAR IS THE ORGAN OF HEARING AND BALANCE. The outer ear consists of a flap called the auricle or pinna and the auditory canal. The main functional parts—the middle and inner ears—are enclosed within the skull. The middle ear consists of three tiny bones, known as auditory ossicles, and the eustachian tube, which links the ear to the back of the nose. The inner ear consists of the spiral-shaped cochlea, and also the semicircular canals and the vestibule, which are the organs of balance. Sound waves entering the ear travel through the auditory canal to the tympanic membrane (eardrum), where they are converted to vibrations that are transmitted via the ossicles to the cochlea. Here, the vibrations are converted by millions of microscopic hairs into electrical nerve signals to be interpreted by the brain.

RIGHT AURICLE (PINNA)

Upper crux of antihelix

Auricle (pinna)

Triangular fossa

Scaphoid fossa

Lower crux of antihelix

Concha

Helix

Auditory canal

Antihelix

Antitragus

Tragus

Intertragic notch

External auditory meatus

Cartilaginous part of meatus

Lobule

Lobule

Temporal bone

Cartilage of auricle

Mastoid process

OSSICLES OF MIDDLE EAR

MALLEUS (HAMMER)   INCUS (ANVIL)   STAPES (STIRRUP)

These three tiny bones connect to form a bridge between the tympanic membrane and the oval window. With a system of membranes they convey sound vibrations to the inner ear.

INTERNAL STRUCTURE OF AMPULLA

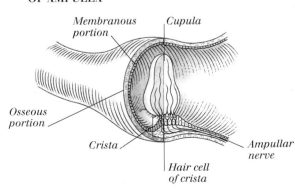

Membranous portion

Cupula

Osseous portion

Crista

Ampullar nerve

Hair cell of crista

LABYRINTH

Osseous (bony) part of meatus

Tympanic membrane (eardrum)

Semicircular canal

Vestibulocochlear nerve

Cochlea

Tensor tympani muscle

Utricle

Saccule

Common crus

Anterior semicircular canal

Lateral semicircular canal

Ampulla

Vestibular nerve

Tympanic canal

Median canal

Vestibular canal

Cochlea

Cochlear nerve

Oval window

Posterior semicircular canal

Internal carotid artery

Eustachian tube

Styloid process

SECTION THROUGH COCHLEA

Organ of Corti

Median canal

Vestibular canal

Vestibular membrane

Spirul ganglion

Cochlear nerve

Hair cells

Tympanic canal

Basilar membrane

Nose, mouth, and throat

WITH EVERY BREATH, air passes through the nasal cavity down the pharynx (throat), larynx ("voice box"), and trachea (windpipe) to the lungs. The nasal cavity warms and moistens air, and the tiny layers in its lining protect the airway against damage by foreign bodies. During swallowing, the tongue moves up and back, the larynx rises, the epiglottis closes off the entrance to the trachea, and the soft palate separates the nasal cavity from the pharynx. Saliva, secreted from three pairs of salivary glands, lubricates food to make swallowing easier; it also begins the chemical breakdown of food, and helps to produce taste. The senses of taste and smell are closely linked. Both depend on the detection of dissolved molecules by sensory receptors in the olfactory nerve endings of the nose and in the taste buds of the tongue.

STRUCTURE OF TONGUE

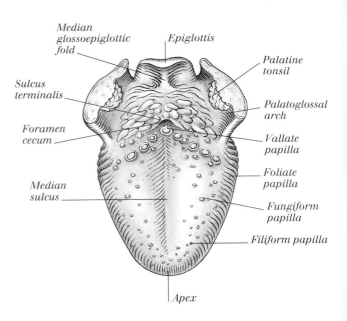

Median glossoepiglottic fold

Epiglottis

Palatine tonsil

Sulcus terminalis

Palatoglossal arch

Foramen cecum

Vallate papilla

Foliate papilla

Median sulcus

Fungiform papilla

Filiform papilla

Apex

STRUCTURES SURROUNDING PHARYNX

Lingual nerve

Tongue

Styloglossus muscle

Hyoglossus muscle

Sublingual gland

Hypoglossal nerve

Mandible (lower jaw)

Superior laryngeal nerve

Submandibular gland

Superior thyroid artery

Hyoid bone

Laryngeal prominence (Adam's apple)

Thyrohyoid muscle

Thyrohyoid membrane

Cricothyroid muscle

Cricothyroid ligament

Thyroid gland

Trachea

TASTE AREAS ON TONGUE

Bitter

Sour

Salt

Sweet

TYPES OF PAPILLAE

FILIFORM PAPILLAE   FUNGIFORM PAPILLAE   VALLATE PAPILLAE

SECTION THROUGH NOSE, MOUTH, AND THROAT

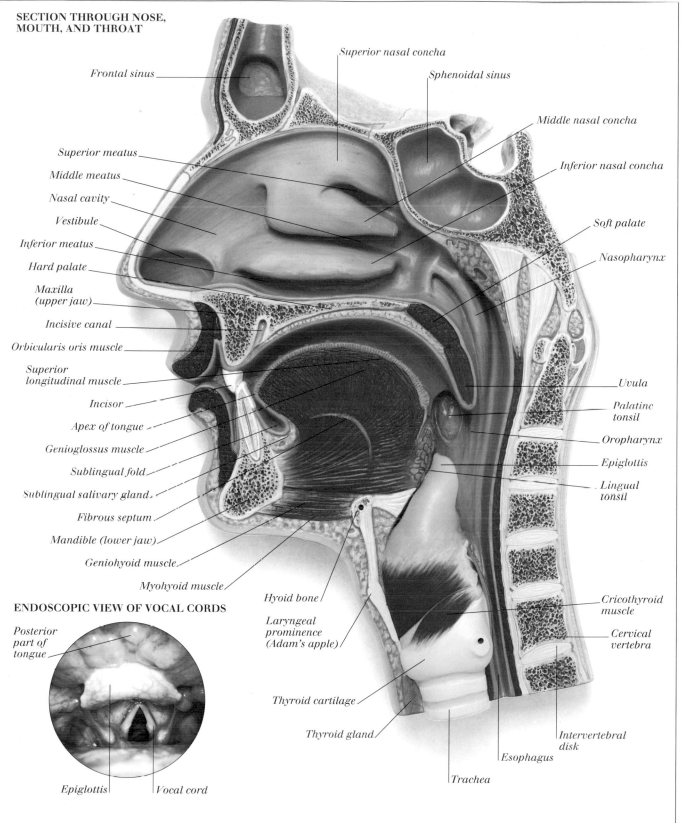

Frontal sinus

Superior nasal concha

Sphenoidal sinus

Middle nasal concha

Inferior nasal concha

Superior meatus

Middle meatus

Nasal cavity

Vestibule

Soft palate

Inferior meatus

Nasopharynx

Hard palate

Maxilla (upper jaw)

Incisive canal

Orbicularis oris muscle

Superior longitudinal muscle

Uvula

Incisor

Palatine tonsil

Apex of tongue

Oropharynx

Genioglossus muscle

Epiglottis

Sublingual fold

Lingual tonsil

Sublingual salivary gland

Fibrous septum

Mandible (lower jaw)

Geniohyoid muscle

Myohyoid muscle

Cricothyroid muscle

ENDOSCOPIC VIEW OF VOCAL CORDS

Hyoid bone

Cervical vertebra

Posterior part of tongue

Laryngeal prominence (Adam's apple)

Thyroid cartilage

Intervertebral disk

Thyroid gland

Esophagus

Epiglottis

Vocal cord

Trachea

Teeth

THE 20 PRIMARY TEETH (also called deciduous or milk teeth) usually begin to erupt when a baby is about six months old. They start to be replaced by the permanent teeth when the child is about six years old. By the age of 20, most adults have a full set of 32 teeth although the third molars (commonly called wisdom teeth) may never erupt. While teeth help people to speak clearly and give shape to the face, their main function is the chewing of food. Incisors and canines shear and tear the food into pieces; premolars and molars crush and grind it further. Although tooth enamel is the hardest substance in the body, it tends to be eroded and destroyed by acid produced in the mouth during the breakdown of food.

DEVELOPMENT OF TEETH IN A FETUS

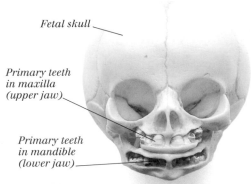

Fetal skull

Primary teeth in maxilla (upper jaw)

Primary teeth in mandible (lower jaw)

FETAL JAWS
By the sixth week of embryonic development areas of thickening occur in each jaw; these areas give rise to tooth buds. By the time the fetus is six months old, enamel has formed on the tooth buds.

DEVELOPMENT OF JAW AND TEETH

Maxilla (upper jaw)

Mandible (lower jaw)

A NEWBORN BABY'S JAWS
The primary teeth can be seen developing in the jawbones; they begin to erupt around the age of six months.

A FIVE-YEAR-OLD CHILD'S TEETH
There is a full set of 20 erupted primary teeth; the permanent teeth can be seen developing in the upper and lower jaws.

A NINE-YEAR-OLD CHILD'S TEETH
Most of the teeth are primary teeth but the permanent incisors and first molars have now emerged.

AN ADULT'S TEETH
By the age of 20, the full set of 32 permanent teeth (including the wisdom teeth) should be in position.

THE PERMANENT TEETH

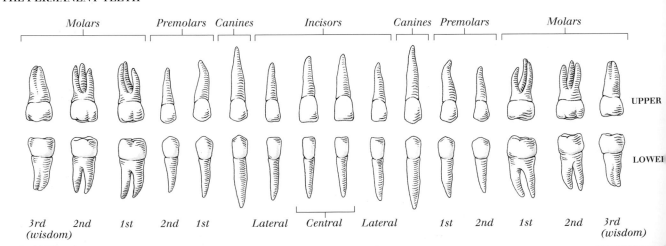

Molars | Premolars | Canines | Incisors | Canines | Premolars | Molars

UPPER

LOWER

3rd (wisdom) | 2nd | 1st | 2nd | 1st | Lateral | Central | Lateral | 1st | 2nd | 1st | 2nd | 3rd (wisdom)

STRUCTURE OF A TOOTH

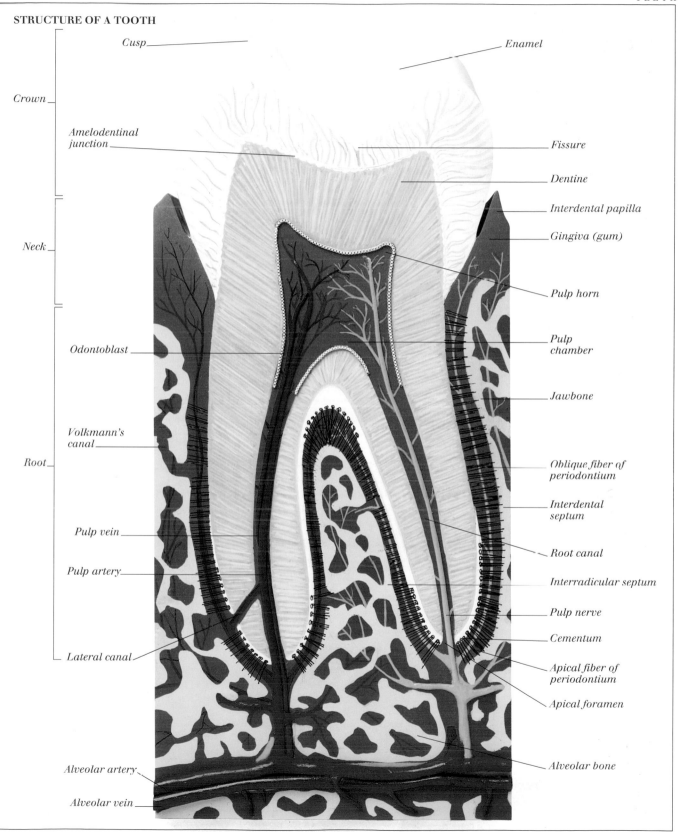

Cusp

Enamel

Crown

Amelodentinal junction

Fissure

Dentine

Interdental papilla

Gingiva (gum)

Neck

Pulp horn

Odontoblast

Pulp chamber

Jawbone

Volkmann's canal

Oblique fiber of periodontium

Interdental septum

Root

Pulp vein

Root canal

Pulp artery

Interradicular septum

Pulp nerve

Cementum

Lateral canal

Apical fiber of periodontium

Apical foramen

Alveolar bone

Alveolar artery

Alveolar vein

Digestive system

THE DIGESTIVE SYSTEM BREAKS DOWN FOOD into particles so tiny that blood can take nourishment to all parts of the body. The system's main part is a 30-foot (9 m) tube from mouth to rectum; muscles in this alimentary canal force food along. Chewed food first travels through the esophagus to the stomach, which churns and liquidizes food before it passes through the duodenum, jejunum, and ileum—the three parts of the long, convoluted small intestine. Here, digestive juices from the gallbladder and pancreas break down food particles; many filter out into the blood through tiny fingerlike villi that line the small intestine's inner wall. Undigested food in the colon forms feces that leave the body through the anus.

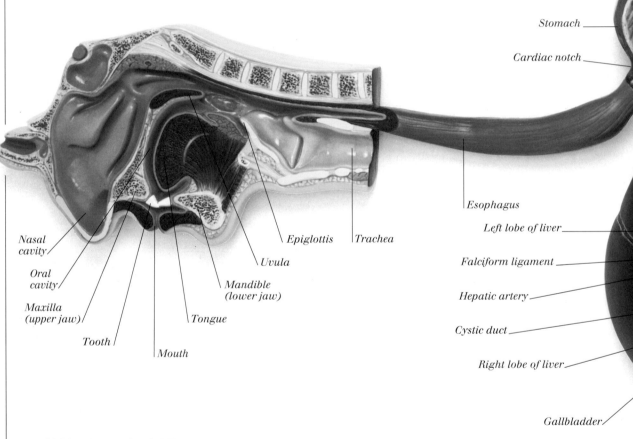

Stomach

Cardiac notch

Esophagus

Left lobe of liver

Falciform ligament

Hepatic artery

Cystic duct

Right lobe of liver

Gallbladder

Nasal cavity

Oral cavity

Maxilla (upper jaw)

Tooth

Mouth

Tongue

Mandible (lower jaw)

Uvula

Epiglottis

Trachea

ENDOSCOPIC VIEWS INSIDE ALIMENTARY CANAL

ESOPHAGUS

Mucosa

STOMACH ENTRANCE

Cardiac orifice

STOMACH

Ruga

STOMACH EXIT

Pylorus

ALIMENTARY CANAL

Fold of mucous membrane

Angular notch

Spleen

Pancreas

Peritoneum

Transverse colon

Tenia colica

Descending colon

Small intestine (jejunum and ileum)

Haustration of colon

Sigmoid colon

Anal sphincter muscle

Rectum

Anal canal

Anus

Terminal ileum

Appendix

Appendix orifice

Cecum

Ileocecal fold

Semilunar fold

Ascending colon

Pyloric sphincter muscle

Bile duct

Duodenum

Plica circulare

DUODENUM

Plica circulare

ILEUM

Villi of mucosa

COLON

Semilunar fold

Blood vessel

RECTUM

Mucosa

249

Heart

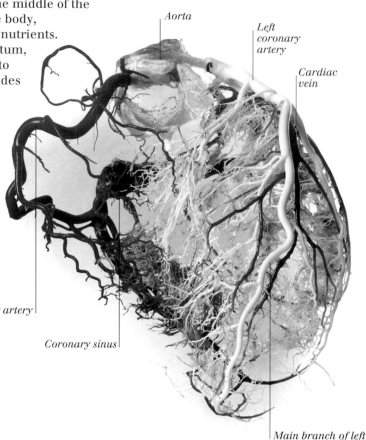

THE HEART IS A HOLLOW MUSCLE in the middle of the chest that pumps blood around the body, supplying cells with oxygen and nutrients. A muscular wall, called the septum, divides the heart lengthwise into left and right sides. A valve divides each side into two chambers: an upper atrium and a lower ventricle. When the heart muscle contracts, it squeezes blood through the atria and then through the ventricles. Oxygenated blood from the lungs flows from the pulmonary veins into the left atrium, through the left ventricle, and then out via the aorta to all parts of the body. Deoxygenated blood returning from the body flows from the vena cava into the right atrium, through the right ventricle, and then out via the pulmonary artery to the lungs for reoxygenation. At rest the heart beats between 60 and 80 times a minute; during exercise or at times of stress or excitement the rate may increase to 200 beats a minute.

ARTERIES AND VEINS SURROUNDING HEART

Aorta

Left coronary artery

Cardiac vein

Right coronary artery

Coronary sinus

Main branch of left coronary artery

SECTION THROUGH HEART WALL

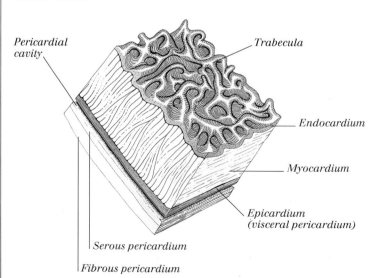

Pericardial cavity

Trabecula

Endocardium

Myocardium

Epicardium (visceral pericardium)

Serous pericardium

Fibrous pericardium

HEARTBEAT SEQUENCE

ATRIAL DIASTOLE

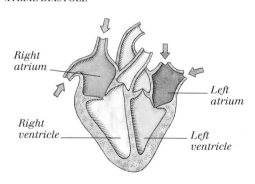

Right atrium

Left atrium

Right ventricle

Left ventricle

Deoxygenated blood enters the right atrium while the left atrium receives oxygenated blood.

STRUCTURE OF HEART

Brachiocephalic trunk

Left subclavian artery

Left common carotid artery

Superior vena cava

Ascending aorta

Right pulmonary artery

Left pulmonary vein

Pulmonary trunk

Pulmonary semilunar valve

Fossa ovalis

Coronary artery

Right pulmonary vein

Right atrium

Chordae tendineae

Opening of inferior vena cava

Muscular part of interventricular septum

Branch of coronary artery

Left ventricle

Papillary muscle

Tricuspid valve

Chordae tendineae

Myocardium of left ventricle

Right ventricle

Trabecula

ATRIAL SYSTOLE (VENTRICULAR DIASTOLE)

Right atrium contracts

Left atrium contracts

Tricuspid valve opens

Mitral valve opens

Right ventricle dilates

Left ventricle dilates

Left and right atria contract, forcing blood into the relaxed ventricles.

VENTRICULAR SYSTOLE

Pulmonary artery

Aorta

Pulmonary valve opens

Aortic valve opens

Tricuspid valve closes

Mitral valve closes

Right ventricle contracts

Left ventricle contracts

Ventricles contract and force blood to the lungs for oxygenation and via the aorta to the rest of the body.

Circulatory system

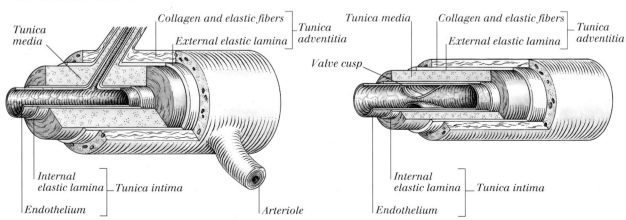

THE CIRCULATORY SYSTEM consists of the heart and blood vessels, which together maintain a continuous flow of blood around the body. The heart pumps oxygen-rich blood from the lungs to all parts of the body through a network of tubes called arteries, and smaller branches called arterioles. Blood returns to the heart via small vessels called venules, which lead in turn into larger tubes called veins. Arterioles and venules are linked by a network of tiny vessels called capillaries, where the exchange of oxygen and carbon dioxide between blood and body cells takes place. Blood has four main components: red blood cells, white blood cells, platelets, and liquid plasma.

ARTERIAL SYSTEM OF BRAIN

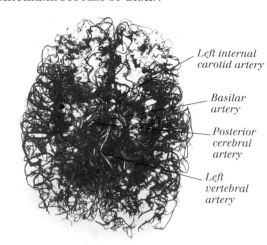

Left internal carotid artery

Basilar artery

Posterior cerebral artery

Left vertebral artery

CIRCULATORY SYSTEM OF LIVER

Inferior vena cava

Portal vein

Common bile duct

Hepatic artery

Gallbladder

CIRCULATORY SYSTEM OF HEART AND LUNGS

Superior vena cava

Aorta

Right ventricle

Left ventricle

SECTION OF MAIN ARTERY

Tunica media

Collagen and elastic fibers

External elastic lamina

Tunica adventitia

Internal elastic lamina

Tunica intima

Endothelium

Arteriole

SECTION OF MAIN VEIN

Tunica media

Collagen and elastic fibers

External elastic lamina

Tunica adventitia

Valve cusp

Internal elastic lamina

Tunica intima

Endothelium

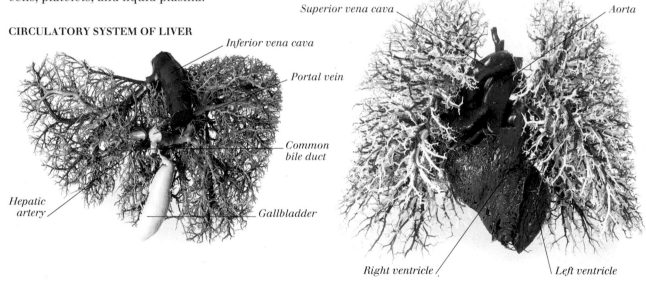

PRINCIPAL ARTERIES AND VEINS OF CIRCULATORY SYSTEM

Common carotid artery

Subclavian artery

Arch of aorta

Axillary artery

Pulmonary artery

Coronary artery

Brachial artery

Gastric artery

Hepatic artery

Splenic artery

Superior mesenteric artery

Radial artery

Ulnar artery

Palmar arch

Digital artery

Common iliac artery

External iliac artery

Internal iliac artery

Femoral artery

Popliteal artery

Peroneal artery

Anterior tibial artery

Posterior tibial artery

Lateral plantar artery

Dorsal metatarsal artery

Internal jugular vein

Brachiocephalic vein

Subclavian vein

Axillary vein

Cephalic vein

Superior vena cava

Pulmonary vein

Basilic vein

Hepatic portal vein

Median cubital vein

Inferior vena cava

Anterior median vein

Gastroepiploic vein

Palmar vein

Digital vein

Inferior mesenteric vein

Superior mesenteric vein

Common iliac vein

External iliac vein

Internal iliac vein

Femoral vein

Great saphenous vein

Short saphenous vein

Dorsal venous arch

Digital vein

TYPES OF BLOOD CELLS

RED BLOOD CELLS
These cells are biconcave in shape to maximize their oxygen-carrying capacity.

WHITE BLOOD CELLS
Lymphocytes are the smallest white blood cells; they form antibodies against disease.

PLATELETS
Tiny cells that are activated whenever blood clotting or repair to vessels is necessary.

BLOOD CLOTTING

Filaments of fibrin enmesh red blood cells as part of the process of blood clotting.

Respiratory system

THE RESPIRATORY SYSTEM supplies the oxygen needed by body cells and carries off their carbon dioxide waste. Inhaled air passes via the trachea (windpipe) through two narrower tubes, the bronchi, to the lungs. Each lung comprises many fine, branching tubes called bronchioles that end in tiny clustered chambers called alveoli. Gases cross the thin alveolar walls to and from a network of tiny blood vessels. Intercostal (rib) muscles and the muscular diaphragm below the lungs operate the lungs like bellows, drawing air in and forcing it out at regular intervals.

BRONCHIOLE AND ALVEOLI

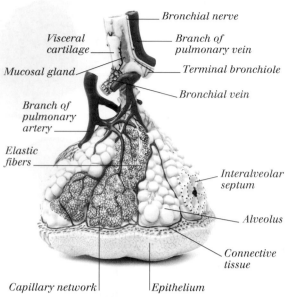

- Bronchial nerve
- Visceral cartilage
- Mucosal gland
- Branch of pulmonary vein
- Terminal bronchiole
- Bronchial vein
- Branch of pulmonary artery
- Elastic fibers
- Interalveolar septum
- Alveolus
- Connective tissue
- Capillary network
- Epithelium

SEGMENTS OF BRONCHIAL TREE

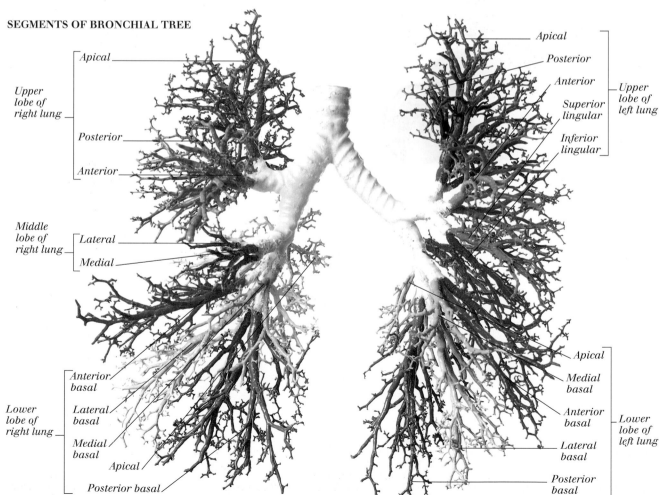

Upper lobe of right lung
- Apical
- Posterior
- Anterior

Middle lobe of right lung
- Lateral
- Medial

Lower lobe of right lung
- Anterior basal
- Lateral basal
- Medial basal
- Apical
- Posterior basal

Upper lobe of left lung
- Apical
- Posterior
- Anterior
- Superior lingular
- Inferior lingular

Lower lobe of left lung
- Apical
- Medial basal
- Anterior basal
- Lateral basal
- Posterior basal

STRUCTURES OF THORACIC CAVITY

Epiglottis

Hyoid bone

Thyroid cartilage

Thyroid gland

Cricoid cartilage

Apex of lung

Trachea

Superior vena cava

Aorta

Upper lobe of right lung

Upper lobe of left lung

Horizontal fissure

Pulmonary trunk

Oblique fissure

Left pulmonary artery

Heart

Lower lobe of left lung

Secondary bronchus

Tertiary bronchus

Lower lobe of right lung

Middle lobe of right lung

Right crus of diaphragm

Abdominal aorta

Left crus of diaphragm

Esophagus

Muscular wall of diaphragm

GASEOUS EXCHANGE IN ALVEOLUS

Oxygen diffuses into blood

Oxygenated blood

Alveolus

Deoxygenated blood rich in carbon dioxide

Carbon dioxide diffuses from blood into alveolus

MECHANISM OF RESPIRATION
INSPIRATION

Lung expands

Air drawn into lungs

Diaphragm contracts and flattens

Intercostal muscles contract

EXPIRATION

Lung contracts

Air forced out of lungs

Diaphragm relaxes and moves up

Intercostal muscles relax

Urinary system

THE URINARY SYSTEM FILTERS WASTE PRODUCTS from the blood and removes them from the body via a system of tubes. Blood is filtered in the two kidneys, which are fist-sized, bean-shaped organs. The renal arteries carry blood to the kidneys; the renal veins remove blood after filtering. Each kidney contains about one million tiny units called nephrons. Each nephron is made up of a tubule and a filtering unit called a glomerulus, which consists of a collection of tiny blood vessels surrounded by the hollow Bowman's capsule. The filtering process produces a watery fluid that leaves the kidney as urine. The urine is carried via two tubes called ureters to the bladder, where it is stored until its release from the body through another tube called the urethra.

ARTERIAL SYSTEM OF KIDNEYS

Aorta

Celiac trunk

Superior mesenteric artery

Right renal artery

Left renal artery

Right ureter

Left ureter

SECTION THROUGH LEFT KIDNEY

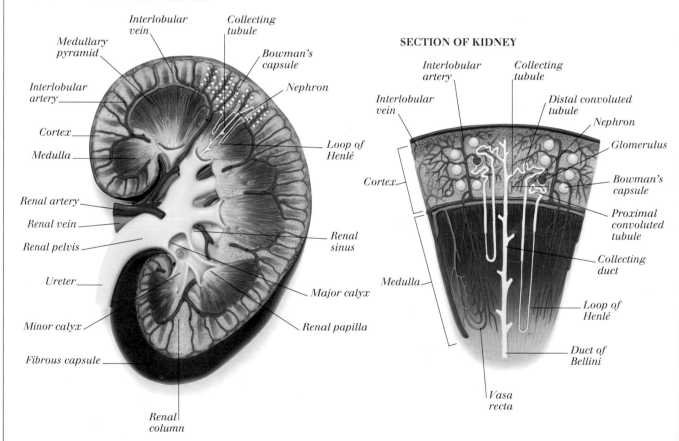

Medullary pyramid

Interlobular vein

Collecting tubule

Bowman's capsule

Nephron

Interlobular artery

Cortex

Medulla

Renal artery

Renal vein

Renal pelvis

Ureter

Minor calyx

Fibrous capsule

Renal column

Loop of Henlé

Renal sinus

Major calyx

Renal papilla

SECTION OF KIDNEY

Interlobular artery

Collecting tubule

Interlobular vein

Distal convoluted tubule

Nephron

Glomerulus

Bowman's capsule

Cortex

Proximal convoluted tubule

Collecting duct

Medulla

Loop of Henlé

Duct of Bellini

Vasa recta

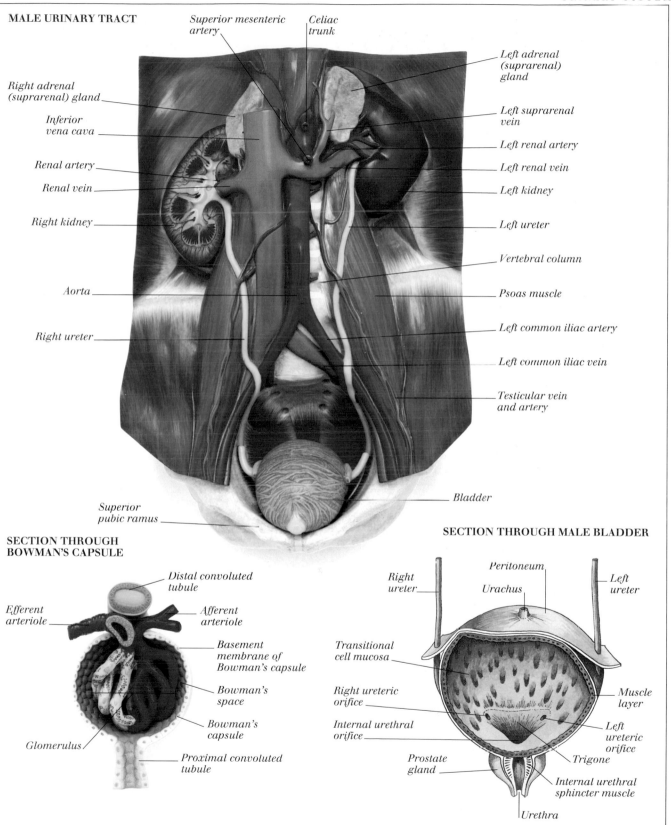

MALE URINARY TRACT

Superior mesenteric artery

Celiac trunk

Left adrenal (suprarenal) gland

Right adrenal (suprarenal) gland

Inferior vena cava

Left suprarenal vein

Left renal artery

Renal artery

Left renal vein

Renal vein

Left kidney

Right kidney

Left ureter

Vertebral column

Aorta

Psoas muscle

Right ureter

Left common iliac artery

Left common iliac vein

Testicular vein and artery

Bladder

Superior pubic ramus

SECTION THROUGH BOWMAN'S CAPSULE

Distal convoluted tubule

Efferent arteriole

Afferent arteriole

Basement membrane of Bowman's capsule

Bowman's space

Bowman's capsule

Glomerulus

Proximal convoluted tubule

SECTION THROUGH MALE BLADDER

Right ureter

Peritoneum

Urachus

Left ureter

Transitional cell mucosa

Right ureteric orifice

Muscle layer

Internal urethral orifice

Left ureteric orifice

Prostate gland

Trigone

Internal urethral sphincter muscle

Urethra

257

Reproductive system

SEX ORGANS LOCATED IN THE PELVIS create new human lives. Each month a ripe egg is released from one of the female's ovaries into a fallopian tube leading to the uterus (womb), a muscular pear-sized organ. A male produces minute tadpole-like sperm in two oval glands called testes. When the male is ready to release sperm into the female's vagina, many millions pass into his urethra and leave his body through the fleshy penis. The sperm travel up through the vagina into the uterus and fallopian tubes, and one sperm may enter and fertilize an egg. The fertilized egg becomes embedded in the uterus wall and starts to grow into a new human being.

SECTION THROUGH OVARY

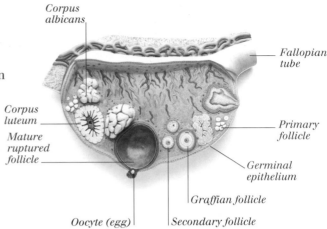

Corpus albicans

Corpus luteum

Mature ruptured follicle

Oocyte (egg)

Fallopian tube

Primary follicle

Germinal epithelium

Graffian follicle

Secondary follicle

SECTION THROUGH FEMALE PELVIC REGION

Ureter

Ampulla of fallopian tube

Fimbria of fallopian tube

Isthmus of fallopian tube

Ovary

Fundus of uterus

Uterus (womb)

Cervix (neck of uterus)

Os

Rectum

Vagina

Anus

Perineum

Bladder

Pubic symphysis

Urethra

Clitoris

External urinary meatus

Labia minora

Labia majora

Introitus (vaginal opening)

FEMALE REPRODUCTIVE ORGANS

Fallopian tube

Fundus of uterus

Isthmus of fallopian tube

Ovarian ligament

Ampulla of fallopian tube

Ovary

Body of uterus (womb)

Fimbria of fallopian tube

Os

Cervix (neck of uterus)

Vagina

MALE REPRODUCTIVE ORGANS

External spermatic fascia

Prostate gland

Ductus vas deferens

Seminal vesicle

Cremasteric fascia

Bulbourethral gland

Internal spermatic fascia

Urethra

Epididymis

Corpus spongiosum

Testis (testicle)

Corpus cavernosum

Scrotum

Prepuce (foreskin)

Glans penis

Urethral opening

SECTION THROUGH MALE PELVIC REGION

Intervertebral disk

Ureter

EXTERNAL STRUCTURE OF SPERM

Acrosomal cap

Head

Mitochondrial sheath

Terminal ring

Tailpiece

Flagellum

Colon

Sacrum

Bladder

Pubis of pelvis

Prostate gland

Seminal vesicle

Penis

Ejaculatory duct

Corpus cavernosum

Corpus spongiosum

Urethra

Epididymis

Glans penis

Testis (testicle)

Scrotum

259

Development of a baby

A FERTILIZED EGG IS NOURISHED AND PROTECTED as it develops into an embryo and then a fetus during the 40 weeks of pregnancy. The placenta, a mass of blood vessels implanted in the uterus lining, delivers nourishment and oxygen, and removes waste through the umbilical cord. Meanwhile, the fetus lies snugly in its amniotic sac, a bag of fluid that protects it against any sudden jolts. In the last weeks of the pregnancy, the rapidly growing fetus turns head down: a baby ready to be born.

EMBRYO AT FIVE WEEKS

Rudimentary ear

Rudimentary eye

Rudimentary mouth

Tail bud

Leg bud

Heart bulge

Arm bud

Rudimentary liver

Rudimentary vertebra

Amniotic fluid

Umbilicus (navel)

Uterine wall

Fetus

SECTION THROUGH PLACENTA

Umbilical cord

Amnion

Umbilical vein

Umbilical artery

Fetal blood vessels

Chorionic plate

Chorion

Trophoblast

Chorionic villus

Pool of maternal blood

Septum

Decidual plate

Maternal blood vessel

Myometrium

SECTION THROUGH PELVIS IN NINTH MONTH OF PREGNANCY

THE DEVELOPING FETUS

Intervertebral disk

Vertebra

Spinal cord

Bladder

Cervix

Rectum

Anus

Pubic bone

Vagina

Urethra

Uterine wall

Placenta

Fallopian tube

Fetus

SECOND MONTH
All the internal organs have developed by this stage.

Umbilical cord

THIRD MONTH
The fetus is fully formed and now begins a period of rapid growth.

FIFTH MONTH
Although the fetus here is in breech (bottom down) position, it will probably turn by 180° before birth. By the fifth month the baby is moving actively and responds to sound.

Cervix

SEVENTH MONTH
The internal organs are maturing in preparation for life outside the uterus. The baby has grown to such a size that there is less room for movement within the uterus.

Placenta

261

GEOLOGY, GEOGRAPHY, AND METEOROLGY

Earth's physical features

MOST OF THE EARTH'S SURFACE (about 70 percent) is covered with water. The largest single body of water, the Pacific Ocean, alone covers about 30 percent of the surface. Most of the land is distributed as seven continents; these are (from largest to smallest) Asia, Africa, North America, South America, Antarctica, Europe, and Australasia. The physical features of the land are remarkably varied. Among the most notable are mountain ranges, rivers, and deserts. The largest mountain ranges—the Himalayas in Asia and the Andes in South America—extend for thousands of miles. The Himalayas include the world's highest mountain, Mount Everest (29,029 feet). The longest rivers are the River Nile in Africa (4,160 miles) and the Amazon River in South America (4,000 miles). Deserts cover about 20 percent of the total land area. The largest is the Sahara, which covers nearly a third of Africa. The Earth's surface features can be represented in various ways. Only a globe can correctly represent areas, shapes, sizes, and directions, because there is always distortion when a spherical surface like the Earth's is projected onto the flat surface of a map. Each map projection is therefore a compromise: some aspects of global features are shown accurately by allowing others to be distorted. Even satellite mapping does not produce completely accurate maps, although they can show physical features with great clarity.

EXAMPLES OF MAP PROJECTIONS

CYLINDRICAL
PROJECTION

CYLINDRICAL-
PROJECTION MAP

SATELLITE MAPPING OF THE EARTH

Satellite takes photographs of the Earth

Solar panel

Earth's rotation

Antenna

Earth

Polar orbit of satellite

Area of Earth's surface on each photograph

Composite picture of Earth created from thousands of separate images

180° 160° 120° 80°

Great Slave Lake
Great Bear Lake
Lake Superior
Greenland
Mackenzie-Peace River
Baffin Island
Bering Sea
Hudson Bay
Rocky Mountains
NORTH AMERICA
Mississippi-Missouri River
Lake Huron
Lake Ontario
Lake Erie
Lake Michigan
Sonoran Desert
Appalachian Mountains
Sierra Madre
ATLANTIC OCEAN
Gulf of Mexico
Chihuahuan Desert
Caribbean Sea
Guiana Highlands
Amazon River
Brazil Highlo
PACIFIC OCEAN
Andes
Atacama Desert
Mato Gross.
Gran Chaco
Parana River
Pampas
Patagonia

120° 80°

180° 160°

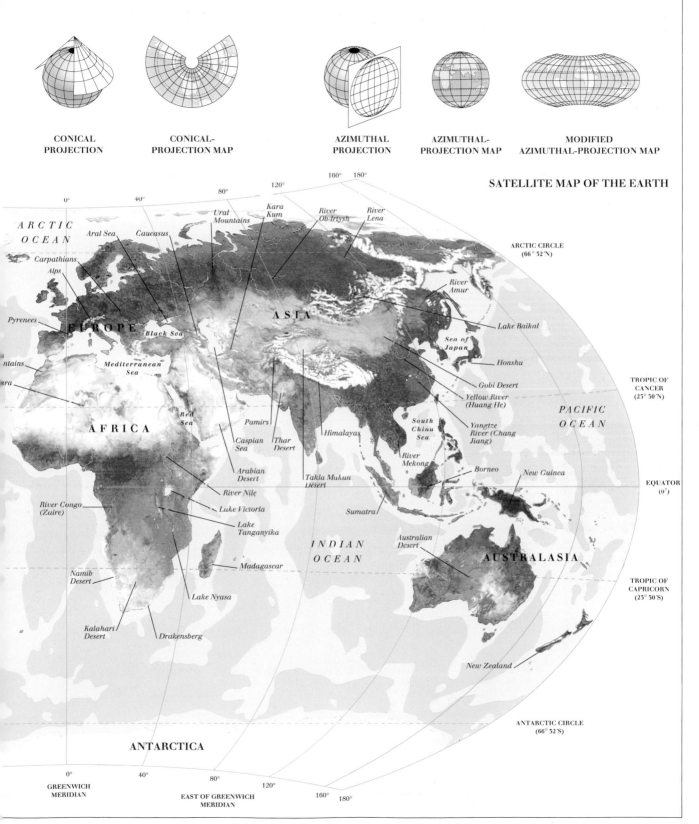

CONICAL PROJECTION

CONICAL-PROJECTION MAP

AZIMUTHAL PROJECTION

AZIMUTHAL-PROJECTION MAP

MODIFIED AZIMUTHAL-PROJECTION MAP

SATELLITE MAP OF THE EARTH

160° 180°
120°
80°
40°
0°

Urat Mountains
Kara Kum
River Ob-Irtysh
River Lena

ARCTIC OCEAN

Aral Sea
Caucasus

ARCTIC CIRCLE
(66° 32´N)

Carpathians
Alps

River Amur

Pyrenees

ASIA

EUROPE

Black Sea

Lake Baikal

ntains

Mediterranean Sea

Sea of Japan

ra

Honshu

TROPIC OF CANCER
(23° 30´N)

Red Sea

Gobi Desert

AFRICA

Pamirs

Himalayas

Yellow River (Huang He)

South China Sea

PACIFIC OCEAN

Caspian Sea
Thar Desert

Yangtze River (Chang Jiang)

Arabian Desert

Takla Makan Desert

River Mekong

River Nile
Lake Victoria

Borneo

New Guinea

EQUATOR
(0°)

River Congo (Zaire)

Lake Tanganyika

Sumatra

Australian Desert

INDIAN OCEAN

Madagascar

AUSTRALASIA

Namib Desert

Lake Nyasa

TROPIC OF CAPRICORN
(23° 30´S)

Kalahari Desert

Drakensberg

New Zealand

ANTARCTIC CIRCLE
(66° 32´S)

ANTARCTICA

0°
40°
80°
120°
160° 180°

GREENWICH MERIDIAN

EAST OF GREENWICH MERIDIAN

The rock cycle

THE ROCK CYCLE IS A CONTINUOUS PROCESS through which old rocks are transformed into new ones. Rocks can be divided into three main groups: igneous, sedimentary, and metamorphic. Igneous rocks are formed when magma (molten rock) from the Earth's interior cools and solidifies (see pp. 274-275). Sedimentary rocks are formed when sediment (rock particles, for example) becomes compressed and cemented together in a process known as lithification (see pp. 276-277). Metamorphic rocks are formed when igneous, sedimentary, or other metamorphic rocks are changed by heat or pressure (see pp. 274-275). Rocks are added to the Earth's surface by crustal movements and volcanic activity. Once exposed on the surface, the rocks are broken down into rock particles by weathering (see pp. 282-283). The particles are then transported by glaciers, rivers, and wind and are deposited as sediment in lakes, deltas, deserts, and on the ocean floor. Some of this sediment undergoes lithification and forms sedimentary rock. This rock may be thrust back to the surface by crustal movements or forced deeper into the Earth's interior, where heat and pressure transform it into metamorphic rock. The metamorphic rock in turn may be pushed up to the surface or may be melted to form magma. Eventually, the magma cools and solidifies—below or on the surface—forming igneous rock. When the sedimentary, igneous, and metamorphic rocks are exposed once more on the Earth's surface, the cycle begins again.

HEXAGONAL BASALT COLUMNS, ICELAND

STAGES IN THE ROCK CYCLE

Magma extruded as lava, which solidifies to form igneous rock

Lava flow

Vent

Main conduit

Secondary conduit

Lava

Ash

THE ROCK CYCLE

Igneous rock

Cooling and solidification (crystallization)

Weathering, transport, and deposition

Sediment

Heat and pressure (metamorphism)

Weathering, transport, and deposition

Weathering, transport, and deposition

Compression and cementation (lithification)

Magma

Melting

Heat and pressure (metamorphism)

Metamorphic rock

Sedimentary rock

Rock surrounding magma changed by heat to form metamorphic rock

Intense heat of rising magma melts some of the surrounding rock

Sedimentary rock crushed and folded to form metamorphic rock

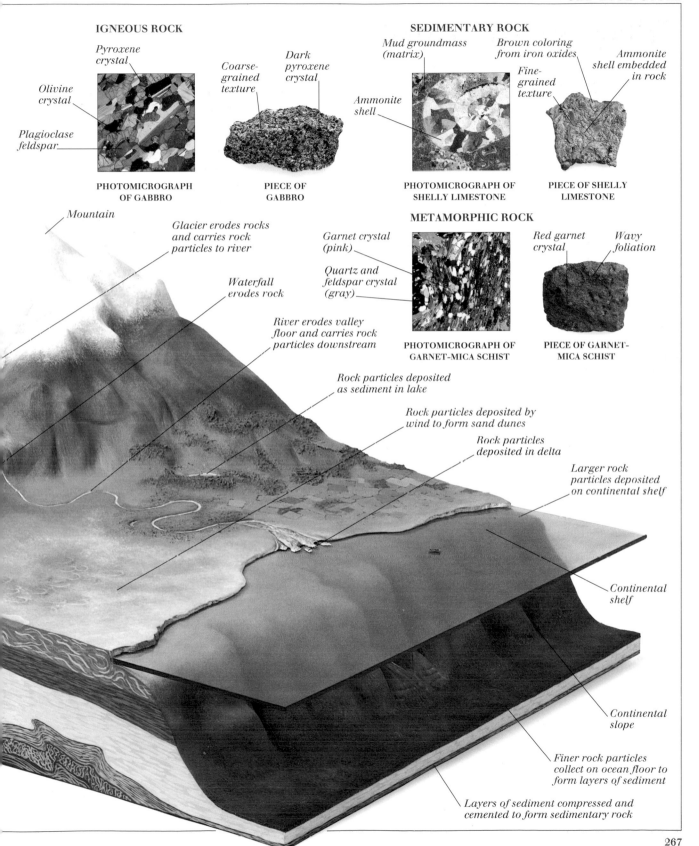

IGNEOUS ROCK

Pyroxene crystal

Olivine crystal

Plagioclase feldspar

Coarse-grained texture

Dark pyroxene crystal

PHOTOMICROGRAPH OF GABBRO

PIECE OF GABBRO

SEDIMENTARY ROCK

Mud groundmass (matrix)

Brown coloring from iron oxides

Ammonite shell

Fine-grained texture

Ammonite shell embedded in rock

PHOTOMICROGRAPH OF SHELLY LIMESTONE

PIECE OF SHELLY LIMESTONE

METAMORPHIC ROCK

Garnet crystal (pink)

Quartz and feldspar crystal (gray)

Red garnet crystal

Wavy foliation

PHOTOMICROGRAPH OF GARNET-MICA SCHIST

PIECE OF GARNET-MICA SCHIST

Mountain

Glacier erodes rocks and carries rock particles to river

Waterfall erodes rock

River erodes valley floor and carries rock particles downstream

Rock particles deposited as sediment in lake

Rock particles deposited by wind to form sand dunes

Rock particles deposited in delta

Larger rock particles deposited on continental shelf

Continental shelf

Continental slope

Finer rock particles collect on ocean floor to form layers of sediment

Layers of sediment compressed and cemented to form sedimentary rock

267

Minerals

A MINERAL IS A NATURALLY OCCURRING SUBSTANCE that has a characteristic chemical composition and specific physical properties, such as habit and streak (see pp. 270-271). A rock, by comparison, is an aggregate of minerals and need not have a specific chemical composition. Minerals are made up of elements (substances that cannot be broken down chemically into simpler substances), each of which can be represented by a chemical symbol. Minerals can be divided into two main groups: native elements and compounds. Native elements are made up of a pure element. Examples include gold (chemical symbol Au), silver (Ag), copper (Cu), and carbon (C); carbon occurs as a native element in two forms, diamond and graphite. Compounds are combinations of two or more elements. For example, sulfides are compounds of sulfur (S) and one or more other elements, such as lead (Pb) in the mineral galena, or antimony (Sb) in the mineral stibnite.

NATIVE ELEMENTS

Dendritic (branching) copper

Limonite groundmass (matrix)

COPPER
(Cu)

SULFIDES

Cubic galena crystal

GALENA
(PbS)

Dendritic (branching) gold

Quartz vein

GOLD
(Au)

White diamond

Kimberlite groundmass (matrix)

DIAMOND
(C)

Hexagonal graphite crystal

GRAPHITE
(C)

OXIDES/HYDROXIDES

Milky quartz groundmass (matrix)

Smoky quartz crystal

SMOKY QUARTZ
(SiO$_2$)

Rounded bauxite grains in groundmass (matrix)

BAUXITE
(FeO(OH) and Al$_2$O$_3$.2H$_2$O)

Mass of specular hematite crystals

SPECULAR HEMATITE
(Fe$_2$O$_3$)

Prismatic stibnite crystal

Quartz groundmass (matrix)

STIBNITE
(Sb$_2$S$_3$)

Perfect octahedral pyrites crystal

Quartz crystal

PYRITES
(FeS$_2$)

Parallel bands of onyx

ONYX
(SiO$_2$)

Kidney ore hematite

Specular crystals of hematite

KIDNEY ORE HEMATITE
(Fe$_2$O$_3$)

PHOSPHATES

Limonite groundmass (matrix)

Rock groundmass (matrix)

Radiating wavellite crystals

Prismatic pyromorphite crystals

WAVELLITE
$(Al_3(PO_4)_2(OH,F)_3.5H_2O)$

PYROMORPHITE
$(Pb_5(PO_4)_3Cl)$

CARBONATES

Striated cerussite crystal

Dog tooth calcite crystal

CERUSSITE
$(PbCO_3)$

CALCITE
$(CaCO_3)$

SULFATES

Rock groundmass (matrix)

Radiating crystal mass of daisy gypsum

Radiating cyanotrichite crystals

CYANOTRICHITE
$(Cu_4Al_2(SO_4)(OH)_{12}.2H_2O)$

DAISY GYPSUM
$(CaSO_4.2H_2O)$

MOLYBDATE

Tabular wulfenite crystal

Dark rock groundmass (matrix)

WULFENITE
$(PbMoO_4)$

SILICATES

Feldspar groundmass (matrix)

Dodecahedral sodalite crystal

Transparent bicolored tourmaline crystal

SODALITE
$(Na_8Al_6Si_6O_{24}Cl_2)$

Striated surface of olivine crystal

TOURMALINE
$(Na(Mg,Fe,Li,Mn,Al)_3Al_6(BO_3)_3Si_6.O_{18}(OH,F)_4)$

OLIVINE
$(Fe_2SiO_4 - Mg_2SiO_4)$

Striated prismatic epidote crystal

Tabular muscovite crystal

EPIDOTE
$(Ca_2(Al,Fe)_3(SiO_4)_3(OH))$

Orthoclase crystal

MUSCOVITE
$(KAl_2(Si_3Al)O_{10}(OH,F)_2)$

ORTHOCLASE
$(KAlSi_3O_8)$

HALIDES

Cubic rock salt crystal

Cubic fluorite crystal

GREEN FLUORITE
(CaF_2)

ORANGE HALITE (ROCK SALT)
$(NaCl)$

Mineral features

MINERALS CAN BE IDENTIFIED BY STUDYING features such as fracture, cleavage, crystal system, habit, hardness, color, and streak. Minerals can break in different ways. If a mineral breaks in an irregular way, leaving rough surfaces, it possesses fracture. If a mineral breaks along well-defined planes of weakness, it possesses cleavage. Specific minerals have distinctive patterns of cleavage. For example, mica cleaves along one plane. Most minerals form crystals that can be categorized into crystal systems according to their symmetry and number of faces. Within each system, several different but related forms of crystal are possible; for example, a cubic crystal can have six, eight, or twelve sides. A mineral's habit is the typical form taken by an aggregate of its crystals. Examples of habit include botryoidal (like a bunch of grapes) and massive (no definite form). The relative hardness of a mineral may be assessed by testing its resistance to scratching. This property is usually measured using Mohs' scale, which increases in hardness from 1 (talc) to 10 (diamond). The color of a mineral is not a dependable guide to its identity as some minerals have a range of colors. Streak (the color the powdered mineral makes when rubbed across an unglazed tile) is a more reliable indicator.

CLEAVAGE

Cleavage in one direction

CLEAVAGE ALONG ONE PLANE

Cleavage in three directions, forming a block cube

CLEAVAGE ALONG THREE PLANES

Horizontal cleavage

Vertical cleavage

CLEAVAGE ALONG TWO PLANES

Cleavage in four directions, forming a double-pyramid crystal

CLEAVAGE ALONG FOUR PLANES

CRYSTAL SYSTEMS

Cubic iron pyrites crystal

Tetragonal idocrase crystal

Representation of tetragonal system

TETRAGONAL SYSTEM

CUBIC SYSTEM

Representation of cubic system

Hexagonal beryl crystal

Representation of hexagonal/trigonal system

HEXAGONAL/TRIGONAL SYSTEM

Orthorhombic barite crystal

Representation of orthorhombic system

ORTHORHOMBIC SYSTEM

FRACTURE

Fire opal with conchoidal (shell-like) fracture

Nickel-iron with hackly (jagged) fracture

CONCHOIDAL FRACTURE

HACKLY FRACTURE

Orpiment with uneven fracture

Garnierite with splintery fracture

UNEVEN FRACTURE

SPLINTERY FRACTURE

Monoclinic selenite crystal

Representation of monoclinic system

Triclinic axinite crystal

MONOCLINIC SYSTEM

Representation of triclinic system

TRICLINIC SYSTEM

HABIT

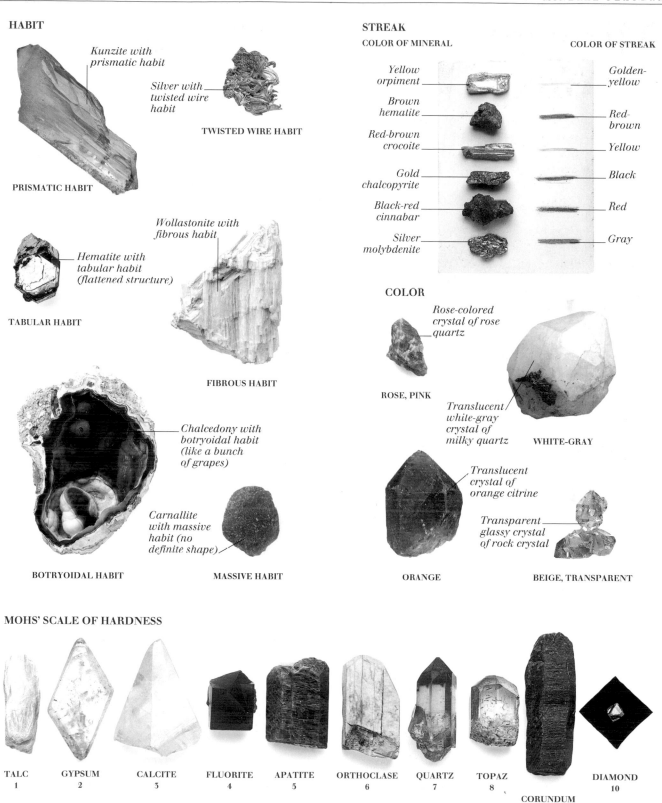

Kunzite with prismatic habit

Silver with twisted wire habit

TWISTED WIRE HABIT

PRISMATIC HABIT

Hematite with tabular habit (flattened structure)

TABULAR HABIT

Wollastonite with fibrous habit

FIBROUS HABIT

Chalcedony with botryoidal habit (like a bunch of grapes)

Carnallite with massive habit (no definite shape)

BOTRYOIDAL HABIT

MASSIVE HABIT

STREAK

COLOR OF MINERAL		COLOR OF STREAK
Yellow orpiment		Golden-yellow
Brown hematite		Red-brown
Red-brown crocoite		Yellow
Gold chalcopyrite		Black
Black-red cinnabar		Red
Silver molybdenite		Gray

COLOR

Rose-colored crystal of rose quartz

ROSE, PINK

Translucent white-gray crystal of milky quartz

WHITE-GRAY

Translucent crystal of orange citrine

Transparent glassy crystal of rock crystal

ORANGE

BEIGE, TRANSPARENT

MOHS' SCALE OF HARDNESS

TALC	GYPSUM	CALCITE	FLUORITE	APATITE	ORTHOCLASE	QUARTZ	TOPAZ	CORUNDUM	DIAMOND
1	2	3	4	5	6	7	8	9	10

Volcanoes

VOLCANOES ARE VENTS OR FISSURES IN THE EARTH'S crust through which magma (molten rock that originates from deep beneath the crust) is forced onto the surface as lava. They occur most commonly along the boundaries of crustal plates; most volcanoes lie in a belt called the "Ring of Fire," which runs along the edge of the Pacific Ocean. Volcanoes can be classified according to the violence and frequency of their eruptions.

Nonexplosive volcanic eruptions generally occur where crustal plates pull apart. These eruptions produce runny basaltic lava that spreads quickly over a wide area to form relatively flat cones. The most violent eruptions take place where plates collide. Such eruptions produce thick rhyolitic lava and may also blast out clouds of dust and pyroclasts (lava fragments). The lava does not flow far before cooling and therefore builds up steep-sided, conical volcanoes. Some volcanoes produce lava and ash eruptions, which build up composite volcanic cones. Volcanoes that erupt frequently are described as active, those that erupt rarely are termed dormant, and those that have stopped erupting altogether are termed extinct. Besides the volcanoes themselves, other features associated with volcanic regions include geysers, hot mineral springs, solfataras, fumaroles, and bubbling mud pools.

Folded, rope-like surface

PAHOEHOE
(ROPY LAVA)

HORU GEYSER,
NEW ZEALAND

VOLCANO TYPES

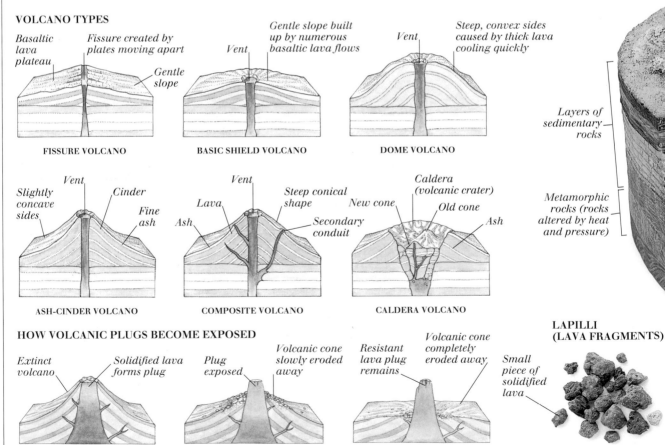

Basaltic lava plateau

Fissure created by plates moving apart

Gentle slope

FISSURE VOLCANO

Gentle slope built up by numerous basaltic lava flows

Vent

BASIC SHIELD VOLCANO

Vent

Steep, convex sides caused by thick lava cooling quickly

DOME VOLCANO

Slightly concave sides

Vent

Cinder

Fine ash

ASH-CINDER VOLCANO

Vent

Lava

Ash

Steep conical shape

Secondary conduit

COMPOSITE VOLCANO

Caldera (volcanic crater)

New cone

Old cone

Ash

CALDERA VOLCANO

Layers of sedimentary rocks

Metamorphic rocks (rocks altered by heat and pressure)

HOW VOLCANIC PLUGS BECOME EXPOSED

Extinct volcano

Solidified lava forms plug

PLUG FORMATION

Plug exposed

Volcanic cone slowly eroded away

INITIAL EROSION AROUND PLUG

Resistant lava plug remains

Volcanic cone completely eroded away

COMPLETE DENUDATION OF PLUG

LAPILLI
(LAVA FRAGMENTS)

Small piece of solidified lava

272

TYPES OF LAVA

Scoria (sharp, angular chunks)

Driblets of lava from roof of tunnel

AA (BLOCKY LAVA)

REMELTED LAVA

LOCATION OF VOLCANOES

▲ Volcano   ⊢╫⊣ Plate boundary

STRUCTURE OF A VOLCANO

Steeply sloping cone consisting of numerous layers of ash and lava

Laccolith

Secondary conduit

Vent

Plug (solidified lava)

Main conduit

Volcanic ash

Cinder cone

Parasitic cone

Mineral spring

Magma reservoir

Lava flow

Groundwater

VOLCANIC FEATURES

Sulfurous gases

Jet of hot water and steam

Water heated by hot rocks

Steam pressure builds up

Hot water

Mud and surface deposits mixed with hot water

Superheated water

Steam

SOLFATARA

GEYSER

MUD POOL

FUMAROLE

Igneous and metamorphic rocks

IGNEOUS ROCKS ARE FORMED WHEN MAGMA (molten rock that originates from deep beneath the Earth's crust) cools and solidifies. There are two main types of igneous rock: intrusive and extrusive. Intrusive rocks are formed deep underground, where magma is forced into cracks or between rock layers to form structures including sills, dikes, and batholiths. The magma cools slowly to form coarse-grained rocks such as gabbro and pegmatite. Extrusive rocks are formed above the Earth's surface from lava (magma that has been ejected in a volcanic eruption). The molten lava cools quickly, producing fine-grained rocks such as rhyolite and basalt. Metamorphic rocks are those that have been altered by intense heat (contact metamorphism) or extreme pressure (regional metamorphism). Contact metamorphism occurs when rocks are changed by heat from, for example, an igneous intrusion or lava flow. Regional metamorphism occurs when rock is crushed in the middle of a folding mountain range. Metamorphic rocks can be formed from igneous rocks, sedimentary rocks, or even other metamorphic rocks.

BASALT COLUMNS

IGNEOUS ROCK STRUCTURES

Cinder cone

Large eroded lava flow

Cedar tree laccolith

Butte

Plug

Cone sheet

Ring dike

Batholith

Dike

Sill

Dike swarm

Lopolith

CONTACT METAMORPHISM

Metamorphic aureole (region where contact metamorphism occurs)

Hot igneous intrusion

Limestone

Shale

Marble (metamorphosed limestone)

Slate (metamorphosed shale)

REGIONAL METAMORPHISM

Mountain range

Slate, formed under low pressure and temperature

Compression

Compression

Crust

Mantle

Magma

Schist, formed under medium pressure and temperature

Gneiss, formed under high pressure and temperature

EXAMPLES OF METAMORPHIC ROCKS

Pale feldspar

Dark mica

Dark mineral band

Pale calcite

GNEISS

FOLDED SCHIST

SKARN

EXAMPLES OF EXTRUSIVE IGNEOUS ROCKS

Porphyritic texture

Fine-grained crystals

Elongated vesicles (gas cavities)

Fine-grained groundmass (matrix)

Conchoidal fracture

Glassy luster

RHYOLITE

BASALT

PUMICE

PORPHYRITIC ANDESITE

OBSIDIAN

Mesa (flat-topped plateau)

Extinct geyser

Lake

Caldera

Sea

Lava flow

Vent

Active juvenile volcano

Parasitic volcano

Main conduit

Sagging caused by weight of volcano

Eroded plug of extinct volcano

Magma reservoir

Batholith

Laccolith

EXAMPLES OF INTRUSIVE IGNEOUS ROCKS

Dark groundmass (matrix)

KIMBERLITE

Plagioclase feldspar

OLIVINE GABBRO

Amphibole crystals

White feldspar

FELDSPAR PEGMATITE

Fine groundmass (matrix)

Pyrites crystal

SLATE WITH PYRITES

Chiastolite crystal

CHIASTOLITE HORNFELS

Green calc-silicate mineral

GREEN MARBLE

High quartz content

HALLEFLINTA

Amphibole crystal

SYENITE

Sedimentary rocks

SEDIMENTARY ROCKS ARE FORMED BY THE ACCUMULATION and consolidation of sediments (see pp. 266-267). There are three main types of sedimentary rock: clastic sedimentary rocks, such as breccia or sandstone, are formed from other rocks that have been broken down into fragments by weathering (see pp. 282-283), which have then been transported and deposited elsewhere; organic sedimentary rocks, such as coal (see pp. 280-281), are derived from plant and animal remains; and chemical sedimentary rocks are formed by chemical processes. For example, rock salt is formed when salt dissolved in water is deposited as the water evaporates. Sedimentary rocks are laid down in layers called beds, or strata. Each new layer is laid down horizontally over older ones. There are usually some gaps in the sequence, called unconformities. These represent periods in which no new sediments were being laid down, or when earlier sedimentary layers were raised above sea level and eroded away.

THE GRAND CANYON, U.S.A.

EXAMPLES OF UNCONFORMITIES

Early beds tilted and eroded   *Later beds horizontal*

ANGULAR UNCONFORMITY

No bedding in early rocks   *Later beds horizontal*

NONCONFORMITY

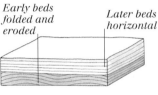

Early beds folded and eroded   *Later beds horizontal*

DISCONFORMITY

SEDIMENTARY LAYERS OF THE GRAND CANYON REGION

Wasatch formation

Kaiparowits formation

Tropic formation

Wahweap sandstone

Dakota sandstone

Carmel formation

Pink Cliffs

Bryce Canyon

Zion Canyon

Gray Cliffs

Sevier fault

White Cliffs

Pipe Spring

Temple Cap sandstone

Navajo sandstone

Kayenta formation

Moenave formation

Chinle formation

Shinarump member

Moenkopi formation

Kaibab limestone

Toroweap formation

Coconino sandstone

Hermit shale

EXAMPLES OF SEDIMENTARY ROCKS

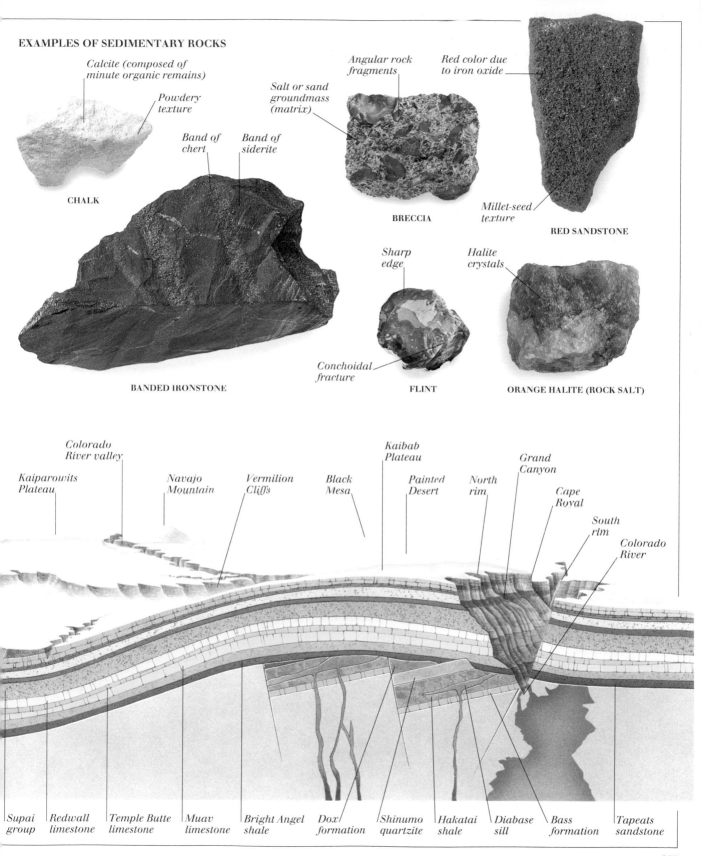

Calcite (composed of minute organic remains)

Powdery texture

CHALK

Band of chert

Band of siderite

BANDED IRONSTONE

Angular rock fragments

Salt or sand groundmass (matrix)

BRECCIA

Red color due to iron oxide

Millet-seed texture

RED SANDSTONE

Sharp edge

Conchoidal fracture

FLINT

Halite crystals

ORANGE HALITE (ROCK SALT)

Kaiparowits Plateau

Colorado River valley

Navajo Mountain

Vermilion Cliffs

Black Mesa

Kaibab Plateau

Painted Desert

North rim

Grand Canyon

Cape Royal

South rim

Colorado River

Supai group

Redwall limestone

Temple Butte limestone

Muav limestone

Bright Angel shale

Dox formation

Shinumo quartzite

Hakatai shale

Diabase sill

Bass formation

Tapeats sandstone

Fossils

FOSSILS ARE THE REMAINS of plants and animals that have been preserved in rock. A fossil may be the preserved remains of an organism itself, an impression of it in rock, or preserved traces (known as trace fossils) left by an organism while it was alive, such as organic carbon outlines, fossilized footprints, or droppings. Most dead organisms soon rot away or are eaten by scavengers. For fossilization to occur, rapid burial by sediment is necessary. The organism decays, but the harder parts—bones, teeth, and shells, for example—may be preserved and hardened by minerals from the surrounding sediment. Fossilization may also occur even when the hard parts of an organism are dissolved away to leave an impression called a mold. The mold is filled by minerals, thereby creating a cast of the organism. The study of fossils (paleontology) not only can show how living things have evolved, but can also help reveal the Earth's geological history—for example, by aiding in the dating of rock strata.

PROCESS OF FOSSILIZATION

Sea — Ammonite — Seabed

ANIMAL DIES

Sea — Shell — Seabed

SOFT PARTS ROT

Sea — Shell — Sediment — Seabed

SHELL BURIED

Shell dissolved away and replaced by minerals — Sea — Sediment — Sediment — Seabed

SHELL FOSSILIZED

EXAMPLES OF FOSSILS

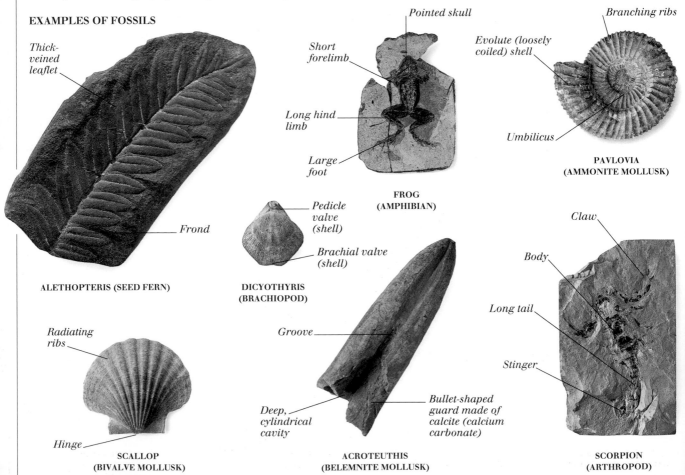

Thick-veined leaflet

Frond

ALETHOPTERIS (SEED FERN)

Pointed skull

Short forelimb

Long hind limb

Large foot

FROG (AMPHIBIAN)

Branching ribs

Evolute (loosely coiled) shell

Umbilicus

PAVLOVIA (AMMONITE MOLLUSK)

Pedicle valve (shell)

Brachial valve (shell)

DICYOTHYRIS (BRACHIOPOD)

Radiating ribs

Hinge

SCALLOP (BIVALVE MOLLUSK)

Groove

Deep, cylindrical cavity

Bullet-shaped guard made of calcite (calcium carbonate)

ACROTEUTHIS (BELEMNITE MOLLUSK)

Claw

Body

Long tail

Stinger

SCORPION (ARTHROPOD)

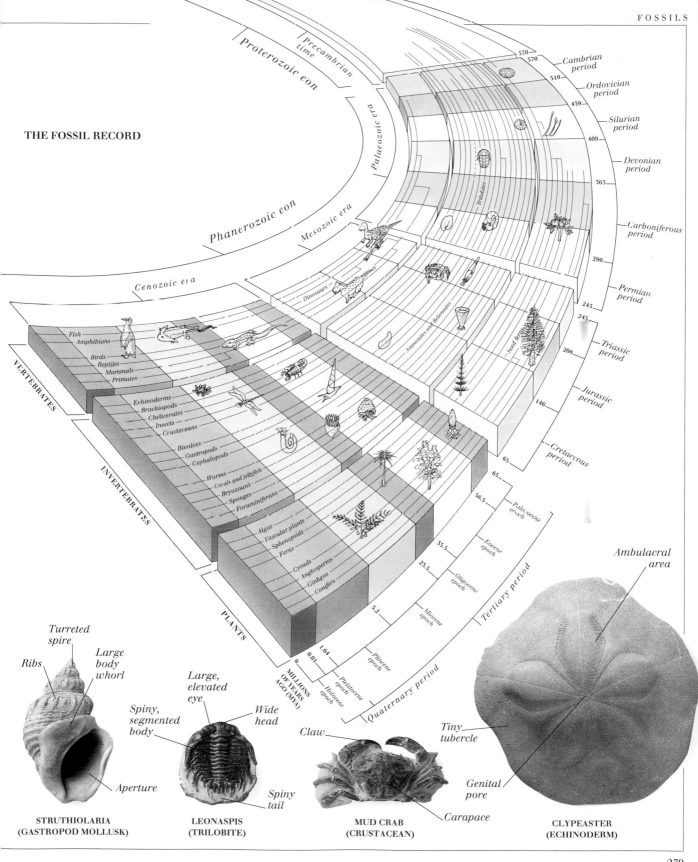

THE FOSSIL RECORD

Precambrian time

Proterozoic eon

Palaeozoic era

Phanerozoic eon

Mesozoic era

Cenozoic era

Cambrian period
Ordovician period
Silurian period
Devonian period
Carboniferous period
Permian period
Triassic period
Jurassic period
Cretaceous period
Tertiary period
Quaternary period

570
570
510
439
409
363
290
245
245
208
146
65
65
56.5
35.5
23.5
5.2
1.64
0
0.01

Trilobites

Dinosaurs

Ammonites and Belemnites

Seed ferns

VERTEBRATES
INVERTEBRATES
PLANTS

Fish
Amphibians
Birds
Reptiles
Mammals
Primates

Echinoderms
Brachiopods
Chelicerates
Insects
Crustaceans
Bivalves
Gastropods
Cephalopods
Worms
Corals and Jellyfish
Bryozoans
Sponges
Foraminiferans

Algae
Vascular plants
Sphenopsids
Ferns
Cycads
Angiosperms
Ginkgos
Conifers

Palaeocene epoch
Eocene epoch
Oligocene epoch
Miocene epoch
Pliocene epoch
Pleistocene epoch
Holocene epoch

MILLIONS OF YEARS AGO (MYA)

Ambulacral area

Turreted spire

Ribs

Large body whorl

Aperture

STRUTHIOLARIA (GASTROPOD MOLLUSK)

Large, elevated eye

Wide head

Spiny, segmented body

Spiny tail

LEONASPIS (TRILOBITE)

Claw

Carapace

MUD CRAB (CRUSTACEAN)

Tiny tubercle

Genital pore

CLYPEASTER (ECHINODERM)

279

Mineral resources

STAGES IN THE FORMATION OF COAL

Stalk

Leaf

PLANT MATTER

MINERAL RESOURCES CAN BE DEFINED AS naturally occurring substances that can be extracted from the Earth and are useful as fuels and raw materials. Coal, oil, and gas—collectively called fossil fuels—are commonly included in this group, but are not strictly minerals, because they are of organic origin. Coal formation begins when vegetation is buried and partly decomposed to form peat. Overlying sediments compress the peat and transform it into lignite (soft brown coal). As the overlying sediments accumulate, increasing pressure and temperature eventually transform the lignite into bituminous and hard anthracite coals. Oil and gas are usually formed from organic molecules that were deposited in marine sediments. Under the effects of heat and pressure, the compressed organic molecules undergo complex chemical changes to form oil and gas. The oil and gas

Decayed plant matter

About 60% carbon

PEAT

About 70% carbon

OIL RIG, NORTH SEA

percolate upward through water-saturated permeable rocks. They may rise to the Earth's surface, or accumulate below an impermeable layer of rock that has been folded or faulted to form a trap—an anticline (upfold) trap, for example. Minerals are inorganic substances that may consist of a single chemical element, such as gold, silver, or copper, or combinations of elements (see pp. 268-269). Some minerals are concentrated in mineralization zones in rock associated with crustal movements or volcanic activity. Others may be found in sediments as placer deposits—accumulations of high-density minerals that have been weathered out of rocks, transported, and deposited (on riverbeds, for example).

Crumbly texture

LIGNITE (BROWN COAL)

Powdery texture

About 80% carbon

HOW COAL IS FORMED

Increasing layers of overlying sediment

Vegetation

Increasing layers of overlying sediment

Increasing pressure and temperature

Increasing pressure and temperature

Increasing pressure and temperature

Peat (about 60% carbon)

Lignite (about 70% carbon)

Bituminous coal (about 80% carbon)

PEAT

LIGNITE (BROWN COAL)

BITUMINOUS COAL

BITUMINOUS COAL

Shiny surface

About 95% carbon

ANTHRACITE COAL

EXAMPLES OF OIL AND GAS TRAPS

Impermeable rock
Oil
Water-saturated permeable rock
Fault

FAULT TRAP

Folded impermeable rock
Pinch-out
Water-saturated permeable rock
Fault
Gas
Oil

PINCH-OUT TRAP

Anticline
Folded impermeable rock
Water-saturated permeable rock
Gas
Oil

ANTICLINE TRAP

Folded impermeable rock
Water-saturated permeable rock
Oil
Impermeable salt dome

SALT-DOME TRAP

MAJOR COAL, OIL, AND GAS DEPOSITS

● Coal   ● Oil and gas

HOW AN ANTICLINE TRAP IS FORMED

Layer of sediment containing decayed plant and animal matter
Sea
Old seabed

DEPOSITION OF ORGANIC MATERIAL

Increasing layers of overlying sediment
Sea
Oil and gas formed by chemical reactions, heat, and pressure

FORMATION OF OIL AND GAS

Land
Sea
Anticline
Impermeable rock layer folded to form oil and gas trap
Gas
Oil
Water-saturated permeable rock

COLLECTION OF OIL AND GAS IN ANTICLINE TRAP

MINERALIZATION ZONES

Continental crust
Volcano
Subduction zone
Oceanic crust
Midocean ridge

Tin, tungsten, bismuth, and copper
Copper, zinc, gold, and chromium
Copper, gold, silver, tin, lead, and mercury
Lead, zinc, and copper
Chromium
Manganese, cobalt, and nickel
Copper and zinc

Weathering and erosion

WEATHERING IS THE BREAKING DOWN of rocks on the Earth's surface. There are two main types: physical (or mechanical), and chemical. Physical weathering may be caused by temperature changes, such as freezing and thawing, or by abrasion from material carried by winds, rivers, or glaciers. Rocks may also be broken down by the actions of animals and plants, such as the burrowing of animals and the growth of roots. Chemical weathering causes rocks to decompose by changing their chemical composition. For example, rainwater may dissolve certain minerals in a rock. Erosion is the wearing away and removal of land surfaces by water, wind, or ice. It is greatest in areas of little or no surface vegetation, such as deserts, where sand dunes may form.

FORMATION OF A ROCK PAVEMENT (HAMADA)

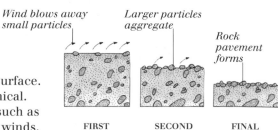

Wind blows away small particles

Larger particles aggregate

Rock pavement forms

FIRST STAGE

SECOND STAGE

FINAL STAGE

FEATURES PRODUCED BY WIND ACTION

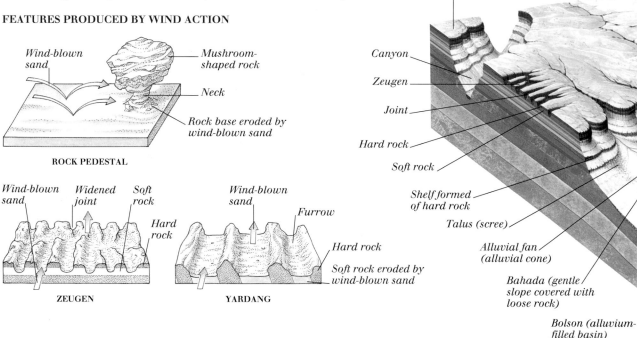

Wind-blown sand

Mushroom-shaped rock

Neck

Rock base eroded by wind-blown sand

ROCK PEDESTAL

Wind-blown sand

Widened joint

Soft rock

Hard rock

ZEUGEN

Wind-blown sand

Furrow

Hard rock

Soft rock eroded by wind-blown sand

YARDANG

FEATURES OF WEATHERING AND EROSION

Mesa (flat-topped plateau)

Canyon

Zeugen

Joint

Hard rock

Soft rock

Shelf formed of hard rock

Talus (scree)

Alluvial fan (alluvial cone)

Bahada (gentle slope covered with loose rock)

Bolson (alluvium-filled basin)

EXAMPLES OF PHYSICAL WEATHERING PROCESSES

Heated rock surface expands

Exfoliation dome

Flaking rock

Fallen debris

EXFOLIATION (ONION-SKIN WEATHERING)

Joint expands and contracts due to temperature changes

Block of fallen rock

BLOCK DISINTEGRATION

Talus (scree)

Joint widened by frozen water

FROST WEDGING

Trunk

Crack widened by tree root

TREE ROOT ACTION

SECTION THROUGH A BARKHAN DUNE

Strong wind

Weak wind

Direction of wind-blown sand

Windward face

Direction of sand movement

Slip face

Foreset strata

Cross-bed set

Topset strata

Bottomset strata

EXAMPLES OF SAND DUNES

Wind direction

Crescent-shaped dune

BARKHAN DUNE

Wind direction

Dune at right angle to wind

TRANSVERSE DUNE

Wind direction

Point where sand ridges meet

STAR DUNE

Wind direction

Parallel dunes

SEIF (LINEAR) DUNE

Canyon

Wadi (dry wash)

Mesa (flat-topped plateau)

Talus (scree)

Butte (flat-topped mesa remnant)

Eroded arch

Residual hill on pediment

Rock pavement (hamada)

Rock pedestal

Barkhan dune

Parabolic dune

Transverse dune

Seif (linear) dune

Inselberg (isolated, steep-sided hill)

Playa (dry lake bed of salt or desiccated clay)

Faultline

Freshwater lake

Fertile oasis

Deflation hollow (created by wind erosion)

Hard granite

Cuesta (asymmetric ridge)

Fault plane

Hard sandstone

Hogback (steep ridge)

Caves

CAVES COMMONLY FORM in areas of limestone, although on coastlines they also occur in other rocks. Limestone is made of calcite (calcium carbonate), which dissolves in the carbonic acid naturally present in rainwater, and in humic acids from the decay of vegetation. The acidic water trickles down through cracks and joints in the limestone and between rock layers, breaking up the surface terrain into clints (blocks of rock), separated by grikes (deep cracks), and punctuated by sinkholes (also called swallow holes or potholes) into which surface streams may disappear. Underground, the acidic water dissolves the rock around crevices, opening up a network of passages and caves, which can become large caverns if the roofs collapse. Various features are formed when the dissolved calcite is redeposited. For example, it may be redeposited along an underground stream to form a gour (series of calcite ridges), or in caves and passages to form stalactites and stalagmites. Stalactites develop where calcite is left behind as water drips from the roof; where the drops land, stalagmites build up.

MERGED STALACTITE

STALACTITE WITH RING MARKS

Ring mark

SURFACE TOPOGRAPHY OF A CAVE SYSTEM

Doline (depression caused by collapse of cave roof)

Sinkhole

Porous limestone

Gorge where cave roof has fallen in

Resurgence

Limestone terrain with clints and grikes

Impermeable rock

STALAGMITE FORMATIONS

Calcite (calcium carbonate) crystalized under water

Thin encrustations of calcite (calcium carbonate)

CRYSTALLINE STALAGMITIC FLOOR

CALCAREOUS TUFA

Encrustations on dead stems of small plants

Calcite (calcium carbonate)

Calcite (calcium carbonate)

STALAGMITIC FLOOR

Encrustations with fungoid structure

STALAGMITIC BOSS

Scar of bare rock

Former water table

Permeable limestone

Resurgence

Layer of impermeable rock

Present water table

DEVELOPMENT OF A CAVE SYSTEM

STRUCTURE OF LIMESTONE STRATA

Impermeable rock
Joint
Bedding plane
Impermeable rock
Permeable limestone

INITIAL CAVE

Water seeps through cracks in rock
Stream enters permeable rock
Calcite (calcium carbonate) deposits begin to form
Resurgence
Tunnel
Underground stream

EXTENDED CAVE SYSTEM

Doline caused by collapse of cave roof
Sinkhole
Stalactite
Stalagmite
Gorge
Cave
Dry gallery
Resurgence

INTERCONNECTED CAVE SYSTEM

Stalactite
Pillar (column)
Gorge
Stalactite
Dry gallery (former course of underground stream)
Gour (series of calcite ridges) deposited by running water
Stalagmite
Joint in rock enlarged by water
Bedding plane
Curtain of deposited calcite (calcium carbonate)
Tunnel
Cave
Passage
Cavern
Gour (series of calcite ridges)

Glaciers

A VALLEY GLACIER IS A LARGE MASS OF ICE that forms on land and moves slowly downhill under its own weight. It is formed from snow that collects in cirques (mountain hollows also known as corries), compressing into ice as more and more snow accumulates. The cirque is deepened by frost wedging and abrasion (see pp. 282-283), and arêtes (sharp ridges) develop between adjacent cirques. Eventually, so much ice builds up that the glacier begins to flow. As the glacier moves it collects moraine (debris), which may range in size from particles of dust to large boulders. The rocks at the base of the glacier erode the glacial valley, giving it a U-shaped cross section. Under the glacier, *roches moutonnées* (eroded outcrops of hard rock) and drumlins (rounded mounds of rock and clay) are left behind on the valley floor. The glacier ends at a terminus (the snout), where the ice melts as fast as it arrives. If the temperature increases, the ice melts faster than it arrives, and the glacier retreats. The retreating glacier leaves behind its moraine and also erratics (isolated single boulders). Glacial streams from the melting glacier deposit eskers and kames (ridges and mounds of sand and gravel) but carry away the finer sediment to form a stratified outwash plain. Lumps of ice carried on to this plain melt, creating holes called kettles.

GLACIER BAY, ALASKA

VALLEY GLACIER

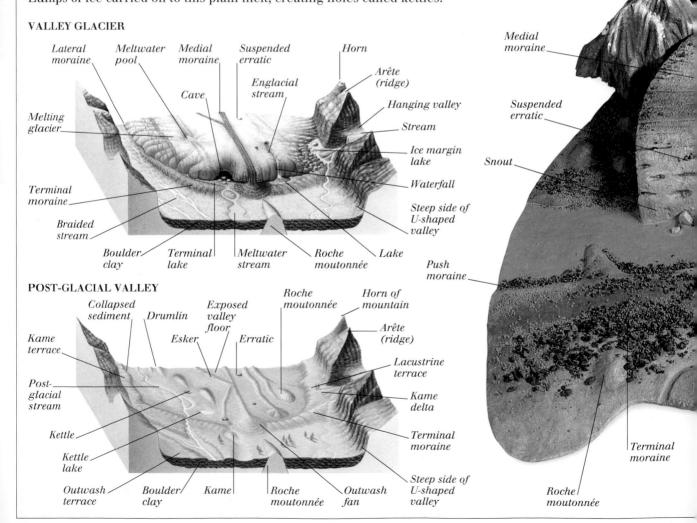

Lateral moraine

Meltwater pool

Medial moraine

Suspended erratic

Horn

Arête (ridge)

Englacial stream

Cave

Hanging valley

Melting glacier

Stream

Ice margin lake

Waterfall

Terminal moraine

Steep side of U-shaped valley

Braided stream

Boulder clay

Terminal lake

Meltwater stream

Roche moutonnée

Lake

Medial moraine

Suspended erratic

Snout

Push moraine

POST-GLACIAL VALLEY

Collapsed sediment

Drumlin

Exposed valley floor

Roche moutonnée

Horn of mountain

Kame terrace

Esker

Erratic

Arête (ridge)

Lacustrine terrace

Post-glacial stream

Kame delta

Kettle

Terminal moraine

Kettle lake

Steep side of U-shaped valley

Outwash terrace

Boulder clay

Kame

Roche moutonnée

Outwash fan

Terminal moraine

Roche moutonnée

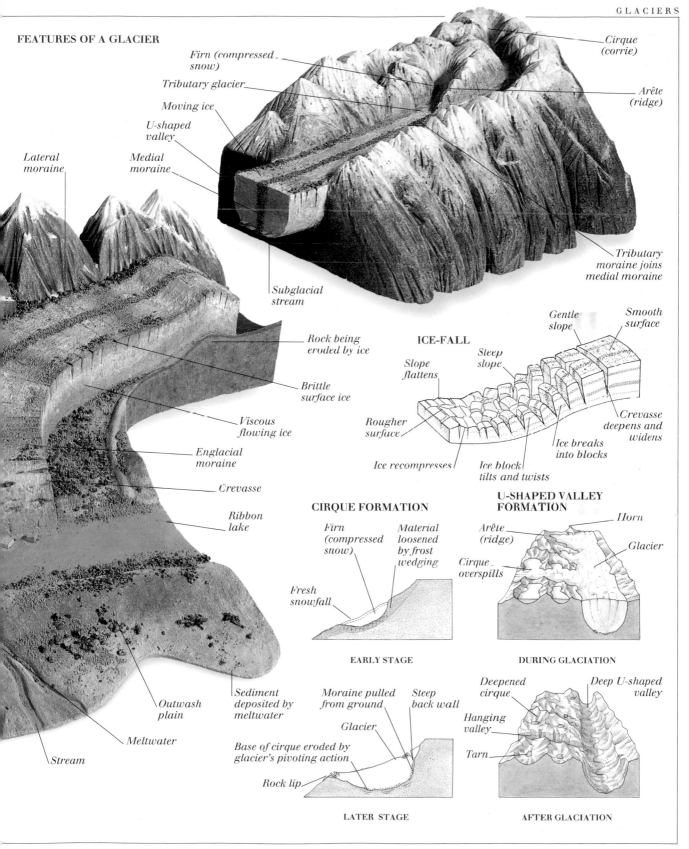

FEATURES OF A GLACIER

Firn (compressed snow)

Tributary glacier

Moving ice

U-shaped valley

Medial moraine

Lateral moraine

Cirque (corrie)

Arête (ridge)

Tributary moraine joins medial moraine

Subglacial stream

Rock being eroded by ice

Brittle surface ice

Viscous flowing ice

Englacial moraine

Crevasse

Ribbon lake

Outwash plain

Sediment deposited by meltwater

Meltwater

Stream

ICE-FALL

Slope flattens

Steep slope

Gentle slope

Smooth surface

Rougher surface

Ice recompresses

Ice block tilts and twists

Ice breaks into blocks

Crevasse deepens and widens

CIRQUE FORMATION

Firn (compressed snow)

Material loosened by frost wedging

Fresh snowfall

EARLY STAGE

Moraine pulled from ground

Steep back wall

Glacier

Base of cirque eroded by glacier's pivoting action

Rock lip

LATER STAGE

U-SHAPED VALLEY FORMATION

Arête (ridge)

Horn

Glacier

Cirque overspills

DURING GLACIATION

Deepened cirque

Deep U-shaped valley

Hanging valley

Tarn

AFTER GLACIATION

Rivers

RIVERS FORM PART of the water cycle—the continuous circulation of water between the land, sea, and atmosphere. The source of a river may be a mountain spring, or lake, or a melting glacier. The course that the river subsequently takes depends on the slope of the terrain and on the rock types and formations over which it flows. In its early, upland stages, a river tumbles steeply over rocks and boulders and cuts a steep-sided V-shaped valley. Farther downstream, it flows smoothly over sediments and forms winding meanders, eroding sideways to create broad valleys and plains. On reaching the coast, the river may deposit sediment, forming an estuary or delta (see pp. 290-291).

RIVER CAPTURE

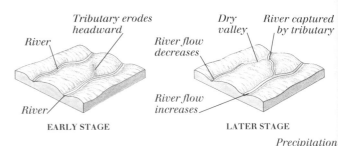

River
Tributary erodes headward
River

EARLY STAGE

River flow decreases
Dry valley
River captured by tributary
River flow increases

LATER STAGE

THE WATER CYCLE

Precipitation falls on high ground
Wind
Water carried downstream by river
Water vapor released into atmosphere by trees and other plants
Wind
Water vapor forms clouds
Water evaporates from sea
Water stored in sea
River flows into sea
Water seeps underground and flows to sea
Water evaporates from lake
Water seeps underground and flows to sea

SATELLITE IMAGE OF GANGES RIVER DELTA, BANGLADESH

River Ganges
Ganges delta
Infertile swampland
Distributary
Large volume of sediment

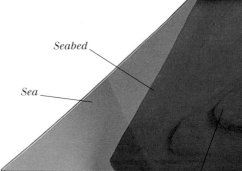

Seabed
Sea
Sediment layers

RIVER DRAINAGE PATTERNS

RADIAL

CENTRIPETAL

PARALLEL

DENDRITIC

DERANGED

TRELLISED

ANNULAR

RECTANGULAR

STAGES IN A RIVER'S DEVELOPMENT

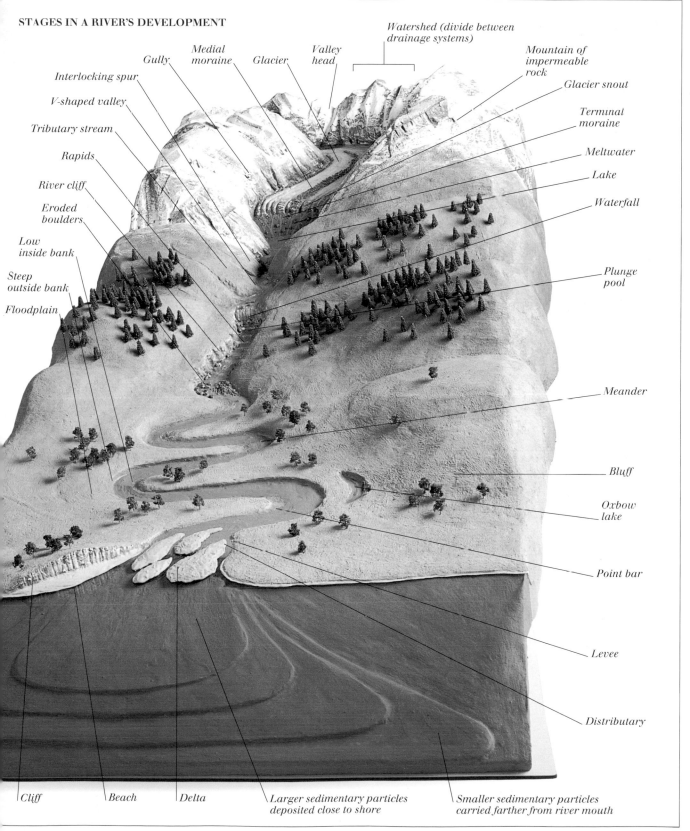

Watershed (divide between drainage systems)

Medial moraine

Gully

Glacier

Valley head

Interlocking spur

V-shaped valley

Tributary stream

Rapids

River cliff

Eroded boulders

Low inside bank

Steep outside bank

Floodplain

Mountain of impermeable rock

Glacier snout

Terminal moraine

Meltwater

Lake

Waterfall

Plunge pool

Meander

Bluff

Oxbow lake

Point bar

Levee

Distributary

Cliff

Beach

Delta

Larger sedimentary particles deposited close to shore

Smaller sedimentary particles carried farther from river mouth

River features

RIVERS ARE ONE OF THE MAJOR FORCES that shape the landscape. Near its source, a river is steep (see pp. 288-289). It erodes downward, carving out V-shaped valleys and deep gorges. Waterfalls and rapids are formed where the river flows from hard rock to softer, more easily eroded rock. Farther downstream, meanders may form and there is greater sideways erosion, resulting in a broad river valley. The river sometimes erodes through the neck of a meander to form an oxbow lake. Sediment deposited on the valley floor by meandering rivers and during floods helps to create a floodplain. Floods may also deposit sediment on the banks of the river to form levees. As a river spills into the sea or a lake, it deposits large amounts of sediment, and may form a delta. A delta is an area of sand bars, swamps and lagoons through which the river flows in several channels called distributaries—the Mississippi delta, for example. Often, a rise in sea level may have flooded the river mouth to form a broad estuary, a tidal section where seawater mixes with fresh water.

HOW WATERFALLS AND RAPIDS ARE FORMED

Hard rock
Softer rock
Plunge pool

WATERFALL

Hard rock
Softer rock
River erodes softer rocks to form rapids
Gently sloping rock strata

RAPIDS

A RIVER VALLEY DRAINAGE SYSTEM

Headward erosion

Waterfall

Gorge

Steep gorge cut by river

Mountain

GORGE

Floodplain

Stream

Sediment bar

BRAIDING

Entrenched meander

Braiding

Lake

River terrace

Levee

River erodes headward

HEADWARD EROSION

River erodes downward

Natural bridge

Meander

Steep cliffs

ENTRENCHED MEANDER

Old meander

Bridge

River

NATURAL BRIDGE

Oxbow lake

Lake

River mouth

Sediment deposited on seabed

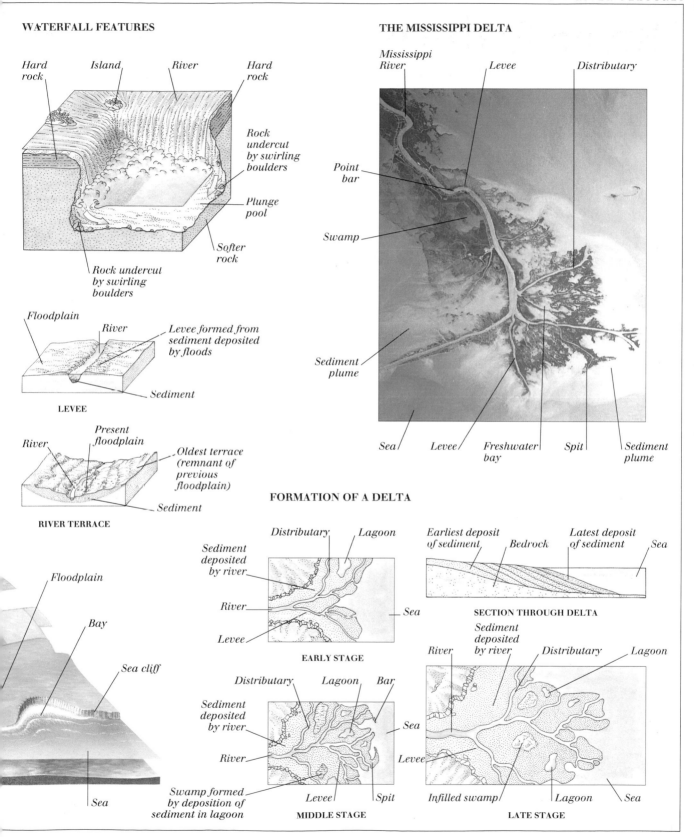

WATERFALL FEATURES

Hard rock
Island
River
Hard rock
Rock undercut by swirling boulders
Plunge pool
Softer rock
Rock undercut by swirling boulders

Floodplain
River
Levee formed from sediment deposited by floods
Sediment

LEVEE

River
Present floodplain
Oldest terrace (remnant of previous floodplain)
Sediment

RIVER TERRACE

Floodplain
Bay
Sea cliff
Sea

THE MISSISSIPPI DELTA

Mississippi River
Levee
Distributary
Point bar
Swamp
Sediment plume
Sea
Levee
Freshwater bay
Spit
Sediment plume

FORMATION OF A DELTA

Distributary
Lagoon
Sediment deposited by river
River
Levee
Sea

EARLY STAGE

Earliest deposit of sediment
Bedrock
Latest deposit of sediment
Sea

SECTION THROUGH DELTA

Distributary
Lagoon
Bar
Sediment deposited by river
River
Levee
Spit
Sea

Swamp formed by deposition of sediment in lagoon

MIDDLE STAGE

River
Sediment deposited by river
Distributary
Lagoon
Levee
Infilled swamp
Lagoon
Sea

LATE STAGE

Lakes and groundwater

NATURAL LAKES OCCUR WHERE a large quantity of water collects in a hollow in impermeable rock or is prevented from draining away by a barrier, such as moraine (glacial deposits) or solidified lava. Lakes are often relatively short-lived landscape features, because they tend to become silted up by sediment from the streams and rivers that feed them. Some of the more long-lasting lakes are found in deep rift valleys formed by vertical movements of the Earth's crust (see pp. 58-59)—for example, Lake Baikal in Russia, the world's largest freshwater lake, and the Dead Sea in the Middle East, one of the world's saltiest lakes. Where water is able to drain away, it sinks into the ground until it reaches a layer of impermeable rock, then accumulates in the permeable rock above it. This water-saturated permeable rock is called an aquifer. The saturated zone varies in depth according to seasonal and climatic changes. In wet conditions, the water stored underground builds up, while in dry periods it becomes depleted. Where the upper edge of the saturated zone—the water table—meets the ground surface, water emerges as springs. In an artesian basin, where the aquifer is below an aquiclude (layer of impermeable rock), the water table throughout the basin is determined by its height at the rim. At the center of such a basin, the water table is above ground level. The water in the basin is thus trapped below the water table and can rise under its own pressure along fault lines or well shafts.

LAKE BAIKAL, RUSSIA

EXAMPLES OF SPRINGS

Permeable limestone
Water table
Spring line
Stream
Spring
Impermeable shale

LIMESTONE SPRING

Permeable gravel
Water table
Spring line
Stream
Spring
Impermeable clay

COASTAL (VALLEY) SPRING

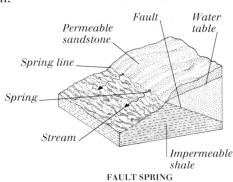

Fault
Water table
Permeable sandstone
Spring line
Spring
Stream
Impermeable shale

FAULT SPRING

Water table
Spring line
Jointed, solidified lava
Spring
Jointed, solidified lava
Stream
Impermeable mudstone

LAVA SPRING

STRUCTURE OF AN ARTESIAN BASIN

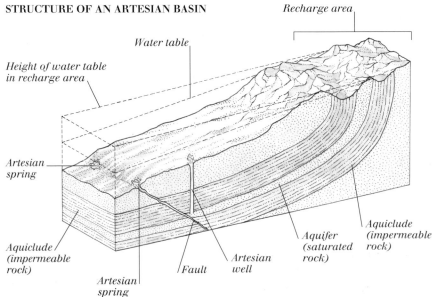

Recharge area
Water table
Height of water table in recharge area
Artesian spring
Aquiclude (impermeable rock)
Artesian spring
Fault
Artesian well
Aquifer (saturated rock)
Aquiclude (impermeable rock)

FEATURES OF A GROUNDWATER SYSTEM

Zone of
aeration

Layer
of soil
moisture

Lake

Stream

Zone of
aeration

Capillary
fringe

Marsh

Water table

Saturated
zone

**CLOSE-UP OF
SURFACE LAYER**

Dry-season
water table

Permanently
saturated zone
(saturated in wet
and dry seasons)

Present water
table (wet season)

Temporarily saturated
zone (saturated only in
wet season)

EXAMPLES OF LAKES

Glacial
deposits

Lake in kettle
(former site of
ice block)

Oxbow lake
(cut-off river
meander)

River

KETTLE LAKE

OXBOW LAKE

Caldera
(collapsed
crater)

Volcanic
lake

Movement
along strike-
slip (lateral)
fault

Strike-slip
(lateral) fault

VOLCANIC LAKE

Lake in
elongated
hollow

STRIKE-SLIP (LATERAL) FAULT LAKE

Rift valley

Steep back wall
eroded by frost
and ice

Moraine or rock
lip damming lake

High
valley
walls

Sinking
graben
(block fault)

Tarn (circular
mountain lake)

GRABEN (BLOCK-FAULT) LAKE

TARN

THE DEAD SEA, ISRAEL/JORDAN

River
Jordan

Dead Sea

Steep rift-
valley walls

Salt left by
evaporation

Israel

Shallow
flats

Jordan

Coastlines

COASTLINES ARE AMONG THE MOST RAPIDLY changing landscape features. Some are eroded by waves, wind, and rain, causing cliffs to be undercut and caves to be hollowed out of solid rock. Others are built up by waves transporting sand and small rocks in a process known as longshore drift and by rivers depositing sediment in deltas. Additional influences include the activities of living organisms such as coral, crustal movements, and sea-level variations due to climatic changes. Rising land or a drop in sea level creates an emergent coastline, with cliffs and beaches standing above the new shoreline. Sinking land or a rise in sea level produces a drowned coastline, typified by fjords (submerged glacial valleys) or submerged river valleys.

FEATURES OF A SEA CLIFF

Cliff top
Cliff face
High tide level
Low tide level
Offshore deposits
Wave-cut platform
Undercut area of cliff

FEATURES OF WAVES

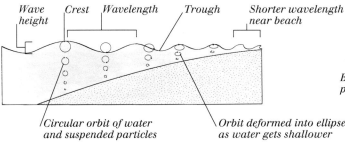

Wave height
Crest
Wavelength
Trough
Shorter wavelength near beach
Circular orbit of water and suspended particles
Orbit deformed into ellipse as water gets shallower

LONGSHORE DRIFT

Pebble
Backwash
Movement of material along beach
Buildup of material against groyne
Beach
Groyne
Waves approaching shore at an oblique angle
Swash zone
Swash

Mature river
Headland
Bedding plane
Sea cliff
Remnants of former headland
Estuary

DEPOSITIONAL FEATURES OF COASTLINES

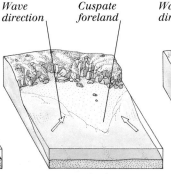

Bay head beach
Wave direction
Headland

Wave direction
Tombolo
Island

Wave direction
Cuspate foreland

Wave direction
Barrier beach
Lagoon

BAY HEAD BEACH

TOMBOLO

CUSPATE FORELAND

BARRIER BEACH

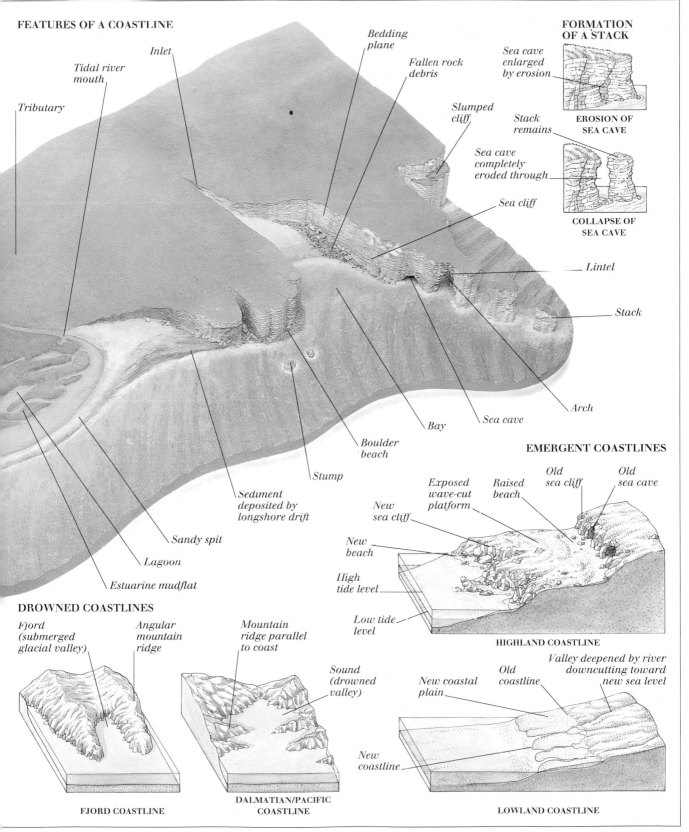

FEATURES OF A COASTLINE

Tributary

Tidal river mouth

Inlet

Bedding plane

Fallen rock debris

Slumped cliff

Sea cliff

FORMATION OF A STACK

Sea cave enlarged by erosion

EROSION OF SEA CAVE

Stack remains

Sea cave completely eroded through

COLLAPSE OF SEA CAVE

Lintel

Stack

Arch

Sea cave

Bay

Boulder beach

Stump

Sediment deposited by longshore drift

Sandy spit

Lagoon

Estuarine mudflat

EMERGENT COASTLINES

Exposed wave-cut platform

Raised beach

Old sea cliff

Old sea cave

New sea cliff

New beach

High tide level

Low tide level

HIGHLAND COASTLINE

DROWNED COASTLINES

Fjord (submerged glacial valley)

Angular mountain ridge

Mountain ridge parallel to coast

Sound (drowned valley)

FJORD COASTLINE

DALMATIAN/PACIFIC COASTLINE

Valley deepened by river downcutting toward new sea level

Old coastline

New coastal plain

New coastline

LOWLAND COASTLINE

295

Oceans and seas

OCEANS AND SEAS COVER ABOUT 70 PERCENT of the Earth's surface and account for about 97 percent of its total water. These oceans and seas play a crucial role in regulating temperature variations and determining climate. Their waters absorb heat from the Sun, especially in tropical regions, and the surface currents distribute it around the Earth, warming overlying air masses and neighboring land in winter and cooling them in summer. The oceans are never still. Differences in temperature and salinity drive deep current systems, while surface currents are generated by winds blowing over the oceans. All currents are deflected—to the right in the Northern Hemisphere, to the left in the Southern Hemisphere—as a result of the Earth's rotation. This deflective factor is known as the Coriolis force. A current that begins on the surface is immediately deflected. This current in turn generates a current in the layer of water beneath, which is also deflected. As the movement is transmitted downward, the deflections form an Ekman spiral. The waters of the oceans and seas are also moved by the constant ebb and flow of tides. These are caused by the gravitational pull of the Moon and Sun. The highest tides (Spring tides) occur at full and new Moon; the lowest tides (neap tides) occur at first and last quarter.

SURFACE CURRENTS

OFFSHORE CURRENTS

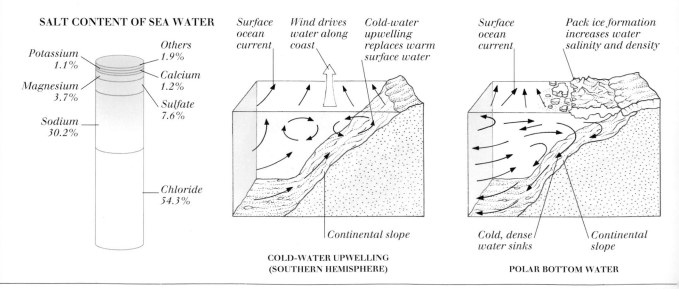

SALT CONTENT OF SEA WATER

Potassium 1.1%
Magnesium 3.7%
Sodium 30.2%
Others 1.9%
Calcium 1.2%
Sulfate 7.6%
Chloride 54.3%

Surface ocean current
Wind drives water along coast
Cold-water upwelling replaces warm surface water
Continental slope

COLD-WATER UPWELLING (SOUTHERN HEMISPHERE)

Surface ocean current
Pack ice formation increases water salinity and density
Cold, dense water sinks
Continental slope

POLAR BOTTOM WATER

EFFECT OF CORIOLIS FORCE

North Pole

Coriolis force

Winds and currents deflected to right in Northern Hemisphere

Equator

Winds and currents deflected to left in Southern Hemisphere

Original direction of wind or current

Actual direction of wind or current

South Pole

EKMAN SPIRAL (NORTHERN HEMISPHERE)

EQUATOR (0°)

Wind

Surface current caused by wind

Subsurface current slightly deflected by Coriolis force

Deep current at 180° to surface current

Midwater current further deflected by Coriolis force

ARCTIC CIRCLE (66° 52'N)

80° 120° 160° 180°

Kuroshio Current

Kuroshio Current

TROPIC OF CANCER (23° 30'N)

Northeast Monsoon Drift

North Equatorial Current

North Equatorial Current

Equatorial Countercurrent

North Equatorial Current

Equatorial Countercurrent

Equatorial Countercurrent

agulhas Current

South Equatorial Current

SOUTH INDIAN GYRE

TROPIC OF CAPRICORN (23° 30'S)

East Australian Current

West Australian Current

ANTARCTIC CIRCLE (66° 52'S)

80° 120° 160° 180°

HOW TIDES ARE CAUSED

HIGH SPRING TIDE

New Moon

LOW NEAP TIDE

Last quarter

Moon's gravitational pull

HIGH SPRING TIDE

Full Moon

Earth's orbit

Earth

Tidal bulge caused by Sun's gravitational pull

Tidal bulge caused by Moon's gravitational pull

Sun's gravitational pull

Sun

Sun's gravitational pull reinforces centrifugal effect, producing large tidal bulge

Sun's gravitational pull diminishes Moon's effect

Equal and opposite tidal bulge produced by centrifugal effect due to Earth's spin

LOW NEAP TIDE

First quarter

Moon's orbit

Tidal bulge where Moon's gravitational pull is strongest

Moon

297

The ocean floor

THE OCEAN FLOOR INCLUDES TWO SECTIONS: the continental shelf and slope, and the deep-ocean floor. The continental shelf and slope are part of the continental crust, but may extend far into the ocean. Sloping quite gently to a depth of about 460 feet, the continental shelf is covered in sandy deposits shaped by waves and tidal currents. At the edge of the continental shelf, the seabed slopes down to the abyssal plain, which lies at an average depth of about 12,500 feet. On this deep-ocean floor is a layer of sediment made up of clays, fine oozes formed from the remains of tiny sea creatures, and occasional mineral-rich deposits. Echo-sounding and remote sensing from satellites has revealed that the abyssal plain is divided by a world-circling system of mountain ranges, far bigger than any on land—the midocean ridge. Here, magma (molten rock) wells up from the Earth's interior and solidifies, widening the ocean floor (see pp. 58-59). As the ocean floor spreads, volcanoes that have formed over hot spots in the crust move away from their magma source; they become extinct and are increasingly submerged and eroded. Volcanoes eroded below sea level remain as seamounts (underwater mountains). In warm waters, a volcano that projects above the ocean surface often acquires a fringing coral reef, which may develop into an atoll as the volcano becomes submerged.

CONTINENTAL-SHELF FLOOR

Bedrock exposed by tidal scour

Shoreline

Parallel strips of coarse material left by strong tidal currents

Sand deposited in wavy pattern by weaker currents

Irregular patches of fine sand deposited by weakest currents

FEATURES OF THE OCEAN FLOOR

Sediment

Submarine canyon

Continental shelf

Course of mud river

Continental rise

Continental slope

Guyot (flat-topped seamount)

Seamount (underwater mountain)

Abyssal plain

Continental crust

Ooze (sediment consisting of remains of tiny sea creatures)

Layer of volcanic rock

Pillow lava

Volcanic crystalline rock

Oceanic crust

DEEP-OCEAN FLOOR SEDIMENTS

KEY

- Calcareous ooze
- Pelagic clay
- Glacial sediments
- Siliceous ooze
- Terrigenous sediments
- Continental margin sediments
- Metalliferous muds
- Major nodule fields

DEVELOPMENT OF AN ATOLL

ECHO-SOUND PROFILE OF OCEAN FLOOR

Sand wave

Event mark indicates synchronization of survey equipment

Sand wave

Seabed profile

Minor oscillations caused by ship's movement

Velocity of sound in water (1,493 m/sec; 4,898 ft/sec)

Reference code

Midocean ridge

Ocean trench

Magma (molten rock)

Sediment

Volcanic island

Sea level

Coral grows on shoreline

FRINGING REEF

Lagoon

Eroded volcanic island subsides

Coral continues to grow, forming barrier reef

BARRIER REEF

Coral continues to grow where waves bring food

Lagoon

Dead coral

Volcanic island becomes submerged

ATOLL

Coral submerged too deeply to grow

Volcanic island is submerged further

SUBMERGED ATOLL

The atmosphere

JET STREAM

THE EARTH IS SURROUNDED BY ITS ATMOSPHERE, a blanket of gases that enables life to exist on the planet. This layer has no definite outer edge, gradually becoming thinner until it merges into space, but over 80 percent of atmospheric gases are held by gravity within about 10 miles of the Earth's surface. The atmosphere blocks out much harmful ultraviolet solar radiation, and insulates the Earth against extremes of temperature by limiting both incoming solar radiation and the escape of re-radiated heat into space. This natural balance may be distorted by the greenhouse effect, as gases such as carbon dioxide have built up in the atmosphere, trapping more heat. Close to the Earth's surface, differences in air temperature and pressure cause air to circulate between the equator and poles. This circulation, together with the Coriolis force, gives rise to the prevailing surface winds and the high-level jet streams.

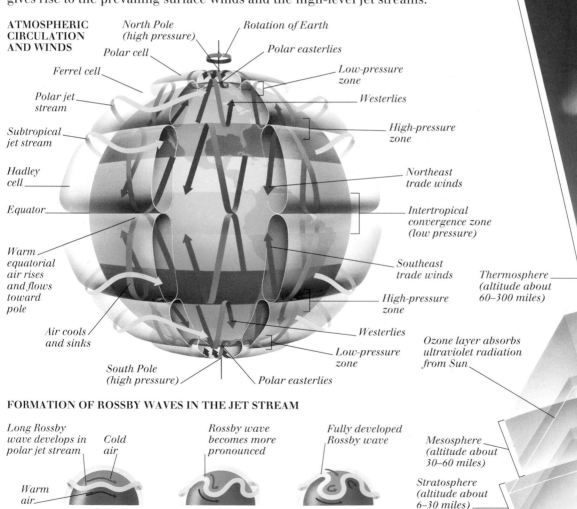

ATMOSPHERIC CIRCULATION AND WINDS

North Pole (high pressure)
Rotation of Earth
Polar cell
Polar easterlies
Ferrel cell
Low-pressure zone
Polar jet stream
Westerlies
Subtropical jet stream
High-pressure zone
Hadley cell
Northeast trade winds
Equator
Intertropical convergence zone (low pressure)
Warm equatorial air rises and flows toward pole
Southeast trade winds
Air cools and sinks
High-pressure zone
Westerlies
South Pole (high pressure)
Low-pressure zone
Polar easterlies

Exosphere (altitude above about 300 miles)
Corona
Thermosphere (altitude about 60–300 miles)
Ozone layer absorbs ultraviolet radiation from Sun
Mesosphere (altitude about 30–60 miles)
Stratosphere (altitude about 6–30 miles)
Troposphere (altitude up to about 6 miles)

FORMATION OF ROSSBY WAVES IN THE JET STREAM

Long Rossby wave develops in polar jet stream
Cold air
Rossby wave becomes more pronounced
Fully developed Rossby wave
Warm air

INITIAL UNDULATION

DEEPENING WAVE

DEVELOPED WAVE

STRUCTURE OF THE ATMOSPHERE

GLOBAL WARMING

Solar radiation re-radiated as heat

Some re-radiated heat escapes into space

Sun

Some re-radiated heat reflected back to Earth

Incoming solar radiation

Earth

Atmosphere

NATURALLY MODERATED GREENHOUSE EFFECT

Meteor (shooting star) burns up as it passes through atmosphere

Less re-radiated heat escapes

Solar radiation re-radiated as heat

More re-radiated heat reflected back to Earth

Aurora

Surface temperature rises

"Greenhouse gases" accumulate in atmosphere

Incoming solar radiation

UNBALANCED GREENHOUSE EFFECT

14% of incoming solar radiation absorbed by atmosphere

7% of incoming solar radiation reflected by atmosphere

COMPOSITION OF THE LOWER ATMOSPHERE

24% of incoming solar radiation reflected by clouds

Other elements less than 0.1%

Argon 0.93%

Cosmic rays (high-energy particles from space) penetrate to stratosphere

Oxygen 21%

Some absorbed heat re-radiated by atmosphere

4% of incoming solar radiation reflected by oceans and land

Nitrogen 78%

51% of incoming solar radiation absorbed by Earth's surface

Some absorbed heat re-radiated by clouds

301

Weather

WEATHER IS DEFINED AS THE ATMOSPHERIC CONDITIONS at a particular time and place; climate is the average weather conditions for a given region over time. Weather conditions include temperature, wind, cloud cover, and precipitation, such as rain or snow. Good weather is associated with high-pressure areas, where air is sinking. Cloudy, wet, changeable weather is common in low-pressure zones with rising, unstable air. Such conditions occur at temperate latitudes, where warm air meets cool air along the polar fronts. Here, spiraling low-pressure cells known as depressions (mid-latitude cyclones) often form. A depression usually contains a sector of warmer air, beginning at a warm front and ending at a cold front. If the two fronts merge, forming an occluded front, the warm air is pushed upward. An extreme form of low-pressure cell is a hurricane (also called a typhoon or tropical cyclone), which brings torrential rain, and exceptionally strong winds.

TYPES OF OCCLUDED FRONT

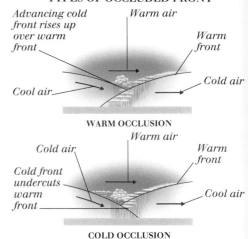

Advancing cold front rises up over warm front

Warm air

Warm front

Cool air

Cold air

WARM OCCLUSION

Cold air

Warm air

Warm front

Cold front undercuts warm front

Cool air

COLD OCCLUSION

FORMS OF PRECIPITATION

Water droplets less than 0.5 mm in diameter fall as drizzle

Water droplets coalesce to form raindrops 0.5–5.0 mm in diameter

Rising air

RAIN FROM CLOUDS NOT REACHING FREEZING LEVEL

Coalesced water droplets fall as rain

Ice crystal

Snowflakes grown from ice crystals fall as snow

Rising air

Snowflakes melt to fall as rain

RAIN AND SNOW FROM CLOUDS REACHING FREEZING LEVEL

Vertical air currents toss frozen water droplets up and down

Alternate freezing and melting builds up layers of ice

Rising air

Ice falls as hailstones

HAIL

TYPES OF CLOUD

Cirrus

Cirrostratus

Cirrocumulus

Freezing level, above which clouds consist of ice crystals

Cumulonimbus

Altocumulus

Altostratus

Nimbus

Stratocumulus

Cumulus

Nimbostratus

Stratus

Condensation level

13
12
11
10
9
8
7
6
5
4
3
2
1
0

Altitude in temperate regions (km)

STRUCTURE OF A HURRICANE

Outward-spiraling high-level winds

Outward-spiraling cirrus clouds

Descending dry air

6–9 miles high

Storm moving at 9–25 mph in direction of prevailing wind

Greatest windspeeds (up to 185 mph) about 12 miles from eye wall

Eye (calm, very low-pressure center)

Precipitation greatest in eye wall

Spiraling bands of wind and rain

Water vapor picked up from sea feeds walls of cumulus clouds

Warm, moist air drawn in

WEATHER MAP

Center of high-pressure area

Center of low-pressure area

Very strong southeasterly wind

Cold front

Continuous rain

Cloudy sky

Light northwesterly wind

Obscured sky

Very cloudy sky

Air pressure 1026 millibars

Occluded front

Occluded front

Strong northeasterly wind

Slightly cloudy sky

Overcast sky

Temperature 21°C (70°F)

Light southerly wind

Sea temperature 8°C (46.4°F)

Cold front

Warm front

Calm

Very cloudy sky

PHYSICS AND CHEMISTRY

The variety of matter

**PLANT AND INSECT
(LIVING MATTER)**

MATTER IS ANYTHING THAT HAS A MASS. It includes everything from natural substances, such as minerals or living organisms, to synthetic materials. Matter can exist in three distinct states—solid, liquid, and gas. A solid is rigid and retains its shape. A liquid is fluid, has a definite volume, and will take the shape of its container. A gas (also fluid) fills a space, so its volume will be the same as the volume of its container. Most substances can exist as a solid, a liquid, or a gas: the state is determined by temperature. At very high temperatures, matter becomes plasma, often considered to be a fourth state of matter. All matter is composed of microscopic particles, such as atoms and molecules (see pp. 308-309). The arrangement and interactions of these particles give a substance its physical and chemical properties, by which matter can be identified. There is a huge variety of matter because particles can arrange themselves in countless ways, in one substance or by mixing with others. Natural glass, for example, seems to be a solid but is, in fact, a supercool liquid: the atoms are not locked into a pattern and can flow. Pure substances known as elements (see p. 310) combine to form compounds or mixtures. Mixtures called colloids are made up of larger particles of matter suspended in a solid, liquid, or gas, while a solution is one substance dissolved in another.

TYPES OF COLLOID

HAIR GEL (SOLID IN LIQUID)

**SHAVING CREAM
(AIR IN LIQUID)**

**MIST
(LIQUID IN GAS)**

EXAMPLES OF MATTER

The element silicon in pure crystalline form

Polythene is made by combining natural materials in new ways

**POLYTHENE
(SYNTHETIC POLYMER)**

**PURE SILICON
(SEMICONDUCTOR)**

Low pressure gases

Central electrode

**BALL CONTAINING
HIGH-TEMPERATURE GAS
(PLASMA)**

Streaks of plasma (mixture of electrons and charged atoms)

Voltage tears electrons from atoms of low pressure gases inside

Obsidian is molten volcanic rock that cools quickly, so atoms cannot form a regular pattern

**OBSIDIAN
(NATURAL GLASS)**

Azurite is found naturally with deposits of copper ore

**AZURITE
(CRYSTALLINE MINERAL)**

Solid crystals dissolve in liquid water

Water

Potassium permanganate crystals

**POTASSIUM PERMANGANATE AND WATER
(SOLUTION)**

STATES OF MATTER

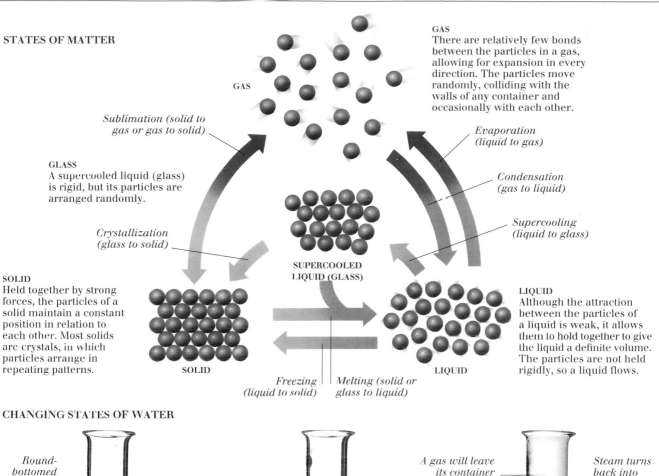

GAS
There are relatively few bonds between the particles in a gas, allowing for expansion in every direction. The particles move randomly, colliding with the walls of any container and occasionally with each other.

Sublimation (solid to gas or gas to solid)

GLASS
A supercooled liquid (glass) is rigid, but its particles are arranged randomly.

Evaporation (liquid to gas)

Condensation (gas to liquid)

Crystallization (glass to solid)

Supercooling (liquid to glass)

SUPERCOOLED LIQUID (GLASS)

SOLID
Held together by strong forces, the particles of a solid maintain a constant position in relation to each other. Most solids are crystals, in which particles arrange in repeating patterns.

SOLID

LIQUID

LIQUID
Although the attraction between the particles of a liquid is weak, it allows them to hold together to give the liquid a definite volume. The particles are not held rigidly, so a liquid flows.

Freezing (liquid to solid)   *Melting (solid or glass to liquid)*

CHANGING STATES OF WATER

Round-bottomed glass flask

Ice cubes have a definite shape

Liquid water

Liquid takes the shape of its container

Water remains liquid up to 212 °F (100 °C)

A gas will leave its container

Bubbles of steam form in boiling water

Steam turns back into liquid water where it meets cooler glass

Eventually, all the liquid will become a gas

SOLID STATE: ICE
The solid state of water, ice, forms when liquid water is cooled sufficiently. Ice cubes are rigid, with a definite shape and volume.

LIQUID STATE: WATER
When the temperature of a substance rises above its freezing point, it melts to become a liquid. Ice changes to water.

GASEOUS STATE: STEAM
Above its boiling point, a substance will become a gas. When heated sufficiently, liquid water turns to steam, a colorless gas.

Atoms and molecules

FALSE-COLOR IMAGE
OF ACTUAL GOLD
ATOMS

ATOMS ARE THE smallest individual parts of an element (see pp. 310-311). They are tiny, with diameters in the order of one ten-thousand-millionth of a meter (10^{-10} m). Two or more atoms join together (bond) to form a molecule of a substance known as a compound. For example, when atoms of the elements hydrogen and fluorine join together, they form a molecule of the compound hydrogen fluoride. So molecules are the smallest individual parts of a compound. Atoms themselves are not indivisible —they possess an internal structure. At their center is a dense nucleus consisting of protons, which have a positive electric charge (see p. 316), and neutrons, which are uncharged. Around the nucleus are negatively charged electrons. It is the electrons that give a substance most of its physical and chemical properties. They do not follow definite paths around the nucleus. Instead, electrons are said to be found within certain regions, called orbitals. These are arranged around the nucleus in "shells," each containing electrons of a particular energy. For example, the first shell (1) can hold up to two electrons, in a so-called s-orbital (1s). The second shell (2) can hold up to eight electrons in s-orbitals (2s) and p-orbitals (2p). If an atom loses an electron, it becomes a positive ion (cation). If an electron is gained, an atom becomes a negative ion (anion). Ions of opposite charges will attract and join together in a type of bonding known as ionic bonding. In covalent bonding, the atoms bond by sharing their electrons in what become molecular orbitals.

ATOMIC ORBITALS

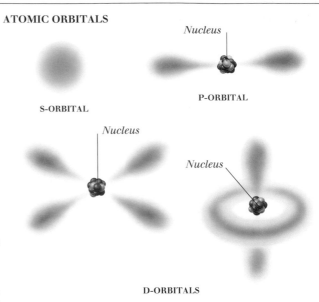

S-ORBITAL

P-ORBITAL

Nucleus

Nucleus

Nucleus

D-ORBITALS

MOLECULAR ORBITALS

Nucleus

Nucleus

Nucleus

Σ- (SIGMA) ORBITAL

π- (PI) ORBITAL

Nucleus

SP⁵-HYBRID ORBITAL

EXAMPLE OF IONIC BONDING

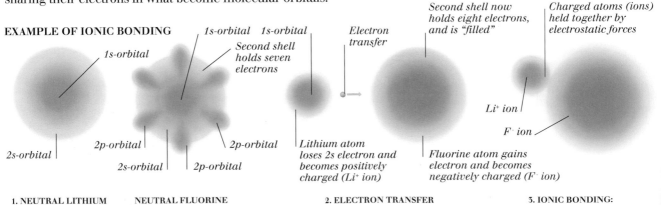

1s-orbital

1s-orbital   1s-orbital

Second shell
holds seven
electrons

Electron
transfer

Second shell now
holds eight electrons,
and is "filled"

Charged atoms (ions)
held together by
electrostatic forces

2s-orbital

2p-orbital

2s-orbital   2p-orbital

2p-orbital

Lithium atom
loses 2s electron and
becomes positively
charged (Li⁺ ion)

Fluorine atom gains
electron and becomes
negatively charged (F⁻ ion)

Li⁺ ion

F⁻ ion

1. NEUTRAL LITHIUM
ATOM (Li)

NEUTRAL FLUORINE
ATOM (F)

2. ELECTRON TRANSFER

3. IONIC BONDING:
LITHIUM FLUORIDE MOLECULE (LiF)

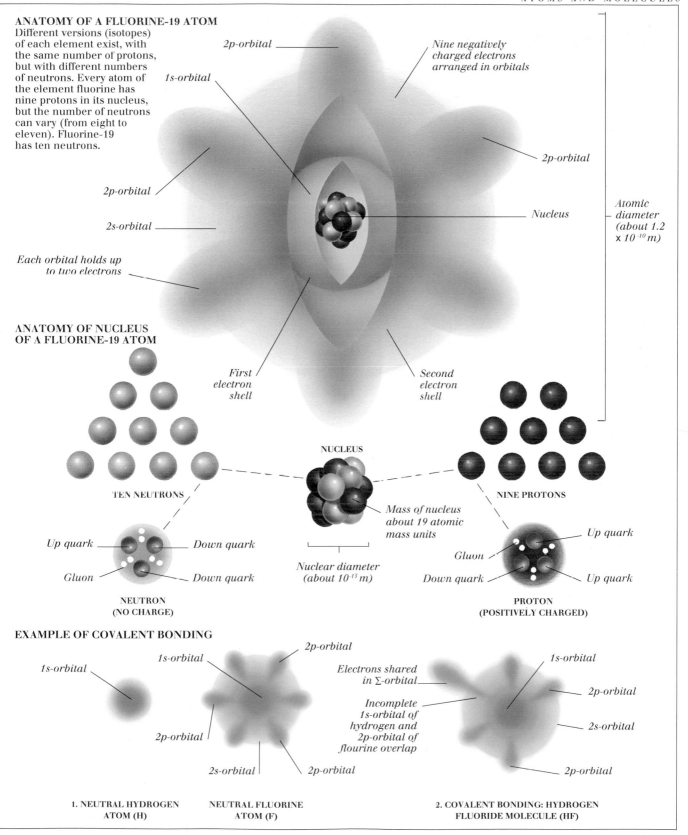

ANATOMY OF A FLUORINE-19 ATOM

Different versions (isotopes) of each element exist, with the same number of protons, but with different numbers of neutrons. Every atom of the element fluorine has nine protons in its nucleus, but the number of neutrons can vary (from eight to eleven). Fluorine-19 has ten neutrons.

2p-orbital

1s-orbital

Nine negatively charged electrons arranged in orbitals

2p-orbital

2p-orbital

2s-orbital

Nucleus

Atomic diameter (about 1.2 x 10^{-10} m)

Each orbital holds up to two electrons

ANATOMY OF NUCLEUS OF A FLUORINE-19 ATOM

First electron shell

Second electron shell

NUCLEUS

Mass of nucleus about 19 atomic mass units

TEN NEUTRONS

NINE PROTONS

Up quark

Down quark

Gluon

Down quark

Nuclear diameter (about 10^{-15} m)

Up quark

Gluon

Down quark

Up quark

NEUTRON (NO CHARGE)

PROTON (POSITIVELY CHARGED)

EXAMPLE OF COVALENT BONDING

1s-orbital

1s-orbital

2p-orbital

2p-orbital

2s-orbital

2p-orbital

Electrons shared in Σ-orbital

Incomplete 1s-orbital of hydrogen and 2p-orbital of flourine overlap

1s-orbital

2p-orbital

2s-orbital

2p-orbital

1. NEUTRAL HYDROGEN ATOM (H)

NEUTRAL FLUORINE ATOM (F)

2. COVALENT BONDING: HYDROGEN FLUORIDE MOLECULE (HF)

309

The periodic table

AN ELEMENT is a substance that consists of atoms of one type only. The 92 elements that occur naturally, and the 17 elements created artificially, are often arranged into a chart called the periodic table. Each element is defined by its atomic number—the number of protons in the nucleus of each of its atoms (it is also the number of electrons present). Atomic numbers increase along each row (period) and down each column (group). The shape of the table is determined by the way in which electrons arrange themselves around the nucleus: the positioning of elements in order of increasing atomic number brings together atoms with a similar pattern of orbiting electrons (orbitals). These appear in blocks. Electrons occupy shells of a certain energy (see pp. 308–309). Periods are ordered according to the filling of successive shells with electrons, while groups reflect the number of electrons in the outer shell (valency electrons). These outer electrons are important—they decide the chemical properties of the atom. Elements that appear in the same group have similar properties because they have the same number of electrons in their outer shell. Elements in Group 0 have filled shells, where the outer shell holds its maximum number of electrons, and are stable. Atoms of Group I elements have just one electron in their outer shell. This makes them unstable—and ready to react with other substances.

METALS AND NON-METALS

Elements at the left-hand side of each period are metals. Metals easily lose electrons and form positive ions. Non-metals, on the right of a period, tend to become negative ions. Semi-metals, which have properties of both metals and non-metals, are between the two.

Atomic number is number of protons in each nucleus

Atomic number goes up by one along each period

1st transition metals

Atomic number	
1	Atomic number
H	Chemical symbol
Hydrogen	Chemical name
1.0	Relative atomic mass

RELATIVE ATOMIC MASS
Atomic mass (formerly atomic weight) is the mass of each atom of an element. It is equal to the number of protons plus the number of neutrons (electrons have negligible mass). The figures given are the averages for all the different versions (isotopes) of each element, measured relative to the mass of carbon-12.

Two series always separated out from the table to give it a coherent shape

s-block *d-block*

Soft, silvery, and highly reactive metal

SODIUM: GROUP 1 METAL

Silvery, reactive metal

MAGNESIUM: GROUP 2 METAL

Hard, silvery metal

CHROMIUM: 1ST TRANSITION METAL

Radioactive metal

PLUTONIUM: ACTINIDE SERIES METAL

TYPES OF ELEMENT KEY:

- Alkali metals
- Alkaline earth metals
- Transition metals
- Lanthanides (rare earths)
- Actinides
- Poor metals
- Semi-metals
- Non-metals
- Noble gases

Bright yellow crystal

Purple-black solid turns to gas easily

IODINE: GROUP 7 SOLID NON-METAL

SULFUR: GROUP 6 SOLID NON-METAL

ALLOTROPES OF CARBON
Some elements exist in more than one form —these are known as allotropes. Carbon powder, graphite, and diamond are allotropes of carbon. They all consist of carbon atoms, but have very different physical properties.

DIAMOND

GRAPHITE

CARBON POWDER

Group 0

Boron and carbon groups | *Nitrogen and oxygen groups* | *Halogens*

| | | | | | 2 **He** Helium 4.0 | *Period* |

Group III | *Group IV* | *Group V* | *Group VI* | *Group VII*

| 5 **B** Boron 10.8 | 6 **C** Carbon 12.0 | 7 **N** Nitrogen 14.0 | 8 **O** Oxygen 16.0 | 9 **F** Fluorine 19.0 | 10 **Ne** Neon 20.2 | *Short period* |

| 13 **Al** Aluminum 27.0 | 14 **Si** Silicon 28.1 | 15 **P** Phosphorus 31.0 | 16 **S** Sulfur 32.1 | 17 **Cl** Chlorine 35.5 | 18 **Ar** Argon 40.0 |

2nd transition metals | *3rd transition metals*

26 **Fe** Iron 55.9	27 **Co** Cobalt 58.9	28 **Ni** Nickel 58.7	29 **Cu** Copper 63.5	30 **Zn** Zinc 65.4	31 **Ga** Gallium 69.7	32 **Ge** Germanium 72.6	33 **As** Arsenic 74.9	34 **Se** Selenium 79.0	35 **Br** Bromine 79.9	36 **Kr** Krypton 83.8	*Long period*
44 **Ru** Ruthenium 101.0	45 **Rh** Rhodium 102.9	46 **Pd** Palladium 106.4	47 **Ag** Silver 107.9	48 **Cd** Cadmium 112.4	49 **In** Indium 114.8	50 **Sn** Tin 118.7	51 **Sb** Antimony 121.8	52 **Te** Tellurium 127.6	53 **I** Iodine 126.9	54 **Xe** Xenon 131.3
76 **Os** Osmium 190.2	77 **Ir** Iridium 192.2	78 **Pt** Platinum 195.1	79 **Au** Gold 197.0	80 **Hg** Mercury 200.6	81 **Tl** Thallium 204.4	82 **Pb** Lead 207.2	83 **Bi** Bismuth 209.0	84 **Po** Polonium 210.0	85 **At** Astatine 210.0	86 **Rn** Radon 222.0
108 **Uno** Unniloctium (265)	109 **Une** Unnilennium (266)									

d-block | *p-block*

Atomic mass is estimated, as element exists fleetingly

Unreactive, colorless gas glows red in discharge tube

Shiny semi-metal

NOBLE GASES
Group 0 contains elements that have a filled (complete) outer shell of electrons, which means the atoms do not need to lose or gain electrons by bonding with other atoms. This makes them stable and they do not easily form ions or react with other elements. Noble gases are also called rare or inert gases.

Yellow, unreactive precious metal

Soft, shiny, reactive metal

GOLD: 3RD TRANSITION METAL

TIN: GROUP 4 POOR METAL

ANTIMONY: GROUP 5 SEMI-METAL

NEON: GROUP 0 COLORLESS GAS

| 61 **Pm** Promethium 147.0 | 62 **Sm** Samarium 150.4 | 63 **Eu** Europium 152.0 | 64 **Gd** Gadolinium 157.3 | 65 **Tb** Terbium 158.9 | 66 **Dy** Dysprosium 162.5 | 67 **Ho** Holmium 164.9 | 68 **Er** Erbium 167.3 | 69 **Tm** Thulium 168.9 | 70 **Yb** Ytterbium 173.0 | 71 **Lu** Lutetium 175.0 |
| 93 **Np** Neptunium 237.0 | 94 **Pu** Plutonium 242.0 | 95 **Am** Americium 243.0 | 96 **Cm** Curium 247.0 | 97 **Bk** Berkelium 247.0 | 98 **Cf** Californium 251.0 | 99 **Es** Einsteinium 254.0 | 100 **Fm** Fermium 253.0 | 101 **Md** Mendelevium 256.0 | 102 **No** Nobelium 254.0 | 103 **Lr** Lawrencium 257.0 |

f-block

Chemical reactions

A CHEMICAL REACTION TAKES PLACE whenever bonds between atoms are broken or made. In each case, atoms or groups of atoms rearrange, making new substances (products) from the original ones (reactants). Reactions happen naturally, or can be made to happen; they may take years, or only an instant. Some of the main types are shown here. A reaction usually involves a change in energy (see pp. 314-315). In a burning reaction, for example, the making of new bonds between atoms releases energy as heat and light. This type of reaction, in which heat is given off, is an exothermic reaction. Many reactions, like burning, are irreversible, but some can take place in either direction, and are said to be reversible. Reactions can be used to form solids from solutions: in a double decomposition reaction, two compounds in solution break down and re-form into two new substances, often creating a precipitate (insoluble solid); in displacement, an element (eg. copper) displaces another element (eg. silver) from a solution. The rate (speed) of a reaction is determined by many different factors, such as temperature, and the size and shape of the reactants. To describe and keep track of reactions, internationally recognized chemical symbols and equations are used. Reactions are also used in the laboratory to identify matter. An experiment with candle wax, for example, demonstrates that it contains carbon and hydrogen.

SALT FORMATION (ACID ON METAL)

Glass beaker

Hydrogen gas (H_2) given off

Zinc (Zn) replaces hydrogen (H) in acid (HCl) to form zinc chloride solution $(ZnCl_2)$

Hydrogen in acid driven off when acid meets a reactive metal

Zinc metal chippings (Zn)

Hydrochloric acid (HCl)

Effervescence

Zinc metal chippings (Zn)

THE REACTION
Hydrochloric acid added to zinc produces zinc chloride and hydrogen.
$$Zn + 2HCl \rightarrow ZnCl_2 + H_2$$

DISPLACEMENT

Copper metal (Cu)

Silver nitrate solution $(AgNO_3)$

Two metals compete for nitrate ions

Glass flask

Copper (Cu) ions displace silver (Ag) ions from silver nitrate solution $(AgNO_3)$

Blue solution of copper nitrate $(Cu(NO_3)_2)$ forms

Needles of silver metal (Ag) form

THE REACTION
Copper metal added to silver nitrate solution produces copper nitrate and silver metal.
$$Cu + 2AgNO_3 \rightarrow Cu(NO_3)_2 + 2Ag$$

BURNING MATTER

Ammonium dichromate $((NH_4)_2Cr_2O_7)$

Flame

In this burning reaction, atoms form simpler substances and give off heat and light

Ammonium dichromate $((NH_4)_2Cr_2O_7)$ converts to chromium oxide (Cr_2O_3)

Nitrogen monoxide (NO) and water vapor (H_2O) given off as colorless gases

THE REACTION
When lit, ammonium dichromate combines with oxygen from air.
$$(NH_4)_2Cr_2O_7 + O_2 \rightarrow Cr_2O_3 + 4H_2O + 2NO$$

A REVERSIBLE REACTION

Flat-bottomed glass flask

Potassium chromate solution (K_2CrO_4)

Bright yellow solution contains potassium and chromate ions

Pipette

Hydrochloric acid (HCl) added in drops

Acid causes reaction to take place

Chromate ions converted to orange dichromate ions

Potassium dichromate (KCr_2O_7) forms

Pipette

Sodium hydroxide (NaOH) neutralizes the acid

Solution turns to bright orange of potassium dichromate

Potassium dichromate (KCr_2O_7) re-forms to potassium chromate (K_2CrO_4)

Sodium hydroxide (NaOH) added in drops

Solution returns to original bright yellow color

1. THE REACTANT
Potassium chromate dissolves in water to form potassium ions and chromate ions.
$$K_2CrO_4 \rightarrow 2K^+ + CrO_4^{2-}$$

2. THE REACTION
Addition of hydrochloric acid changes chromate ions into dichromate ions.
$$2CrO_4^{2-} \rightarrow Cr_2O_7^{2-}$$

3. REVERSING
Addition of sodium hydroxide changes dichromate ions back into chromate ions.
$$Cr_2O_7^{2-} \rightarrow 2CrO_4^{2-}$$

FERMENTATION

Yeast converts sugar into alcohol (C_2H_5OH) and carbon dioxide gas (CO_2)

Airtight stopper

Flat-bottomed glass flask

Yeast mixed with warm water and sugar ($C_6H_{12}O_6$)

Carbon dioxide bubbles (CO_2)

THE REACTION
Yeast converts sugar and warm water into alcohol and carbon dioxide.
$C_6H_{12}O_6 \rightarrow 2C_2H_5OH + 2CO_2$

DOUBLE DECOMPOSITION

Potassium iodide solution (KI)

Lead nitrate solution ($Pb(NO_3)_2$)

Two solutions swap partners

Potassium iodide solution added to lead nitrate solution

Lead iodide (PbI_2), a yellow solid, forms

Potassium nitrate solution (KNO_3) forms

1. THE REACTANTS
Potassium iodide in water (KI) and lead nitrate in water ($Pb(NO_3)_2$) each form colorless solutions.

2. THE REACTION
When the solutions are mixed, lead iodide, a precipitate, and potassium nitrate solution are formed.
$2KI + Pb(NO_3)_2 \rightarrow PbI_2 + 2KNO_3$

TESTING CANDLE WAX, AN ORGANIC COMPOUND

Burning produces carbon dioxide gas (CO_2) and water vapor (H_2O)

Delivery tube

Clamp stand

Unburned carbon forms soot particles

Gases are trapped in funnel

Stopper

Delivery tube

Stopper

Tube connection to pump that sucks gases through

Flame

Thistle funnel

U-tube

Stopper

Burning candle wax

Water vapor condenses to form liquid water (H_2O)

Water vapor trapped by solid drying agent, anhydrous copper sulfate ($CuSO_4$)

Clamp

Anhydrous copper sulfate ($CuSO_4$)

Carbon dioxide gas (CO_2) given off

Calcium hydroxide ($Ca(OH)_2$) and carbon dioxide (CO_2) form insoluble calcium carbonate ($CaCO_3$): lime water becomes milky

Test tube

Calcium hydroxide solution (lime water, $Ca(OH)_2$))

Candle wax ($C_{18}H_{38}$), a hydrocarbon, contains the elements carbon and hydrogen

Anhydrous copper sulfate crystals ($CuSO_4$) combine with water vapor (H_2O) to form darker blue hydrated copper sulfate ($CuSO_4 . 10H_2O$)

1. THE BURNING REACTION
Burning wax produces carbon dioxide gas and water vapor.
$2C_{18}H_{38} + 55O_2 \rightarrow 36CO_2 + 38H_2O$

2. TESTING FOR WATER VAPOUR
A solid drying agent traps water vapor, proving the presence of hydrogen in the candle wax.
$CuSO_4 + 10H_2O \rightarrow CuSO_4 . 10H_2O$

3. TESTING FOR CARBON DIOXIDE
Calcium hydroxide in solution reacts with carbon dioxide, forming a carbonate and turning milky.
$Ca(OH)_2 + CO_2 \rightarrow CaCO_3 + H_2O$

Energy

ANYTHING THAT HAPPENS—from a pin drop to an explosion
—requires energy. Energy is the capacity for doing work
(making something happen). Various forms of energy exist,
including light, heat, sound, electrical, chemical, nuclear,
kinetic, and potential energies. The Law of Conservation
of Energy states that the total amount of energy in the
Universe is fixed—energy cannot be created or destroyed,
it can only change from one form to another (energy
transfer). For example, potential energy is energy that
is stored, and can be used in the future. An object gains
potential energy when it is lifted; as the object is released,
potential energy changes into the energy of motion (kinetic
energy). During transference, some of the energy converts
into heat. A combined heat and power station can put some
of the "waste" heat to useful effect in local schools and
housing. Most of the Earth's energy is provided by the Sun,
in the form of electromagnetic radiation (see pp. 316-317).
Some of this energy transfers to plant and animal life, and
ultimately to fossil fuels, where it is stored in chemical
form. Our bodies obtain energy from the food we eat,
while energy needed for other tasks, such as heating and
transportation, can be obtained by burning fossil fuels
—or by harnessing natural forces like wind or moving
water—to generate electricity. Another source is nuclear
power, where energy is released by reactions in the nucleus
of an atom. All energy is measured by the international
unit, the joule (J). As a guide, one joule is about equal to
the amount of energy needed to lift an apple one yard.

SANKEY DIAGRAM SHOWING ENERGY FLOW IN A COAL-FIRED COMBINED HEAT AND POWER STATION

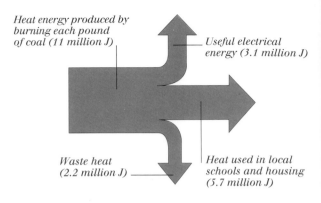

Heat energy produced by burning each pound of coal (11 million J)

Useful electrical energy (3.1 million J)

Waste heat (2.2 million J)

Heat used in local schools and housing (5.7 million J)

CROSS-SECTION OF HYDROELECTRIC POWER STATION WITH FRANCIS TURBINE

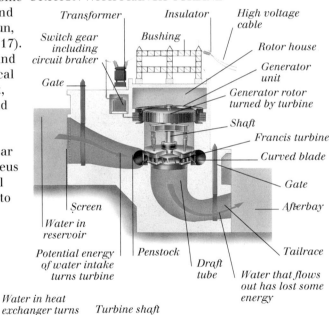

Transformer

Insulator

High voltage cable

Switch gear including circuit braker

Bushing

Rotor house

Generator unit

Gate

Generator rotor turned by turbine

Shaft

Francis turbine

Curved blade

Gate

Screen

Afterbay

Water in reservoir

Potential energy of water intake turns turbine

Penstock

Draft tube

Tailrace

Water that flows out has lost some energy

CROSS-SECTION OF NUCLEAR POWER STATION WITH PRESSURIZED WATER REACTOR

Steam generator

Concrete shielding

Water pressurizer

Steel girder framework

Control rod

Reactor core

Pump

Moderator (water)

Enriched uranium fuel

Coolant (water) takes heat from reactor core to heat exchanger

Heat exchanger

Water pumped back into steam generator

Pump

Water in heat exchanger turns to steam

Steam drives turbine

Turbine shaft turns generator

Generator produces electric current at 25,000 volts

Water cools used steam

Steam loses energy to turbine and condenses back to water

Transformer increases voltage to 300,000 volts

High voltage cable

Pylon carries high voltage electricity

Hot water to cooling tower

Cold water from cooling tower

ENERGY SYSTEMS

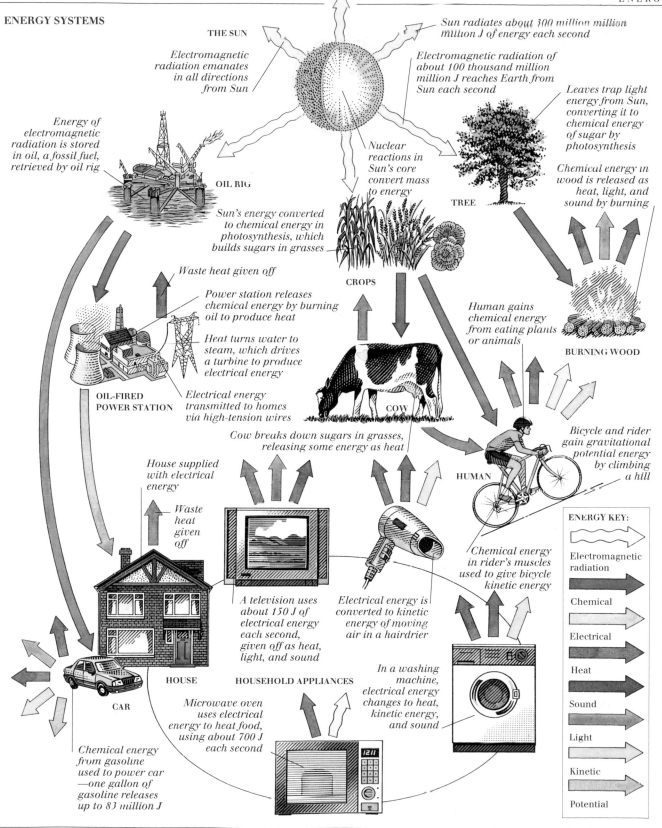

THE SUN

Electromagnetic radiation emanates in all directions from Sun

Sun radiates about 300 million million million J of energy each second

Electromagnetic radiation of about 100 thousand million million J reaches Earth from Sun each second

Leaves trap light energy from Sun, converting it to chemical energy of sugar by photosynthesis

TREE

Chemical energy in wood is released as heat, light, and sound by burning

Energy of electromagnetic radiation is stored in oil, a fossil fuel, retrieved by oil rig

OIL RIG

Nuclear reactions in Sun's core convert mass to energy

Sun's energy converted to chemical energy in photosynthesis, which builds sugars in grasses

CROPS

Waste heat given off

Power station releases chemical energy by burning oil to produce heat

Heat turns water to steam, which drives a turbine to produce electrical energy

OIL-FIRED POWER STATION

Electrical energy transmitted to homes via high-tension wires

Human gains chemical energy from eating plants or animals

BURNING WOOD

COW

Cow breaks down sugars in grasses, releasing some energy as heat

House supplied with electrical energy

Waste heat given off

HUMAN

Bicycle and rider gain gravitational potential energy by climbing a hill

Chemical energy in rider's muscles used to give bicycle kinetic energy

A television uses about 150 J of electrical energy each second, given off as heat, light, and sound

Electrical energy is converted to kinetic energy of moving air in a hairdrier

HOUSE

HOUSEHOLD APPLIANCES

Microwave oven uses electrical energy to heat food, using about 700 J each second

In a washing machine, electrical energy changes to heat, kinetic energy, and sound

CAR

Chemical energy from gasoline used to power car —one gallon of gasoline releases up to 83 million J

ENERGY KEY:

Electromagnetic radiation

Chemical

Electrical

Heat

Sound

Light

Kinetic

Potential

Electricity and magnetism

ELECTRICAL EFFECTS result from an imbalance of electric charge. There are two types of electric charge: positive (carried by protons) and negative (carried by electrons). If charges are opposite (unlike), they attract one another, while like charges repel. These forces of attraction and repulsion (electrostatic forces) exist between any two charged particles. Matter is normally uncharged, but if electrons are gained, an object will gain an overall negative charge; if they are removed, it becomes positive. Objects with an overall negative or positive charge are said to have an imbalance of charge, and exert the same forces as individual negative and positive charges. On this larger scale, the forces will always act to regain the balance of charge. This causes static electricity. Lightning, for example, is produced by clouds discharging a huge excess of negative electrons. If charges are free—in a wire or material that allows electrons to pass through it—the forces cause a flow of charge called an electric current. Some substances exhibit the strange phenomenon of magnetism—which also produces attractive and repulsive forces. Magnetic substances consist of small regions called domains. Normally unmagnetized, they can be magnetized by being placed in a magnetic field. Magnetism and electricity are inextricably linked, a fact put to use in motors and generators.

LIGHTNING

VAN DE GRAAFF (ELECTROSTATIC) GENERATOR

Positive charges at many thousands of volts

Metal dome

Rotation of belt

Positively charged belt strips negative charges (electrons) from dome via metal comb, giving dome a positive charge

Pulley wheel

Moving rubber belt gains a positive charge

Insulating column prevents charges leaking away

Positive metal comb strips negative charges (electrons) from belt

Negatively charged metal pla

Connection to positive electrical supply

Pulley wheel

Rotation of belt

Connection to negative electrical supply

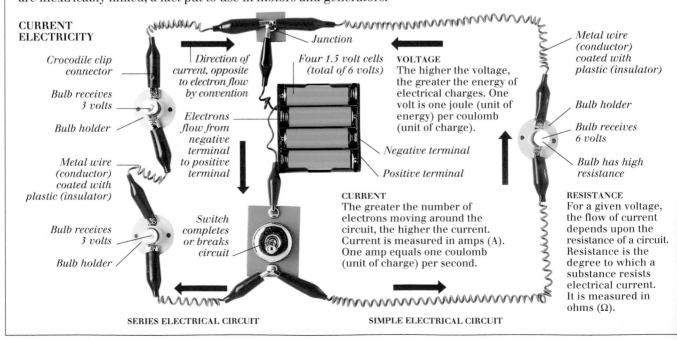

CURRENT ELECTRICITY

Crocodile clip connector

Bulb receives 3 volts

Bulb holder

Metal wire (conductor) coated with plastic (insulator)

Bulb receives 3 volts

Bulb holder

Junction

Direction of current, opposite to electron flow by convention

Electrons flow from negative terminal to positive terminal

Switch completes or breaks circuit

Four 1.5 volt cells (total of 6 volts)

Negative terminal

Positive terminal

VOLTAGE
The higher the voltage, the greater the energy of electrical charges. One volt is one joule (unit of energy) per coulomb (unit of charge).

CURRENT
The greater the number of electrons moving around the circuit, the higher the current. Current is measured in amps (A). One amp equals one coulomb (unit of charge) per second.

Metal wire (conductor) coated with plastic (insulator)

Bulb holder

Bulb receives 6 volts

Bulb has high resistance

RESISTANCE
For a given voltage, the flow of current depends upon the resistance of a circuit. Resistance is the degree to which a substance resists electrical current. It is measured in ohms (Ω).

SERIES ELECTRICAL CIRCUIT

SIMPLE ELECTRICAL CIRCUIT

MAGNETIC FIELDS AND FORCES

Iron filings.

Profile of magnetic field

Bar magnet

North-seeking pole

Like poles repel

North-seeking pole

Unlike poles attract

North-seeking pole

South-seeking pole of electromagnet

North-seeking pole

South-seeking pole

Unlike poles attract

Direction of force

South-seeking pole

South-seeking pole

Like poles repel

Electromagnet

Wire to battery

MAGNETIC DOMAINS

Domain

Direction of magnetization within domain is random

Direction of magnetization within domain has aligned

Domain aligned with magnetization has grown

Domain boundary

Domain not aligned with magnetization has shrunk

Direction of overall magnetization

UNMAGNETIZED IRON

MAGNETIZED IRON IN A MAGNETIC FIELD

GENERATING MAGNETISM FROM ELECTRICITY

Direction of magnetic field (from north pole to south pole)

Electric current produces magnetic field

Magnetic field

Coil carries electric current

Direction of current

Metal wire (conductor) coated with plastic (insulator)

Negative terminal

Positive terminal

Four 1.5 volt cells (total of 6 volts)

CIRCUIT WITH ELECTROMAGNET

GENERATING ELECTRICITY FROM MAGNETISM

Terminal box

Coil of wire

Permanent magnet

Bearing

Non-drive end

Coil of wire

Terminal

Stator

Main rotor turns in magnetic field produced by coil of wire in stator

Fan

Drive end

Coil of wire

Shaft

Secondary (exciter) rotor

ELECTRIC GENERATOR
In a generator, the rotor rotates within the magnetic field of the stator to produce an electric current.

Coil of wire rotates within magnetic field of permanent magnet

Permanent magnet

Iron core

Steel casing

Coated copper winding

Commutator

Terminal

Spindle

End of shaft

Terminal

ELECTRIC MOTOR
In a motor, magnetic forces between the winding and permanent magnet produce a rotary motion.

Light

LIGHT IS A FORM OF ENERGY. It is a type of electromagnetic radiation, like X rays or radio waves. All electromagnetic radiation is produced by electric charges (see pp. 316-317): it is caused by the effects of oscillating electric and magnetic fields as they travel through space. Electromagnetic radiation is considered to have both wave and particle properties. It can be thought of as a wave of electricity and magnetism. In that case, the difference between the various forms of radiation is their wavelength. Radiation can also be said to consist of particles, or packets of energy, called photons. The difference between light and X rays, for instance, is the amount of energy that each photon carries. The complete range of radiation is referred to as the electromagnetic spectrum, extending from low energy, long wavelength radio waves to high energy, short wavelength gamma rays. Light is the only part of the electromagnetic spectrum that is visible. White light from the Sun is made up of all the visible wavelengths of radiation, which can be seen when it is separated by using a prism. Light, like all forms of electromagnetic radiation, can be reflected (bounced back) and refracted (bent). Different parts of the electromagnetic spectrum are produced in different ways. Sometimes visible light—and infrared radiation—is generated by the vibrating particles of warm or hot objects. The emission of light in this way is called incandescence. Light can also be produced by fluorescence, a phenomenon in which electrons gain and lose energy within atoms.

MAXWELLIAN DIAGRAM OF ELECTROMAGNETIC RADIATION AS WAVES

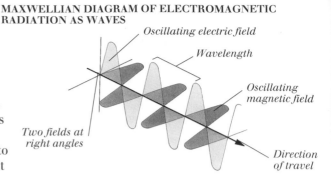

Oscillating electric field

Wavelength

Oscillating magnetic field

Two fields at right angles

Direction of travel

ELECTROMAGNETIC RADIATION AS PARTICLES

Photon thought of as wave packet of energy

Red light has long wavelength

PHOTON OF RED LIGHT

Blue light has about twice the energy of red light

Blue light has shorter wavelength: waves are more tightly packed

PHOTON OF BLUE LIGHT

SPLITTING WHITE LIGHT INTO THE SPECTRUM

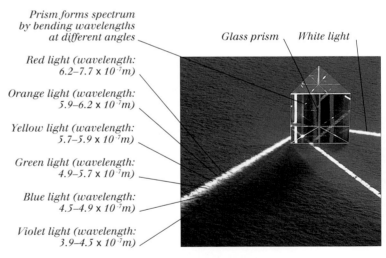

Prism forms spectrum by bending wavelengths at different angles

Glass prism

White light

Red light (wavelength: $6.2–7.7 \times 10^{-7}$m)

Orange light (wavelength: $5.9–6.2 \times 10^{-7}$m)

Yellow light (wavelength: $5.7–5.9 \times 10^{-7}$m)

Green light (wavelength: $4.9–5.7 \times 10^{-7}$m)

Blue light (wavelength: $4.5–4.9 \times 10^{-7}$m)

Violet light (wavelength: $3.9–4.5 \times 10^{-7}$m)

THE ELECTROMAGNETIC SPECTRUM

ENERGY (JOULES)	10^{-28}	10^{-27}	10^{-26}	10^{-25}	10^{-24}	10^{-23}	10^{-22}	10^{-21}	10^{-20}

WAVELENGTH (METERS) 10^4 10^3 10^2 10 1 10^{-1} 10^{-2} 10^{-3} 10^{-4} 10^{-5}

Long-wave radio | Medium-wave radio | Shortwave radio | Very high-frequency (VHF) radio | Microwaves | Infrared radiation

Radio waves

ARTIFICIAL LIGHT SOURCES

FLUORESCENT TUBE

Glass tube filled with mercury vapor

Coiled tungsten filament

Ceramic end-piece

Electrical contact

Glass support

Filament heated and negatively charged electrons emitted

Electrons accelerate from one coil to the other

Electrons collide with mercury atoms

Mercury atom

Free electron

Energy from collision produces ultraviolet light (shortwave radiation)

Phosphor coating

Glass

Action of ultraviolet light on phosphor produces visible light (long-wave radiation)

SECTION OF PHOSPHOR COATING OF FLUORESCENT TUBE: HOW FLUORESCENT LIGHT IS PRODUCED

INCANDESCENT LIGHT BULB

SECTION OF FILAMENT OF INCANDESCENT LIGHT BULB: HOW INCANDESCENT LIGHT IS PRODUCED

Moving electrons collide with metal atoms

Hot filament gives out light

Vibration of metal atoms increases temperature

Lead-in wire

Glass bulb

Seal

Glass support

Screw fitting

Electrical contact

Coiled tungsten filament

Mixture of unreactive gases at low pressure

Electrical contact

REFLECTION OF LIGHT

Incident laser light

Mirror

Mirror support

Light strikes smooth surface at an angle, which reflects it at the same angle

Reflected light

REFRACTION OF LIGHT

Glass (transparent substance)

Incident laser light

Light enters substance

Light slows down and bends as it passes from air to glass

Light speeds up as it leaves glass

Refracted (bent) light

10^{-18} | 10^{-17} | 10^{-16} | 10^{-15} | 10^{-14} | 10^{-13} | 10^{-12} | 10^{-11} | 10^{-10} | 10^{-9} | 10^{-8} |

10^{-7} | 10^{-8} | 10^{-9} | 10^{-10} | 10^{-11} | 10^{-12} | 10^{-13} | 10^{-14} | 10^{-15} | 10^{-16} | 10^{-17} |

Visible light

Ultraviolet radiation

X rays

Gamma rays

Force and motion

FORCES ARE PUSHES OR PULLS that change the motion of objects. To make a stationary object move, or a moving object stop, a force is needed. A force is also required to change the speed or direction of an object. This change in speed or direction is known as acceleration. Acceleration depends on the size (magnitude) of the force, and on the mass of the object. The effects of forces were first summarized by Isaac Newton in his three laws of motion. The international unit of force, named after him, is the newton (N), which is approximately equal to the weight of one apple. Gravity—the force of attraction between any two masses—can be measured using a newton meter (spring balance). Forces are put to useful effect in machines. A simple machine, such as a wheel and axle, is a device that changes the size or direction of an applied force. It allows an applied force (the effort) to produce another force (the load). A lever uses a bar that turns on a fulcrum to exert force. In all simple machines, there is a relationship between force and distance. A small force (in a compound pulley, for instance) moves through a large distance to lift a heavy object a small distance. This is called the Law of Simple Machines.

SIMPLE MACHINES

Single-pulley system (simple pulley)

Pulley wheel

Simple pulley only changes direction of a force

Effort is the same size as the load (10 N) and is pulled the same distance

One rope attached to load

Load of 10 N

Two-pulley system (simple pulley)

Pulley wheel

Effort is half the load (5 N), but the rope must be pulled twice the distance

Two ropes share the force and distance

Pulley wheel

Load of 10 N

Four-pulley system (compound pulley)

Two pulley wheels

Effort is one quarter of the load (2.5 N), but the rope must be pulled four times the distance

Four ropes share the force and distance

SIMPLE AND COMPOUND PULLEYS

Two pulley wheels

Load of 10 N

NEWTON METERS (SPRING BALANCES)

Weight is measured using a spring

When weight pulls downward, pointer moves along scale and measures force

Weight is 10 N

Weight is 20 N

Mass of 1 kg

Mass of 2 kg

WEIGHT AND MASS
The mass of an object is a measure of the quantity of matter that it possesses. Mass is usually measured in grams (g) or kilograms (kg). The weight of an object is the force exerted on the object's mass by gravity. Since weight is a force, its unit is the newton (N).

Wheel and axle multiplies the effort

Force is transmitted to the wheels by the chain

Pedal

Crank

Effort, provided by cyclist's muscles, is smaller than the load, but moves through a greater distance

A larger force, the load, is produced at the axle

WHEEL AND AXLE

A screw, acting like a wedge wrapped around a shaft, multiplies the effort

Effort, a turning force supplied through a screwdriver

Pitch (the angle of the screw thread)

The smaller the angle of pitch, the less force is required, but more turns are needed to move it through a greater distance

A larger force, the load, pulls the screw into wood

SCREW

Effort pushes axe into wood

A larger force, the load, moves through a smaller distance to push wood apart

Axe blade has wedge shape

Wedge multiplies effort

WEDGE

NEWTON'S THREE LAWS OF MOTION

NEWTON'S FIRST LAW
When no force acts on a body, it will continue in a state of rest or uniform motion.

Newton meter shows no applied force

Mass of 1 kg

Mass of trolley is negligible

Trolley is not in motion, and will remain at rest until a force acts

NO FORCE, NO ACCELERATION: STATE OF REST

Constant speed

Mass of 1 kg

Newton meter shows no applied force

Trolley is in motion, and will continue at a constant speed in a straight line until a force acts

NO FORCE, NO ACCELERATION: UNIFORM MOTION

NEWTON'S SECOND LAW
When a force acts on a body, the motion of the body will change. The size of the change will depend upon the mass of the object and the magnitude of the applied force.

Acceleration is 2 ms⁻²

Trolley and mass (1 kg) gain 2 meters per second of speed each second (2 ms⁻²)

Newton meter registers force of 2 N

Mass of 1 kg

Acceleration is 1 ms⁻²

Trolley and mass (2 kg) gain 1 meter per second of speed each second (1 ms⁻²)

Newton meter registers force of 2 N

Mass of 2 kg

With the same applied force, an object with 2 kg mass accelerates at half the rate of object with 1 kg mass

FORCE AND ACCELERATION: SMALL MASS, LARGE ACCELERATION　　**FORCE AND ACCELERATION: LARGE MASS, SMALL ACCELERATION**

NEWTON'S THIRD LAW
If one object exerts a force on another, an equal and opposite force, called the reaction force, is applied by the second object on the first.

Newton meters pull on each other with equal and opposite forces

Acceleration: the trolley and mass accelerate at 2 ms⁻²

Newton meter registers force of 2 N to the left

Newton meter registers force of 2 N to the right

Mass of 1 kg

Person experiences a reaction force

ACTION AND REACTION

THREE CLASSES OF LEVER

Fulcrum, between effort and load

Effort

Load is greater than effort, but moves through smaller distance

CLASS 1 LEVER
Pliers consist of two class 1 levers.

Fulcrum

Load, between effort and fulcrum

Effort is smaller than load, but moves through greater distance

CLASS 2 LEVER
Nutcrackers consist of two class 2 levers.

Load is applied at open end

Effort forces tongs together

Load is smaller than effort, but moves through greater distance

Effort, between fulcrum and load

Fulcrum

CLASS 3 LEVER
Tongs consist of two class 3 levers.

RAIL AND ROAD

Steam locomotives

WAGONS THAT ARE PULLED along tracks have been used to transport material since the 16th century, but these trains were drawn by men or horses until the invention of the steam locomotive. Steam locomotives enabled the basic railroad system to realize its true potential. In 1804, Richard Trevithick built the world's first working steam locomotive in South Wales. It was not entirely successful, but it encouraged others to develop new designs. By 1829, the British engineer Robert Stephenson had built the Rocket, considered to be the forerunner of the modern locomotive. The Rocket was a self-sufficient unit, carrying coal to heat the boiler and a water supply for generating steam. Steam passed from the boiler to force the pistons back and forth, and this movement turned the driving wheels, propelling the train forward. Used steam was then expelled in characteristic puffs. Later steam locomotives, like Ellerman Lines and the Mallard, worked in a similar way, but on a much larger scale. The simple design and reliability of steam locomotives ensured that they changed very little in 120 years of use, before being replaced in the 1950s by more efficient diesel and electric power (see pp. 326-329).

ROCKET STEAM LOCOMOTIVE, 1829

Chimney

Smokebox

Leaf spring

Rocket nameplate

Pipe takes steam from boiler to cylinder

Regulator (throttle)

Wrought iron boiler

Remains of firebox

Valve chest

Valve setting control

Wooden buffer beam

Wooden driving wheel

Metal tire

Axle

Ballast

Rail chair

Wrought iron rail

Wooden sleeper

Piston rod

Cylinder

Carrying wheel

Driver's platform

ELLERMAN LINES, 1949 (CUTAWAY VIEW)

Vacuum reservoir

Water filler

Hand rail

Panel brace

Panel sheeting

Water tank

Coal space

Tender hand brake

Cab

Firebox

Brick arch

Stay

Buffer

Brake vacuum pipe

Wheel guard

Axle

Axle box

Tender wheel

Brake rigging

Water float to indicate water level

Water float lever

Step

Axle box cover

Coupling

Coil spring

Trailing wheel

Footplate

Grate

Fire drawn into fire tubes

TENDER

CAB INTERIOR OF MALLARD EXPRESS STEAM LOCOMOTIVE, 1938

Steam sanding control

Blower isolator valve

Pressure gauge isolator valve

Vacuum brake isolator valve

Steam heating isolator valve

Steam chest pressure gauge

Sliding roof vent

Vacuum brake pressure gauge

Boiler pressure gauge

Blower control

Gauge glass to show level of water in boiler

Regulator controls flow of steam to cylinders

Exhaust steam water injector control

Cab side window

Steam heating pressure gauge

Vacuum brake lever

Glass deflector

Live steam water injector control

Whistle lever

Manual sanding lever

Cylinder drain lever

Reverser handle

Control valve for hot water hose

Driver's seat

Fireman's seat

Steam-operated reversing shaft lock control

Oil can warming tray

Firebox

Firehole

Firebox door

Steam heat safety valve

Fire tube

Steam dome

Mechanical lubricator

Pipe takes steam from boiler to cylinder

Chimney

Thermal siphon

Regulator valve

Superheater tube inside flue tube

Boiler

Blast pipe

Smoke box

Smoke box door

Lubricating pipe

Piston valve

Buffer

Brake shoe

Expansion lever

Slide bar

Screw coupling

Brake rigging

Driving wheel

Combination lever

Crank

Connecting rod

Piston, linked to connecting rod

Leading wheel

Coupling rod

Cylinder

STEAM LOCOMOTIVE

Diesel trains

RUDOLF DIESEL FIRST DEMONSTRATED the diesel engine in Germany in 1898, but it was not until the 1940s that diesel locomotives were successfully established on both passenger and freight services in the U.S. Early diesel locomotives like the Union Pacific were more expensive to build than steam locomotives, but were more efficient and cheaper to operate, especially where oil was plentiful. One feature of diesel engines is that the power output cannot be coupled directly to the wheels. To convert the mechanical energy produced by diesel engines, a transmission system is needed. Almost all diesel locomotives have electric transmissions, and are known as diesel-electric locomotives. The diesel engine works by drawing air into the cylinders and compressing it to increase its temperature; a small quantity of diesel fuel is then injected into it. The resulting combustion drives the generator (more recently an alternator) to produce electricity, which is fed to electric motors connected to the wheels. Diesel-electric locomotives are essentially electric locomotives that carry their own power plants, and are used worldwide today. The Deltic diesel-electric locomotive, similar to the one shown here, replaced classic express steam locomotives, and ran at speeds up to 100 mph.

FRONT VIEW OF UNION PACIFIC DIESEL-ELECTRIC LOCOMOTIVE, 1950s

Exhaust vent   *Windshield wiper*   *Horn*   *Cab front window*   *Headlight*

Cab door

Name of operating railroad

Illuminated locomotive unit number

Railroad crest

Cab step   *Step*   *Motor-driven bogie axle*   *Air-brake coupling hose*   *Center buck-eye coupler*

PROTOTYPE DELTIC DIESEL-ELECTRIC LOCOMOTIVE, 1956

Engine room vent   *Inspection hatch*   *Engine exhaust port*   *Radiator fan*   *Engine room window*   *Engine room vent*

DELTIC

Fuel tank   *Water for heating boiler*   *Inspection socket*   *Folding step*   *Drain for radiator coolant*   *Radiator coolant*   *Sand box*   *Telescopic damper*   *Drain for control reservoir*

DIESEL ENGINE OF BRITISH RAIL CLASS 20
DIESEL-ELECTRIC LOCOMOTIVE

Exhaust vent

Cylinder head
(V-four configuration)

Turbo-charged diesel
engine drives generator

Generator
cooling fan

Generator
compartment
vent

Auxiliary
generator

Main generator
produces
electricity that
drives wheels

Main chassis
member

Innermost
wheel set on
cab-end bogie

Air brake pipe

Brake
rigging

Battery
box

Engine crankcase

Air reservoir and
isolator valves

Lubricating oil
primary pump and
fuel supply pump

Cab
door

Driver's seat

Warning horn

Cab

Windshield

Windshield wiper

Cab window

Manufacturer's
logo

Cab vent

Indicator
light

Sand box

Buffer

Brake cylinder

Roller-bearing
axle box

Brake
shoe

Brake
actuating chain

Transverse leaf spring
secondary suspension

Coil spring primary
suspension

EXAMPLES OF FREIGHT CARS

BOX CAR

HOPPER CAR

REFRIGERATOR CAR

LIVESTOCK CAR

FLAT CAR WITH BULKHEADS

AUTOMOBILE CAR

Electric and high-speed trains

THE FIRST ELECTRIC LOCOMOTIVE ran in 1879 in Berlin, Germany. In Europe, electric trains developed as a more efficient alternative to the steam locomotive and diesel-electric power. Like diesels, electric trains employ electric motors to drive the wheels but, unlike diesels, the electricity is generated externally at a power station. Electric current is picked up either from a catenary (overhead cable) via a pantograph, or from a third rail. Since it does not carry its own power-generating equipment, an electric locomotive has a better power-to-weight ratio and greater acceleration than its diesel-electric equivalent. This makes electric trains highly suitable for urban routes with many stops. They are also faster, quieter, and cause less pollution. The latest electric French TGV (Train à Grande Vitesse) reaches 186 mph; other trains, like the London to Paris and Brussels Eurostar, can run at several voltages and operate between different countries. Simpler electric trains perform special duties—the "People Mover" at Gatwick Airport, London, runs between terminals.

HOW ALTERNATING CURRENT (AC) ELECTRIC TRAINS WORK

Running rail for return current

Feeder station provides current

Catenary

Vacuum circuit breaker

Pantograph collects current

Thyristor converter converts current (ac) to direct current (dc)

Traction motor turns wheel

Control circuit

Transformer steps down voltage

Axle brush

FRONT VIEW OF PARIS METRO

Route number

Windshield wiper

Unit number

Operator's initials (Régie Autonome des Transports Parisien)

Rubber running wheel

Guard for rubber wheel

Door open/shut indicator light

Driver's seat

Handle

Front light (white)

Rear light (red)

Buffing pad

Rubber guide wheel

FRONT VIEW OF ITALIAN STATE RAILWAYS CLASS 402 ELECTRIC LOCOMOTIVE

Collector strip for electric current

Double-arm pantograph

Headlight

Windshield wiper

Italian State Railways crest

Number of electric (E) locomotive (class 402 No. 5)

Buffer

Jumper cable

Conventional hook-screw coupling

Front light (white)

Rear light (red)

SIDE VIEW OF GATWICK EXPRESS "PEOPLE MOVER"

Pneumatic rubber wheel

Concrete track

Automatic door

No driver (train controlled by central computer)

EUROSTAR MULTI-VOLTAGE ELECTRIC TRAIN

Cab window

Grill over warning horn

Rear light (red)

Headlight (white)

Fiberglass reinforced plastic cover

Fiberglass reinforced plastic cover

Aerofoil wheel guard

Aerofoil wheel guard

Sanding pipe

FRONT VIEW

Cab side window

Cab front window

Electric equipment compartment

Cab door

Side vent

Leading driven axle

Horizontal telescopic damper

Third (electric) rail collector shoe

Coil spring suspension

SIDE VIEW

TGV ELECTRIC HIGH-SPEED TRAIN

Luggage rack

Reading light

Double-glazed and tinted side window

Sliding curtain

Seat

Main overhead lighting

Automatic electric carriage end door

Antimacassar

Headrest

Armrest

Center gangway

INTERIOR OF TGV

Cab door

Hand rail

Side vent

Roof vent

Cab side window

Cab front window

Windshield wiper

Emergency exit door

Access panel for servicing

Nose air deflector dam

306

SNCF

Vertical damper

Horizontal damper

SIDE VIEW OF TGV

Train equipment

MODERN RAILROAD TRACK consists of two parallel steel rails clipped onto a support called a sleeper. Sleepers are usually made of reinforced concrete, although wood and steel are still used. The distance between the inside edges of the rails is the track gauge. It evolved in Britain, which uses a gauge of 4 ft 8½ in (1,435 mm), known as the standard gauge. As engineering grew more sophisticated, narrower gauges were adopted because they cost less to build. The loading gauge, which is equally important, determines the size of the largest loaded vehicle that may pass through tunnels and under bridges with adequate clearance. Safe train operation relies on following a signaling system. At first, signaling was based on a simple time interval between trains, but it now depends on maintaining a safe distance between successive trains traveling in the same direction. Most modern signals are colored lights, but older mechanical semaphore signals are still used. On the latest high-speed lines, train drivers receive control instructions by electronic means. Signaling depends on reliable control of the train by effective braking. For fast, modern trains, which have considerable momentum, it is essential that each vehicle in the train can be braked by the driver or by a train control system, such as Automatic Train Protection (ATP). Braking is achieved by the brake shoe acting on the wheel rim (rim brakes), by disc brakes, or, increasingly, by electrical braking.

MECHANICAL SEMAPHORE SIGNAL

Red, square-ended arm in raised position means "all clear"

Red glass

Green glass

Actuating lever system

Motor operating "home" stop signal

Green glass

Yellow glass

Yellow, "distant" warning arm in horizontal position means "caution"

Tubular steel post

Ladder

Electrical relay box

FOUR-ASPECT COLORED LIGHT SIGNAL

Glass (yellow)

Glass (green)

Yellow glass (lit)

Glass (red)

FRONT VIEW

Lifting lug

Lamp shield

Clip

Base

SIDE VIEW

HOW A MODERN MAIN-LINE SIGNALING SYSTEM WORKS

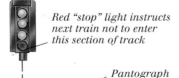

Red "stop" light instructs next train not to enter this section of track

Green "all clear" light instructs train B to proceed into this section of track

Green "all clear" light instructs train B to proceed into this section of track

Green "all clear" light instructs train B to proceed into this section of track

Green "all clear" light instructs train B to proceed into this section of track

Pantograph

Catenary

Train B

Track

EXAMPLES OF INTERNATIONAL TRACK GAUGES

3 ft 3½ in (1,000 mm) East Africa, India, Malaysia, Chile, and Argentina

3 ft 6 in (1,067 mm) Japan, Australia, Sudan, West Africa, South Africa, and New Zealand

4 ft 8½ in (1,435 mm) U.S., Canada, China, Egypt, Turkey, Iran, Japan, Peru, Britain, Europe, Australia, Brazil, and Mexico

5 ft 0 in (1,524 mm) Russia, Spain, Portugal, and Finland

5 ft 3 in (1,600 mm) Ireland, Australia, and Brazil

5 ft 6 in (1,676 mm) India, Pakistan, and Argentina

EXAMPLES OF INTERNATIONAL LOADING GAUGES

KEY:
Britain: 9 ft 0 in (2.75 m) x 12 ft 11 in (3.95 m)
Europe: 10 ft 2 in (3.1 m) x 14 ft 9 in (4.5 m)
U.S.: 10 ft 10 in (3.3 m) x 16 ft 2 in (4.9 m)
Russia: 11 ft 2 in (3.4 m) x 17 ft 4 in (5.3 m)

4 ft 8½ in (1,435 mm) Standard track gauge

5 ft 0 in (1,524 mm) Track gauge of Russia, with largest loading gauge

FLAT-BOTTOMED RAIL

Flat-bottomed steel rail

Steel spring secures rail to sleeper

Synthetic insulating pad

Sleeper supports track and maintains gauge

BULL-HEAD RAIL

Wooden "key" secures rail in chair

Bull-head pattern steel rail

Steel tapered screw fastens chair to sleeper

Cast-iron chair

Wooden sleeper

DISC BRAKES ON MODERN WAGON BOGIE

Base of wagon

Airbag secondary suspension

Damper

Hand brake wheel

Axle

Brake disc

Brake calliper

Wheel

Two yellow "preliminary caution" lights instruct train B that it must stop in two signals time

Yellow "caution" light instructs train B that it must stop at next signal

Green "all clear" light instructs train A to proceed into this section of track

Red "stop" light instructs train B not to enter this section of track

Braking distance

Train A

Trolleys and buses

METROLINK TROLLEY, MANCHESTER, BRITAIN

WHEN CITY POPULATIONS exploded in the 1800s, there was an urgent need for mass transportation. Trolleys were an early solution. The first trolleys, like buses, were horse-drawn, but in 1881, electric streetcars appeared in Berlin, Germany. Electric trolleys soon became widespread throughout Europe and North America. Trolleys run on rails along a fixed route, using electric motors that receive power from overhead cables. As road networks developed, motorized buses offered a flexible alternative to trolleys. By the 1930s, they had replaced trolley systems in many cities. City buses typically have doors at both the front and rear to make loading and unloading easier. Double-decker designs are popular, occupying the same amount of street space as single-decker buses but able to transport twice the number of people. Buses are also commonly used for inter-city travel and touring. Tour buses have reclining seats, large windows, luggage space, and toilets. Recently, as city traffic has become increasingly congested, many city planners have designed new electric streetcar routes to run alongside bus routes as part of an integrated transport system.

EARLY TROLLEY, c.1900

- Trolley boom
- Trolley head
- Trolley base
- Drop window
- Upper deck
- Quarter light
- Brake
- Stair
- Lower deck
- Underframe
- Platform
- Controller
- Truck
- Lifeguard

MCW METROBUS, LONDON, ENGLAND

- Upper deck air intake
- Window vent
- Upper deck windshield
- Route information
- Destination screen
- Side mirror
- Asymmetric windshield
- Windshield wiper
- Sidelight
- Headlight
- Grill
- Fog light
- License plate
- Manufacturer's logo
- Route number
- Side mirror
- Permit holder
- Turning indicator

LONDON NORTHERN

41

Hornsey Rise   Crouch End
Turnpike Lane
West Green Road

ARCHWAY STN.

PAY DRIVER

mcw

KYV 739X

FRONT VIEW

- Square roof dome
- Mirror for driver to see upstairs
- Operator's logo
- Destination screen
- Side mirror
- Front bumper
- Entrance door
- Emergency door control
- Turning indicator

LONDON NORTHERN

SINGLE-DECKER BUS, NEW YORK CITY, NEW YORK

Wheelchair access · Sliding window · Sloped roof dome · Marker light · Repeater indicator · Entrance door · Side mirror · Tinted glass · Route number · Headlight · Turning indicator · Air intake · Exit door · Access panel · Entrance door · License plate · Bumper · Tire · Axle · Sidelight · Bumper

SIDE VIEW   **FRONT VIEW**

DOUBLE-DECKER TOUR BUS, PARIS, FRANCE

Tinted glass · Raked windshield · Air intake · Panoramic window · Access panel · Turning indicator · Skirt · Bumper · Access door · Side entrance · Single front axle · Tire · Plug-style entrance door · Twin rear axle

Paris Vision

Sliding window vent · Upper saloon window · Advertising panel · Air intake · Lower saloon window · Fleet number · Engine access panel · Rear bumper · Emergency door control · Two-leaf style exit door · Legal lettering · London Buses logo · Tire · Skirt · Axle

LONDON BUSES

HT   M1041

SIDE VIEW

The first cars

THE EARLIEST ROAD VEHICLE powered by an engine, the Cugnot steam traction engine, was built in 1770. More practical steam carriages, such as the Bordino, were available in the early 19th century, but they were heavy and cumbersome. Restrictive laws and the introduction of railways, faster and able to carry more passengers, saw the decline of "cars" powered by steam. It was not until 1860 that the first practical power unit for road vehicles was developed with the invention of the internal combustion engine by the Belgian Étienne Lenoir. By around 1890, Karl Benz and Gottlieb Daimler in Germany and Albert de Dion and Armand Peugeot in France were building cars for sale to the public. These early cars, despite being primitive, expensive, and produced in limited numbers, heralded the age of the automobile.

STEAM-POWERED CUGNOT "FARDIER," 1770

Chimney
Steam pipe
Haystack boiler
Twin cylinder engine
Rocking beam
Steering tiller
Brake pedal
Seat
Wooden frame
Wooden wheel (artillery wheel)
Load space
Carrying fork
Piston rod
Ratchet wheel
Single front driving wheel
Step
Log basket
Broad, rough tire

BORDINO STEAM CARRIAGE, 1854

Chimney
Top iron (landau iron)
Landau body
Drop-down window
Leather top
Fire-tube boiler
Sprung chassis
Safety valve
Water tank
Safety valve weight
Coal hopper
Chauffeur's seat (stoker's seat; spider seat; tiger seat)
Step
Tie bar
Full-elliptic leaf spring
Iron tire
Wooden spoke
Wooden wheel (artillery wheel)
Hub
Unsprung chassis
Tie rod
Connecting rod
Steam chest
Twin-cylinder steam engine
Steam distributor valve

SIDE VIEW OF GASOLINE-DRIVEN BENZ MOTORWAGEN, 1886

Steering tiller

Brake quadrant

Brake lever

Cooling water tank

Steering column

Full-elliptic leaf spring

Steering rack

Bevel gear

Steering link

Final drive sprocket

Steering head

Seat spring

Driven pulley

Wheel fork

Tubular chassis

Driving chain

Driving sprocket

Hub

Solid rubber tire

Tangent-spoked wire wheel

REAR VIEW OF BENZ MOTORWAGEN, 1886

Pinion

Lubricator

Cooling tank

Crown wheel

Driving pulley

Fuel tank

Drive belt

Big-end bearing

Groove for rope starter

Crankshaft

Flywheel

Seat cushion

Candle lamp

Driver's seat

Steering tiller

Brake lever

Dashboard

Headlight

Round pin

Splinter bar

Towing hook

Forecarriage

Steam pipe

Spoke

Frame

OVERHEAD VIEW OF BENZ MOTORWAGEN, 1886

Steering link

Footboard (floorboard)

Steering tiller

Brake lever

Tool and battery box

Trembler coil box

Intake pipe

Single cylinder

Fuel tank

Cooling water tank

Oil-filled lubricator

Flywheel

Crown wheel

Crankshaft

Driving pulley

Drive belt

Elegance and utility

DURING THE FIRST DECADE OF THE 20TH CENTURY, the motorist who could afford it had a choice of some of the finest cars ever made. These handbuilt cars were powerful and luxurious, using the finest wood, leather, and cloth, and bodywork made to the customer's individual requirements. Some had six-cylinder engines as big as 15 liters. The price of such cars was several times that of an average house, and their yearly running costs were also very high. As a result, basic, utilitarian cars became popular. Costing perhaps one-tenth of the price of a luxury car, these cars had very little trim and often had only single-cylinder engines.

1904 OLDSMOBILE SINGLE-CYLINDER ENGINE

Oil bottle dripfeed

Crankcase

Exhaust pipe

Starting handle bracket

Cylinder head

Cylinder

Starter cog

Carburetor

Engine timing gear

Crankshaft

Flywheel

Gear band

FRONT VIEW OF 1906 RENAULT

SIDE VIEW OF 1906 RENAULT

Canopy

Mahogany-framed windshield

Cast aluminum wheel spider

Rear window

British Automobile Association badge

Bedford cord upholstery

Window blind

British Royal Automobile Club badge

Blind pull

Window lift strap

Rearview mirror

Broad lace trim

Lamp bracket

Oil side lamp

Windshield support

Dashboard radiator

Fender

Brass bevel

Access panel

Hood catch

Bail handle

Lifting handle

Mirror reflector

Acetylene headlight

Steering spindle

Elliott steering knuckle

Chevron-tread tire

Dumb iron

Screwdown greaser

Front axle

Starting handle

Tie rod

Luggage grid

Button-quilted upholstery

Mahogany-framed plate glass window

Round-corner single limousine coachwork

Rear oil lamp

Shock absorber

Hub

Hubcap

Beaded edge tire

Tire security bolt

1904 OLDSMOBILE TRIM AND BODYWORK

Reflector

Rear lamp

Engine cover handle

Engine cover

Fender

Fender stay

Seat back rest frame

Dashboard

Tiller

Brake pedal

Throttle pedal

Mirror

Ignition switch

Seat cushion (squab)

1904 OLDSMOBILE CHASSIS

Front steering tie rod

Front spring

Brake rod

Full-elliptic steering spring

Steering wiffletree

Rear spring

Starting handle bracket

Front axle

Combined spring and chassis unit

Non-skid tire

Brass scrollwork

Blind pull

Canopy

Openable windshield

Brass bevel

Division

Dashboard

Oil side lamp

Hood

Broad lace trim

Leather upholstery

Handbrake

Steering wheel

Water pipe

Gear lever

Plug lead conduit

Acetylene headlight

Fuel/air intake pipe

Bi-block engine

Bulb horn

Spare tire

Jump seat (opera seat; strapontin)

Rim clamp

Tire carrier

Running board

Leather valance

Dashboard radiator

Tire strap

Hood support

Exhaust manifold

Starting handle

Wooden artillery wheel

Mass production

THE FIRST CARS WERE HAND-ASSEMBLED from individually built parts, a time-consuming procedure that required skilled mechanics and made cars very expensive. This problem was solved, in America, by a Detroit car manufacturer named Henry Ford. He introduced mass production by using standardized parts, and later combined these with a moving production line. The work was brought to the workers, each of whom performed one simple task in the construction process as the chassis moved along the line. The first mass-produced car, the Ford Model T, was launched in 1908. At first it was available in a limited range of body styles and colors. However, when the production line was introduced in 1914, the color range was cut back; the Model T became available, as Henry Ford said, in "any color you like, so long as it's black." Ford cut the production time for a car from several days to about 12 hours, and eventually to minutes, making cars much cheaper than before. As a result, half the cars in the world were Model T Fords by 1920.

FRONT VIEW OF 1913 FORD MODEL T

Throttle lever

Openable windshield

Steering wheel

Ignition lever

Windshield stay

Dashboard

Side lamp

Spring shock absorber

Bulb horn

Fender

Headlight

Radiator

Front transverse leaf spring

License plate

Starting handle

Steering knuckle

Front axle

Steering spindle connecting-rod

STAGES OF FORD MODEL T PRODUCTION

Left half of differential housing

Pinion

Hub bolt

Rear leaf spring (cross-member)

Steering arm

King pin

Removable wheel

Hub brake shoe

Tie rod

Steering wheel

Pinion housing

Front transverse leaf spring

Differential housing

Chassis frame

Rear spring perch

Radius rod

Rear axle

Front cross-member

Battery carrier

Body mount

Bearing sleeve

King pin

Half-shaft

Right half of differential housing

Crown wheel

Rear axle bearing

Bevel pinion

Front axle

Removable wheel

Radius rod

Torque tube

Running board support

Hub brake shoe

SIDE VIEW OF 1913 FORD MODEL T

The "people's car"

WORKING PARTS OF VOLKSWAGEN BEETLE

THE MOST POPULAR CAR in the history of car manufacture is the Volkswagen Beetle, originally called the KdF Wagen. The car was developed in Germany in the 1930s by Dr. Ferdinand Porsche. At that time, Germany had only half the number of cars of Britain or France, and Adolf Hitler took a personal interest in the development of the Volkswagen ("people's car"). The intention was to provide a new industry, new jobs, and a car so inexpensive that anyone with a job could afford it. Dr. Porsche designed a car that was cheap to build and run; its rear-mounted, air-cooled engine cut down the number of parts needed and also reduced weight. However, few civilians managed to obtain the Beetle before the outbreak of the Second World War in 1939. After the war, the Beetle proved so popular that eventually more than 20 million were sold.

CUSTOMIZED VOLKSWAGEN BEETLE

FLAT-FOUR CYLINDER ARRANGEMENT

Fuel tank

Fuel tank sender unit

Steering tie-rod

Fuel filler neck

Windshield-wiper motor assembly

Steering box assembly

Steering idler

Suspension strut

Frame head

Anti-roll bar

Brake back plate

Track control arm

Pedal cluster

Strut cartridge (shock absorber)

Dust shroud

Gear lever knob

Front suspension top mount

Front road spring

Seat mount

Front suspension top mount

Handbrake

Floor pan (platform chassis)

Torsion bar cover

Rear brake drum

Trailing arm

Tire

Sports wheel

Drive shaft

Rear shock absorber

Heat exchanger

Transaxle (gearbox and final drive)

Starter motor

Clutch and flywheel

Flat-four engine

Air filter

Tail pipe

Taillight

Air scoop

Vent window

Luggage compartment lid

Turn signal and parking light

Tail pipe

Pressed steel wheel

Fuel filler cap

Counterweight

Piston

Crankshaft

Big end

Connecting rod (con-rod)

**BODY SHELL OF
VOLKSWAGEN BEETLE**

Front bumper

Release
handle

Left side
headlight unit

Chrome
trim strip

Right side
headlight unit

Left front
parking light
and turn
signal lens

Right front
parking light
and turn
signal lens

Luggage
compartment
lid

Left front
fender

Right front
fender

Front
fender
piping

Spare-
wheel
well

Front
fender
piping

Hood
hinge

Blade

Vent
window

Mirror

Arm

Right side
running
board

Windshield wiper

Left side
running
board

Door catch

Steering
column

Wind
deflector
(baffle)

Sun roof

Quarter
light

Door
handle

Window winder
handle

Passenger door

Window
winder
regulator

Body shell

Drop glass

Rear
fender
piping

Rear
fender
piping

Air intake
vents

Engine lid
(engine cover)

Left side
rear fender

Air
intake
vents

Rear valance

Right rear
fender

License
plate
light

License plate

Left taillight

Right taillight

WRV
408L

Rear bumper

Early engines

STEAM AND ELECTRICITY were used to power cars until early this century, but neither power source was ideal. Electric cars had to stop frequently to recharge their heavy batteries, and steam cars gave smooth power delivery but were too complicated for the average motorist to use. A rival power source, the internal combustion engine, was invented in 1860 by Étienne Lenoir (see pp. 334-335). This engine converted the force of a controlled explosion into rotary motion to turn the wheels of a vehicle. Early variations on this basic model included sleeve valves, separately cast cylinders, and the two-stroke combustion cycle. Today, many internal combustion engines, including the Wankel rotary and diesels (see pp. 346-347), use the four-stroke cycle, first demonstrated by Nikolaus Otto in 1876. The Otto cycle has proved the best method of ensuring that the engine turns over smoothly and that exhaust emissions are controllable.

TROJAN TWO-STROKE ENGINE, 1927

Port linking combustion chambers of upper and lower cylinders

Water connection

Upper paired cylinder

Spark plug

Wide piston-ring

Transfer port

Wire gauze pad

Upper piston

Flywheel

Flexible, forked connecting-rod

Counterweight

Big end

Crankcase

BERSEY ELECTRIC CAB, 1896

Mounting for tray of 40 batteries

Housing for electric motors

SECTIONED WHITE STEAM CAR, 1903

Steering wheel

Throttle wheel

Brake lever

Reverse lever

Flash steam generator

Automatic cylinder lubricator

Lamp bracket

High-pressure cylinder

Rocking lever

Exhaust pipe

Water pump

Condenser

Low-pressure cylinder

Fuel tank

Semi-elliptic spring

Brake drum

Spiral tubes

Steel-reinforced wooden chassis

Steering drop arm

Water tank

Drag link

Dumb iron

CYCLE OF A FOUR-STROKE INTERNAL COMBUSTION ENGINE

INDUCTION STROKE

- Exhaust port closed
- Intake valve
- Intake port opens
- Piston moves downward
- Fuel and air (the "charge") sucked into cylinder
- Counterweight
- Crankshaft
- Crankpin

COMPRESSION STROKE

- Exhaust port closed
- Charge compressed by piston
- Intake port closed
- Connecting rod (con-rod)
- Piston moves upward

POWER STROKE

- Spark plug
- Exhaust port closed
- Explosion pushes piston downward
- Intake port closed
- Charge ignited by spark plug
- Big end

EXHAUST STROKE

- Exhaust valve
- Exhaust port opens
- Piston moves upward
- Intake port closed
- Burned gases forced out of cylinder

16-HORSEPOWER HUMBER ENGINE, 1911

- Brass housing for ignition cable
- Intake port
- Water pipe
- Valve cap
- Spark plug
- Side valve (inlet valve)
- Cylinders (cast in pairs)
- Water jacket
- Fan bracket
- Tappet
- Valve spring
- Timing chain
- Timing cover
- Flywheel
- Camshaft
- Oil pump
- Oil pan
- Crankcase
- Starting handle

DAIMLER DOUBLE-SLEEVE VALVE ENGINE, 1910

- Spark plug socket
- Junk ring
- Cylinder head
- Intake port
- Exhaust port
- Intake manifold
- Outer sleeve valve
- Water jacket
- Cylinder wall
- Inner sleeve valve
- Piston
- Carburetor
- Engine bearer
- Flywheel

OUTER SLEEVE VALVE

- Oil groove

INNER SLEEVE VALVE

- Sleeve port
- Eye for connecting con-rods to secondary crankshaft

Modern engines

TODAY'S GASOLINE ENGINE WORKS on the same basic principles as the first car engines of a century ago, although it has been greatly refined. Modern engines, often made from special metal alloys, are much lighter than earlier engines. Computerized ignition systems, fuel injectors, and multi-valve cylinder heads achieve a more efficient combustion of the fuel/air mixture (the charge) so that less fuel is wasted. As a result of this greater efficiency, the power and performance of a modern engine are increased, and the level of pollution in the exhaust gases is reduced. Exhaust pollution levels today are also lowered by the increasing use of special filters called catalytic converters, which absorb many exhaust pollutants. The need to produce ever more efficient engines means that it can take up to seven years to develop a new engine for a family car, at a cost of many millions of dollars.

FRONT VIEW OF A FORD COSWORTH V6 12-VALVE

Idle control valve
Plenum chamber
Valve rocker
Power steering pump reservoir
Steering pump pulley
Cogged drive belt
Alternator
Viscous coupling
Oil pan
Oil dipstick
High-tension ignition lead (spark plug lead)
Fan
Crankshaft pulley

FRONT VIEW OF A FORD COSWORTH V6 24-VALVE

Idle control valve
Exhaust gas recirculation valve
Steering pump drive pulley
Belt tensioner
Alternator cooling fan
Oil pan
Crankshaft pulley
Plenum chamber
Camshaft timing gear
Camshaft chain
Air-conditioning compressor
Drive belt

SECTIONED VIEW OF A JAGUAR STRAIGHT 6

Cam follower (bucket tappet)
Valve spring
Cam lobe
Cam
Combustion chamber
Compression ring
Cam cover
Distributor
Fan
Air-conditioning refrigerant pipe
Suspension self-leveling pump
Power steering pump
Swash plate
Drive belt
Compressor piston
Air-conditioning compressor
Oil-control ring (scraper ring)
Crankcase
Anti-surge baffle
Oil pick-up pipe
Oil pan
Crankshaft counterweight
Transmission adaptor plate
Big end
Main bearing housing
Connecting rod (con-rod)
Piston
Water jacket
Cylinder liner
Exhaust valve
Valve stem
Cylinder head
Camshaft

FRONT VIEW OF A JAGUAR V12

Air cleaner

Camshaft sprocket

Distributor

Fuel injector nozzle

Intake manifold tract

Piston

Crankshaft

Plenum chamber

Camshaft

Cam follower

Piston ring land

Piston ring groove

Exhaust manifold

Piston skirt

Wrist pin

Coolant outlet

Cam cover

STRAIGHT 4 CYLINDER ARRANGEMENT

Viscous coupling

Cooling fan

Fan drive shaft

Belt pulley

Alternator

Alternator pulley

Counterweight

Connecting rod (con-rod)

V12 CYLINDER ARRANGEMENT

SECTIONED VIEW OF A JAGUAR V12

Distributor drive shaft

Fuel pipe

Throttle butterfly

Intake manifold

Ignition amplifier

Throttle linkage

Air inlet

Exhaust valve

Cam cover

Inlet valve

Oil feed pipe

Timing chain

Cylinder head

Piston crown

Water outlet

Piston ring land

Exhaust heat shield

Water pump

Exhaust manifold

Piston

Oil pipe banjo

Accessory drive pulley

Drive plate

Timing chain drive sprocket

Starter ring

Connecting rod (con-rod)

Oil filter

Counterweight (balance weight)

Main bearing

Pipe to oil cooler

Crankcase

Oil pan

Alternative engines

THE MOST COMMON TYPE OF ALTERNATIVE ENGINE is the diesel engine. Instead of igniting the compressed fuel/air mixture with a spark, the diesel engine uses compression alone, which heats the mixture to the point where it explodes. A diesel engine's fuel consumption is low in comparison with similarly sized piston engines, despite its heavier, reinforced moving parts and cylinder block. Another type of engine is the rotary-combustion, first successfully developed by Felix Wankel in the 1950s. Its two trilobate (three-sided) rotors revolve in housings shaped in a fat figure eight. The four sequences of the four-stroke cycle, which occur consecutively in a piston engine, occur simultaneously in a rotary engine, producing power in a continuous stream.

ROTARY-ENGINED MAZDA RX-7 TURBO II

Aerodynamic windshield
Headrest
Top boot
Front spoiler (chin spoiler)
Side marker lamp
Body-side molding
Cast alloy wheel

WANKEL ROTARY ENGINE

OIL-PUMP HOUSING
Distributor fixing point (drive point)
FRONT SIDE HOUSING
Intake port
FRONT ROTOR CHAMBER
Trailing spark plug hole
INTERMEDIATE HOUSING
Oil filler
Dipstick tube
Intake port
REAR ROTOR CHAMBER
Aluminum alloy backing

Oil-pump drive
Coolant passage
Exhaust port
Water drain bolt
Trailing spark plug hole
Leading spark plug hole
Leading spark plug hole

THE WANKEL ROTARY CYCLE

Exhaust port
Intake port
Fuel/air mixture being compressed
Water passage
Trilobate rotor
Burning gas expands

Exhaust port closed
Vacuum sucks in fuel/air mixture
Gas continues to expand
Stationary gear (fixed gear)
Compression continues

Burned gas exhausts
Rotor gear
Compressed gas ignites
Fuel/air mixture continues to enter

Burned gas continues to exhaust
Output shaft turns
Compression begins
Burned gas begins to expand

FORD TURBOCHARGED DIESEL ENGINE

Engine lifting bracket
Valve cover
Baffle plate
Intake track
Turbo impeller (inlet rotor)
Turbo propeller (exhaust rotor)
Exhaust
Bell housing

Oil filler cap
Cam follower
Valve return spring
Water jacket
Water pump pulley
Compression ring
Oil-control ring
Piston
Accessory drive belt
Water jacket
Oil cooler
Oil cooler matrix

Oil pan
Engine block
Oil return pipe for turbocharger
Oil filter

REAR SIDE HOUSING

Chrome plating

Exhaust port

ROTOR AND SEALS

Outer oil seal
Inner oil seal spring
Inner oil seal
Rotor bearing
Rotor gear
Side gear

Corner seal spring
Corner seal insert
Corner seal
Rotor
Balancing drilling
Apex seal
Apex seal spring

Inner oil seal groove
Outer oil seal groove
Hole for output shaft
Side seal spring
Side seal
Side seal groove
Apex seal groove

Outer oil seal spring

OUTPUT SHAFT

Front counterweight
Front eccentric rotor journal
Oil passage
Rear stationary gear (fixed gear)

V-belt pulley
Front stationary gear (fixed gear)
Main journal
Eccentric shaft
Oil jet
Rear eccentric rotor journal

Flywheel with balance weight

Bodywork

RENAULT
LOGO

THE BODY OF A MODERN mass-produced car is built on the monocoque (single-shell) principle, in which the roof, side panels, and floor are welded into a single integral unit. This bodyshell protects and supports the car's internal parts. Steel and glass are used to construct the bodyshell, creating a unit that is both light and strong. Its lightness helps to conserve energy, while its strength protects the occupants. Modern bodywork is designed with the aid of computers, which are used to predict factors such as aerodynamic efficiency and impact-resistance. High-technology is also employed on the production line, where robots are used to assemble, weld, and paint the body.

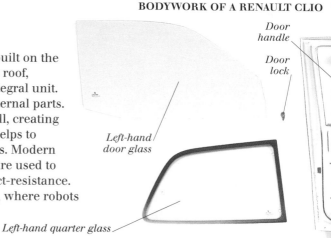

Door handle

Door lock

Left-hand door glass

Left-hand quarter glass

tailgate support

Window washer jet

Heating element contact

Rear window glass

Tailgate support

Tailgate

Rear bumper

Bodyshell

Fuel cap

Right-hand quarter glass

Right-hand door glass

Door key and lock

Door handle

Zinc phosphating

Degreased bare metal

Primer

Base coat color

Cataphoresic coating

Clear coat

Chrome passivation

Left-hand door

Left-hand mirror assembly

Door hinge

Electric window motor

Radio antenna

Rear hatch

Side marker lamp

SIDE VIEW OF A RENAULT CLIO

Spoiler bumper

Hood-release cable

Hood

Hood catch

Hood hinge

Window winder cable

Windshield glass

Front bumper

Window winder handle

Door hinge

Right-hand door

Right-hand mirror assembly

Hood

Headrest

Headlight

Spoiler bumper

Fog-light

FRONT VIEW OF A RENAULT CLIO

Mechanical components

A TYPICAL MODERN CAR has several thousand
individual mechanical components. These are
assembled to form the car's various mechanical
systems: engine and exhaust, transmission,
steering, suspension, and brakes. To ensure that
each system functions properly, components are
manufactured to extremely fine tolerances—to within
about one ten-thousandth of an inch in some cases.

Alloy wheel

Hubcap

Hub nut

Hub seal

Exhaust downpipe

Muffler

Catalytic converter

Suspension spring

Rear muffler

Fuel tank

Vent pipe

Shock absorber

Electric fuel pump

Brake cylinder (wheel cylinder)

Brake shoe

Hub seal

Hub nut

Hubcap

Wheel cover

Fuel tank filler neck

Torsion bar

Left rear suspension arm

Anti-roll bar

Right rear suspension arm

Handbrake

Gear lever

Steering wheel

Steering rack

Steering column

Clutch pedal

Hub and brake drum

Brake pedal

Accelerator pedal

Brake backplate

Clutch cable

Accelerator cable

Steel wheel

MECHANICAL COMPONENTS
OF A RENAULT CLIO, 1991

Brake shield

Alloy wheel

Clutch throw-out bearing

Brake disc

Hub

Left drive shaft

Clutch pressure plate

Tie-rod end

Upper suspension arm

Brake hose

Top radiator hose

Tie rod

Brake pad

Power steering pump

Clutch center plate

Lower suspension arm

Gear-change rod

Gearbox (transmission)

Bottom radiator hose

Anti-roll bar

Starter motor

Flywheel

Subframe

Power steering belt

Fan motor

Electronic ignition unit

Intake manifold

Exhaust manifold

Brake cylinder (wheel cylinder)

Water pump

Brake power-assist servo

Fan motor support bracket

Alternator

Alternator belt

Engine

Suspension strut

Brake caliper fixing bolt

Distributor

Brake caliper locking plate

Air cleaner

Brake caliper

Hub carrier

Right drive shaft

Brake hose

Radiator

Lock nut and washer

Brake disc

Front hub bearing

Brake shield

Steel wheel

Wheel cover

Water bottle

Car trim

A MODERN CAR HAS TWO TYPES OF TRIM, according to the materials used: hard (chrome and plastics) and soft (upholstered materials). Safety and comfort are priorities in the trim's design: seats help the occupants maintain a comfortable posture, rubber seals keep out dirt and moisture, and headlights light the way. Older cars had interior or leather paneling cut and fitted by craftsmen; modern cars use precisely molded plastics and seat fabrics cut by robot-controlled lasers to reduce costs and production time. Doors are now assembled off the production line so that complex wiring can be built in.

TRIM OF A RENAULT CLIO, 1991

Rear quarter trim panel

Inner roof trim

Roof seal

Quarter trim panel

Quarter panel molding

Rear seat belt

Center seat belt

Rear seat belt stalk (catch)

Gear lever surround

Rear tire

Rear shelf

Split, folding rear seat assembly

Rear shelf radio speaker

Rear shelf radio speaker

Tailgate trim

Rear wiper blade

Tailgate seal

Rear wiper arm

License plate light

Rear turn signal and stop lamp assembly

Wheel cover (rear wheel embellisher)

Untrimmed headrest

Rear seat belt

Quarter panel molding

Quarter trim panel

Rear quarter trim panel

Roof seal

Inner roof trim

Roof molding

Rear tire

HALOGEN HEADLIGHT BULB

SPOTLIGHT BULB

Filament

MARKER LIGHT BULB

Filament

FESTOON BULB

Contact

Bayonet fixing

Contact

Contact

Window winder handle

Door seal

Door lock handle

Door pull handle

Front tire

Wheel cover (front wheel embellisher)

Turn signal lamp

Fog light

Inner sill trim

Door molding (rubbing strip)

Inner windshield molding

Front seat belt

Front door radio speaker

Dash radio speaker

Headlight

Front seat assembly

Sun visor

Dash panel (instrument panel)

Windshield wiper bracket and spindles

Windshield wiper blade

Interior light

Heater unit

Washer jet

Fan blade

Radio

Rearview mirror

Center console

Steering wheel

Windshield seal

Fascia (dash)

Headlight

Sun visor

Front seat frame

Windshield wiper arm

Front seat belt

Control stalk

Dash radio speaker

Front door radio speaker

Door trim panel

Inner sill trim

Door molding (rubbing strip)

Inner windshield molding

Door seal

Fog light

Door pull handle

Window winder handle

Turn signal lamp

Door lock handle

Front tire

Wheel cover (front wheel embellisher)

Hybrid car

THERE HAVE BEEN SEVERAL proposed alternatives to conventional gas- or diesel-powered cars, including cars that use solar or battery power. The object is to lower harmful emissions and conserve natural resources. One of the alternatives already in production is the hybrid car. A hybrid vehicle uses two or more fuels. Examples include diesel-electric trains and mopeds. The latter combine the power of a gasoline engine with pedal power. In a hybrid car, gasoline consumption is reduced by the provision of additional power by an electric motor during acceleration. The motor is driven by power from on-board batteries that are recharged when the car is cruising or decelerating by an engine-driven generator. Some hybrid cars transfer energy from the wheels to a flywheel during braking. The flywheel drives the generator, which recharges the batteries.

HONDA INSIGHT

Antenna
Aerodynamic roof
Windshield
Side mirror
Plastic front wings
Front air dam
Plastic fender
Aerodynamic underside components
Cooling intake
Aluminum hood

SIDE VIEW OF 1-LITER VTEC ENGINE

FRONT VIEW OF 1-LITER VTEC ENGINE

Motor power cables
Air-intake duct
Ignition coils
Coolant pipe
Electric motor housing
Lightweight plastic intake manifold
Lightweight magnesium alloy oil sump pan
Oil filter
Air-conditioning compressor
Engine drive belt

Dipstick
Rocker cover
Ignition coils
Water pump
Belt tensioner
Air-conditioning compressor
Crankshaft pulley
Drive belt

HOW HYBRID POWER WORKS

Gasoline engine provides power for acceleration and to generator

Inverter

Battery

Inverter controls direction of electrical current

Inverter cooling fan

Motor electronic control module (ECM)

Battery electronic control module (ECM)

Battery cooling fan

REAR VIEW

Electric motor

Power from generator recharges battery during deceleration

Power from battery to motor during acceleration

INVERTER AND BATTERY

Inverter housing

DC converter

High-voltage connector

High-voltage cables

Motor electronic control module (ECM)

Battery electronic control module (ECM)

⚠ DANGER
HIGH VOLTAGE

INVERTER ASSEMBLY

Inverter cooling fan connector

Magnesium housing for air intake

DC converter connection

Junction board

Cover mounting bracket

BATTERY ASSEMBLY

Battery cooling fan

Manifold connector

O_2 sensor

Catalyst

Rear exhaust section connector

EXHAUST WITH CATALYTIC CONVERTER

Racecars

SINCE THE ADVENT OF DRIVING, racecars have been a major focus of innovation in car design. Features that are now commonplace, such as disk brakes, turbochargers, and even seat belts, were used first on competition cars. Research into racecars has contributed to a new understanding of engine performance, aerodynamics, and tire adhesion, and has led to the development of ultralight materials such as carbon-fiber for car bodies. A modern McLaren Formula One car has a low, streamlined body and an open cockpit but, unlike its forerunner, it also has front and rear wings that push the wheels firmly onto the track, huge tires for extra grip, and electronic sensors that continually relay information to the pits about the car's performance.

72° V10 ENGINE

Fuel injection trumpet guard

Cam cover

Gearbox fixing stud

Water and oil pump assembly

Harmonically tuned exhaust system

Cylinder head

Stressed cylinder block

BACK VIEW OF MCLAREN MERCEDES MP4-13

Upper flap

Grooved racing tire

Warning light

Half-shaft

Diffuser

Differential

Exhaust pipe

Rear wing endplate

One-piece side pod and engine cover

Side pod air outlet

SIDE VIEW OF MCLAREN MERCEDES MP4-13

Rear wing endplate

Winglet

Engine cover

Head rest

Onboard TV mini-camera

Engine air intake

Alloy wheel

Wheel nut

Side pod

OVERHEAD VIEW OF MCLAREN MERCEDES MP4-13

Front wing endplate

Driver's radio antenna

Rearview mirror

One-piece side pod and engine cover

Radius arm

Rear wing endplate

Front wing

Slot

Nose cover

Upper flap

Lower wishbone

Upper wishbone

Front brake duct

Turning vane

Safety harness

Driver protection

Grooved racing tire

Rear wing upper mainplane

Grooved racing tire

FRONT VIEW OF MCLAREN MERCEDES MP4-13

Rear wing upper mainplane

Engine air intake

Rear-view mirror

Driver's radio aerial

Radiator air intake

Front brake duct

Upper wishbone

Grooved racing tyre

Lower wishbone

Endplate

Rearview mirror

Forward rollover structure

Steering link

Wing supports

Front wing

Driver's radio antenna

Alloy wheel

High nose

Turning vane

Wheel nut

Front wing endplate

Bicycle anatomy

THE BICYCLE IS A TWO-WHEELED, lightweight machine, which is propelled by human power. It is efficient, cheap, easily manufactured, and one of the world's most popular forms of transportation. The first pedal-driven bicycle was built in Scotland in 1839. Since then the basic design—of a frame, wheels, brakes, handlebars, and a saddle—has been gradually improved, with the addition of a chain, gear system, and pneumatic tires (tires inflated with air). The recent invention of the mountain bike (all-terrain bike) has been an important development. With its strong, rugged frame, wide tires, and 21 gears, a mountain bike enables riders to reach rough and hilly areas that were previously inaccessible to cyclists.

REAR WHEEL

Tire

Spoke

Hub

Rim

Saddle (seat)

Seat post

Seat post quick release bolt

Cable guide

Straddle wire

Seat tube

Rear cantilever brake

6000

Seat stay

Front derailleur

Rear dropouts

Rear hub quick release spindle

Bottom bracket shell

Bottom bracket axle

Crank bolt

Washer

17-tooth sprocket

13-tooth sprocket

Adjustable cup

Fixed cup

Bottom bracket sleeve

Caged ball bearings

Lock ring

Lock washer

Freewheel lock nut

Jockey wheel

Chain

Lock washer

Rear derailleur

23-tooth sprocket

Derailleur cage plate

Jockey wheel

46-tooth chain ring

Toe clip

Sprocket spacer

30-tooth sprocket

GEAR SYSTEM

Spider

Spoke guard

FREEWHEEL SPROCKETS

Toe strap

Pedal

Right arm

Gear cable

Gearshift

Handlebar stem

Gearshift

Handlebar

Handlebar grip

Expander bolt

Lock nut

Top tube

Rear brake cable

Brake lever

Brake lever

Top race

Lock washer

Front brake cable

Hub

Spoke

Cable guide

Head tube

Top cup

Caged ball bearings

BICYCLE FRAME

Down tube

Bottom cup

Rubber bearing seal

Steerer tube

Straddle wire

Bottom race

Toe clip

Front cantilever brake

Cantilever brake boss

Rim

Inner tube

Fork blade

Toe strap

Pedal

Left arm

24-tooth chain ring

Front hub quick release spindle

36-tooth chain ring

Handlebar

Saddle

Frame

Brake lever and gearshift

Valve cap

Valve

Pedal

Tire

FRONT WHEEL

Chain

Bicycles

ALTHOUGH ALL BICYCLES are made up of the same basic components, they can vary greatly in design. A racing bike, such as the Eddy Merckx model, with its light frame and steep head- and seat-angles, is built for speed. Its design forces the rider to adopt the aero tuck, a crouched, aerodynamic position. While a touring bike resembles a racing bike in many respects, it is designed for comfort and stability on long-distance journeys. Touring bikes are characterized by more relaxed frame angles, heavy chain stays that support the rear panniers, and a long wheelbase (the distance between the wheel axles) for reliable handling. All-purpose bicycles, known as hybrids, combine the light weight and speed of sports bikes with the rugged durability of mountain bikes (see pp. 358-359). Bicycles that are not designed for conventional road use include time-trial bikes, which have a short head tube, sloping top tube, aero handlebars, and aerodynamic tubing. Most Human Powered Vehicles (HPVs) are recumbents—the rider has a recumbent position—which maximize power output and minimize drag (resistance). Essential to the safety of all riders are helmets, and both front and rear lights; locks protect against theft.

FRONT AND REAR LIGHTS

White front light

Red rear light

HELMET

Hard outer shell

Air vent

Polystyrene padding

Quick-release strap

EDDY MERCKX RACING BICYCLE

Saddle (seat)

Saddle clamp

Seat post

Cable guide

Seat-post bolt

Rear brake cable

Top tube (crossbar)

Steel frame

Brake-block bolt

Brake block

Seat stay

Seat tube

Down tube

Tire

Water-bottle cage

Tire tread

Front derailleur

Tire wall

Wheel rim

Freewheel sprocket

STEEL LOCK

Key

Hardened steel

Pick-proof lock

Rear derailleur

Pulley bolt

Tension pulley

Chain

Chain stay

Chain ring

Crank bolt

Crank

Spider

Pedal

Toe clip

CANNONDALE SH600 HYBRID BICYCLE

Gel-filled saddle

Lightweight frame

Straight handlebar

Brake bridge

Cantilever brake

All-surface tire

CANNONDALE ST1000 TOURING BICYCLE

Rear fender

Water bottle

Drop handlebar

Front fender

Rear pannier

Long chain stay

Large diameter aluminum tubing

Front pannier

Headset

Stem

Binder bolt

Handlebar

Front brake cable

Brake lever

Head tube

Brake pivot bolt

Brake pad

Fork

Hub quick-release lever

Spoke

Spoke nipple

Presta valve

Hub

ROSSIN ITALIAN TIME-TRIAL BICYCLE

Aero handlebar

Sloping top tube

Hollow disk wheel

Steep seat tube

Short head tube

Narrow tire

Clipless pedal

Tri-spoke wheel

WINDCHEETAH SL MARK VI "SPEEDY" RACING HPV BICYCLE

Fleecy headrest

Fiberglass bucket seat

Joystick

Brake lever

53-tooth chain ring

Clipless pedal

Extended racing chain

7-speed freewheel

Aluminum tubing

Drum brake

The motorcycle

THE MOTORCYCLE HAS EVOLVED from a motorized cycle—a basic bicycle with an engine—into a sophisticated, high-performance machine. In 1901, the Werner brothers established the most viable location for the engine, positioning it low in the center of the chassis (see pp. 364-365): the new Werner became the basis for the modern motorcycle. Motorcycles are used for many purposes —for commuting, delivering messages, touring, and racing—and different machines have been developed to suit the demands of different types of riders. The Vespa scooter, for instance, which is small-wheeled, economical, and easy-to-ride, was designed to meet the needs of the commuter. Sidecars provided transportation for the family until the arrival of cheap cars caused their popularity to decline. Serious riders generally favor larger capacity machines that are capable of greater performance and offer more comfort. Four-cylinder machines have been common since the Honda CB750 appeared in 1969. Despite advances in motorcycle technology, many riders are attracted to the traditional look of motorcycles like the twin-cylinder Harley-Davidson. Harley-Davidson Glides exploit the style of the classic American V-twin engine, where the cylinders are placed in a V-formation.

1901 WERNER MOTORCYCLE

Vacuum-operated inlet valve
Bicycle-type saddle
Pulley rim rear brake
Fuel tank
Electric ignition control
Inlet-over-exhaust (IOE) engine
A2201
Alloy crankcase
Twisted rawhide drive belt
Cast iron cylinder barrel

1988 HARLEY-DAVIDSON FLHS ELECTRA GLIDE

1965 BMW R/60 WITH 1952 STEIB CHAIR

Handlebar
Headlight
Adjustable link
Mirror
Windshield
Sidecar
Fuel tank
Side light
Fender
Horizontally opposed engine
Sidecar chassis rail
Sidecar wheel
Sidecar lower link
Exhaust pipe
Square-section tire
FRONT VIEW

Backrest
Passenger seat
Passenger grab rail
Saddlebag
Luggage rack
Licence plate
Taillight
Indicator
Side reflector

Fender
Canvas shroud
Speedometer
Ignition lock
Taillight
Grab rail
Tool tray
Fender clamp
Lockable luggage trunk
Silencer
Silencer bracket
Suspension linkage
Bullet-shaped sidecar body
Drum brake
Disc brake
Knock-off wheel nut
SIDE VIEW
Long leading-link fork (Earles fork)
Crash bar
Exhaust clamp

1969 HONDA CB750

1963 VESPA GRAND SPORT 160 MARK 1

Taillight

Seat

Mirror

Front brake lever

Seat strap

Indicator

Shock absorber

Oil tank

Telescopic fork

Fender clamp

Disc brake

Clutch cover

Single overhead camshaft engine

Mirror

Heat shield

Passenger footrest

Exhaust pipe

Brake master cylinder

Handgrip

Front brake lever

Light switch

Padded seat

Manufacturer's logo

Oil tank filler cap

Fuel tank

Oil tank

Passenger foot rest

Gearbox

Air filter

45° V-twin engine

Exhaust pipe

Foot rest

Brake pedal

Crash bar

Duplex tubular cradle frame

Brake calliper

Disc brake

Cast alloy wheel

Twist grip gear change

Monocoque chassis

Seat strap

Throttle

Front brake lever

Clutch lever

Engine cover

Seat

Headlight

Cooling grille

Horn

Taillight

Choke

Shock absorber

Gas tap

Kick-starter

Center stand

Foot brake

Silencer

Rubber foot mat

Drum brake

Single-sided trailing-link fork

Windshield

Clutch cable

Throttle cable

Windshield adjustor

Headlight

Fog lamp

Indicator

Telescopic fork

Side reflector

Fender

The motorcycle chassis

THE MOTORCYCLE CHASSIS is the main "body" of the motorcycle, to which the engine is attached. Consisting of the frame, wheels, suspension, and brakes, the chassis performs various functions. The frame, which is built from steel or alloy, keeps the wheels in line to maintain the handling of the motorcycle, and serves as a structure for mounting other components. The engine and gearbox unit is bolted into place, while items such as the seat, the fenders, and the fairing are more easily removable. Suspension cushions the rider from irregularities in the road surface. In most suspension systems, coil springs controlled by an oil damper separate the main mass of the motorcycle from the wheels. At the front, the spring and damper are usually incorporated in a telescopic fork; the rear employs a pivoted swing arm. The suspension also helps to retain maximum contact between the tires and the road, necessary to effective braking and steering. Drum brakes were common until the 1970s, but modern motorcycles use disc brakes, which are more powerful.

1985 HONDA VF750 WITH BODYWORK

Racing number plate
Frame-mounted fairing
Fuel tank
Dual seat
Telescopic fork
Fender
Disc brake
Box-section swing arm
V4 engine unit
Box-section tubular cradle frame
Floating disc brake

1985 HONDA VF750 WITH BODYWORK REMOVED

Brake master cylinder
Headstock
Bracing tube
Shock absorber top mounting
Engine mounting plate
Square-section steel tubing
Rear sub-frame
Bodywork mounting point
Shock absorber
Exhaust mounting strap
Exhaust pipe
Light alloy wheel
Axle adjustor
Disc brake
Disc brake calliper
Box-section swing arm
Brake torque arm
Brake master cylinder
Swing arm pivot
Brake pedal
Foot rest hanger
Multiplate clutch
Oil level window
Oil sump
Engine cover
Engine mounting bolt
V4 engine unit
Radiator
Oil cooler
Radiator pipe

DRUM BRAKE

EXTERIOR OF DRUM BRAKE

Bolt hole
Torque arm
Air cooling scoop
Axle hole
Cooling fin
Speedometer drive
Cable stop
Brake plate
Operating arm

INTERIOR OF DRUM BRAKE

Torque arm
Bolt hole
Brake shoe
Pivot
Brake shoe return spring
Axle hole
Operating cam
Brake shoe return spring
High-friction material

OPERATING PARTS OF DISC BRAKE SYSTEM

Brake-fluid reservoir
Master cylinder
Push-rod
Piston
Hydraulic brake fluid
Wheel disc
Calliper assembly
Piston
Brake pad

Clutch cable
Hydraulic brake hose

Telescopic fork leg
Fork slide
Light alloy wheel
Axle
Floating disc brake
Brake calliper

SPRING/DAMPER UNIT

Rubber mounting bush
Twin rate spring
Damper rod
Damper body
Pre-load adjustor
Rubber mounting bush

HOW A SPRING/DAMPER UNIT WORKS

Rubber mounting bush
Spring
Damper rod
Compressible gas
Nonreturn valve
Hydraulic fluid
Hydraulic fluid chamber
Rubber mounting bush

TYPES OF TIRE

RACING SLICK
No tread pattern

TUBELESS SPORTS
Radial groove

TRIALS
Knobby tread pattern

STANDARD
Hard-wearing rubber compound

Motorcycle engines

MOTORCYCLE ENGINES must be lightweight and compact, and have a good power output. They have between one and six cylinders, can be cooled by air or water, and the capacity of the combustion chamber varies from 49cc (cubic centimeters) to 1500cc. Two types of internal combustion engine are common: the four-stroke, which is used in cars (see pp. 342-343), and the two-stroke. A basic two-stroke engine has only three moving parts—the crankshaft, the connecting rod, and the piston—but the power output is high. The engine fires every two strokes (rather than every four), giving a "power stroke" every revolution (see p. 343). Power is conveyed from the engine to the rear wheel by the transmission system. This usually consists of a clutch, a gearbox, and a final drive system. Clutches are multiplate devices, which run in oil. Gearboxes have five or six speeds and are operated by foot pedal. Shaft and belt drive systems are used in some cases, but chain drive to the rear wheel is most common.

EXTERIOR OF STANDARD TWO-STROKE ENGINE

Spark plug cap
Fuel tap
Carburetor mounting
Kick-starter
Carburetor
Cylinder head
Cooling fin
Exhaust port
Case screw
Clutch activating arm
Engine cover
Gear lever

TRANSMISSION SYSTEM

GEARBOX

Gear lever selector shaft
5th gear
2nd gear
3rd gear
4th gear
6th gear
1st gear
Input shaft
Splines for mounting gear lever
Bearing
Output shaft
Splines for mounting final drive sprocket
Gear tooth
Selector fork
Copper oil feed pipe
Aluminum outer casing

MULTIPLATE CLUTCH

Fiber plate
Outer clutch drum, connected to engine
Pressure plate, connected to inner clutch drum
Springs force plates together
Metal plate
Key locks fiber plate to outer drum
Straight-cut primary-drive gear

MODERN O-RING DRIVE CHAIN

Small front sprocket
Roller with sealed-in lubricant
Hole for retaining bolt
Plate
Large rear sprocket
Mounting hole
Sprocket tooth

**VELOCETTE OVERHEAD
VALVE (OHV) ENGINE**

Screw and lock nut
tappet adjustor

Oil feed pipe

Inlet port

Spark plug lead

Cam follower

Magneto drive

Camshaft gear

Engine
mounting
bolt hole

Oil passageway

Crankcase

Oil pump

Mounting lug

Rocker arm

Rocker cover
retaining bolt

Cylinder head

Exhaust port

Cylinder head

Combustion chamber

Cooling fin

Piston

Push rod

Valve lifter

Timing gear

Engine
mounting
bolt hole

Crankshaft

Nonreturn valve

Oil sump

Competition motorcycles

THERE ARE MANY TYPES of motorcycle sports and in each, a special machine has evolved to perform to specific requirements. Races take place on roads or tracks or "off-road," in fields, dirt tracks, and even the desert. "Grand Prix" world championships in roadracing are contested by three classes: 125cc, 250cc two-strokes; the top class of 500cc two-strokes; and 900cc four-stroke machines. The latest racing sidecars have more in common with racing cars than motorcycles. The rider and passenger operate within an all-enclosing, aerodynamic fairing. The Suzuki RGV500 shown here, like other Grand Prix machines, carries advertising, which helps to cover the cost of developing motorcycle technology. In Speedway, which originated in the U.S. in 1902, motorcycles operate without brakes or a gearbox. Off-road competition motorcycles have less emphasis on high power output. In Motocross, for example, which is held on rough terrain, they must have high ground clearance, flexible long-travel suspension, and tires with a chunky tread pattern.

1992 HUSQVARNA MOTOCROSS TC610

Throttle cable
Handlebar brace
Long seat
Racing number
Hand protector
Radiator air vent
Flexible plastic fender
Lightweight exhaust system
Telescopic fork
Plastic guard
Axle
Overhead camshaft engine
Gear lever
Disc brake
Knobby tire
Shock absorber
Disc brake
Brake calliper
Alloy swing arm
Shock absorber linkage

1992 SUZUKI RGV500
SIDE VIEW

Exhaust pipe
Racing number
Air vent
One-piece seat and tail unit
Shock absorber
Minimal seat padding
Arched alloy swing arm

Exhaust pipe
Vent
Handlebar
Silencer
Foot rest
Shock absorber mounting
Rear brake pedal
Three-spoke alloy wheel
Drive chain
Exhaust pipe
Wide, slick tire
Axle adjustor
Disc brake
Rear brake calliper
Slick racing tire
Drive chain
Foot rest
Exhaust pipe
Brake pedal
Disc brake master cylinder
Lightweight alloy frame

REAR VIEW

1981 WESLAKE SPEEDWAY

Throttle

Throttle cable

Carburetor cover

Fuel cap

Oil cap

Fender

Seat

Fuel tank

Fender

Wheel cover

Throttle

Wide tire

Telescopic fork

Narrow tire

Brakeless wheel hub

Silencer

Foot rest

Oil pump

Overhead valve engine

Tubular open cradle frame

1968 KIRBY BSA RACING SIDECAR

FRONT VIEW

Rev counter

Windshield

All-enclosing fairing

Fuel tank

Battery

Wheel guard

60

BSA

Square-section tire

Passenger windshield

Passenger grab rail

SIDE VIEW

Throttle cable

Exhaust pipe

Rev counter

All-enclosing fairing

60

Sidecar chassis

Engine

Fuel cap

Fiberglass wheel guard

Fairing stay

Throttle cable

Fuel tank breather

MOTUL

Fuel tank

Throttle

Front brake lever

SUZUKI

TEAM LUCKY STRIKE SUZUKI MOTUL

Telescopic fork

Fender

LUCKY STRIKE

KYABB

MOTUL

HELIN

Sponsor's logo

Air vent

Braided steel hydraulic hose

Brake calliper

Carbon-fiber disc brake

Three-spoke alloy wheel

Slick racing tire

Quickly detachable (QD) fairing

Windshield

Racing number

Clutch lever

Fairing

TEAM LUCKY STRIKE SUZUKI MOTUL

34

TEAM LUCKY STRIKE SUZUKI MOTUL

Radiator

Front brake lever

SUZUKI

Hydraulic brake hose

Fender

Axle

Slick tire

FRONT VIEW

Sea and Air

Ships of Greece and Rome

ROMAN ANCHOR

Stock

Shank

Palm

Acutely angled arm

Ring

Crown

IN THE EXPANSIVE EMPIRES OF GREECE AND ROME, powerful fleets were needed for battle, trade, and communication. Greek galleys were powered by a sail and many oars. A new armament, the embolos (ram), was fitted on to the galley bow. As ramming duels required fast and maneuverable boats, extra rows of oarsmen were added, culminating in the trireme. During the fifth and fourth centuries B.C., the trireme dominated the Mediterranean. It was powered by 170 oarsmen, each pulling one oar, and ranged on three levels, as the model opposite shows. The trireme also carried archers and soldiers for boarding enemy craft. Galleys were pulled out of the water when not in use, and were kept in dockyard ship-sheds. The merchant ships of the Greeks and Romans were mighty vessels, too. The full-bodied Roman corbita, for example, could hold up to 400 tons of cargo, such as spices, gems, silk, and animals. The construction of these boats was based on a stout hull with planking secured by mortice and tenon. Some of these ships made long trading voyages, sailing even as far as India. To make them easier to steer, corbitas set a foresail called an "artemon." It flew from a forward-leaning mast that was the forerunner of the long bowsprits carried by the great clipper ships of the 19th century.

ATTIC VASE SHOWING A GREEK GALLEY

Kalos (brailing rope)

Mast

Embolos (ram; beak)

Ophthalmos (eye)

Bronze mast truck

Keraia (yard)

Kubernetes (helmsman)

Sternpost

Pedalia (twin rudder)

Oar port sleeve

Kope (oar)

ROMAN CORBITA

Double halyard

Bullseye

Antenna (yard)

Fore mast

Buntline

Brace

Artemon (fore sail)

Oculus (eye)

Tabling

Bolt rope

Prow

Windlass

Scala (ladder)

Catena (riding bitt)

Ancorale (anchor rope; anchor rode)

Hatch board

Deck beam

Roband (rope band)

Ceruchi (lift)

Heraldic device

Ring

Ruden (brail line)

Fore stay

Anchor

Sheet

Zosteres (rubbing strake)

Cargo hold

Masthead

Single clump block

Malus (mast)

Rope parrel

Bullet block

Antenna (yard)

Timber fairlead

Shroud

Leather reinforcing strip

Scala (ladder)

Velum (main sail)

Sheer pole

Deadeye

Lanyard

Poop break

Poop deck

Clew

Midships fence

Constratum (deck)

Bitt

ROWING POSITIONS ON A GREEK TRIREME (TRIERE)
The katastroma (deck) has been removed from this model to show the positions taken by oarsmen on a trireme.

Deck rail

Tropeter (leather grommet)

Paraxeiresia (outrigger)

Kope (oar)

Stanchion

Zugon (thwart; seat)

Thranite (upper level oarsman)

Zygian (middle level oarsman)

Thalamian (lower level oarsman)

Hyperesion (oarsman's cushion)

Pine hull

Main double halyard

Main brace

Main sheet

Hole and peg joint

Poop deck house

Clavus (tiller)

Swan neck ornament

Stern balustrade

Ring bolt

Sternpost

Gubernator (helmsman)

Wale

Planking

Shaft

Oar lanyard

Blade

Gubernacula (rudders)

MORTICE-AND-TENON FASTENINGS FOR HULL PLANKS

Mortice

Gomphoi (dowel)

Tenon

Hull plank

373

Viking ships

IN THE DARK AGES (roughly 500 A.D. to 1000 A.D.) the longships of Scandinavia were among the most feared sights for people of northern Europe. The Vikings launched raids from Scandinavia every summer in longships equipped with a single steering oar on the right, or "steerboard" side (hence, "starboard"). A longboat had one row of oars on each side and a single sail. The hull was clinker-built, with overlapping planks. Prowheads adorned fighting ships during war campaigns. The longship was also used for coastal travel. The karv below was probably built as transport for an important family, while the smaller faering was a rowing boat only. The fleet of William of Normandy that invaded England in 1066 owed much to the Viking boat building tradition, and has been depicted in the Bayeux Tapestry (right). Seals of port towns and royal courts through the ages provide a record of contemporary ship design. The seal opposite shows a European craft from somewhat later than the Viking period. Fighting platforms, or castles, and the addition of more masts and sails changed the character of the medieval ship. Note also that the steering oar has been replaced by a centered rudder.

BOAT BUILDERS' TOOLS

Shave

Broad axe

Breast auger

Sheer

Master shipwright

Stempost

Hood end

Keel

T-handle auger

Axe

Strake

Tree cut for planking

Roband

Leather diagonal reinforcement

Square sail of homespun yarn

Leech (leach)

Clew

Tye halyard

Foot

Zoomorphic head

Eye

Tooth

Braiding

Serpentine neck

Lozenge-shaped recess

Rectangular cross-band

Snake-tail ornament

VIKING KARV (COASTER)

Tiller

Sternpost

Boss (rudder pivot)

Steering oar (side rudder)

Oar

Starboard (steerboard) side

DRAGON PROWHEAD

FAERING (VIKING ROWING BOAT)

Grommet

Tiller

Knee

Grommet

Kabe (oar pivot)

Plank scarf

Prow

Clench nail

Stepped stempost

Stepped sternpost

Sheer strake

Pivot

Side rudder

Keel

Thwart (seat)

Double-ended hull

Oar

Masthead

Masthead pulley for tye halyard

Yard

Head

Head earing

Parrel

COURT SEAL SHOWING A THREE-MASTED, SQUARE-RIGGED SHIP

Weaponry

Banner/ windvane

Topcastle

Main mast

Furled forecourse

Furled lateen mizzen sail

Jack staff

Mizzen mast

Fore mast

Aftercastle

Forecastle

Rudder

Gudgeon strap

Stempost

Main sail

Anchor

Leechline

Mast

Snake-head ornament

Sail foot control line

Open, double-ended hull

Stempost

Starboard main sheet

Oar port

Scroll work

Clinker-built oak planking (overlapping planking)

Stowage crutch for oars

Clench nail

Medieval warships and traders

FROM THE 16TH CENTURY, SHIPS WERE BUILT WITH A NEW FORM OF HULL, constructed with carvel (edge-to-edge) planking. Warships of the time, like King Henry VIII of England's Mary Rose, boasted awesome fire power. This ship carried both long-range bronze cannon, and short-range, anti personnel guns in iron. Elsewhere, ships took on a multiformity of shapes. Dhows transported slaves from East Africa to Arabia, their fore-and-aft rigged lateen sails allowing them to sail close to the wind around the lands of the Indian Ocean. The Chinese sailed to East Africa and Arabia in junks, trading goods that were carried in watertight compartments. New astronomical tools helped medieval sailors to find their way. Cross-staves and astrolabes were used to measure the altitude of the sun or stars. One of the cross-pieces was slid along the staff of the cross-stave—which was graduated in degrees of altitude—until its top aligned with the celestial body and its base with the horizon. The sighting rule of the astrolabe was simply lined up with a known body, and its altitude read from marks on the metal disk. Sundials used the shadow of the sun to show sailors the time of day.

SAILING WARSHIP

Fore topsail yard
Fore topmast
Fore topcastle
Lift
Fore yard
Fore mast
Ratline
Shroud
Fore stay
Woolling
Forecastle
Forecastle castle-deck gunport
Beakhead
Rigging rail
Chain wale (channel)
Hawse hole
Anchor cable
Stempost

DHOW

Main yard
Furled lateen main sail
Mizzen yard
Parrel
Furled lateen mizzen sail
Main mast
Shroud
Parrel tackle
Mizzen mast
Stem head
Tiller
Rudder
Eye
Raking stempost

JUNK

Su-wei (fourth mast)
Topsail
Chung-ta-wei (main mast)
Wei-wei (mizzen mast)
Fore topmast stay
Bowsprit
Halyard
Erh-wei (second mast)
Sail batten
Sprit yard
T'on-wei (port fore-mast)
Lug sail
Rudder head
Transom
Quarterdeck house
Rudder
Cargo hatch
Oar
Grapnel-type anchor

Main topgallant mast

Main topgallant yard

Main top yard

Main topmast topcastle

Mizzen topmast

Mizzen top yard

Mizzen topcastle

Main topmast stay

Main topmast

Lift

Main topcastle

Bonaventure top yard

Lift

Bonaventure topmast

Main yard

Parrel

Tye

Jeer

Bonaventure topcastle

Brace

Main stay

Bonaventure yard

Mizzen mast

Bonaventure mast

Mizzen yard

Aftercastle

Main mast

Swifting tackle

Aftercastle castle-deck gunport

Outrigger

Upper deck gunport

Chain wale (channel)

Lid

Deadeye

Gangway

Gun carriage

Transom

Rudder

Sternpost

Keel

Blindage (removable archery screen)

Wale

Main deck gunport

Carvel planking

Port bower anchor

CROSS-STAVE (CROSS-STAFF)

90 degree cross-piece (transversary)

Clamp

Boxwood staff

60 degree cross-piece

Altitude scale in degrees and minutes

30 degree cross-piece

Ocular end

10 degree cross-piece (dutch shoe)

SUNDIAL

Style of the gnomon (edge)

Gnomon

Needle

Pivot

Hour line

Dial

Swivel suspension ring

Graduated ring

ASTROLABE

Scale of degrees

Pivot

Alidade (sighting rule)

Bottom ballast

Scribed arc decoration

The expansion of sail

BY THE 18TH CENTURY, SAILING SHIPS had become fast and effective floating fortresses. The navies of the north European powers competed with each other by building heavily-armed fighting ships called "men-of-war." The distinctive round stern of the ship below, with its open gallery, balcony, and elaborate wood carving is typical of the period. Hulls around this time were semicircular in cross section, although many boat designers were soon to return to the V-shaped hulls used by the Vikings. Ships of the period carried more sail than ever before. A labyrinth of rigging supported the masts and yards from which the profusion of square sails were set. Ships grew higher as extra masts were fitted above the lower masts, and the bowsprit became longer, to allow the ship to carry staysails, spritsails, and jibs. Ships went into battle in single file, so that broadsides from the multiple decks of guns would have maximum effect. Ships were classified by rates, the rating of a vessel depending on how many guns it had. A first rate ship had more than 100 guns. The guns fired solid round shot, usually made of iron.

WOODEN SAILING SHIP

BOW

SAIL PATTERN OF A 74-GUN SHIP

Main topgallant stay

Fore topgallant mast

Fore topgallant backstay

Gilded truck

Fore topgallant stay

Mouse and collar

Main topmast stay

Fore topmast shroud

Main topmast preventer stay

Fore topmast backstay

Fore shroud

Main stay

Mainstay tackle

Fore hatch tackle

Anchor buoy

Ratline

Fore topmast

Fore top

Fore mast

Rope woolding

Fore stay

Fish davit

Mainrail head

Mizzen topgallant sail

Main topgallant sail

Fore topgallant sail

Fore topsail

Inner jib

Outer jib

Mizzen topsail

Mizzen course

Main course

Main topsail

Fore course

Fore staysail

Top spritsail

Spritsail

Fore topmast stay

Fore topmast preventer stay

Truck

Jack staff

Cap

Bee

Top spritsail yard

Spritsail yard

Foot rope

Bowsprit

Bobstay

Figurehead

Rail

Trailboard

Draft mark

Bower anchor

Tallow coating

Capstan   Clewline   Gunport   Gun   Gripe

Jibboom

STERN

Main topgallant yard

Fore topgallant yard

Main topsail yard

Yardarm

Fore topsail yard

Main yard

Fore yard

Mizzen topmast yard

Stern lantern

Captain's cabin (great cabin)

Upper gallery

Port

Balcony

Stern quarter gallery

A ship of the line

THE 74-GUN THIRD-RATER WAS A MAINSTAY of British and French battlefleets in the late 18th and early 19th centuries. (The biggest ships in the fledgling American navy of the time were 44-gun frigates.) The length of such a man-of-war was determined by the number of guns needed for each deck, allowing room for crews to man them. The gun deck of this vessel was about 170 ft (52 m) long. Her decks had to be strong to carry the weight of the guns. The deck planks have been removed in the model below to illustrate the number of beams needed to make the hull strong enough. Only timber with perfect grain was used. The upper deck was open at the waist, but forward and aft were officers' cabins. The forecastle (foc's'l) and quarterdeck carried light guns and provided platforms for handling the rigging and for reconnaissance. The ship's longboats, or launches, were carried on skids between the gangways.

LONGBOAT

UPPER DECK OF A 74-GUN SHIP

Truck
Mast
Jib halyard
Fore stay halyard
Shrouds
Fore staysail halyard
Parrel
Bowsprit
Traveler
Stem
Waterline
Deadeyes
Flag halyard
Backstay
Topping lift
Peak halyard
Main sheet
Gaff
Boom
Oar
Side bench

Thole pins
Planking
Rabbit line
Sheerplank
Windlass bar
Frame
Floor
Transom
Tiller
Keel
Rudder
Thwart (seat)

Stock
Hoop
Cathead
Ring
Knightheads
Head (privy)
Figurehead
Head beam
Head rail
Roundhouse (privy)
Boomkin
Anchor cable
Sheave for cat tackle
Fluke
Hoop
Stock
Arm
Deck beam
Foremast hole
Carling (carline)

Steam grating
Timber head
Fore bitts
Galley stove chimney
Belfry
Deadeye
Waterway
Gangway
Capstan
Breastwork
Forked beam
Bulwark
Pawl
Main companion way
Skid beam

Head
Forecastle (foc's'l)
Waist

BOW

Figurehead

Main rail

Headboard

Middle rail

Lower rail

Head rail

Supporter

Eiking

Cat block

Cheek

Catted anchor

Riband

Frame

Side step

Hawse piece

Main wale

Hawse hole

Stempost

Deadwood

STERN

Cove

Taffrail

Screen bulkhead

Balcony

Side counter timber

Upper counter rail

Counter timber

Drop

Tuck

Lower counter rail

Tuck rail

Gunport lid

After fashion piece

Filling transom

Cant frame

Wing transom

Timber under transom

Side step

Eye bolt

Main bitts

Ledge (batten)

Hatch coaming/ shot garland

Spirketting

Backstay stool

Companion ladder

Master's sea cabin

Mizzen mast hole

Great cabin (captain's cabin)

Channel

Coaming

Pilaster

Ledge (batten)

Screen bulkhead

Standard knee

Main mast hole

Mast partners

Grating

Lodging knee

Gunport lid

Rail at break of poop deck

Mizzen bitts

Clerk's cabin

Poop rail

Gunport drip (eyebrow; rigol)

Necking

Wardroom

Upper finishing

Stern carving

Taffrail

Quarter gallery

Quarterdeck

Poop deck

Rigging

MOST SAILING SHIPS HAVE TWO TYPES OF RIGGING. Standing rigging—kept taut by turnbuckles or old-fashioned lanyards and deadeyes—refers to the ropes, wires, and chains that support the masts and yards (horizontal spars). Running rigging, which includes types of block and tackle, halyards, and sheets, is used to hoist, lower, or trim sails.

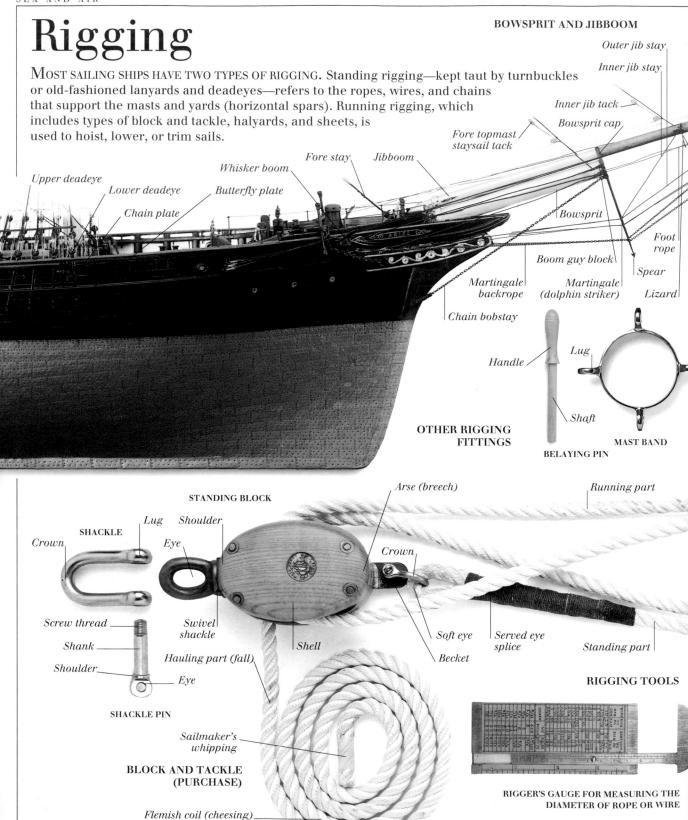

BOWSPRIT AND JIBBOOM

Outer jib stay
Inner jib stay
Inner jib tack
Bowsprit cap
Fore topmast staysail tack
Fore stay
Whisker boom
Jibboom
Upper deadeye
Lower deadeye
Butterfly plate
Chain plate
Bowsprit
Foot rope
Boom guy block
Martingale backrope
Martingale (dolphin striker)
Spear
Lizard
Chain bobstay

OTHER RIGGING FITTINGS

Handle
Lug
Shaft
BELAYING PIN
MAST BAND

STANDING BLOCK

Arse (breech)
Running part
Lug
Shoulder
Eye
Crown
Becket
SHACKLE
Crown
Shoulder
Eye
Swivel shackle
Shell
Soft eye
Served eye splice
Standing part
Screw thread
Shank
Shoulder
Eye
SHACKLE PIN
Hauling part (fall)
Sailmaker's whipping
BLOCK AND TACKLE (PURCHASE)

RIGGING TOOLS

RIGGER'S GAUGE FOR MEASURING THE DIAMETER OF ROPE OR WIRE

Flemish coil (cheesing)

Fore royal stay

Flying jib tack

Outer jib tack

Outer martingale stay

Middle martingale stay

Inner martingale stay

Eye

SCORED BULLSEYE FAIRLEAD

Eye

Strap

SHEET LEAD

Base

RUNNING BLOCK

Cheek

Pin cover plate

Double rope becket

DUTCH TRIPLE FIDDLE BLOCK

Flat seizing

Swallow

Strop

Sheave

Back   Shank

HOOK

Crown

Fixed lug   Bill

SPLICING FID

ROPE SERVING MALLET

HEAVER FOR WIRE SERVING

PRICKERS

HOLLOW SPIKE FOR WIRE

MARLINESPIKE

LANYARD AND DEADEYES

TURNBUCKLE (RIGGING SCREW)

Leather parceling

Shroud

Marline serving

Turk's head

Flat wire seizing

Hitched hauling end

Solid heart thimble

UPPER DEADEYE

Cotter pin

Fork end

Tail

Standing part

Right hand screw

Open body

LANYARD

Left hand screw

Safe working load mark

LOWER DEADEYE

Seizing

Grooving (scone)

Shoulder

Binding

Face

Eye

Bolt

Nut

Crown

Sails

THERE ARE TWO MAIN TYPES OF SAILS: Old-fashioned square sails hang from yards at right angles to the mast, and are powerful drivers with following winds; fore-and-aft sails are set parallel to the length of the boat, with the luff (leading edge) of the sail attached to a mast or a stay. They are more efficient for all-round sailing, and almost all modern sailboats are rigged this way. Some fore-and-aft sails have a gaff at the head; Marconi-rig sails are pointed at the top (below). The bottom (foot) of the sail is on a boom. Sails are made of strips of cloth sewn together. Cotton and flax are traditional sail materials but synthetic fabrics are now more often used.

TOP OF A MARCONI SAIL

Seizing LUFF (LEADING EDGE) Luff slide Bolt rope Head

Round thimble

Rope strand

Grommet

Head cringle

Sharp point

LEECH (LEACH)

Flat seam

Synthetic flax (duradon)

SERVING MALLET

Groove for spunyarn (twine)

Flatboard

NEEDLES AND SAIL TWINE

Tabling

Handle

Sail twine

Rat's tail

Needle packet

Needle

SAILMAKER'S FID

Grip

SAILCLOTHS

KEVLAR ON FLEX FILM

HEAVYWEIGHT NYLON CLOTH

SAIL HOOK

SAILMAKER'S PALM

Strap

Thumbhole

Crown

Cowhide face

MYLAR

NYLON AND SILICON CLOTH

Bill Shank

Metal needle pad

BEESWAX

SYNTHETIC FLAX (DURADON)

DACRON

Handle

SAILMAKER'S MALLET

Cheek

Whipping

Hide grip

Seizing

Groove made by thread

SAILMAKING TOOLS

Copper face

Mizzen
gaff
topsail

Main sail

Main gaff
topsail

Fore staysail

Jib

Mizzen
sail

KETCH

Lugger topsail

Lug foresail

Lug
mainsail

LUGGER

**SAILS AND RUNNING RIGGING OF A
DOUBLE TOPSAIL SCHOONER**

Upper
topsail
lift

Lower
topsail
brace

Main topsail
halyard

Fore
upper
topsail

Triatic
stay

Flying jib
halyard

Foot rope

Main gaff
topsail

Fisherman's
staysail

**FORE-AND-AFT
SAILING RIGS**

Fore sail

Main sail

Fore staysail

Jib

GAFF–HEADED SCHOONER

Upper topsail brace

Outer jib halyard

Fore peak halyard

Lower topsail
clewline

Fore yard lift

Fore lower topsail

Inner jib halyard

Fore throat halyard

Fore staysail halyard

Fore sail

Mast hoop
(parrel)

Inner jib downhaul

Outer jib downhaul

Outer jib sheet

Flying jib sheet

Inner jib sheet

Flying jib
downhaul

Flying
jib

Outer jib

Reef point

Inner jib

Fore
staysail

Fore staysail sheet

Yard

Head

Gaff

Luff

Boom

Foot

385

Mooring and anchoring

IN MOST HARBORS AND PORTS, a ship can moor (tie up or "make fast") directly to a pier, wharf, or quay (pronounced "key"), using heavy hawsers and docking lines attached to bitts or bollards. Hawsers are tied to each other with knots called bends. In open water, however, ships that are not under way must drop an anchor, which attaches the ship securely to the seabed. The earliest anchors were simply heavy stones. Later, various anchor designs were developed for different uses. Most small vessels today use Danforth or plow anchors, which dig deeply into the sea bottom. A permanent mooring is an anchor set in the bottom to which a ship can tie up without using its own anchor. On old sailing ships, anchors were pulled up, or "weighed," by sailors pushing against bars that turned a capstan, which wound up the anchor cable. Now, most capstans are powered by electricity.

Rope hole

TYPES OF ANCHOR

CLOSE-STOWING ANCHOR

CQR ANCHOR (PLOW ANCHOR)

BRITISH ADMIRALTY ANCHOR TYPE ACII

YACHTSMAN'S ANCHOR (KEDGE)

STOCKLESS ANCHOR

MUSHROOM ANCHOR (PERMANENT MOORING ANCHOR)

End link   **ANCHOR CHAIN**   *Common link*   *Patent link*

SHACKLE, SWIVELS, AND LINK

DANFORTH ANCHOR

Shank

Crown

Bolt   *Lug*

Screw thread

GALVANIZED "D" SHACKLE   **MOORING SWIVEL**   **CHAIN SWIVEL**   **SCREW LINK**

Pea (bill)

Fluke (palm)

TWIN BOLLARDS (BITTS), WITH RAKED PILLARS AND A HAWSER (HEAVY ROPE)

Flat

Throat

Rim

Stock

Tripping palm   *Crown*   *Base*

BERTHING ROPES (HAWSERS)

Ship
Bitts
Stern line
Bow line
Stern breast line
After spring
Fore spring
Bow breast line
Quayside
Bollard

MOORING ROPE BENDS

HAWSER BEND (TWO BIGHTS WITH DOUBLE HALF HITCHES)

Standing part
Seizing

CARRICK BEND

Seizing

SINGLE SHEET BEND (BECKET BEND)

Bare end
Standing part
Thin rope
Thick rope

Three-strand hawser belayed with figure of eight turns

Outboard end
Pillar
Foundry plug
Horn
Bolt hole
Cross piece
Bitter end (inboard end)

Bar hole (pigeon hole)
Cap
Upper head (drumhead)
Strengthening chock
Barrel
Trenail (treenail)
Strengthening chock
Whelp
Pawl slot
Lignum vitae bearing
Tapered spindle

WOOD CAPSTAN WITH A VERTICAL SPINDLE

Pin

Ropes and knots

ALL KINDS OF ROPES ARE USED AT SEA, from thin twines and yarn to thick hawsers. Synthetic fibers are much in use today. Nylon ropes stretch, and so are ideal for anchoring; polyester (frequently called by the trade name Dacron) has little stretch and is used for halyards and sheets. Different knots have different uses. Knots that join two ropes are often called bends; hitches join a rope to another object. Ropes, usually called "lines" on board ship, can also be joined by seizing (lashing them together side by side) or splicing (unraveling the ends and weaving them together).

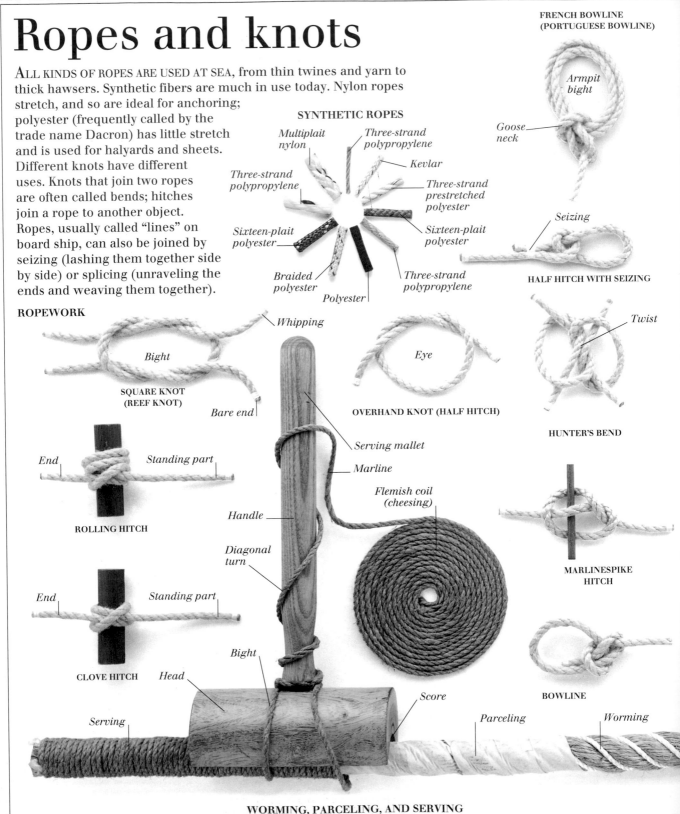

FRENCH BOWLINE (PORTUGUESE BOWLINE)

Armpit bight

Goose neck

SYNTHETIC ROPES

Multiplait nylon

Three-strand polypropylene

Kevlar

Three-strand polypropylene

Three-strand prestretched polyester

Sixteen-plait polyester

Sixteen-plait polyester

Braided polyester

Three-strand polypropylene

Polyester

Seizing

HALF HITCH WITH SEIZING

ROPEWORK

Whipping

Bight

SQUARE KNOT (REEF KNOT)

Bare end

Eye

OVERHAND KNOT (HALF HITCH)

Twist

HUNTER'S BEND

End

Standing part

ROLLING HITCH

Serving mallet

Marline

Flemish coil (cheesing)

Handle

Diagonal turn

MARLINESPIKE HITCH

End

Standing part

CLOVE HITCH

Bight

Head

Score

BOWLINE

Serving

Parceling

Worming

WORMING, PARCELING, AND SERVING

THUMB KNOT

SPANISH BOWLINE

**ROUND SEIZING
(FLAT SEIZING)**

DOUBLE CARRICK BEND

End

*Frapped
turn*

*Heaving
line knot*

LIGHTERMAN'S HITCH

HEAVING LINE BEND

*Standing
part*

**JURY MAST KNOT
(MAST HEAD BEND)**

**SHEET BEND
(BECKET BEND)**

**MANHARNESS KNOT
(BUTTERFLY KNOT;
ARTILLERY LOOP)**

Flemish coil (cheesing)

Marlinespike

HEAVING LINE

PINNED SHEEPSHANK

Rat tail

Jaw

*Hawser laid three-strand manila
rope with right-handed lay*

Paddle wheels and propellers

THE INVENTION OF THE STEAM ENGINE IN THE 18TH CENTURY made mechanically driven ships fitted with paddle wheels or propellers a viable alternative to sails. Paddle wheels have fixed or feathered floats, and the model shown below features both types. Feathered floats give more propulsive power than fixed floats because they are almost upright at all times in the water. Paddle wheels were superseded by the propeller on oceangoing vessels in the mid-19th century. Propellers are more efficient, work better in rough water, and are less vulnerable in collisions. The first propellers were two-bladed, but later three- and four-bladed versions are more powerful; the shape and pitch of the blades have also been refined over the years. At the beginning of the 18th century, tillers were replaced on many larger ships by the ship's wheel as a means of steering.

SHIP'S WHEEL

King spoke handle

Handle

Spoke

Rim plate

Felloe (rim section)

Maker's name

Nave plate

Nave

PADDLE WHEEL WITH FIXED FLOATS

Wrist pin

Limb

Fixed float

Hub

Deck beam

OSCILLATING STEAM ENGINE

Slip eccentric for slide valve

Ahead/astern controls

Slide valve

Main crank

THREE-BLADED PROPELLER

Blade

Tapered shaft hole

Hub

Keyway

Strut

Frame

Piston rod (tail rod)

Stuffing box

Oscillating cylinder

Bottom plate (bedplate)

Slide valve rod

Control platform

Propeller blade tip trace

Pitch

Blade

Propeller diameter

Hub

Propeller hub trace

PROPELLER ACTION

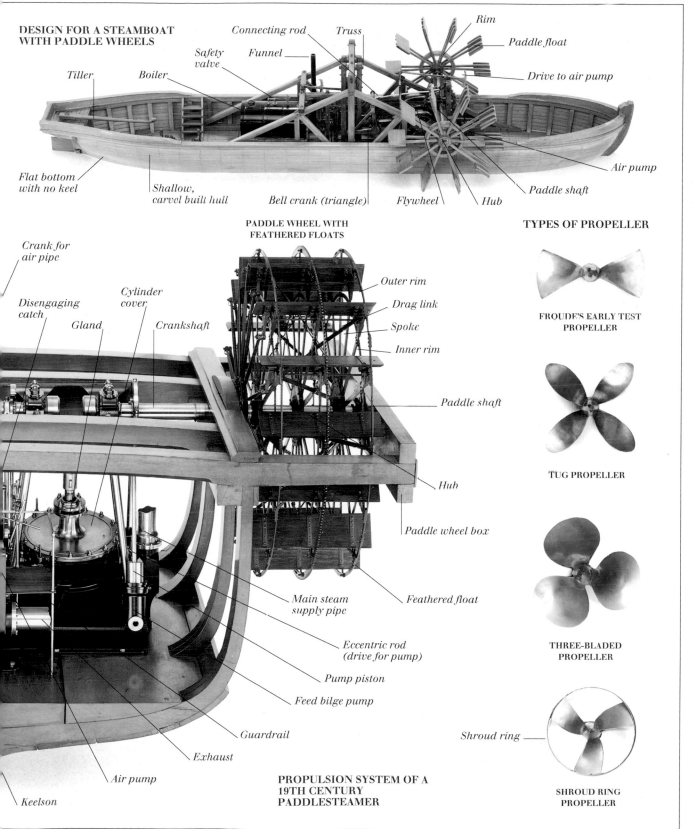

DESIGN FOR A STEAMBOAT WITH PADDLE WHEELS

Connecting rod

Truss

Rim

Paddle float

Safety valve

Funnel

Drive to air pump

Tiller

Boiler

Flat bottom with no keel

Shallow, carvel built hull

Bell crank (triangle)

Flywheel

Hub

Air pump

Paddle shaft

PADDLE WHEEL WITH FEATHERED FLOATS

TYPES OF PROPELLER

Crank for air pipe

Disengaging catch

Cylinder cover

Gland

Crankshaft

Outer rim

Drag link

Spoke

Inner rim

Paddle shaft

Hub

Paddle wheel box

Feathered float

FROUDE'S EARLY TEST PROPELLER

TUG PROPELLER

Main steam supply pipe

Eccentric rod (drive for pump)

Pump piston

Feed bilge pump

Guardrail

Exhaust

Air pump

Keelson

THREE-BLADED PROPELLER

Shroud ring

PROPULSION SYSTEM OF A 19TH CENTURY PADDLESTEAMER

SHROUD RING PROPELLER

Anatomy of an iron ship

IRON PARTS WERE USED IN WOODEN SHIPS AS EARLY AS 1675, often in the same form as the wooden parts that they replaced. Eventually, as on the tea clipper Cutty Sark (below), iron standing rigging was found to be stronger than the traditional rope. The first "ironclads" were warships whose wooden hulls were protected by iron armor plates. Later ironclads actually had iron hulls. The model opposite is based on the British warship HMS Warrior, launched in 1860, the first battleship built entirely of iron. The plan of an iron paddlesteamer (bottom), built somewhat later, shows that the craft had the masts and bowsprit of a sailing ship; but it also boasted a steam propulsion plant amid ships that turned two side paddlewheels. Early iron plates were painstakingly riveted together (below), but by the 1940s, steel vessels were welded together, whole sections at a time. The Liberty ships built in America during World War II are prime examples of such "production-line" vessels.

TEA CLIPPER

Steel yard

Iron wire stay

Steel lower mast

Steel bowsprit

Forged iron anchor

Wooden planking with copper sheathing

RIVETED PLATES

Pan head rivet

Plate

Button head rivet (snap head)

Seam

LIBERTY SHIP

Gun section

Accommodation section

Cargo derrick

Weld line

Stern section

Midships section

Cargo hold

Bow section

PLAN OF AN IRON PADDLESTEAMER

Steering position

Steering gear

Stern

Vertical frame ladder

Mast step

Rudder

Rudder post

Heel of rudder post

Mizzen mast

Poop deck

Lounge

Guardrail

Deck lantern

Binnacle

State room

Main mast

Steam whistle

After funnel

Skylight

Eccentric

Crankshaft

Guardrail

Connecting rod

Paddle wheel

Bar keel

Afterpeak

Cabin

Tank

Main mast step

Donkey boiler

Box boiler

Foundation

Reversing wheel

Bottom plate

Side lever

Cylinder

Stern framing

CUTAWAY SECTION OF AN "IRONCLAD"

Bulwark cap

Bulwark

Upper sheer strake

Teak backing

Topside strake

Wrought iron armor plate

Main sheer strake

Main deck tie plate

Lower deck tie plate

Frame

Bilge stringer

Bilge strake

Bilge keelson

Side keelson

Bottom plating

Garboard strake

Keel

Waterway

Scupper

Deck planking

Upper deck stringer (tie) plate

Upper deck beam

Upper deck pillar (stanchion)

Main deck beam

Main deck pillar (stanchion)

Lower deck beam

Pillar (hold stanchion)

Centerline keelson

Lighting hole

Angle bar (I bar)

Box sister keelson

Limber hole

Floor

Forward funnel

Main deck

Fore mast

Ventilator cowl

Skylight

Capstan

Chimney

Hatch

Bowsprit

Hawse pipe

Stem

Beam

Chain locker

Bulkhead stiffener

Deep floor

Forefoot

Deck beam

Smoke box

Combustion chamber

Cabin

'Tween decks ladder

Lower deck

Center girder

Forepeak

The battleship

IN THE EARLY YEARS OF THE 20TH CENTURY, sea warfare—attacking enemy vessels or defending a ship—was revolutionized by the introduction of Dreadnought-type battleships like the Brazilian vessel below. These new ships combined the latest advances in steam propulsion, gunnery, and armor plating. Their gun turrets, protected by armor up to 12 in (30 cm) thick, were designed to fire shells over great distances. The ship shown here, the Minas Geraes, was 500 ft (152 m) long. It was built at Elswick, England, and launched in 1908. Its chief armament was of 12 in (30 cm) guns (firing shells with a 12 in diameter). Other naval weapons developed in the 20th century include the torpedo—as portrayed on the upper cigarette card (right). This was a self-propelled underwater missile, often steered by gyro-control. Depth charges were designed in the First World War for use against submerged U-boats. They are canisters filled with explosives that are detonated by depth-sensitive pistols. The lower cigarette card shows depth charges being fired by a "thrower," fired from a torpedo tube, and rolled from the stern. Ship's shields were fitted to warships from the late 19th century onwards. The shield shown opposite depicts a traditional ship's cannon.

20TH CENTURY WEAPONRY

Torpedo tube

Sight

Warhead

TORPEDOES

DEPTH CHARGES

Side-thrown canister

Stern-rolled canister

Torpedo-fired canister

BRAZILIAN BATTLESHIP

Boat handling derrick

Gunnery spotting top

Purchase wire

Searchlight

Searchlight platform

Leading block

Tripod mast

Boat winch

Rangefinder

Forward funnel

Light screen

Lifeboat

Compass

Compass and rangefinder platform

Ship's wheel

Navigating bridge

Conning tower

Captain's shelter/ chart house

Weather shutter for gun

"F" turret

12 in (30 cm) gun

Arms of Brazil

Jack staff

Skylight

Stem (false ram bow)

Porthole

Belt armor

Forward accommodation ladder

Sighting hood

"A" turret

Turret barbette

Open gun mounting

4.7 in (12 cm) gun

Steam launch

Guest boat boom

SHIP'S SHIELD

Muzzle molding

Rope molding

Swell of muzzle

Chase

Reinforce

Ogee

Astragal

Trunnion

Lion crest

Radio antenna

Upper wireless and telegraphy yard (Upper W/T yard)

Topgallant mast

Wireless and telegraphy yard (W/T yard)

Lower yard

Signal gear

Lifeboat davit

Ladder way

Brake slip

Davit

Clump cathead

Guardrail

Hawser fairlead

Sheet anchor

Starboard bower anchor

Breakwater

Cable holder

Anchor chain

Bollard

Hawse pipe

Boat boom

Towing fairlead

Port bower anchor

Exhaust pipe

Searchlight

Vedette boat

Gig

After funnel

Funnel stay

Searchlight platform

After compass platform

After bridge

3 pound (1.3 kg) gun ("three pounder")

"X" turret

"Y" turret

Officer's accommodation ladder

Davit for whaler

Whaler

Flagmast

Stern walk

Scarph

Stern anchor

"P" turret

Ash chute

Hen coop

Gun battery

Bilge keel

Torpedo net boom

Turret roof rail

Propeller shaft boss

Torpedo net

Propeller shaft

Propeller

Rudder

Life buoy

Frigates and submarines

FROM THE MID-19TH CENTURY, ARMORED SHIPS provided a new challenge to enemy craft. In response, huge revolving gun turrets were developed. These could shoot in any direction, were loaded quickly from the breech, and fired exploding shells. Today's fighting ships, like the Royal Navy frigate opposite, also carry missile launchers and helicopters. Submarines operate underwater, have great speed, and some can fire missiles while submerged. A nuclear sub can operate for several years without refueling.

Rangefinder

Look out periscope

Local control cabinet

Breech wheel

Breech block

Loading arm

Slide

Slide locking lever

Sighting hood

Recoil cylinder

Guide for gun loading cage

Rammer lever

Gun loading cage

Training rack gearing

Stabilizer fin

Aft hydroplane

Propeller

Lower rudder

Elevating wheel

Blast bag (breeches)

Floor of gun house

Turret roller

Roller path

Working chamber

Training gear

Rammer

Waiting position

Roller path support

Floor

"Walking pipe" (hydraulic supply)

GUN TURRET
In this turret for two 15 in (37 cm) guns carried on the British "Queen Elizabeth class" battleship, shells are carried in a hoisting cage. The shell is rammed into the gun, followed by the propellant (charge). Once the breech is closed, the gun is ready for firing. The whole operation requires around 70 sailors.

Barbette (armor)

Main hoisting cage

Cordite handling room

Cordite supply shuttle

Cordite case

Turret trunk

Ensign staff

Lynx helicopter

SONAR torpedo decoy

Rudder

Practice projectile

High-explosive projectile

Shell bogie

Shell room

Hydraulic grab

Shell-handling gear

Variable pitch propeller

Accommodation ladder

Steam pipework

Machinery raft

Main turbine

Machinery control room

Conning tower

Switchboard room

Snorkel mast

Electronic warfare mast

Periscope

Control room

Sonar room

Galley

Officers' mess

ROYAL NAVY NUCLEAR "HUNTER-KILLER" SUBMARINE

SONAR transducer array

Main engine steam condenser

Distiller

Diesel motor compartment

Reactor space

Wireless office

Junior enlisted men's mess

Carbon dioxide scrubber compartment

Torpedo compartment

Torpedo tube

Forward hydroplane

Junior enlisted men's bunk space

Senior enlisted men's mess

Muzzle

Barrel

6 in (15 cm) SHELL
This shell is designed to burst in the air above its target.

Bursting charge (explosive)

Flash tube

Body

Wooden packing

Expelling plate

CROSS SECTION OF THE SHELL

Transit plug

Bullet (shrapnel)

Driving band

SHELL CASE

FRIGATE HMS ALACRITY

Surveillance RADAR

Navigation/helicopter control RADAR antenna

RADAR for gunnery and missile control

Mast

Aerial rig

Signaling lamp

Oerlikon gun position

Enclosed bridge

Exocet missile launcher

Gun turret

4.5 in (11 cm) gun

Jack staff

Seacat missile launcher

Motor whaler

Vent

Funnel

Stern gallery

Aerial

F174

RADAR for gunnery and missile control

Stabilizer

Liferaft cylinder

Signal flag compartment

Reel

Fairlead

Anchor

Anti-submarine torpedo tube

Triple "chaff" rocket launcher

Bilge keel

Pennant number

SONAR bulge

Porthole

Bollard

Breakwater

Draft mark

Pioneers of flight

FLIGHT HAS FASCINATED MANKIND for centuries, and countless unsuccessful flying machines have been designed. The first successful flight was made by the French Montgolfier brothers in 1783, when they flew a balloon over Paris. The next major advance was the development of gliders, notably by the Englishman Sir George Cayley, who in 1845 designed the first glider to make a sustained flight, and by the German Otto Lilienthal, who became known as the world's first pilot because he managed to achieve controlled flights. However, powered flight did not become a practical possibility until the invention of lightweight, gas-driven internal-combustion engines at the end of the 19th century. Then, in 1903, the American brothers Orville and Wilbur Wright made the first powered flight in their Wright Flyer biplane, which used a four-cylinder, gas-driven engine. Aircraft design advanced rapidly, and in 1909 the Frenchman Louis Blériot made his pioneering flight across the English Channel (see pp. 400-401). The American Glenn Curtiss also achieved several "firsts" in his Model-D Pusher and its variants, most notably winning the world's first competition for airspeed at Reims in 1909.

FRONT VIEW OF WRIGHT FLYER, 1903

Biplane elevator

Pusher propeller (rear-mounted propeller)

Chain drive to starboard propeller

Fuel tank

Propeller-shaft bracing strut

Offset pilot's cradle

Takeoff and landing skid

Side-mounted engine to balance pilot's weight

SIDE VIEW OF CURTISS MODEL-D PUSHER, 1911

Nine-cylinder Salmson radial engine

Pusher propeller (rear-mounted propeller)

Aileron operating arm

Wing strut

Fuel filler cap

Oil filler cap

Body cradle that pivots to control ailerons

Fuel and oil tank

Rudder control wheel

Elevator wire for diving

Seatbelt

Control column

Throttle

Nose wheel brake

Footrest

Aileron

Turnbuckle

Fuel pipe

Pneumatic tire

Rubber-tired nose wheel

Seat support strut

Pilot's seat

Elevator wire for climbing

Wing-protecting skid

Thin, cambered lower wing

Engine and propeller thrust frame

Starboard main landing gear

SIDE VIEW OF WRIGHT FLYER, 1903

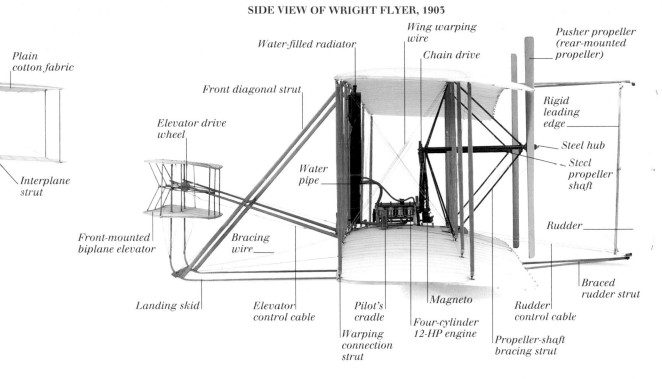

Plain cotton fabric

Interplane strut

Water-filled radiator

Wing warping wire

Chain drive

Pusher propeller (rear-mounted propeller)

Front diagonal strut

Elevator drive wheel

Rigid leading edge

Steel hub

Steel propeller shaft

Water pipe

Front-mounted biplane elevator

Bracing wire

Rudder

Landing skid

Elevator control cable

Pilot's cradle

Magneto

Rudder control cable

Braced rudder strut

Warping connection strut

Four-cylinder 12-HP engine

Propeller-shaft bracing strut

Softwood strut

Laminated wooden boom

Rudder bracing wire

Tail plane

Elevator control wire

Rudder

Elevator operating arm

Elevator

FRONT VIEW OF CURTISS MODEL-D PUSHER, 1911

Rudder control wheel

Anti-lift wire

Fuel and oil tank

Nine-cylinder Salmson radial engine

Elevator operating arm

Aileron operating arm

Starboard aileron

Port aileron

Carved interplane strut

Wing-protecting skid

Wing-protecting skid

Lift wire

Control column

Seat beam

Footrest

Axle

Main landing gear lateral brace

Tubular steel leg

Interplane strut pin-jointed to front spar

Early monoplanes

RUMPLER MONOPLANE, 1908

MONOPLANES HAVE ONE WING on each side of the fuselage. The principal disadvantage of this arrangement in early wooden-framed aircraft was that single wings were weak. They required strong wires to brace them to king posts above and below the fuselage. However, single wings also had advantages: they experienced less drag than multiple wings, allowing greater speed; they also made aircraft more maneuverable because single wings were easier to warp (twist) than double wings, and warping the wings was how pilots controlled the roll of early aircraft. By 1912, the French pilot Louis Blériot had used a monoplane to make the first flight across the English Channel, and the Briton Robert Blackburn and the Frenchman Armand Deperdussin had proved the greater speed of monoplanes. However, a spate of crashes caused by broken wings discouraged monoplane production, except in Germany, where all-metal monoplanes were developed in 1917. The wings of all-metal monoplanes did not need strengthening by struts or bracing wires, but despite this, such planes were not widely adopted until the 1930s.

FRONT VIEW OF BLACKBURN MONOPLANE, 1912

Taut fabric

Carved wooden propeller

King post

Hub bolted to propeller

Nose ring

Pilot's viewing aperture

Exhaust valve push-rod

Gnome seven-cylinder rotary engine

Elevator hinge

Elevator

Landing gear rear cross-member

Wheel fairing

Rubber-sprung wheel

Landing gear front strut

Tailskid

Axle

Landing skid

Landing gear rear strut

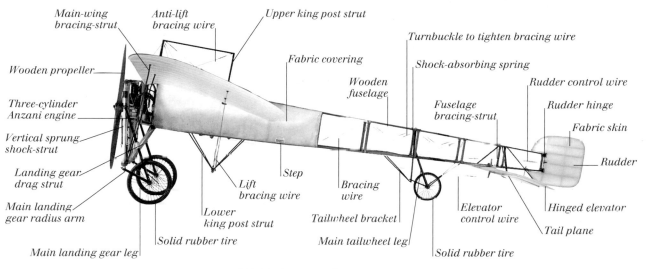

Main-wing bracing-strut
Anti-lift bracing wire
Upper king post strut
Fabric covering
Turnbuckle to tighten bracing wire
Wooden propeller
Wooden fuselage
Shock-absorbing spring
Rudder control wire
Three-cylinder Anzani engine
Fuselage bracing-strut
Rudder hinge
Fabric skin
Vertical sprung shock-strut
Rudder
Landing gear drag strut
Main landing gear radius arm
Lift bracing wire
Step
Bracing wire
Elevator control wire
Hinged elevator
Lower king post strut
Tailwheel bracket
Tail plane
Main landing gear leg
Solid rubber tire
Main tailwheel leg
Solid rubber tire

SIDE VIEW OF BLÉRIOT XI, 1909

Anti-lift bracing wire
Leading edge
Rib
Bracing wire anchor bolt
Turnbuckle to tighten bracing wire
Concave undersurface
Lift bracing wire

Warped wing
Carved wooden propeller
King post
Aluminum cowl
Anti-lift bracing wire
Lateral control wheel
Rudder post
Tail plane
Domed top deck
Large fin
Hub
Rudder
Engine mount
Elevator
Lift bracing wire
Forward fuselage structure
Diagonal bracing
Triangular-section rear fuselage
Landing gear rear strut
Elevator operating bracket
Tailskid
Braced landing gear structure
Landing skid
Rubber-sprung wheel

SIDE VIEW OF BLACKBURN MONOPLANE, 1912

Biplanes and triplanes

BIPLANES DOMINATED AIRCRAFT DESIGN until the 1930s, largely because some early monoplanes (see pp. 400-401) were too fragile to withstand the stresses of flight. The struts between biplanes' wings made the wings strong compared with those of early monoplanes, although the greater surface area of biplanes' wings increased drag and reduced speed. Many aircraft designers also developed triplanes, which had a particular advantage over biplanes: more wings meant a shorter wingspan to achieve the same lifting power, and a shorter wingspan gave greater maneuverability. Triplanes were most successful as fighters during World War I, the German Fokker triplane being a notable example. However, the greater maneuverability of triplanes was no advantage for normal flying, so most manufacturers continued to make biplanes. Many other aircraft designs were attempted. Some were quadruplanes, with four pairs of wings. Some had tandem wings (two pairs of monoplane wings, one behind the other). One of the most bizarre designs was by the Englishman Horatio Phillips; it had 20 sets of narrow wings and looked rather like a Venetian blind.

LAMINATED PROPELLER

SIDE VIEW OF AVRO TRIPLANE IV, 1910

Rudder hinge

RAF Central Flying School badge

Rudder

Fin

Navigation light

K 3215

Elevator

Rudder cable

Tail plane

Tailwheel

Bracing strut

Valve rocker

Air cooling baffle

Magneto

Wing strut

Fuel tank

Throttle

Harness

Pilot's seat

Crankcase breather pipe

Directly driven propeller

Main front strut to engine mount

Limit of fuselage skin

Skid upper bracing strut

Turnbuckle

Axle

Skid rear strut

Ash skid

Rubber cord suspension

Rubber tire

Wheel rim

Lateral bracing strut

Wire wheel

**AVRO TUTOR
BIPLANE, 1931**

Pin joint

Aileron hinge strut

Aileron control wire

Navigation light

Slat-arm fairing

Lift bracing wire

Instructor's cockpit

Wooden-domed deck

Padded coaming

Student's cockpit

Engine cowl

RAF roundel

Propeller hub

Laminated-wood, fixed pitch propeller

Metal leading edge

3215

Exhaust collector ring

Exhaust pipe

Aircraft registration code

Inspection cover

Main landing gear leg

Inflation valve

Radius rod

Manufacturer's logo

Fabric-covered steel-tube fuselage

Fabric-covered aluminum and steel wing

Recessed nose of aileron

FRONT VIEW OF AVRO TRIPLANE IV, 1910

Unpainted, varnished fabric

Leading edge

Fuel filler and vent

Fixed-pitch wooden propeller

Anti-lift bracing wire

Top wing

Wing strut

Middle wing

Rib

Bottom wing

Landing skid

Lift bracing wire

Axle

Elevator

Tail plane

Triangular-section fuselage

Fuselage bracing wire

Rudder control cable

Triangular-section fuselage

Lateral bracing strut

Tail plane

Rudder

Metal plate anchorage

Elevator control cable

Longeron

Rubber cord suspension

Tailskid pivot

Tailskid

Elevator

World War I aircraft

FLYING HELMET

WHEN WORLD WAR I STARTED in 1914, the main purpose of military aircraft was reconnaissance. The British-built BE 2, of which the BE 2B was a variant, was well suited to this duty; it was very stable in flight, allowing the occupants to study the terrain, take photographs, and make notes. The BE 2 was also one of the first aircraft to drop bombs.

One of the biggest problems for aircraft designers during the war was mounting machine guns. On aircraft that had front-mounted propellers, the field of fire was restricted by the propeller and other parts of the aircraft. The problem was solved in 1915 by the Dutchman Anthony Fokker, who designed an interrupter gear that prevented a machine gun from firing when a propeller blade passed in front of the barrel. The German LVG CVI had a forward-firing gun to the right of the engine, as well as a rear-cockpit gun, and bombing capability. It was one of the most versatile aircraft of the war.

PORT WINGS FROM A BE 2B

Interplane-strut attachment
Intermediate leading-edge rib
Airspeed-indicator tube
Leading edge
Wingtip
Airspeed-indicator tube
Main rib
Root
Airspeed pitot tube
Interplane strut
Trailing edge
Interplane-strut attachment
Upper side of lower wing
Attachment lug

BE 2B, 1914

Cabane strut fairing
Observer's windshield
Engine air intake (ram scoop)
Top-wing center section
Wooden propeller
Cabane strut
Lift bracing wire
Air-cooled V8 engine
Pilot's windshield
Crankcase
Plywood skin
Control column
Padded coaming
Buffed metal cowling
Silencing heat exchanger
Exhaust pipe
Landing gear front strut
Elevator rocking arm
Ash skid
Step
Step
Lateral control wire
Reconnaissance camera bracket
Pneumatic rubber tire
Bomb rack
Wheel cover
V-strut
Lower-wing attachment
112 lb (51 kg) bomb

SIDE VIEW OF LVG CVI, 1917

Pilot's cockpit

Observer's cockpit

Starboard aileron

7.92-mm Parabellum machine gun

Cold-water pipe

Exhaust pipe

230-HP Benz six-cylinder water-cooled engine

Rudder

Fin

Rudder control wire

Elevator

Laminated wooden propeller

Steel-drive bracket

Pivoted sprung tailskid

Aircraft registration code

Air ventilator inlet

Pitot head

Pneumatic rubber tire

Elevator control wire

Interplane strut

Aileron control cable

Axle

Aircraft type

Bracing wire

Tire inflation aperture

FRONT VIEW OF LVG CVI, 1917

Lozenge-patterned fabric

Forward-firing machine gun

Exhaust stack

230-HP Benz six-cylinder water-cooled engine

Wooden propeller

Pitot head

Interplane strut

Anti-lift bracing wire

Lift bracing wire

Main fuel tank

Pneumatic rubber tire

Multiple rubber-cord suspension

Axle

Tailskid

Landing gear strut

Gravity-feed fuel tank

Turnbuckle

Rib

Rudder

Fixed tail plane

Fabric covering

Elevator

Fabric lacing

Tail plane attachment

Rudder post

Steel lug

Elevator hinge

687

Aircraft registration code

Spar

Shock-absorbing spring

Steel V-strut

Pivoted tailskid

National marking

Leading edge

Rib

Trailing edge

HORIZONTAL TAIL OF A BE 2B

Early passenger aircraft

UNTIL THE 1930s, most passenger aircraft were biplanes, with two pairs of wings and a wooden or metal framework covered with fabric or, sometimes, plywood. Such aircraft were restricted to low speeds and low altitudes because of the drag on their wings. Many had an open cockpit, situated behind or in front of an enclosed—but unpressurized—cabin that carried a maximum of 10 people. The passengers usually sat in wicker chairs that were not bolted to the floor, and the journey could be bumpy when flying through turbulence. Warm clothing, and earplugs to reduce the effects of prolonged noise, were often required. During the 1930s, powerful, streamlined, all-metal monoplanes, such as the Lockheed Electra shown here, became widespread. By 1939, the advent of pressurized cabins allowed fast flights at high altitudes, where there is less turbulence. Flying boats were still necessary on many routes until 1945 because of inadequate runways and the frequency of emergency sea landings. World War II, however, resulted in enough good runways being built for land planes to become standard on all major airline routes.

Green starboard navigation light

Flush-riveted metal-skinned wing

Leading edge

Fuel-jettison valve

Static discharge wick

Split flap in landing position

PASSENGER CABIN TRIM PANELS

Roof trim panel

Forward bulkhead upper panel

Passenger service panel aperture

Starboard wall forward panel

Ashtray

Cockpit door panel

Forward bulkhead lower panel

Starboard wall mid-forward panel

SIDE VIEW OF LOCKHEED ELECTRA, 1934

Cockpit windshield

Sliding window

Emergency escape hatch

Steel firewall

Air intake

Passenger window

Ventilator exit

Oil tank

Nose

Propeller pitch-change cylinder

Blade counterweight

Spinner mounting disk

Variable-pitch propeller

Pratt & Whitney nine-cylinder radial engine

Exhaust collector ring

Red port navigation light

Main landing gear

Aluminum wheel

Landing gear door

Exhaust pipe

Brake pipe

Mudguard

Static discharge wick

Aileron

Electrically driven split flap

Passenger door

Metal-skinned wing

Cylinder-cooling gills

Variable-pitch propeller

Cockpit windshield

High-visibility tip

Streamlined spinner

Pratt & Whitney nine-cylinder radial engine

Valve push-rod tube

Inner wing containing fuel tank

Fixed landing light

Red filter signal light

Exhaust pipe

Pitot mast

Tank drain tap

Landing gear door

Landing gear fork

Single-leg main landing gear

Battery compartment

Electrical service compartment

Single-leg main landing gear

Axle

Brake pipe

Pneumatic rubber tire

Axle

Inspection cover

Tailwheel

Brake pipe

Landing gear fork

Disc brake

Pneumatic rubber tire

Roof trim

PASSENGER SEAT

Starboard wall aft panel

Bulkhead starboard trim

Backrest

Document panel

Seat button

Seat belt

Armrest

Bulkhead port trim

Starboard wall mid-aft panel

Seat anchor bolt hole

Wall anchor

Floor anchor

Interior cabin trim for aft bulkhead between cabin and luggage hold

Seat cushion

PORT ENGINE COWLS

Rotating beacon

Starboard rudder

Inspection door

Fixed tail plane

Starboard trim tab

Tail plane

Port fin

Aluminum flush-riveted skin

120° cowl segment

Propeller-hub spinner

Port trim tab

Ventilator exit

NC5171N

Tail plane tip

Aircraft registration code

Swiveling rubber-tired tailwheel

120° cowl panel

Joining latch

World War II aircraft

WHEN WORLD WAR II began in 1939, air forces had already replaced most of their fabric-skinned biplanes with all-metal stressed-skin monoplanes. Aircraft played a far greater role in military operations during World War II than ever before. The wide range of aircraft duties and the introduction of radar tracking and guidance systems put pressure on designers to improve aircraft performance. The main areas of improvement were speed, range, and engine power. Bombers became larger and more powerful—converting from two to four engines—in order to carry a heavier bomb load; the U.S. B-17 Flying Fortress could carry up to 6 tons of bombs over a distance of about 2,000 miles (3,200 km). Some aircraft increased their range by using drop tanks (fuel tanks that were jettisoned when empty to reduce drag). Fighters needed speed and maneuverability: the Hawker Tempest shown here had a maximum speed of 435 mph (700 kph) and was one of the few Allied aircraft capable of catching the German jet-powered V1 "flying bomb." By 1944, Britain had introduced its first turbojet-powered aircraft, the Gloster Meteor fighter, and Germany had introduced the fastest fighter in the world, the turbojet-powered Me 262, which had a maximum speed of 540 mph (868 kph).

PROPELLER

High-visibility yellow tip

Light-alloy propeller spinner

Variable-pitch aluminum-alloy blade

COMPONENTS OF A HAWKER TEMPEST MARK V, c.1943

STARBOARD ENGINE COWLINGS

Radiator-access cowling

Lower side cowling

Upper side cowling

Cowling fastener

2,400-HP Napier Sabre 24-cylinder engine

Cartridge starter

Propeller governor

Radiator header tank

Propeller drive shaft

Distributor

Ejector exhaust

Magneto

Starter motor

Engine top cowling

Cowling fastener

Upper side cowling

Lower side cowling

Radiator-access cowling

PORT ENGINE COWLINGS

SECTIONED B-17G FLYING FORTRESS BOMBER, c.1943

Astronavigation dome

Hand-held gun

Plastic nose

Pilot's seat

Oxygen bottle

Upper gun turret

1,000 lb (454 kg) bomb

Radio operator's seat

Ammunition belt

Ammunition box

Waist gun

Dorsal fin

Fin

VHF antenna

Rudder

"Cheyenne-type" tail-gun turret

Tail gunner's compartment

Ammunition feed

Retracted tailwheel

Entrance door

Oxygen bottle

Sperry ball gun turret

Ammunition feed

Navigator's seat

Bomb door

Direction-finding-antenna fairing

Bombardier's viewing panel

Chin gun turret

HF radio antenna

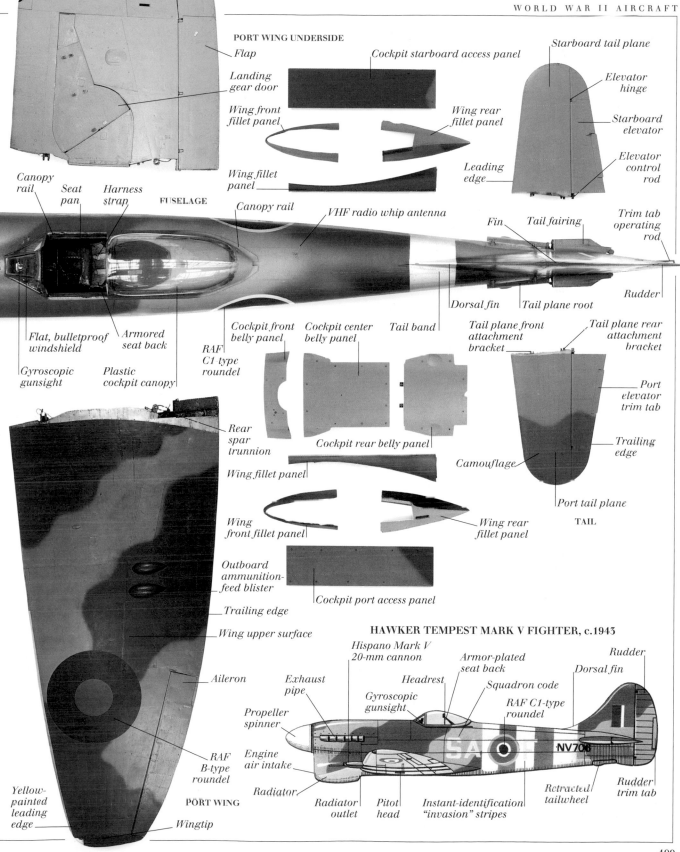

PORT WING UNDERSIDE

Flap

Cockpit starboard access panel

Starboard tail plane

Landing gear door

Wing front fillet panel

Wing rear fillet panel

Elevator hinge

Starboard elevator

Elevator control rod

Wing fillet panel

Leading edge

Canopy rail

Seat pan

Harness strap

FUSELAGE

Canopy rail

VHF radio whip antenna

Fin

Tail fairing

Trim tab operating rod

Rudder

Flat, bulletproof windshield

Armored seat back

RAF C1 type roundel

Dorsal fin

Tail plane root

Gyroscopic gunsight

Plastic cockpit canopy

Cockpit front belly panel

Cockpit center belly panel

Tail band

Tail plane front attachment bracket

Tail plane rear attachment bracket

Port elevator trim tab

Rear spar trunnion

Cockpit rear belly panel

Camouflage

Trailing edge

Wing fillet panel

Port tail plane

TAIL

Wing front fillet panel

Wing rear fillet panel

Outboard ammunition-feed blister

Cockpit port access panel

Trailing edge

Wing upper surface

HAWKER TEMPEST MARK V FIGHTER, c.1943

Hispano Mark V 20-mm cannon

Armor-plated seat back

Rudder

Dorsal fin

Aileron

Exhaust pipe

Headrest

Squadron code

Gyroscopic gunsight

RAF C1-type roundel

Propeller spinner

RAF B-type roundel

Engine air intake

Radiator

Yellow-painted leading edge

PORT WING

Wingtip

Radiator outlet

Pitot head

Instant-identification "invasion" stripes

Retracted tailwheel

Rudder trim tab

Modern piston aircraft engines

PISTON ENGINES today are used mainly to power the vast numbers of light aircraft and ultralights, as well as crop sprayers and crop dusters, small helicopters, and fire-bombers (which dump water on large fires). Virtually all heavier aircraft are now powered by jet engines. Modern piston aircraft engines work on the same basic principles as the engine used by the Wright brothers in the first powered flight in 1903. However, today's engines are more sophisticated than earlier engines. For example, modern aircraft engines may use a two-stroke or a four-stroke combustion cycle; they may have from one to nine air- or liquid-cooled cylinders, which may be arranged horizontally, in-line, in V formation, or radially; and they may drive the aircraft's propeller either directly or through a reduction gearbox. One of the more unconventional types of modern aircraft engine is the rotary engine shown here, which has a trilobate (three-sided) rotor spinning in a chamber shaped like a fat figure-eight.

MID WEST TWO-STROKE, THREE-CYLINDER ENGINE

MID WEST 75-HP TWO-STROKE, THREE-CYLINDER ENGINE

- Spark plug
- Coolant outlet
- Cylinder head
- Exhaust manifold
- Piston
- Cylinder barrel
- Exhaust port
- Cylinder liner
- Upper crankcase

- Reduction gearbox
- Driven gear
- Propeller drive flange
- Torsional vibration damper
- Sprag clutch
- Gearbox mounting plate

- Gearbox drive splines
- Small end
- Connecting rod (con-rod)
- Big end
- Counterweight
- Crankshaft
- Lower crankcase

- Pump drive belt
- Coolant pump
- Generator rotor
- Stator
- Ignition trigger housing
- Engine mounting plate

ROTOR AND HOUSINGS OF A MID WEST SINGLE-ROTOR ENGINE

- Propeller bolt hole
- Propeller drive flange
- Propeller shaft rear bearing

GEARBOX CASE

- Dowel
- Stud
- Roller
- Eccentric-shaft bearing
- Coolant jacket
- Dowel

FRONT HOUSING (FRONT END PLATE)

- Coolant jacket
- Stud hole
- Stud hole
- Dowel hole
- Rotor chamber
- Inlet tract
- Exhaust tract

TROCHOID HOUSING

MID WEST 90-HP TWIN-ROTOR ENGINE

Propeller-bolt collar

Propeller drive flange

Reduction gearbox

Lubricating oil feed

Engine front mounting plate

Blanking plate over air inlet

Upper rubber anti-vibration engine mount

Carburetor

Rotor-cooling air duct

Pipe clamp joint

Rotor-cooling air pump

Upper rotor-cooling air duct

Generator housing

Electric cable

Starter motor

Flywheel

Front bearing mount

Oil pump drive shaft cover

Torsional vibration damper

Fuel pipe inlet connection

Fuel drip tray

Blanking plate over exhaust port

Exhaust pipe flange

Lower rubber anti-vibration engine mount

Engine rear mounting plate

OUTPUT SHAFT OF A MID WEST ROTARY ENGINE

Balance weight

Drive gear

Front bearing

Drive gear spline

Starter-ring teeth

Oil seal spacer ring

Flywheel retaining thread

Eccentric shaft

Rotor bearing

Rear bearing

Flywheel

Corner bolt

Fixed gear (stationary gear)

Engine mounting

Outlet manifold

Water pump cover and oil pump housing

Rotor tip seal

Rotor tip spring

Tip seal groove

Balancing drilling

Rotor-gear teeth

Rotor side seal

Pump drive shaft

Fixing stud

Rotor bearing

Side seal spring

Side seal groove

Bolt hole

Thermostat

Cooling fins

Side seal groove

Stud hole

Dowel hole

Coolant jacket

Inlet manifold

Oil pump

ROTOR AND SEALS

REAR HOUSING (REAR END PLATE)

WATER-PUMP HOUSING

Modern jetliners 1

BAE 146 JETLINER

MODERN JETLINERS HAVE ENABLED ordinary people to travel to places where once only the wealthy could afford to go. Compared with the first jetliners (which were introduced in the 1940s), modern jetliners are much quieter, burn fuel more efficiently, and produce less air pollution. These advances are largely due to the replacement of turbojet engines with turbofan engines (see pp. 418-419). The greater power of turbofan engines at low speeds enables modern jetliners to carry more fuel and passengers than turbojet aircraft; a modern Boeing 747-400 (popularly known as a "jumbo jet") can fly 400 people for 8,500 miles (13,700 km) without needing to refuel. Jetliners fly at high altitudes, typically cruising at 26,000-36,000 ft (8,000-11,000 m), where they can use fuel efficiently and usually avoid bad weather. The pilot always controls the aircraft during takeoff and landing, but at other times the aircraft is usually controlled by an autopilot. Autopilots are complex onboard mechanisms that detect deviations from an aircraft's route and make appropriate adjustments to the flight controls. Flight decks are also equipped with radar that warns pilots of approaching hazards, such as mountain ranges, bad weather, and other aircraft.

Shoulder nacelle

Engine pylon

Hinged nacelle panel

Nose cowling

Fan duct nozzle

Fire extinguisher discharge indicator

Core-engine jet pipe

Oil-filler door

Push-in door for hand-held fire extinguisher

TURBOFAN ENGINE COWLING

Drain mast

STRUCTURAL COMPONENTS OF A BAE 146 JETLINER

Oil-filler door for integrated-drive generator

FUSELAGE NOSE-SECTION

FUSELAGE MID-SECTION

Electrically heated, birdproof windshield

Side window

Anchor for open door

Rain gutter

Hinge

Peephole

Finger recess

Static air-pressure plate

Forward main door aperture

Passenger window aperture

VHF omni-range and instrument-landing-system antennas

Light-alloy door frame

Main external operating handle

Multiple-pinned lock

Floor level

Radome

Toilet service connector

FORWARD MAIN DOOR

Anchor for open door

Air temperature probe

Stall-warning vane

Pitot head for dynamic air pressure

Overwing
fuel-filler cap

Systems
connector

Overwing fuel-
filler cap

Fuel contents
indicator

STARBOARD
WING
ASSEMBLY

Center-line (spine)
of aircraft

Single-piece skin
over inboard wing

Rubber sealing strip

Rubber sealing strip

Trailing edge

Trailing edge
of fixed wing

Spoiler anchorage

Hydraulic actuator
attachment

Pivot point

Flap-track fairing

Screw
joint

Aft section

Hinge

INBOARD LIFT
SPOILERS

Stainless-steel
flap seal

MOVABLE FLAP TRACK AND FAIRING

Track roller

Upper carriage
attached to flap

Anchor
bearing

Track

Tab hinge line

FOWLER FLAP

Leading edge

Root

Gearbox
mount

Bellcrank
lever

Gearbox unit

Carriage
drive nut

Flap drive
screw

Lower carriage

Skin lap-
joint

Leading
edge

Main spar
bridge

Root rib

Wing-root mount
containing central
fuel tank

Inboard
tab

Attachment structure for
wing-to-fuselage fillet

Cabin air-pressure
discharge valve

Floor
level

Fairing of
landing gear bay

Fairing of landing
gear pivot

Yellow anti-
corrosion paint

Modern jetliners 2

Landing and taxiing light

Heated deicing leading edge

Roll-spoiler hinge

Roll-spoiler hydraulic actuator attachment

STARBOARD WING

Fixed trailing edge

Aileron hinge

Starboard navigation light

Hinge

Hydraulic actuator attachment

Spoiler arm

Aerodynamic balance

Hinge bracket

Horn balance

Recessed hinge

INTERMEDIATE LIFT SPOILER

Flap seal

OUTBOARD ROLL SPOILER

AILERON

Trim tab

MAIN FOWLER FLAP

Leading edge

Static discharge wick attachment

Flap tip

FUSELAGE SPINE FAIRING

Outboard tab

Tab-hinge line

Landing gear door

Hydraulic brake line

Main pivot

Finger recess

Peephole

Hot-air deicing duct

Electrical harness

Oleo lock-jack

Skin lap joint

Passenger window aperture

Light-alloy beam

Direction bar

Brake line

Main external operating handle

Hinge

Shock-strut bearing

Side brace and retraction jack trunnions

Hinge

Pneumatic tire

Outer wheel axle

Lower pivot

Pivoted trailing-link arm

Hydraulic brake line

Wheel hub

Anchor for open door

Cabin air-discharge aperture

STARBOARD TWIN-WHEEL MAIN LANDING GEAR

AFT MAIN DOOR

BAE 146 MODERN JETLINER

Tail plane

Logo

Rudder

Fin

Starboard aft service door

Flap-track fairing

Core-engine jet pipe

Landing light

Main landing-gear fairing

VHF antenna

Water-drain mast

VHF radio antenna

Forward door for crew and service

Radome

STARBOARD ELEVATOR

Horn balance

Tab hinge

Aerodynamic balance

Recessed hinge

Root

Trim tab

Servo-tab

TAIL PLANE FAIRINGS

Intermediate fairing (fin tip)

Aft fairing

Fin trailing edge

Forward fairing

Side fairing

Elevator chassis box

Tail plane attachment bracket

Heated deicing leading edge

FIN

Forward spar

Fairing panel

Aft spar

Fin-attachment skin

Access to yaw dampers and rudder trim jack

TAIL PLANE

Elevator hinge

Rain gutter

Fin leading-edge attachment

Auxiliary power unit (APU) inlet

Heated deicing leading edge

Operating arm

Center line (spine)

Auxiliary power unit (APU) vent

Oil-cooler duct

Hinge

Skin lap joint

Trailing edge

Tail plane tip

Aft main door aperture

Heated drain mast

FUSELAGE TAIL SECTION

STARBOARD AIR BRAKE

415

Supersonic jetliners

SUPERSONIC AIRCRAFT FLY FASTER than the speed of sound (Mach 1). There are many supersonic military aircraft, but only two supersonic passenger-carrying aircraft (also called SSTs, or supersonic transports) have been produced: the Russian Tu-144, and the Concorde, produced jointly by Britain and France. The Tu-144 was withdrawn in 1978, after only seven months in service. The Concorde has remained in service since 1976, with a break for modifications from July 2000 until October 2001. Its features include a droop nose, which is lowered during takeoff and landing to aid visibility from the cockpit, and the pumping of fuel between forward and aft trim tanks to help stabilize the aircraft. The Concorde has a narrow fuselage and short-span wings to reduce drag during supersonic flight. Its noisy turbojet engines with afterburners enable it to carry 100 passengers at a cruising speed of Mach 2 at 50,000-60,000 ft (15,000-18,000 m). Once an aircraft is flying faster than Mach 1, it produces a continuous air-pressure wave, which is heard as a "sonic boom."

COMPUTER-
DESIGNED SST

Strake
Fin
Standby pitot head
Inboard elevon-actuator fairing
Nose gear leg
Starboard outboard engine air intake

FRONT VIEW OF CONCORDE

Toilets
Electrothermal deicing panel
Starboard forward trim tank
Overhead luggage compartments
Passenger accommodation
Underfloor air-conditioning duct
Seat attachment rail
Life raft
VHF antenna
Wardrobe

OVERHEAD VIEW OF CONCORDE

Variable nozzle
Leading edge
Forward galley
Additional crew's seat
Aluminum-alloy layers and insulation
Flight engineer's seat
Erosion-resistant radome
Cockpit windshield
Retractable visor
"A" frame
Weather radar
Visor jack
Droop-nose hinge
Captain's seat
Cockpit air-conditioning duct
Standby flight-control hydraulic jack
Plug-type passenger door
Nose gear door
Nose gear leg
Steering actuator
Multi-ply high-pressure tire
Lateral bracing strut
Telescopic strut
Port forward trim tank
Machined skin panel
Pivoted retractable frame
Tail cone
Upper rudder
Fin
Dorsal fin
Emergency exit
Aft door
Elevon (combined elevator and aileron)
Hot-section steel and titanium skin
Engine cowling
Landing gear door
Bogie main landing gear

G-BOAG

SECTIONED VIEW OF CONCORDE

Fire-suppression bottle access panel
Pressurized keel box
Fuel tank
Main air duct
Emergency exit
Cold-air unit
Static discharge wick
Elevon (combined elevator and aileron)
Cabin air duct
Inspection panel
Flight-control mixing unit
HF radio antennas fairing
Emergency oxygen cylinders
Upper rudder
Auxiliary power unit
VHF omni-range antenna
Lower rudder power control unit
Servo control-unit fairing
Tail cone
Fuel-jettison pipe
Twin-wheel tail bumper
Air-conditioning duct
Rear bulkhead
Aft galley unit
Rear emergency door
Tank inspection access
Inboard elevon (combined elevator and aileron)
Landing gear hydraulics
Port main landing-gear leg well
Variable nozzle
Nozzle actuator
Heat exchanger exhaust
Elevon power control unit
Spar
Rib
Leading edge
Middle passenger door
Fuel pipe
VHF antenna
Port engine fuel pumps
Four-wheel bogie
Port main landing gear leg
Forward ramp drive
Main landing gear cross beam
Upper lip of port engine air intakes
Retraction jack
Engine front support link
Rolls-Royce Olympus Mark 610 turbojet
Heat exchanger
Fuel tank
Honeycomb elevon structure

SIDE VIEW OF CONCORDE

VHF antenna
Emergency exit
Passenger window
Flight deck windshield
Retracted visor
Nose in drooped position
Standby pitot head
Nose gear leg
Aerodynamic strake
Nose leg telescopic strut
Starboard forward door
Radome
Steerable twin-wheel nose gear

Jet engines

JET ENGINES ARE USED BY MOST MILITARY and heavy aircraft and by many helicopters. The simplest type of jet engine, or gas turbine, is the turbojet. It works by continuously burning a mixture of fuel and air in a combustion chamber to produce a jet of hot exhaust gas that is expelled through a nozzle to produce thrust. The hot gas also spins turbine blades which, in turn, spin the blades of an air compressor; the compressor forces air into the combustion chamber. Many of the fastest aircraft use turbojets, with additional booster units called afterburners, but their use is restricted by their high noise emission. Most jetliners use quieter turbofan jet engines. An enormous fan, driven by a low-pressure turbine, feeds some air into the compressor but feeds most of it through bypass ducts to join the exhaust jetstream in the tail cone. The bypass stream produces most of the thrust. Many smaller, propeller-driven aircraft use turboprop jet engines, in which the engine powers a propeller.

NPT 301 MODERN TURBOJET

Fuel sprayer
Reverse-flow combustion chamber
Radial diffuser
Turbine rotor
Centrifugal compressor
Exhaust diffuser
Inducer
Tail cone
Air intake
Jet pipe
Exhaust nozzle
Nose cone
Igniter
Alternator
Nozzle guide vane
Air impingement starter
Combustion chamber casing

Plenum ring for hot anti-icing air
Flow splitter
Transmission bevel drive
Integral oil tank
High-pressure compressor
Combustion chamber
Fuel manifold
High-pressure turbine
Fuel nozzle
Centrifugal compressor
Temperature and pressure sensor
Low-pressure fan
Inlet cone (rotating spinner)
Pressure line
Fan case with special structure to contain broken fan
Electronic engine control and airframe interface connector
Fan duct
Electronic engine control (EEC) unit
Compressor front bearing
Engine front mount
Electrical wiring harness
Fuel and oil heat exchanger
Oil filter
Compressor air-bleed connection

PRATT & WHITNEY CANADA PW120 SERIES MODERN TURBOPROP

Alternator mount pad
Propeller speed probe
Reduction transmission
Propeller hub flange
Propeller brake pad
Engine front mount
Torquemeter mount
Transmission oil scavenge line
Accessory drive pad
Fuel-cooled oil cooler
Throttle lever
Fuel filter
Fuel heater
Intercompressor bleed valve
Fuel manifold
High-pressure bleed venturi connector
Turbine support case
Jet pipe connection
Oil pipe
Thermocouple bus bar
Fuel nozzle
Igniter plug
Engine rear mount
Intercompressor diffuser pipe
Oil-pressure regulating valve
Oil tank
Oil filter
Electronic engine control (EEC) unit
Air intake
Autofeather unit

HOW JET ENGINES WORK

TURBOFAN

Fan sucks air in
Fan blade
Rotating blades compress air
Inner drive shaft
Fuel inlet
Outer drive shaft
Exhaust gases provide extra thrust
Bypass air provides main thrust
High-pressure turbine spins outer drive shaft to drive compressor
Fuel/air mixture ignites

TURBOPROP

Compressor sucks air in
Propeller spins to provide main thrust
Reduction gearbox
Rotating blades compress air
Fuel inlet
Combustion chamber
Turbine shaft drives propeller and compressor
Three-stage turbine driven by hot gas
Exhaust gases add a little thrust

TURBOJET

Compressor sucks air in
Rotating blades compress air
Fuel inlet
Fuel/air mixture ignites
Combustion chamber
Turbine drives compressor via drive shaft
Turbine blades driven by hot gas
Exhaust gases provide all the thrust

Low-pressure turbine
Heat shield
Blade tip sealing shroud
Exhaust cone
Core jet pipe (exhaust fairing)
Scavenge oil line
Inter-module bolted joint
Fuel shut-off valve cable

SECTIONED PRATT & WHITNEY CANADA PW305 MODERN TURBOFAN

Modern military aircraft

MODERN MILITARY AIRCRAFT ARE AMONG THE MOST SOPHISTICATED and expensive products of the 21st century. Fighters need computer-operated controls for maneuverability, powerful engines, and effective air-to-air weapons. Most modern fighters also have guided missiles, radar, and passive, infrared sensors. These developments enable today's fighters to engage in combat with adversaries who are outside visual range. Bombers carry a large weapon load and enough fuel for long-range flights. A few military aircraft, such as the Tornado and the F-14 Tomcat, have variable-sweep ("swing") wings. During takeoff and landing their wings are fully extended, but for high-speed flight and low-level attacks the wings are pivoted fully back. A recent development is the "stealth" bomber, which is designed to absorb or deflect enemy radar in order to remain undetected. Earlier bombers, such as the Tornado, use terrain-following radars to fly so close to the ground that they avoid enemy radar detection.

FRONT VIEW OF A PANAVIA TORNADO

Instrument landing system antenna

Birdproof windshield

Air data probe

Port variable-incidence air intake

Wing-root glove fairing

Starboard inboard stores pylon

Taileron

Starboard main landing-gear door

Main landing-gear leg

Laser ranger and marked-target seeker

Starboard nose gear door

Steerable twin-wheel nose gear

Radome containing ground-mapping, attack, and terrain-following radars

Taxiing light

Wing extended for takeoff and landing

Wing pivoted back for high-speed flight

SWING-WING F-14 TOMCAT FIGHTER

SIDE VIEW OF A PANAVIA TORNADO GR1A (RECONNAISSANCE VERSION), 1986

Pilot's cockpit

Navigator's instrument console

Navigator's cockpit

Single canopy over both cockpits

Engine air intake

Navigation light

Flat, birdproof windshield

High-velocity air duct to disperse rain

Upper "request identification" antenna

Air data probe

RESCUE

Radome containing ground-mapping, attack, and terrain-following radars

UHF antenna

Angle-of-attack probe

Tacan (tactical air navigation) antenna

Emergency canopy release handle

Nose gear door

Steerable nose gear leg

Pitot head

Twin nose-wheel

Hinged auxiliary air intake

Cold-air intake (ram scoop)

Heat exchanger exhaust duct

Window covering infrared reconnaissance camera

NORTHROP B-2 ("STEALTH" BOMBER), 1989

Starboard split rudder

Inboard elevons (combined elevators and ailerons)

Refractory (heat-resistant) skin behind exhaust outlet

Variable-incidence gust alleviator

Wing leading edge coated with radar-absorbent material

Port wingtip rudder

Outboard elevon (combined elevator and aileron)

Leading-edge antenna

Engine aft bulkhead

Wing containing fuel tank

Weapon-bay rear bulkhead

Flight refueling receptacle

Auxiliary air intake

Weapon-bay front bulkhead

Air intake coated with radar-absorbent material

Space for extra crew member

Ejector-seat roof hatches

Two-seater cockpit

Port outboard stores pylon

Port navigation light

Fin tip antenna fairing

Radar warning receiver looking forward

Instrument landing system antenna

Fin

Radar warning receiver looking rearward

Heat exchanger air intake (ram scoop)

Extended port air brake

Rudder

Wing-root glove fairing

Wing-root pneumatic seal

Heat exchanger hot-air exhaust

Fin-root antenna fairing

Air brake jack

Spine end fairing

Thrust-reverser (closed)

Port fully variable afterburner nozzle

Port flap

Port taileron (combined tail plane and aileron)

Port inboard stores pylon

Wingtip antenna fairing

Hydraulic hand pump

Port navigation light

Lower "request identification" antenna

Powered leading-edge slat

Main-gear door

Port main landing gear

Port outboard stores pylon

421

Helicopters

BELL 47G-3B1

HELICOPTERS USE ROTATING BLADES for lift, propulsion, and steering. The first machine to achieve sustained, controlled flight using rotating blades was the autogiro built in the 1920s by Juan de la Cierva of Spain. His machine had unpowered blades above the fuselage that relied on the flow of air to rotate them and provide lift while the autogiro was driven forward by a conventional propeller. Then, in 1939, the Russian-born American Igor Sikorsky produced his VS-300, the forerunner of the modern helicopter. Its engine-driven blades provided lift, propulsion, and steering. It could take off vertically, hover, and fly in any direction, and had a tail rotor to prevent the helicopter body from spinning. The introduction of gas turbine jet engines to helicopters in 1955 produced quieter, safer, and more powerful machines. Because of their versatility in flight, helicopters are used today for many purposes, including crop spraying, traffic surveillance, and transporting crews to deep-sea oil rigs, as well as acting as gunships, air ambulances, and air taxis.

BELL 47G-3B1

Droop stop

Blade counterweight

Main rotor hub

Blade-root attachment

Main rotor mast

Stabilizer-bar weight

Direct-vision panel

Fuel vent line

Protective sleeve

Frameless plastic canopy

Fuel tank

Fuel-tank cradle

Tail rotor drive shaft

Radio

Exhaust pipe

Air-intake pipe

Instrument panel

Electric fuel pump

Cyclic-pitch lever

Battery

Battery overspill

Electrical inverter

Pitot head

Breather line

Anti-collision beacon

Oil tank

Landing light

Carburetor hot-air intake pipe

Landing skid

Air filter

VHF omni-range antenna

Navigation light

Ground-handling wheel

Valve-rocker cover

Ventilator

Electric power socket

Lycoming six-cylinder engine

Collective-pitch lever

Riveted light-alloy forward fuselage section

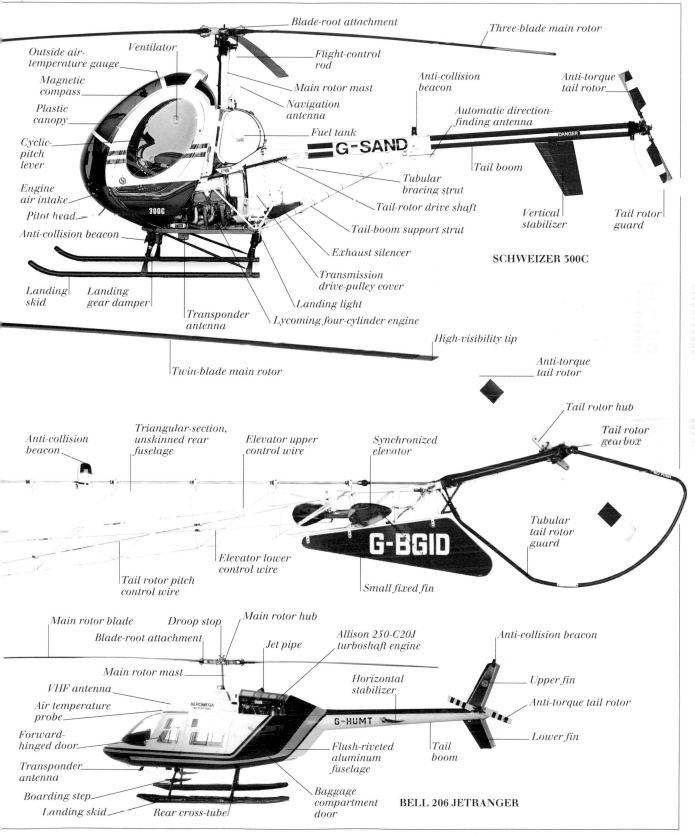

SCHWEIZER 300C

Blade-root attachment

Three-blade main rotor

Outside air-temperature gauge

Ventilator

Flight-control rod

Magnetic compass

Main rotor mast

Anti-collision beacon

Anti-torque tail rotor

Plastic canopy

Navigation antenna

Automatic direction-finding antenna

Cyclic-pitch lever

Fuel tank

G-SAND

Engine air intake

Tubular bracing strut

Tail boom

Pitot head

Tail-rotor drive shaft

Anti-collision beacon

Tail-boom support strut

Vertical stabilizer

Tail rotor guard

Exhaust silencer

Landing skid

Landing gear damper

Transmission drive-pulley cover

Transponder antenna

Landing light

Lycoming four-cylinder engine

High-visibility tip

Twin-blade main rotor

Anti-torque tail rotor

Tail rotor hub

Anti-collision beacon

Triangular-section, unskinned rear fuselage

Elevator upper control wire

Synchronized elevator

Tail rotor gearbox

G-BGID

Tubular tail rotor guard

Elevator lower control wire

Tail rotor pitch control wire

Small fixed fin

BELL 206 JETRANGER

Main rotor blade

Droop stop

Main rotor hub

Allison 250-C20J turboshaft engine

Anti-collision beacon

Blade-root attachment

Jet pipe

Main rotor mast

VHF antenna

Horizontal stabilizer

Upper fin

Air temperature probe

Anti-torque tail rotor

Forward-hinged door

Lower fin

AEROMEGA HELICOPTERS

G-HUMT

Tail boom

Transponder antenna

Flush-riveted aluminum fuselage

Boarding step

Landing skid

Rear cross-tube

Baggage compartment door

Light aircraft

Port wingtip

LIGHT AIRCRAFT, SUCH AS THE ARV SUPER 2 shown here, are small, lightweight, and of simple construction. More than a million have been built since World War I, mainly for recreational use by private owners. Virtually all light aircraft have piston engines, most of which are air-cooled, although some are liquid-cooled. Open cockpits, almost universal in the 1920s, have now been replaced by enclosed cabins. The cabins of high-wing aircraft have one or two doors, while those of low-wing aircraft usually have a sliding or hinged canopy. Most modern light aircraft are made of aluminum alloy, although some are made of wood or of fiber-reinforced materials. Light aircraft today also usually have navigational instruments, an electrical system, cabin heating, wheel brakes, and a two-way radio.

Aileron mass balance

Aileron torque tube

Port aileron

PORT MAIN LANDING GEAR

Inner tube

Tire

Hub

Brake disk

Stub axle

Landing gear leg

Brake mount

Brake pipe

Hydraulic brake caliper

Dorsal fin

TAIL PLANE AND RUDDER

Elevator

Rudder tip fairing

Rudder mass balance

Fin tip fairing

Rudder

Fin

Rear fuselage top skin

Rear attachment-bracket for wing

REAR FUSELAGE

Longeron

Elevator trim tab

Frame

Battery box

Diaphragm

Drive pillar

Side skin

Coolant outlet

Attachment plate

Rear fuselage bottom skin

"Skin-grip" pin

Aluminum radiator

Air scoop

Coolant intake

CONTROL RODS AND CABLES

Elevator push-rod

Flap torque tube

Elevator push-rod

Aileron rod

Tail plane

Rocking elevator arm

Navigational antenna

Aileron torque tube

Flap drive-rod

Rudder cable

Flap drive-rod

SIDE VIEW OF ARV SUPER 2

Canopy

Wing

Communications antenna

Fin

STARBOARD MAIN LANDING GEAR

Spinner

Engine cowling

Dorsal fin

Rudder

Brake caliper

Brake mount

Brake pipe

Elevator

G-BNHB

Landing gear leg

Nose gear

Radiator

Tail plane

Brake disk

Step

Wing strut

Tailskid

Inner tube

Stub axle

Venturi for instruments

Main landing gear

Aircraft registration code

Tire

Hub

PORT WING

Port top-wing fairing

Port underwing fairing

Headrest

Backrest

Wing strut

Port flap

Pitot head

Airspeed-indicator tube

SEAT ASSEMBLY

Seat cushion

Quick-release mechanism

Seatbelt

Seatbelt length adjuster

Bolted anchor

CANOPY

Direct-vision panel

Pressurized strut

Hinge

Leading-edge fairing

Canopy latch

Molded plastic

Outside air-temperature gauge

COCKPIT

Fiberglass canopy frame

Fuel tank top skin

Rudder pedal

Cockpit coaming

Forward attachment bracket for wing

Control-column aperture

Semi-bulkhead

Engine mount

Nose leg upper mount

Firewall

Fiberglass fuel tank

Bulkhead

Seatbelt attachment bracket

"Skin-grip" pin

THREE-CYLINDER ENGINE

Port engine cowling

Air intake box

Water outlet

Carburetor

Backplate

Fuel hose

Cylinder head

Gearbox

Propeller drive flange

Exhaust manifold

PROPELLER

Spinner

Flanged plate

Starboard engine cowling

CONTROL COLUMN AND FLAP LEVER

Torque tube assembly

Control column

Elevator arm

Elevator push-rod

Flap lever

Flap lever detent box

Release button

Throttle lever

Brake lever

Elevator trim tab lever

Carburetor hot air lever

Bearing assembly

Pilot's handgrip

INSTRUMENT PANEL

Flight instruments

Engine instruments

Glove compartment

Radio plugs

NOSE GEAR

Steering stop

Nose leg down tube

Rubber bungee shock absorber

Damper unit

Pivoted fork

Hoop

Axle bolt

Nose wheel

STARBOARD WING

Wing strut

Starboard underwing fairing

Starboard top-wing fairing

Gliders, hang gliders, and ultralights

HANG GLIDER

MODERN GLIDERS ARE AMONG the most graceful and aerodynamically efficient of all aircraft. Unpowered but with a large wingspan (up to about 82 ft, or 25 m), gliders use currents of hot, rising air (thermals) to stay aloft, and a rudder, elevators, and ailerons for control. Modern gliders have achieved flights of more than 900 miles (1,450 km) and altitudes above 49,000 ft (15,000 m). Hang gliders consist of a simple frame across which rigid or flexible material is stretched to form the wings. The pilot is suspended below the wings in a harness or body bag and, gripping a triangular A-frame, steers by shifting weight from side to side. Like gliders, hang gliders rely on thermals for lift. Ultralights are basically powered hang gliders. A small engine and an open fiberglass car (trike), which can hold a crew of two, are suspended beneath a stronger version of a hang glider frame; the frame may have rigid or flexible wings. Ultralight pilots, like hang glider pilots, steer by shifting their weight against an A-frame. Ultralights can reach speeds of up to 100 mph (160 kph).

NOSE SHELL

Grommet for front pylon strut

Instrument panel

King post

Apex

PEGASUS XL SE ULTRALIGHT

Stiffening rib

Center-line beam

Main suspension

Rear-mounted propeller (pusher propeller)

Fuel tank

Wheel part

Main wheel

Trike nacelle

Apex wire

Nose shell

Nose gear mount

Fixed nose wheel

HANG GLIDER BODY BAG

Clip-in latch for pilot

Shoulder strap

Layers of insulating fabric

Camera pouch

Armhole

Shoulder pad

Body bag

End of rib

Trailing edge

Dacron skin

SCHLEICHER K23 GLIDER

Downturned wingtip acts as skid

Single pilot cockpit

Forward-opening canopy

Towing hook

Nose wheel

Nonretractable main wheel

Aileron

Aluminum air brake

Radio antenna

EVW

Fuselage of fiberglass and foam layers

Tail plane

Hinged elevator

T-type cantilevered fin

Rudder

Tailwheel

SOLAR WINGS PEGASUS QUASAR ULTRALIGHT

Foot throttle

Pilot's steering bar

Passenger's steering bar and footrest

Seat belt

Fuel tank filler nozzle

Wheel part

Engine mount

Pylon fairing

Aircraft name

Air outlet

Rear engine cowling

Pylon strut

Footbrake

Pilot's seat

Hand throttle

Pylon-strut strap

Passenger's seat

Main wing strut

TRIKE UNIT

Trailing edge

Leading edge

TWIN-CYLINDER ENGINE

Propeller-drive gearbox

Twin carburetors

Air filter

Dual ignition plugs

Air-cooling fan

Exhaust connection

Engine rear mount

Metal hub

Sealed lid

Waterproof stowage box

TRIKE NACELLE

EXHAUST PIPE

PROPELLER

Eyelet tensioning trailing edge to rib

Bracing cable

Rib

WINGFRAME

Center-line beam

After muffler

Main exhaust muffler

Single spar

King post

Leading edge

Semirigid fiberglass skin

Lift bracing wire

427

THE VISUAL ARTS

Drawing

DRAWINGS CAN BE FINISHED WORKS OF ART, or preparatory studies for paintings and other visual arts. They can be made using a wide variety of drawing instruments such as pencils, graphite sticks, chalks, charcoal, pens and inks, and silver wires. The most common drawing instrument is the graphite pencil. A graphite pencil consists of a thin rod of graphite mixed with clay, encased in wood. Charcoal is one of the oldest drawing instruments. It is produced by firing twigs of willow, vine, or other woods at high temperatures in airtight containers. Erasers can be used to rub out marks made by drawing materials such as graphite pencils or charcoal, or to achieve a particular effect—such as smudging. Fixative is often applied—using a mouth diffuser or aerosol spray fixative—to prevent smudging once a drawing is finished. Silver lines can be produced by drawing silver wire across specially prepared paper—a technique known as silverpoint. The lines are permanent and cannot be erased. In time the silver lines oxidize and turn brown.

FIXATIVE AND MOUTH DIFFUSER

Hinge

Liquid fixative consisting of dissolved resin

Fixative is sucked into tube and sprayed onto drawing

DRAWING INSTRUMENTS

Medium-soft, light line

2B GRAPHITE PENCIL

Very soft, dark line

8B GRAPHITE PENCIL

SILVER WIRE IN A METAL HOLDER

DRAWING BOARD

Drawing board

Paper

Drawing clip

ERASERS

Hard texture

PLASTIC ERASER

Soft texture

KNEADED ERASER

CHALK, CRAYON, AND CHARCOAL

Calcite (calcium carbonate) mixed with pigment

BLUE CHALK

Iron oxide mixed with chalk

SANGUINE CRAYON

Carbonized wood

WILLOW CHARCOAL

DRAWING MATERIALS

Graphite stick

Binder clip

Colored pencil

Dip pen

Pencil sharpener

Sketch book

Ink bottle

Silver lines oxidize to a light brown color

Figures drawn in ink on top of lines

Line drawn in silverpoint using a ruler

Vanishing point located on head of man riding rearing horse

Lines of squared pavement slabs recede toward a single vanishing point

Complex perspective drawing done as a preparatory study for a painting

Paper prepared with size (glue) and pigment

EXAMPLE OF A SILVERPOINT DRAWING
The Adoration of the Magi, Leonardo da Vinci, 1481
Pen and ink over silverpoint on paper
6½ x 11½ in (16.5 x 29.2 cm)

Handmade, tinted paper

One of a series of drawings recording London during 1944–1945

Charcoal lines softened by rubbing and smudging

Broad charcoal mark

Charcoal gives strong, expressive lines

Lines rapidly drawn on site

EXAMPLE OF A CHARCOAL DRAWING
St. Paul's and the River, David Bomberg, 1945
Charcoal on paper
20 x 25⅛ in (50.8 x 65.8 cm)

Tempera

ILLUMINATED
MANUSCRIPT

THE TERM TEMPERA is applied to any paint in which pigment is tempered (mixed) with a water-based binding medium—usually egg yolk. Egg tempera is applied to a smooth surface such as vellum (for illuminated manuscripts) or more commonly to hardwood panels prepared with gesso—a mixture of chalk and size (glue). Bristle brushes are used to apply the gesso. A layer of gesso grosso (coarse gesso) is followed by successive layers of gesso sotile (fine gesso) that are sanded between coats to provide a smooth, yet absorbent ground. The paint is applied with fine sable brushes in thin layers, using light brushstrokes. Tempera dries quickly to form a tough skin with a satin sheen. The luminous white surface of the gesso combined with the overlaid paint produces the brilliant crispness and rich colors particular to this medium. Egg tempera paintings are frequently gilded with gold. Leaves of finely beaten gold are applied to a bole (reddish-brown clay) base and polished by burnishing.

MATERIALS FOR GILDING

Parchment for protecting gold leaf from drafts

Brush

Bowl containing diluted bole

Gold leaf

Gilder's knife

Gilder's tip for picking up gold leaf

Gilder's cushion

Gold leaf smoothed and polished with a burnisher

Surface prepared with gesso

Gold leaf applied in overlapping layers

Bole brushed onto gesso

Burnisher

Agate tip

MATERIALS FOR TEMPERA PANEL PAINTING

Yolk

EGG

White

SIZE (GLUE)

GESSO

Mortar

Lip

MORTAR AND PESTLE

Pestle for crushing and grinding pigments

EGG YOLK BINDING MEDIUM

EXAMPLES OF BRUSHES

FLAT BRISTLE BRUSH

SABLE BRUSH NO. 6

SABLE BRUSH NO. 1

EXAMPLE OF A TEMPERA PAINTING
Presentation in the Temple, Ambrogio Lorenzetti, 1342
Tempera on wood, 8 ft 5⅛ in x 5 ft 6⅛ in (257 x 168 cm)

**PIGMENTS FOR
FLESH-COLOR
PAINTING**

*Altarpiece
commissioned for
Siena Cathedral, Italy*

*The red tinge of
the bole is just
visible beneath
the gold*

*Vine black used
to create the
dim cathedral
interior*

*Red drapery
painted in
vermilion*

*Receding floor
tiles create the
impression of
depth*

*Textured gold ornament made
by punching motifs into the
gilded surface*

*Edge of a sheet
of gold leaf*

*Crisp edge
characteristic of
tempera painting*

*Highlights on
the beard made
by applying thin
layers of white
over dried paint*

*Raised right hand
and pointing finger
is the gesture of
prophecy*

*Patch of discolored
varnish, left from
last cleaning*

VERDACCIO

**VERMILION AND
LEAD WHITE**

VERMILION

**RED EARTH
(IRON OXIDE)**

EXAMPLES OF PIGMENTS

MALACHITE

**ULTRAMARINE
LAPIS LAZULI**

VINE BLACK

LEAD TIN YELLOW

*Warm flesh
tones achieved
by layering
vermilion and
white over an
undercoat of
verdaccio*

*Ultramarine
lapis lazuli, as
costly as gold,
was reserved for
significant
figures such as
the Virgin Mary*

*Patterned gold
halo glitters in
candlelight*

*Craquelure
(pattern of
cracks in
the paint)*

**DETAIL FROM "PRESENTATION
IN THE TEMPLE"**

Fresco

FRESCO IS A METHOD OF WALL PAINTING. In buon fresco (true fresco), pigments are mixed with water and applied to an intonaco (layer of fresh, damp lime-plaster). The intonaco absorbs and binds the pigments as it dries making the picture a permanent part of the wall surface. The intonaco is applied in sections called giornate (daily sections). The size of each giornata depends on the artist's estimate of how much can be painted before the plaster sets. The junctions between giornate are sometimes visible on a finished fresco. The range of colors used in buon fresco are limited to lime-resistant pigments such as earth colors (below). Slaked lime (burnt lime mixed with water), bianco di San Giovanni (slaked lime that has been partly exposed to air), and chalk can be used to produce fresco whites. In fresco secco (dry fresco), pigments are mixed with a binding medium and applied to dry plaster. The pigments are not completely absorbed into the plaster and may flake off over time.

CROSS-SECTION SHOWING FRESCO LAYERS

Wall

Arricio (layer of coarse plaster)

Intonaco

Pigment applied to intonaco

Mortar

Sinopia (design) drawn on surface of arricio

EXAMPLES OF EARTH COLOR PIGMENTS

EXAMPLES OF FRESCO BRUSHES

RAW UMBER

RED EARTH (IRON OXIDE)

GREEN EARTH

RAW SIENNA

Round bristle brush

Rust-resistant twine binding

Dome-shaped bristle brush

Pointed bristle brush

INGREDIENTS FOR FRESCO WHITES

Marble slab for mixing ingredients

Bianco di San Giovanni

Slaked lime

Chalk

TONDO

MUCCINI

RIGA

EXAMPLE OF A FRESCO
The Expulsion of the Merchants from the Temple, Giotto, c.1306
Fresco, 78 x 72 in (200 x 185 cm)

One of a series of frescoes in the Arena Chapel, Padua, Italy

Temple acts as a backdrop for the action

Bianco di San Giovanni often used for fresco whites

Gold leaf applied to apostle's halo

Green earth pigment applied to robe

Child painted on top of apostle's robe

Patches of azurite blue have turned green due to reaction with carbon dioxide

Hairline junction between giornate is visible

Red earth pigment applied in buon fresco has retained rich hue

Azurite blue applied in fresco secco has flaked off to reveal the plaster beneath

Dry, matt surface characteristic of buon fresco

Paint applied in buon fresco to child's face

White dove represents the Holy Ghost

Paint applied in fresco secco to child's body has flaked off

DETAIL FROM "THE EXPULSION"

Artist has to finish giornata before plaster dries

A fresco was generally worked in zones from the top down

Junction between giornate

Area with little detail can be painted quickly, allowing a larger giornata to be completed

Highly detailed area takes a longer time to paint, restricting the size of the giornata

Sinopia (design) sketched in red earth

GIORNATE (DAILY SECTIONS) IN "THE EXPULSION"

Oils

OIL PAINTS ARE MADE BY MIXING and grinding pigment with a drying vegetable oil such as linseed oil. The paint can be applied to many different surfaces and textures—the most common being canvas. Before painting, the canvas is stretched on a wooden frame and its surface is prepared with layers of size (glue) and primer. The two main types of brushes used in oil painting are stiff hog hair bristle brushes—generally used for covering large areas; and soft hair brushes made from sable or synthetic material—generally used for fine detail. Other tools, including painting knives, can also be used to achieve different effects. Oil paint can be applied thickly (a technique known as impasto), or can be thinned down using a solvent such as turpentine. Varnishes are sometimes applied to finished paintings to protect their surface and to give them a matt or gloss finish.

KIDNEY-SHAPED PALETTE

DAMMAR RESIN VARNISH

Crystals are dissolved and applied to painting to protect its surface

COMMERCIAL OIL PAINTS

CADMIUM RED

Lightfast opaque color

ULTRAMARINE

Transparent color

LINSEED OIL

Oil derived from seeds of flax plant

EXAMPLES OF PIGMENTS

CADMIUM RED

CERULEAN BLUE

DOUBLE DIPPER (PALETTE ATTACHMENT)

Screw-top lid

Container for storing solvent or drying oil

BRISTLE BRUSHES

Filbert bristle brush

Flat bristle brush

Flat bristle brush

Filbert bristle brush

SYNTHETIC BRUSH

Round bristle brush

EQUIPMENT FOR MAKING OIL PAINT

Airtight jar for storing paint

Palette knife for mixing drying oil and pigment

PAINTING KNIVES

TROWEL-SHAPED PAINTING KNIFE

DIAMOND-SHAPED PAINTING KNIFE

SABLE BRUSH

Blade

Blade

Glass muller for grinding drying oil and pigment

Glass slab with abrasive surface

Cranked, steel shank

Cranked, steel shank

Long, wooden handle

Protective, plastic case

EXAMPLES OF BRUSHES

EXAMPLE OF AN OIL PAINTING
Fritillarias, Vincent van Gogh, 1886
Oil on canvas, 29 x 24 in (73.5 x 60.5 cm)

Artist's signature scratched in wet paint with the end of the brush

Background enlivened by dabs of white and green

Each leaf painted in a single, rapid stroke

Orange and blue (complementary colors) placed together to give maximum contrast and enhance one another to appear brighter

Impasto (deep ridges of paint applied in thick strokes)

Strong directional brushstrokes on table draw attention to the vase

Features of vase highlighted by generous touches of yellow

STUDIO EASEL

Top sliding-block adjusts to canvas height

Canvas support

Height adjustment key

Angle adjustment key

Tripod

CANVAS STRETCHED ON WOODEN FRAME (VIEWED FROM THE BACK)

Staple

Canvas prepared with glue (size) and primer

Wooden frame

Unprimed canvas

EXAMPLES OF CANVASES

COTTON DUCK

FINE LINEN

COARSE LINEN

Watercolor

WATERCOLOR PAINT IS MADE OF GROUND PIGMENT mixed with a water-soluble binding medium, usually gum arabic. It is usually applied to paper using soft hair brushes such as sable, goat hair, squirrel, and synthetic brushes. Watercolors are often diluted and applied as overlaying washes (thin, transparent layers) to build up depth of color. Washes can be laid in a variety of ways to create a range of different effects. For example, a wet-in-wet wash can be achieved by laying a wash on top of another wet wash. The two washes blend together to give a fused effect. Sponges are used to modify washes by soaking up paint so that areas of pigment are lightened or removed from the paper. Watercolors can also be applied undiluted—a technique known as dry brush—to create a broken-color effect. Watercolors are generally transparent and allow light to reflect from the surface of the paper through the layers of paint to give a luminous effect. They can be thickened and made opaque by adding body color (Chinese white).

GUM ARABIC

Natural sap from acacia tree

NATURAL SPONGE

ANATOMY OF A SABLE BRUSH

Soft red sable hair

Toe (tip)

Wooden handle

SOFT HAIR BRUSHES

Hair trimmed and cemented into ferrule

ROUND SABLE BRUSH (NO. 6)

Round ferrule

Hair tied with clove hitch knot

ROUND SABLE BRUSH (NO. 1)

TUBES OF WATERCOLOR PAINT

SYNTHETIC WASH BRUSH

WINSOR GREEN

Winsor Green
Wet Winsor
Winsorgrün
Verde Winsor
Verde Winsor
0102 720 SL Series 1 A

SQUIRREL MOP WASH BRUSH

Cadmium Yellow
Jaune de Cadmium
Kadmiumgelb
Amarillo de cadmio
Giallo di cadmio
0102 108 SL Series 4 A

PORTABLE BOX OF WATERCOLOR PAINTS

CADMIUM YELLOW

Painted color swatch

Chinese white

Pan of watercolor paint

Chinese White
Blanc de Chine
Chinesischweiss
Bianco di China

Lid can be used for mixing colors

LARGE GOAT HAKE WASH BRUSH

EXAMPLE OF A WATERCOLOR
Burning of the Houses of Parliament, Turner, 1834
Watercolor on paper, 11½ x 17½ in (29.2 x 44.5 cm)

Transparent washes laid on top of each other to create tonal depth

Transparent washes allow light to reflect off the surface of the paper to give a luminous effect

Highlight scratched out with a scalpel

Paper shows through thin wash to give flames added highlight

Crowd painted with thin strokes laid over a pale wash

Undiluted paint applied, then partly washed out, to create the impression of water

EXAMPLES OF WATERCOLOR PAPERS

SMOOTH-TEXTURED PAPER

EXAMPLES OF WASHES

WASH OVER DRY BRUSH
Wash laid over paint applied with dry brush gives two-tone effect

GRADED WASH
Strong wash applied to tilted paper gives graded effect

DRY BRUSH
Undiluted paint dragged across surface of paper gives broken effect

MEDIUM-TEXTURED PAPER

WET-IN-WET
Two diluted washes left to run together to give fused effect

COLOR WHEEL OF WATERCOLOR PAINTS

ROUGH-TEXTURED PAPER

Yellow (primary color)

Secondary colors made by mixing yellow and blue

Secondary colors made by mixing red and yellow

Blue (primary color)

Red (primary color)

Secondary colors made by mixing blue and red

Pastels

PASTELS ARE STICKS OF PIGMENT made by mixing ground pigment with chalk and a binding medium, such as gum arabic. They vary in hardness depending on the proportion of the binding medium to the chalk. Soft pastel—the most common form of pastel—contains just enough binding medium to hold the pigment in stick form. Pastels can be applied directly to any support (surface) with sufficient tooth (texture). When a pastel is drawn over a textured surface, the pigment crumbles and lodges in the fibers of the support. Pastel marks have a particular soft, matt quality and are suitable for techniques such as blending, scumbling, and feathering. Blending is a technique of rubbing and fusing two or more colors on the support using fingers or various tools such as tortillons (paper stumps), soft hair brushes, kneaded erasers, and soft bread. Scumbling is a technique of building up layers of pastel colors. The side or blunted tip of a soft pastel is lightly drawn over an underpainted area so that patches of the color beneath show through. Feathering is a technique of applying parallel strokes of color with the point of a pastel, usually over an existing layer of pastel color. A thin spray of fixative can be applied— using a mouth diffuser (see pp. 430-431) or aerosol spray fixative—to a finished pastel painting, or in between layers of color, to prevent smudging.

EQUIPMENT FOR MAKING PASTELS

Glass muller

Chalk

Glass slab with abrasive surface *Gum arabic* *Ivory-black pigment* *Cobalt-blue pigment*

EXAMPLES OF SOFT PASTELS

COBALT-BLUE
HALF PASTEL

VERMILION
HALF PASTEL

OLIVE-GREEN
FULL PASTEL

MAUVE
FULL PASTEL

BOXED PASTEL SET

Boxed set containing a mixture of portrait and landscape colors

Foam compartments protect the pastels

Soft pastel

Wooden tray

EQUIPMENT USED WITH PASTELS

KNEADED ERASER

AEROSOL
SPRAY FIXATIVE

SOFT
HAIR BRUSH

BREAD

Soft bread suitable for erasing and blending

TORTILLONS (PAPER STUMPS)

Soft point used for blending

Tight roll of paper

EXAMPLE OF A PASTEL PAINTING
Woman Drying her Neck, Edgar Degas, c.1898
Pastel on cardboard, 24½ x 25½ in (62.5 x 65.5 cm)

Pastels applied directly to support

Colors are blended together using fingers or tools such as tortillons

Built up layers of pastel

Pure bright colors laid side by side produce strong contrasts

Rich color of fabric created by overlaying yellows and oranges

Broken colors, characteristic of scumbling technique

Toned color of paper visible beneath thinly applied pastels

DETAIL FROM "WOMAN DRYING HER NECK"

Feathering technique used to produce skin tones

EXAMPLES OF TEXTURED PAPERS AND PASTEL BOARDS

WATERCOLOR PAPER (ROUGH TEXTURE)

GLASS PAPER

WATERCOLOR PAPER (MEDIUM TEXTURE)

INGRES PAPER

FLOCKED PASTEL BOARD

CANSON PAPER

EXAMPLES OF COLORED AND TINTED PAPERS

Acrylics

ACRYLIC PAINT IS MADE BY MIXING PIGMENT with a synthetic resin. It can be thinned with water but dries to become water insoluble. Acrylics are applied to many surfaces, such as paper and acrylic-primed board and canvas. A variety of brushes, painting knives, rollers, air-brushes, plastic scrapers, and other tools are used in acrylic painting. The versatility of acrylics makes them suitable for a wide range of techniques. They can be used opaquely or—by adding water—in a transparent, watercolor style. Acrylic mediums can be added to the paint to adjust its consistency for special effects such as glazing and impasto (ridges of paint applied in thick strokes) or to make it more matt or glossy. Acrylics are quick-drying, which allows layers of paint to be applied on top of each other almost immediately.

EXAMPLES OF BRUSHES

Sable brush

Bristle sash brush

Synthetic bristle brush

Synthetic sable brush

Bristle brush

Goat hair brush

Synthetic wash brush

Ox hair brush

EXAMPLES OF PAINTS USED IN ACRYLICS

Azo yellow

Phthalo green

Cerulean blue

Phthalo blue

Quinacridone red

Titanium white

Yellow ochre

Burnt umber

Burnt sienna

Pad of disposable paper palettes

Flexible, plastic blade

PAINTING TOOLS

Stippled effect achieved using thick paint

Credit card

Paint spread evenly

PLASTIC PAINTING KNIFE

Striated effect

Glue spreader

PLASTIC SCRAPERS

Plastic handle

Blended tones

Paint cup

Main lever

Nozzle

AIR-BRUSH

SPONGE ROLLER

Uniform tone

Air hose

EXAMPLE OF AN ACRYLIC PAINTING
A Bigger Splash, David Hockney, 1967
Acrylic on canvas, 95½ x 96 in (242.5 x 243.8 cm)

Paint applied evenly using a roller

Cotton duck canvas support (surface)

Flatness of rollered areas enhanced by adding gel medium to the paint

Masking tape stuck onto canvas to define main shapes, and paint applied within these areas using a roller

Thin strip of pool edge left unpainted

Splash painted using thicker paint and small brush

Imprecise edge on end of spring board where paint has seeped under masking tape

EXAMPLES OF ACRYLIC PAINTS AND TECHNIQUES

Opaque effect

Extruded (squeezed) effect

Paint applied using painting knife

PURPLE ACRYLIC PAINT

YELLOW ACRYLIC PAINT

ORANGE ACRYLIC PAINT

Transparent, watercolor effect

Translucent, impasto glaze

Thick impasto with coarse texture

BLUE ACRYLIC PAINT DILUTED WITH WATER

GREEN ACRYLIC PAINT MIXED WITH GEL MEDIUM

RED ACRYLIC PAINT MIXED WITH TEXTURE PASTE

Calligraphy

CALLIGRAPHY IS BEAUTIFULLY FORMED LETTERING. The term applies to written text and illumination (the decoration of manuscripts using gold leaf and color). The essential materials needed to practice calligraphy are a writing tool, ink, and a writing surface. Quills are among the oldest writing tools. They are usually made from goose or turkey feathers, and are noted for their flexibility and ability to produce fine lines. A quill point, however, is not very durable and constant recutting and trimming is required. The most commonly used writing instrument in western calligraphy is a detachable, metal nib held in a penholder. The metal nib is very durable, and there are a wide range of different types. Particular types of nibs—such as copperplate, speedball, and round-hand nibs—are used for specific styles of lettering. Some nibs have integral ink reservoirs and others have reservoirs that are detachable. Brushes are also used for writing, and for filling in outlined letters and painting decoration. Other writing tools used in calligraphy are fountain pens, felt-tipped pens, rotring pens, and reed pens. Calligraphy inks may come in liquid form, or as a solid ink stick. Ink sticks are ground down in distilled water to form a liquid ink. The most common writing surfaces for calligraphy are good quality, smooth -surfaced papers. To achieve the best writing position, the calligrapher places the paper on a drawing board set at an angle.

EQUIPMENT USED IN BRUSH LETTERING

Brush rest

Wolf hair brush

Goat hair brush

BRUSHES AND BRUSH REST

Liquid ink made by grinding down ink stick in distilled water

Solid carbon ink stick

Ink stone

INK STICK AND STONE

Feather

PENS, NIBS, AND BRUSHES USED IN CALLIGRAPHY

PENHOLDER

COPPERPLATE NIB

SPEEDBALL NIB

FELT-TIPPED PEN

ROUND-HAND NIB AND DETACHABLE INK RESERVOIR

GOAT HAIR BRUSH

AUTOMATIC PEN

WOLF HAIR BRUSH

REED PEN

Feather stripped for better handling

FOUNTAIN PEN AND INK

Barrel

Bottle of permanent black ink

SQUARE SABLE BRUSH

Barrel

Clip

Nib

POINTED SABLE BRUSH

Hand-cut point

GOOSE-FEATHER QUILL

Outer cap

EXAMPLES OF LETTERING STYLES

Apex

Bowl

Curved stroke

Stem

Inner counter

Stem

Stem

Arm

Counter

A B C D E

Crossbar

Inner counter

Counter

Inner counter

ROMAN CAPITALS

Cap line

Ascender

Curved stroke

Ear

Arch

X line

Abcgmpt

Base line

Crossbar

Descender line

Serif

Neck

Descender

Height of letter determined by ladder of nib widths

ITALIC ROMAN

Slightly pinched (curved) vertical stroke

Letter filled in using brush

Inner counter

ORSW

Tail

Spine

Pointed apex

VERSAL

AN ILLUMINATED MANUSCRIPT

Style of lettering called Gothic book script

Large decorative letter used to mark the opening of a chapter

Words written carefully by hand

Gold leaf

Grid lines provide guide to position of words and pictures

CHINESE LETTERING

Rice paper

Broad brush-stroke

Chinese character meaning long life

Artist's stamped signature

ARTIST'S STAMP

Stamp

Stamped signature of the artist

Ink pad

DRAWING BOARD

Adjustable set square

Blade with parallel motion

EXAMPLES OF CALLIGRAPHY PAPERS

Standard European paper

Indian handmade paper

Flecked, tinted paper

Imitation parchment paper

Printmaking 1

PRINTS ARE MADE BY FOUR BASIC printing processes – intaglio, lithographic, relief, and screen. In intaglio printing, lines are engraved or etched onto the surface of a metal plate. Lines are engraved using sharp metal tools. They are etched by corroding the metal plate with acid, using acid-resistant ground to protect the areas not to be etched. The plate is then inked and wiped, leaving the grooves filled with ink and the surface clean. Dampened paper is laid over the plate, and both paper and plate are passed through the rollers of an etching press. The pressure of the rollers forces the paper into the grooves, so that it takes up the ink, leaving an impression on the paper. Lithographic printing is based on the antipathy between grease and water. An image is drawn on a surface—usually a stone or metal plate—with a greasy medium, such as tusche (lihographic ink). The greasy drawing is fixed onto the plate by applying an acidic solution, such as gum arabic. The surface is then dampened and rolled with ink. The ink adheres only to the greasy areas and is repelled by the water. Paper is laid on the plate and pressure is applied by means of a press. In relief printing, the non-printing areas of a wood or linoleum block are cut away using gouges, knives, and other tools. The printing areas are left raised in relief and are rolled with ink. Paper is laid on the inked block and pressure is applied by means of a press or by burnishing (rubbing) the back of the paper. The most common forms of relief printing are woodcut, wood engraving, and linocut. In screen printing, the printing surface is a mesh stretched across a wooden frame. A stencil is applied to the mesh to seal the non-printing areas and ink is scraped through the mesh to produce an image.

THE FOUR MAIN PRINTING PROCESSES

Paper — Printed image
— Engraved or etched image
Metal plate — Inked area

INTAGLIO

Printed image
Damp surface rejects ink
Ink adheres to greasy image
Paper
Image drawn on stone with greasy medium

LITHOGRAPHIC

Paper — Printed image
Raised figure
Wood block — Inked surface

RELIEF

Ink forced through mesh
Paper
Wooden frame
Stencil
Printed image

SCREEN

LEATHER INK DABBER

EQUIPMENT USED IN INTAGLIO PRINTING

ROCKER   **SCRIBER**   **ROULETTE**   **SCRAPER**   **BURNISHER**   **CLAMP**

ETCHING PRESS USED FOR INTAGLIO PRINTMAKING

Flywheel

Paper

Felt blanket cushions and distributes pressure exerted by rollers

Screw pressure adjustor

Spoke

Handle

Top roller

Position guide

Printed image

Inked-up copper plate

Sliding bed (plank) is wound between steel rollers

GROUND

Acid-resistant ground rolled onto metal plate before etching

EXAMPLES OF PRINTING PAPERS

GROUND ROLLER

Gelatine roller

Wooden handle

EXAMPLE OF AN INTAGLIO PRINT
Annie with a Sun Hat, Jock McFadyen, 1993
Etched copper plate, 16 x 15¾ in (41 x 40 cm)

Printmaking 2

EXAMPLE OF A LITHOGRAPHIC STONE AND PRINT
Crown Gateway 2, Mandy Bonnell, 1987
Lithograph, 19½ x 15¾ in (50 x 40 cm)

IMAGE DRAWN ON STONE   **LITHOGRAPIC PRINT**

EXAMPLE OF A SCREEN PRINT
Sea Change, Patrick Hughes, 1992
Screen print, 30 x 37 in (77 x 94.5 cm)

SCREEN AND SQUEEGEE

Squeegee

Rubber blade

Mesh

Wooden frame

EQUIPMENT USED IN LITHOGRAPHIC PRINTING

CRAYON AND HOLDER

LITHOGRAPHIC PENCIL

TUSCHE (LITHOGRAPHIC INK) PEN

ERASING STICK

EXPANDABLE SPONGE

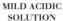

TUSCHE (LITHOGRAPHIC INK) STICK

RUBBING INK

INK ROLLER

MILD ACIDIC SOLUTION   **GUM ARABIC SOLUTION**

WATER-BASED SCREEN PRINTING INKS

BLUE ACRYLIC INK   **RED ACRYLIC INK**   **BROWN TEXTILE INK**

EQUIPMENT USED IN RELIEF PRINTING

V-SHAPED GOUGE

INK ROLLER

Rubber roller

LINOLEUM AND WOODCUT BLOCK

U-SHAPED GOUGE

GRAVER

Linoleum

KNIFE

SCORPER

WOOD ENGRAVING

Side grain wood block

END-GRAIN WOOD BLOCK

INKED-UP ENGRAVED BLOCK

WOOD ENGRAVING PRINT

RELIEF-PRINTING PRESS

Spiral spring

Crown

Tympan lowered onto printing block

Piston

Printed image

Bar (pressure handle)

Staple (frame)

Printing block

Bed is rolled under platen

Drum handle

Platen

Rail

Counterweight

Drum (rounce)

Leg

Pillar (post)

Foot

Mosaic

MOSAIC IS THE ART OF MAKING patterns and pictures from tesserae (small, colored pieces of glass, marble, and other materials). Different materials are cut into tesserae using different tools. Smalti (glass enamel) and marble are cut into pieces using a hammer and a hardy (a pointed blade) embedded in a log. Vitreous glass is cut into pieces using a pair of pliers. Mosaics can be made using a direct or indirect method. In the direct method, the tesserae are laid directly into a bed of cement–based adhesive. In the indirect method, the design is drawn in reverse on paper or cloth. The tesserae are then stuck face down on the paper or cloth using water-soluble glue. Adhesive is spread with a trowel onto a solid surface—such as a wall—and the back of the mosaic is laid into the adhesive. Finally, the paper or cloth is soaked off to reveal the mosaic. Gaps between tesserae can be filled with grout. Grout is forced into gaps by dragging a grouting squeegee across the face of the mosaic. Mosaics are usually used to decorate walls and floors, but they can also be applied to smaller objects.

EQUIPMENT FOR BREAKING MARBLE

Strip of marble, ready for breaking into cubes

Mosaic hammer

Alicante (red marble) pieces

Hardy (pointed blade) embedded in a log

PLIERS

Hardwearing, tungsten carbide tip

Handle with rubber grip

SMALTI (GLASS ENAMEL)

RED SMALTI

EXAMPLE OF A MOSAIC (DIRECT METHOD)
Seascape, Tessa Hunkin, 1993
Smalti mosaic on board
31½ in (80 cm) diameter

Gold-leaf smalti

YELLOW SMALTI

BLUE SMALTI

MOSAIC TOOLS

CEMENT-BASED ADHESIVE

GROUT

TROWEL

Notch

Steel blade

Wooden handle

GROUTING SQUEEGEE

Wooden handle

Rubber blade

STAGES IN THE CREATION OF A MOSAIC (INDIRECT METHOD)

MOSAIC POT

Geometric design

Grout

COLOR SKETCH
A color sketch is drawn
in oil pastel to give a clear
impression of how the finished
mosaic will look.

REVERSE IMAGE
Tesserae are glued face down
on reverse image on paper.
Mosaic is then attached to solid
surface and paper is removed.

MOSAIC MOSQUE DESIGN

Floral design

Geometric border

Andamenti
(line along
which tesserae
are laid)

Grout fills
the gaps
between the
tesserae

Mosaic
mounted
on board

Vitreous
glass cut into
triangular
shape with
pliers

Gold tessera
with ripple
finish

Gold tessera
placed upside-
down

VITREOUS GLASS

**GREEN VITREOUS
GLASS WITH GOLD LEAF**

Plain
finish

Ripple
finish

**RED VITREOUS
GLASS**

SHEETS OF VITREOUS GLASS

**BLUE VITREOUS
GLASS**

FINISHED MOSAIC
Goldfish, Tessa Hunkin, 1993
Vitreous glass mosaic on board
14 x 10 in (35.5 x 25.5 cm)

Border of square
vitreous glass

Sculpture 1

THE TWO TRADITIONAL SCULPTURE METHODS are carving and modeling. A carved sculpture is made by cutting away the surplus from a block of hard material such as stone, marble, or wood. The tools used for carving vary according to the material being carved. Heavy steel points, claws, and chisels that are struck with a lump hammer are generally used for stone and marble. Sharp gouges and chisels that are struck with a wooden mallet are used for wood. Sculptures formed from hard materials are generally finished by filing with rasps, rifflers, and other abrasive implements. Modeling is a process by which shapes are built up, using malleable materials such as clay, plaster, and wax. The material is cut with wire-ended tools and modeled with the fingers or a variety of hardwood and metal implements. For large or intricate modeled sculptures an armature (frame), made from metal or wood, is used to provide internal support. Sculptures formed in soft materials may harden naturally or can be made more durable by firing in a kiln. Modeled sculptures are often first designed in wax or another material to be cast later in a metal (see pp. 454-455) such as bronze. The development of many new materials in the 20th century has enabled sculptors to experiment with new techniques such as construction (joining preformed pieces of material such as machine components, mirrors, and furniture) and kinetic (mobile) sculpture.

2½ lb
(1.1 kg)
iron head

Ash
handle

LUMP HAMMER

CALLIPERS

Curved leg

Gap measures
distance between
two points on a
sculpture

Wing nut

EXAMPLES OF WOOD-CARVING TOOLS

CABINET RASP

STRAIGHT GOUGE

SALMON BEND GOUGE

CHISEL

*Stone for
sharpening
wood-carving
tools*

*Cedar
box*

**ARKANSAS
HONE-STONE**

**CARVING
MALLET**

**EXAMPLES OF RIFFLERS
(FOR STONE, MARBLE, AND WOOD)**

12 IN (30 CM) RIFFLER

6 IN (15 CM) RIFFLER

WIDE
MARBLE
CLAW

NARROW
MARBLE
CLAW

POINT

FLAT CHISEL

BULLNOSE CHISEL

*Surface for
sharpening
stone-carving
tools*

DIAMOND WHETSTONE

*Tiny holes along
the hairline made
with a point*

DETAIL OF
SLAVE'S HEAD

*Soft skin texture tooled
with a fine-toothed
marble claw*

EXAMPLE OF A CARVED WOOD SCULPTURE
Mary Magdalene, Donatello, 1454-1455
Poplar wood, height 6 ft 2 in (188 cm)

EXAMPLE OF A CARVED MARBLE SCULPTURE
The Rebel Slave, Michelangelo, 1513-1516
Marble, height 7ft (213 cm)

*Hair worked
with a narrow
claw*

*Delicately
modeled
hand carved
with a chisel*

*Translucent white
marble, quarried at
Carrara, Italy*

*Hair
highlighted
with gold
leaf*

*Figure cut
from single
length of
poplar*

*Deep
ridges of
hair cut
with a
gouge*

*Surface rubbed
smooth with
rifflers and
pumice*

*Strut gives added
support to long
slender limb*

*Wood prepared
with gesso
(chalk and glue)
and painted*

*Base scored with
jagged parallel
cuts made with
point and lump
hammer*

*Series of tiny
punch holes,
made with a
fine point,
outline the
form*

*Foot carved in
deep relief*

*Rough surface
made by driving
a point into the
marble at an
oblique angle*

*The dimensions of the marble block
determine the size of the sculpture*

DETAIL OF SLAVE'S FOOT

Sculpture 2

EXAMPLES OF MODELING TOOLS

WIRE-ENDED CUTTING TOOL

CURVED MOLDING TOOL

SPATULA-ENDED WAX MODELING TOOL

ROUNDED WAX MODELING TOOL

EXAMPLES OF BRONZE FINISHING TOOLS

HOOKED RIFFLER

POINTED RIFFLER

ALCOHOL BURNER (FOR HEATING WAX MODELING TOOLS)

Wick

Brass holder

Glass bowl

Denatured alcohol

STAGES IN THE LOST-WAX METHOD OF CASTING
Based on Mars, Giambologna, c.1546

Wax-covered wire armature

Wax riser (vertical, hollow rod)

Chaplet (iron nail)

Wax runner (horizontal, hollow rod)

Fire-resistant clay

ORIGINAL MODEL
An original, solid wax model is made and preserved so that numerous replicas can be cast.

HOLLOW WAX FIGURE IS CAST
A new, hollow wax model is cast from the original model. It is filled with a plaster core that is held in place with nails. Wax runners and risers are attached.

FIGURE IS BAKED IN CASTING MOLD
The model is encased in clay and baked. The wax melts away (through the channels made by the wax rods) and is replaced by molten bronze.

MODELING STAND AND ARMATURE

Aluminum wire figure

Fixed iron armature support

Marine ply modeling board

Screw-hole for fastening the iron to modeling board

Rotating table top

Aluminum table stand

Height adjustor

Tripod

Clay smoothed to create the effect of soft skin

Incision made with serrated tool

Strips of clay, added to the model, give the effect of folded drapery

EXAMPLE OF A CLAY MODEL
Madonna and Child, Henry Moore, 1943
Terracotta, height 7¼ in (18.4 cm)

Maquette (small sketch) modeled from a solid lump of clay

Terracotta clay, fires at 1,832°F to 1,922°F (1,000°C to 1,050°C)

Model for a much larger bronze sculpture

Roughly worked clay

Metal riser

Metal runner

Stump left by rod will be filed down

Golden brown color of untreated bronze

Dark brown patina

Hole left by nail will be plugged with bronze

STATUE IS STRIPPED OF CLAY
When the bronze has cooled, the clay mold is broken open to reveal the bronze statue with solid metal runners and risers.

STATUE IS FINISHED
The nails are pulled out and a large hole is made to remove the plaster core. When the metal rods have been sawn off, the sculpture is filed to refine the surface.

STATUE IS CLEANED
Finally the work is cleaned and polished. An artificial patina (coloring) is achieved by treating the surface with chemicals.

ARCHITECTURE

Ancient Egypt

THE CIVILIZATION OF THE ANCIENT EGYPTIANS (which lasted from about 3100 BC until it was finally absorbed into the Roman empire in 30 BC) is famous for its temples and tombs. Egyptian temples were often huge and geometric, like the Temple of Amon-Re (below and right). They were usually decorated with hieroglyphs (sacred characters used for picture writing) and painted reliefs depicting gods, Pharaohs (kings), and queens. Tombs were particularly important to the Egyptians, who believed that the dead were resurrected in the afterlife. The tombs were often decorated—for example, the surround of the false door opposite—in order to give comfort to the dead. The best-known ancient Egyptian tombs are the pyramids, which were designed to symbolize the rays of the sun. Many of the architectural forms used by the ancient Egyptians were later adopted by other civilizations. For example, columns and capitals were later used by the ancient Greeks (see pp. 460-461) and ancient Romans (see pp. 462-465).

FRONT VIEW OF HYPOSTYLE HALL, TEMPLE OF AMON-RE

Cornice decorated with cavetto molding

Campaniform (open papyrus) capital

Architrave

Papyrus-bud capital

Socle

Side aisle

Central nave

Side aisle

SIDE VIEW OF HYPOSTYLE HALL, TEMPLE OF AMON-RE, KARNAK, EGYPT, c.1290 BC

Horus, the sun-god

Architrave

Stone slab forming flat roof of side aisle

Kepresh crown with disc

Chons, the moon-god

Amon-Re, king of the gods

Hathor, the sky-goddess

Papyrus motif

Cartouche (oval border) containing the titles of the Pharaoh (king)

Socle

Aisle running north–south

LIMESTONE FALSE DOOR WITH HIEROGLYPHS, TOMB OF KING TJETJI, GIZA, EGYPT, c.2400 BC

Lintel

Hieroglyph representing a house

Disc representing sun or light

Eroded image of Tjetji

Limestone stela (slab)

Hoe-shaped hieroglyph representing "mr" sound

Head of false door

Image of Tjetji's wife

Image of Tjetji's daughter

PLANT CAPITAL OF THE PTOLEMAIC-ROMAN PERIOD, EGYPT, 332-30 BC

Palm leaf

Papyrus flower

Papyrus leaf

Papyrus stem

Lotus bud

Lotus stem

Cornice decorated with cavetto molding

Bead molding

Trellis window

Rectangular pier decorated with hieroglyphs

Elevated roof of central nave

Clerestory

Disc representing sun or light

Architrave

Square abacus

Papyrus-bud capital

Papyriform column

Shaft

Scene depicting a Pharaoh (king) paying homage to the god Amon-Re

Central nave

ANCIENT EGYPTIAN BUILDING DECORATION

DECORATED WINDOW, MEDINET HABU, EGYPT, C.1198 BC

ROPE AND PATERAE DECORATION

CAPITAL WITH THE HEAD OF THE SKY-GODDESS HATHOR, TEMPLE OF ISIS, PHILAE, EGYPT, 283-47 BC

LOTUS AND PAPYRUS FRIEZE DECORATION

Ancient Greece

THE CLASSICAL TEMPLES OF ANCIENT GREECE were built according to the belief that certain forms and proportions were pleasing to the gods. There were three main ancient Greek architectural orders (styles), which can be distinguished by the decoration and proportions of their columns, capitals (column tops), and entablatures (structures resting on the capitals). The oldest is the Doric order, which dates from the seventh century BC and was used mainly on the Greek mainland and in the western colonies, such as Sicily and southern Italy. The Temple of Neptune, shown here, is a classic example of this order. It is hypaethral (roofless) and peripteral (surrounded by a single row of columns). About a century later, the more decorative Ionic order developed on the Aegean Islands. Features of this order include volutes (spiral scrolls) on capitals and acroteria (pediment ornaments). The Corinthian order was invented in Athens in the fifth century BC and is typically identified by an acanthus leaf on the capitals. This order was later widely used in ancient Roman architecture.

CAPITALS OF THE THREE ORDERS OF ANCIENT GREEK ARCHITECTURE

Abacus
Echinus
Annulet
Trachelion (neck)

DORIC CAPITAL, THE PROPYLAEUM (GATEWAY), THE ACROPOLIS, ATHENS, GREECE, 449 BC

Abacus
Lesbian leaf pattern
Coussinet (cushion)
Cyma reversa profile
Volute
Echinus with egg and dart decoration
Eye
Palmette

IONIC CAPITAL, THE PROPYLAEUM (GATEWAY), TEMPLE OF ATHENA POLIAS, PRIENE, GREECE, c.334 BC

Mask
Abacus
Volute
Cauliculus
Acanthus leaf
Bell-shaped core

CORINTHIAN CAPITAL FROM A STOA (PORTICO), PROBABLY FROM ASIA MINOR

TEMPLE OF NEPTUNE, PAESTUM, ITALY, c.460 BC

Raking cornice
Trachelion (neck)
Taenia
Triglyph
Metope
Glyph (channel)
Pediment
Doric entablature
Pteron (external colonnade)
Euthynteria
Drum
Stylobate
Column of the Doric order

PLAN OF THE TEMPLE OF NEPTUNE, PAESTUM

Pronaos (vestibule)

Naos wall

Anta (pilaster terminating naos wall)

Naos (cella)

Peristyle

Opisthodomos (rear portico)

Pteron (external colonnade)

Hexastyle pteron (colonnade of six columns)

ANCIENT GREEK BUILDING DECORATION

Volute

FACADE, TREASURY OF ATREUS, MYCENAE, GREECE, 1350-1250 BC

Meander

FRETWORK, PARTHENON, ATHENS, GREECE, 447-436 BC

ACROTERION, TEMPLE OF APHAIA, AEGINA, GREECE, 490 BC

Griffon (gryphon)

Raking cornice

ANTEFIXA, TEMPLE OF APHAIA, AEGINA, GREECE, 490 BC

Palmette

Volute

Regula (short fillet beneath taenia)   Eaves

Cornice

Frieze

Architrave

Capital

Shaft

Crepidoma (stepped base)

Entasis (slight curve of a column)   Intercolumniation   Fluting

461

Ancient Rome 1

IN THE EARLY PERIOD OF THE ROMAN EMPIRE extensive use was made of ancient Greek architectural ideas, particularly those of the Corinthian order (see pp. 460-461). As a result, many early Roman buildings—such as the Temple of Vesta (opposite)—closely resemble ancient Greek buildings. A distinctive Roman style began to evolve in the first century AD. This style developed the interiors of buildings (the Greeks had concentrated on the exterior) by wing arches, vaults, and domes inside the buildings and by ornamenting internal walls; many of these features can be seen in the Pantheon. Exterior columns were often used for decorative rather than structural purposes, as in the Colosseum and the Porta Nigra (see pp. 464-465). Smaller buildings had timber frames with wattle-and-daub walls, as in the mill (see pp. 464-465). Roman architecture remained influential for many centuries, with some of its principles being used in the 11th century in Romanesque buildings (see pp. 468-469) and also in the 15th and 16th centuries in Renaissance buildings (see pp. 474-477).

ANCIENT ROMAN BUILDING DECORATION

FESTOON, TEMPLE OF VESTA, TIVOLI, ITALY, C.80 BC

RICHLY DECORATED ROMAN OVUM

INTERIOR OF THE PANTHEON, ROME, ITALY, 118-c.128

Inner dome, following the curve of a depressed arch

Outer saucer dome

Oculus

Series of concentric, steplike rings

Dentil ornament

Engaged pediment

Raking cornice

Pediment

Rotunda

Outer saucer dome

Intermediate block

Entablature with inscription

Octastyle portico (eight-column portico)

FRONT VIEW OF THE PANTHEON

SIDE VIEW OF THE PANTHEON

Entablature

Intermediate block

Upper cornice

Pitched roof

Eaves

Relieving arch

Opening for ventilation

Cornice

Colonnade

Ornamental band decorated with festoons

Attached fluted pilaster

Entablature

Curved cornice

Lesene

Cornice

Triangular pediment

Concave niche

Marble veneer

Segmental pediment

Pedestal

FRIEZE, FORUM OF TRAJAN, ROME, ITALY, 98-113

KEYSTONE, ARCH OF TITUS, ROME, ITALY, 81

TEMPLE OF VESTA, TIVOLI, ITALY, c.80 BC

Circular naos (cella)

Architrave

Ceiling

Fascia

Corinthian entablature

Corinthian capital

Pteron (colonnade)

Naos (cella) window

Opus incertum (concrete wall faced with irregularly shaped stones)

Egg and dart decoration

Upper torus

Scotia

Jamb with corrugated surface

Naos (cella) door

Cornice

Threshold

Podium

Lower torus

Oculus illuminating interior of rotunda

Coffer

Stepped side of coffer

Frieze decorated with arabesques, urns, and winged horses

Steplike ring

Barrel vault

Passageway

Coffer

Engaged pediment

Monolithic shaft (shaft made from a single stone)

Barrel vault

Raking cornice

Pediment

Entablature

Corinthian column

Entablature

Aedicule (tabernacle)

Festoon

Fluting

Corinthian pilaster

Base

Corinthian capital

Rotunda

Portico

Ancient Rome 2

SIDE VIEW OF A ROMAN MILL

Lath
Pantile
Principal rafter
Verge
Wall plate
Eaves
Wall post
Plain fascia
Top plate
Floorboard
Plaster coating
Intermediate floor joist
Sill
Stud
Foundation
Grille
Joist
Boarding

FRONT VIEW OF A ROMAN MILL, 1ST CENTURY BC

Half-round ridge tile
King strut
Lath
Pitched roof
Principal rafter
Ashlar post
Tie beam
Plain fascia
Wall plate
Flat soffit
Intermediate floor joist
Mill wheel
Top plate
Wall post
Sill
Binder
Wattle-and-daub with plaster coating
Supporting post
Floor joist
Foundation post

THE COLOSSEUM (FLAVIAN AMPHITHEATER), ROME, ITALY, 70-82

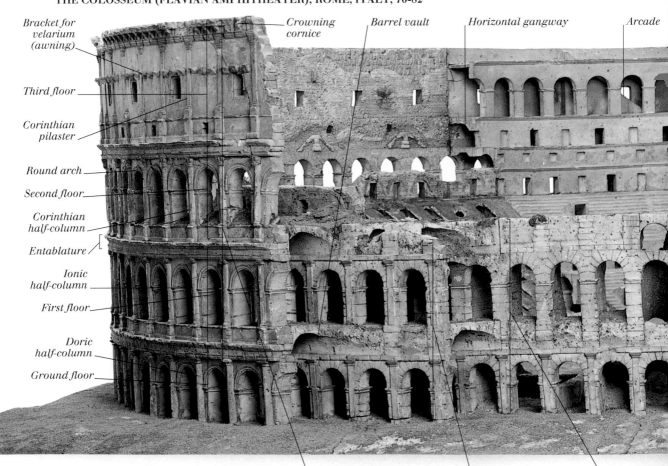

Bracket for velarium (awning)
Crowning cornice
Barrel vault
Horizontal gangway
Arcade
Third floor
Corinthian pilaster
Round arch
Second floor
Corinthian half-column
Entablature
Ionic half-column
First floor
Doric half-column
Ground floor
External travertine shell
Intermediate shell
Inner shell

PORTA NIGRA, TRIER, GERMANY, c.240-260

Crowning cornice

Impost

Semicircular tower

Parapet

Keystone

Arcaded passageway

Round-arched window

Lesene

Voussoir

Cornice

Semicircular tower

Frieze

Entablature

Relieving arch

Architrave

Arcading

Apse (added in Middle Ages)

Attached column

Courtyard

Round arch

Entrance to town

Capital

Shaft

Base

Facade

ROMAN WATTLE-AND-DAUB WALL, 1ST CENTURY BC

Opening to staircase

Maenianum summum) (gallery)

Hazel twig framework

Rectangular window

Clay mixture

String course

Paintwork

Plaster

Cuneus (wedge of seating)

Opus quadratum (square masonry)

Arched opening to staircase

Radiating, wedge-shaped chamber

Radial wall

Opus incertum (concrete wall faced with irregularly shaped stones)

Cornice

Ambulatory corridor

Attached rectangular pier

Keystone

Impost

Tuscan capital

Voussoir

Tuscan pilaster

Medieval castles and houses

WARFARE WAS COMMON IN EUROPE in the Middle Ages, and many monarchs and nobles built castles as a form of defense. Typical medieval castles have outer walls surrounding a moat. Inside the moat is a bailey (courtyard), protected by a chemise (jacket wall). The innermost and strongest part of a medieval castle is the keep. There are two main types of keep: towers called donjons, such as the Tour de César and Coucy-le-Château in France, and rectangular keeps ("hall-keeps"), such as the Tower of London. Castles were often guarded by salients (projecting fortifications), like those of the Bastille. Medieval houses typically had timber cruck (tent-like) frames, wattle-and-daub walls, and pitched roofs, like those on medieval London Bridge (opposite).

DONJON, TOUR DE CESAR, PROVINS, FRANCE, 12TH CENTURY

Oculus
Loophole
Battlements (crenellations)
Conical spire
Hemispherical cupola
Flying buttress
Gallery
Hexahedral hall
Squinch
Semicircular turret
Vaulted room
Fireplace
Main entrance
Bailey
Staircase to chemise (jacket wall)
Embrasure
Chemise (jacket wall)
Plain impost
Depressed cupola
Vaulted staircase
Motte

Loophole

SALIENT, CAERNARVON CASTLE, BRITAIN, 1283-1323

Timber cruck frame
Cornice
Buttress

CRUCK-FRAMED HOUSE, BRITAIN, c.1200

Blind, rounded relieving arch
Merlon
Battlements (crenellations)
Tetrahedral spire
Crenel
Loophole
Rectangular turret
Wooden staircase leading to entrance above ground level
Quoin
Timber-framed house
Round-arched window with twin openings
Cruck frame
Paling

TOWER OF LONDON, BRITAIN, FROM 1070

Curtain wall
Pointed relieving arch
Semicircular relieving arch
Plain string course
Bracket decorated with scroll molding

Rectangular window
Sunken rectangular panel
Round-arched window
Semicircular salient
Loophole
Lateral circular salient

THE BASTILLE, PARIS, FRANCE, 14TH CENTURY

MEDIEVAL LONDON BRIDGE, BRITAIN, 1176 (WITH 14TH-CENTURY BATTLEMENTED BUILDING, NONESUCH HOUSE, AND TWO-TOWERED GATE)

Gate-house   Battlemented building   Chapel pier   Railing   Onion-shaped dome   Pitched roof

Shaped gable

Timber framing with ornamental woodwork

Nonesuch House

Crypt of Becket Chapel

Starling

Pier

Two-towered gate

Pointed Gothic stone arch

Oriel window

Timber framing

DONJON, COUCY-LE-CHATEAU, AISNE, FRANCE, 1225-1245

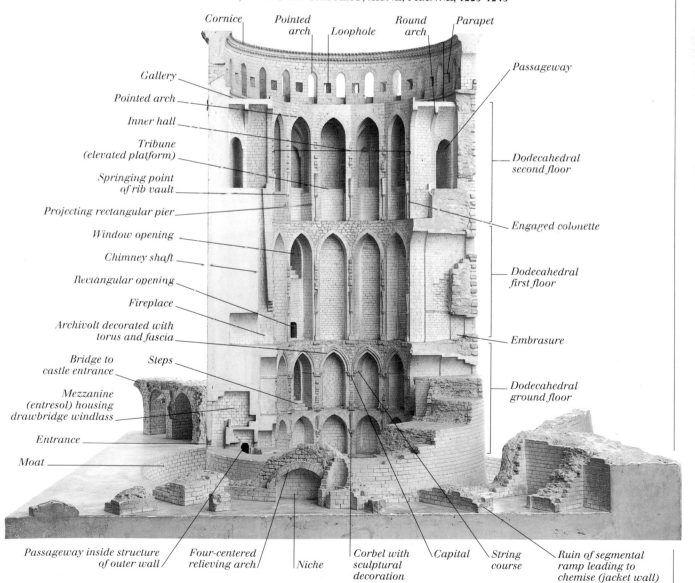

Cornice   Pointed arch   Loophole   Round arch   Parapet

Passageway

Gallery

Pointed arch

Inner hall

Tribune (elevated platform)

Springing point of rib vault

Projecting rectangular pier

Window opening

Chimney shaft

Rectangular opening

Fireplace

Archivolt decorated with torus and fascia

Bridge to castle entrance

Steps

Mezzanine (entresol) housing drawbridge windlass

Entrance

Moat

Dodecahedral second floor

Engaged colonette

Dodecahedral first floor

Embrasure

Dodecahedral ground floor

Passageway inside structure of outer wall

Four-centered relieving arch

Niche

Corbel with sculptural decoration

Capital

String course

Ruin of segmental ramp leading to chemise (jacket wall)

Medieval churches

ABBEY OF ST. FOI, CONQUES, FRANCE, c.1050-c.1130

LARGE NUMBERS OF CHURCHES were built in Europe in the Middle Ages. European churches of this period typically have high vaults supported by massive piers and columns. In the 10th century, the Romanesque style developed. Romanesque architects adopted many Roman or early Christian architectural ideas, such as cross-shaped ground plans—like that of Angoulême Cathedral (opposite)—and the basilican system of a nave with a central vessel and side aisles. In the mid-12th century, flying buttresses and pointed vaults appeared. These features later became widely used in Gothic architecture (see pp. 470-471). Bagneux Church (opposite) has both styles: a Romanesque tower and a Gothic nave and choir.

CHURCH ROOF BOSS, BRITAIN

ROMANESQUE CAPITALS

"THE FLIGHT INTO EGYPT" CAPITAL, CATHEDRAL OF ST. LAZARE, AUTUN, FRANCE, 1120-1130

"CHRIST IN MAJESTY" CAPITAL, BASILICA OF ST. MADELEINE, VEZELAY, FRANCE, 1120-1140

Finial

Incline

Circular staircase-turret

Loophole

Round-arched window

Series of archivolts decorated with torus

Series of jambs decorated with colonettes

Octahedral spire

Octahedral crossing tower

Pitched roof

Tribune (elevated platform)

Semicircular transverse arch

Vaulting shaft

Attached half-column

Round arcade arch

Romanesque capital

Arcade

Square central shaft

Twin opening of gallery bays

Compound pier

Barrel vault

Lean-to roof

Transept

Quadrant arch

Colonette

Round stilted arch

Attached half-column

Side aisle

Main vessel

Side aisle

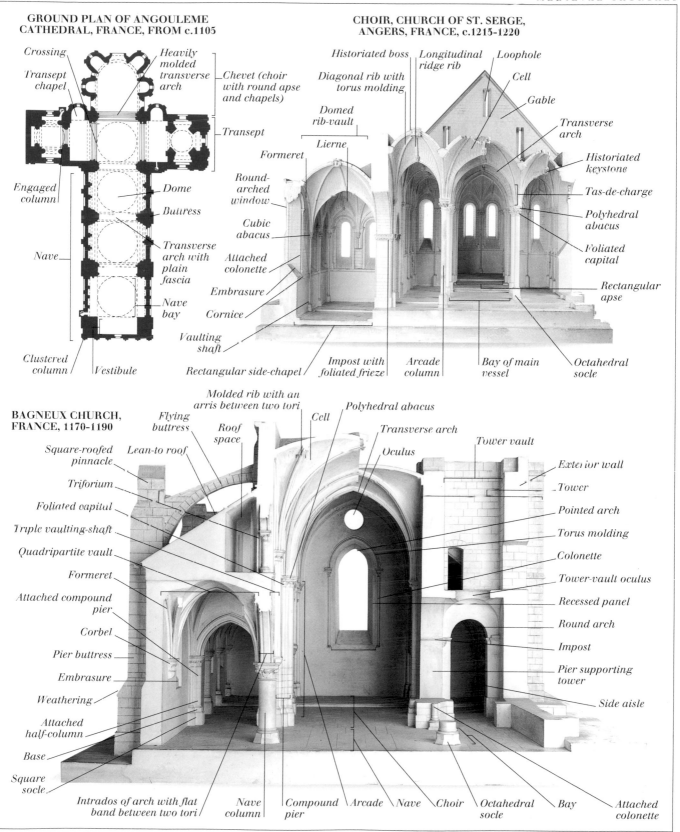

GROUND PLAN OF ANGOULEME CATHEDRAL, FRANCE, FROM c.1105

Crossing

Transept chapel

Heavily molded transverse arch

Chevet (choir with round apse and chapels)

Transept

Engaged column

Dome

Buttress

Nave

Transverse arch with plain fascia

Nave bay

Clustered column

Vestibule

CHOIR, CHURCH OF ST. SERGE, ANGERS, FRANCE, c.1215-1220

Historiated boss

Longitudinal ridge rib

Loophole

Cell

Gable

Diagonal rib with torus molding

Domed rib-vault

Lierne

Formeret

Round-arched window

Cubic abacus

Attached colonette

Embrasure

Cornice

Vaulting shaft

Transverse arch

Historiated keystone

Tas-de-charge

Polyhedral abacus

Foliated capital

Rectangular apse

Rectangular side-chapel

Impost with foliated frieze

Arcade column

Bay of main vessel

Octahedral socle

BAGNEUX CHURCH, FRANCE, 1170-1190

Molded rib with an arris between two tori

Flying buttress

Roof space

Cell

Polyhedral abacus

Transverse arch

Oculus

Tower vault

Square-roofed pinnacle

Lean-to roof

Triforium

Foliated capital

Triple vaulting-shaft

Quadripartite vault

Formeret

Attached compound pier

Corbel

Pier buttress

Embrasure

Weathering

Attached half-column

Base

Square socle

Exterior wall

Tower

Pointed arch

Torus molding

Colonette

Tower-vault oculus

Recessed panel

Round arch

Impost

Pier supporting tower

Side aisle

Intrados of arch with flat band between two tori

Nave column

Compound pier

Arcade

Nave

Choir

Octahedral socle

Bay

Attached colonette

Gothic 1

GOTHIC STAINED GLASS WITH FOLIATED SCROLL MOTIF, ON WOODEN FORM

GOTHIC BUILDINGS are characterized by rib vaults, pointed or lancet arches, flying buttresses, decorative tracery and gables, and stained-glass windows. Typical Gothic buildings include the Cathedrals of Salisbury and old St. Paul's in England, and Notre Dame de Paris in France (see pp. 472-473). The Gothic style developed out of Romanesque architecture in France (see pp. 468-469) in the mid-12th century and then spread throughout Europe. The decorative elements of Gothic architecture became highly developed in buildings of the English Decorated style (late 13th-14th century) and the French Flamboyant style (15th-16th century). These styles are exemplified by the tower of Salisbury Cathedral and by the staircase in the Church of St. Maclou (see pp. 472-473), respectively. In both of these styles, embellishments such as ballflowers and curvilinear (flowing) tracery were used liberally. The English Perpendicular style (late 14th-15th century), which followed the Decorated style, emphasized the vertical and horizontal elements of a building. A notable feature of this style is the hammer-beam roof.

GROUND PLAN OF SALISBURY CATHEDRAL

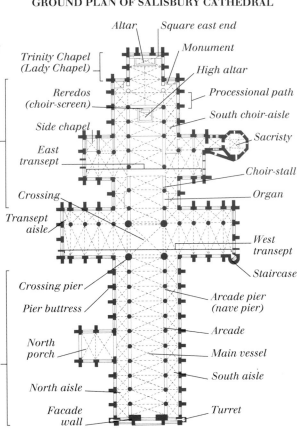

Altar
Square east end
Trinity Chapel (Lady Chapel)
Monument
High altar
Reredos (choir-screen)
Processional path
South choir-aisle
Side chapel
Choir
East transept
Sacristy
Crossing
Choir-stall
Organ
Transept aisle
West transept
Crossing pier
Staircase
Pier buttress
Arcade pier (nave pier)
Arcade
North porch
Main vessel
Nave
South aisle
North aisle
Facade wall
Turret

GOTHIC TORUS WITH BALLFLOWERS

Limestone block
Block members carved into rolls
Block members cut polygonally
Pencil guideline
Early stage of ballflower carving

BLOCK AFTER INITIAL CUTTING

BLOCK WITH MEMBERS CUT INTO ROLLS

Torus
Ballflower
Fillet
Mason's mark

FINISHED BLOCK

Trinity Chapel (Lady Chapel)
Choir
Octahedral pinnacle with small spire
Finial
Blind semi-arch
Staggered triple lancet windows
Turretlike pinnacle
Parapet decorated with blind arches filled with trefoils
Mullion
Stained glass
Base
Cornice
Buttress
Lean-to roof
East transept facade

Orb

Weather-vane

NORTH SIDE, SALISBURY CATHEDRAL, BRITAIN, 1220-1280 (STEEPLE AND SPIRE ADDED DURING 14TH CENTURY)

WEST FACADE, SALISBURY CATHEDRAL

Spire

Band with lozenge decoration

Semi-attached gable with small pilasters

Turretlike pinnacle

Ballflower decoration

Traceried parapet with lozenge decoration

Octahedral turret

Spirelike pinnacle

Blind gabled arch

Gable

Row of blind arches filled with trefoils

Battlemented cornice

Octofoil

Cinquefoil molding

Trefoil in a spandrel

Aureole

Gable

Blind rhombus tracery filled with a quatrefoil

Staggered triple lancet window

Finial

Pitched roof

Spire

Parapet

Staggered triple lancet window

Row of blind trefoil arches

Parapet

Blind pointed arches filled with twin lancets and quatrefoils

Small gable crowning buttress

Angle buttress

Projecting turret

Row of gabled niches under trefoil arches

North porch

Blind semi-arch

Lateral porch

Crocket

Main porch

Niche under small gabled roof

Nave

Blind lancet

Flying buttress

Spire

Molded side of gable

Spirelike pinnacle

Pitched roof

Flying buttress

Lateral turret

Small gable crowning buttress

Crocket

Buttress

Angle buttress

West transept facade

Weathering

Pier buttress

Trefoil decoration

North porch

Archivolt

Twin lancet window under pointed arch, crowned by a quatrefoil

Gothic 2

CURVILINEAR (FLOWING) TRACERY FROM A BALUSTRADE, 14TH OR 15TH CENTURY

Cyma reversa (reversed ogee curve)

Cavetto molding

Plain fascia

Molded cornice

Cavetto molding with elongated lower part

Mouchette (curved dagger)

Ogee curve

Cusp

Drop shape

Cavetto molding

SPIRAL STAIRCASE TO ORGAN, CHURCH OF ST. MACLOU, ROUEN, FRANCE, c.1519

Trefoil

Flamboyant tracery

Mouchette (curved dagger)

Foliated scrollwork

Cherub

Crocket

Pointed arch

Figure

Winding cornice

Rectangular buttress

Niche

Attached gable

Attached gable

Gabled canopy

Statue

Square pillar

Base

Dagger

Basket arch

Round arch

Socle

Base decorated with ovolo moldings

Cross motif

TOWER AND PART OF THE NAVE AND CHOIR, OLD ST. PAUL'S CATHEDRAL, LONDON, BRITAIN, 1087-1666

Octahedral spire

Parapet

Turretlike pinnacle

Angle buttress

Lancet window with twin lancets and crowned with a quatrefoil

Tower

Niche

Pointed arch filled with geometrical tracery

Turretlike pinnacle

Flying buttress

Mullion

Pitched roof

Lancet window

Blind lancet arch

Window filled with early English Perpendicular-style tracery

Buttress

Octagonal chapter house

Oculus

Cloister

Early English-style window

Gable

Couronnement

Parapet decorated with quatrefoils

Pointed arch filled with tracery and three lancet windows

Clerestory wall

Lean-to roof

Outer wall of side aisle

Weathering

Oculus filled with multifoil

Nave

Transept facade

Choir

Ridge

Common rafter

Architrave of window zone, also acting as collar beam

Principal

Attached column

Attached baluster

Strut

Raised surface

Hammer-post

Beveled edge

Arched brace

Wooden panel

Hammer-beam

Gothic window tracery

Collar beam decorated with pearl motif

Gothic window

Arched brace

Bracket

Brace

Impost

SPIRE AND TRANSEPT ROOF, CATHEDRAL OF NOTRE DAME DE PARIS, FRANCE, c.1163-1250

TRUSS OF HAMMER-BEAM ROOF, THE UPPER FRATER (LATER BLACKFRIARS' PLAYHOUSE), LONDON, BRITAIN, PROBABLY 14TH CENTURY

TYPICAL GOTHIC FEATURES

FLYING BUTTRESS OVER SIDE AISLES, MILAN CATHEDRAL, ITALY, C.1385-1485

GARGOYLE, HORSLEY CHURCH, DERBYSHIRE, BRITAIN, C.1450

HAMMER-BEAM ROOF, CHURCH OF ST. BOTOLPH, TRUNCH, NORFOLK, BRITAIN, 1360-1380

Rafter

Straight brace

Octahedral spire

Beam

Gable

Round arch

Pinnacle

Oculus

Blind trefoil

Lancet arch

Trefoil arch

Cusp

Quatrefoil

Colonette

Pointed arch

Lesene

Lancet arch

Balustrade

Mullion

Triangular cornice

Geometrical tracery

Cornice with chamfered edge

Trefoil arch

Balustrade

Stud

Upper collar

Scissor brace

Ridge board

Principal rafter

Common rafter

Roof truss of nave and transept

Vertical strut

Intermediate collar

Raised valley-rafter

Beam

Jack-rafter

Clasped purlin

Lower collar

King post

Queen post

Scissor-beam

Tie beam

Passing brace

Renaissance 1

THE RENAISSANCE was a period in European history—lasting roughly from the 14th century to the mid-17th century—during which the arts and sciences underwent great changes. In architecture, these changes were marked by a return to the classical forms and proportions of ancient Roman buildings. The Renaissance originated in Italy, and the buildings most characteristic of its style can be found there, such as the Palazzo Strozzi shown here. Mannerism is a branch of the Renaissance style that distorts the classical forms; an example is the Laurentian Library staircase. As the Renaissance style spread to other European countries, many of its features were incorporated into the local architecture. For example, the Château de Montal in France (see pp. 476-477) incorporates aedicules (tabernacles).

Crowning cornice

Arched window

Round arch

Light

Rustication

Arched doorway

Rectangular window

SIDE VIEW OF PALAZZO STROZZI, FLORENCE, ITALY, 1489 (BY G. DA SANGALLO, B. DA MAIANO, AND CRONACA)

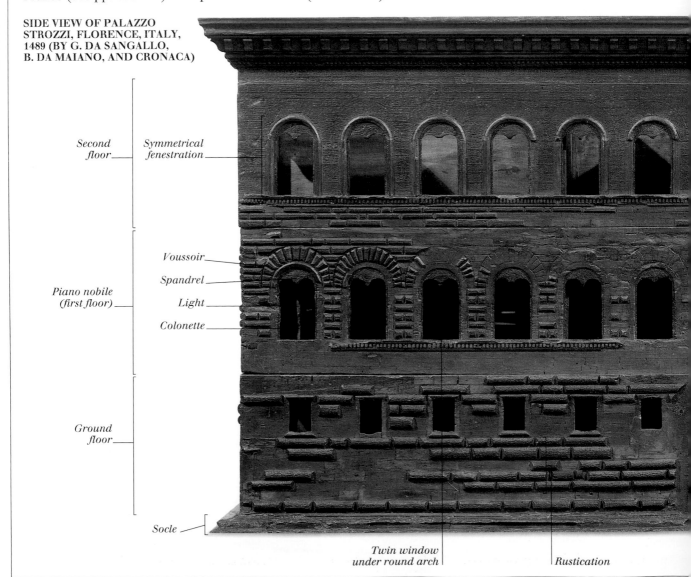

Second floor

Symmetrical fenestration

Voussoir

Spandrel

Light

Colonette

Piano nobile (first floor)

Ground floor

Socle

Twin window under round arch

Rustication

DETAILS FROM ITALIAN RENAISSANCE BUILDINGS

**PANEL FROM DRUM OF DOME,
FLORENCE CATHEDRAL, 1420-1436**

**COFFERING IN DOME,
PAZZI CHAPEL,
FLORENCE, 1429-1461**

**STAIRCASE,
LAURENTIAN LIBRARY,
FLORENCE, 1559**

**PORTICO, VILLA ROTUNDA,
VICENZA, 1567-1569**

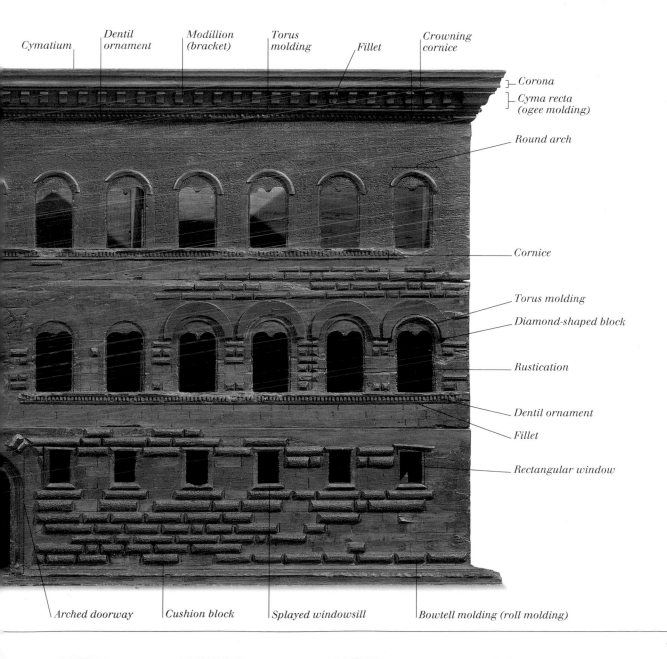

Cymatium

Dentil ornament

Modillion (bracket)

Torus molding

Fillet

Crowning cornice

Corona

Cyma recta (ogee molding)

Round arch

Cornice

Torus molding

Diamond-shaped block

Rustication

Dentil ornament

Fillet

Rectangular window

Arched doorway

Cushion block

Splayed windowsill

Bowtell molding (roll molding)

Renaissance 2

NORTH WING, CHATEAU DE MONTAL, LOT, FRANCE, FROM 1523

DETAILS FROM EUROPEAN RENAISSANCE BUILDINGS

STONE WALL, QUOINS, AND SHELL DECORATION, CASA DE LAS CONCHAS, SALAMANCA, SPAIN, 1475-1483

SPIRAL-STAIRCASE TOWER, CHATEAU DE BLOIS, FRANCE, 1514-1550

CONICAL DOME, CHATEAU DE CHAMBORD, FRANCE, 1519-1547

PAIR OF CHIMNEY STACKS, PALAIS DE FONTAINEBLEAU, FRANCE, FROM 1528

Hipped roof

Conical spire of turret

Fish-scale tile

Chimney stack

Ridge of half-round tiles

Belvedere

Pitched roof

Finial

Medallion

Pinnacle

Foliated volute with dolphin head

Gable

Head-shaped keystone

Keystone decorated with scroll ornament

Dormer window

Cornice decorated with fascias and an ogee molding

Frieze with shell-pattern decoration

Finial

Rectangular window

Ionic capital with head-shaped decoration

Transom

Putto holding candelabrum

Aedicule (tabernacle)

Blind pediment

Double pilaster

Grotesque figure

Mullion

Medallion with bust of Robert de Montal

Shell

Concave arched niche

Lesene decorated with paterae

Small pier decorated with statuette in concave niche

Frieze decorated with sculptural wreaths, tendrils, and grotesque figures

Lesene

Cornice

Pedestal

Frieze with scroll motif

Dado

Plinth Cornice Architrave Portal Pilaster

Pseudo-Corinthian capital

476

NORTH WING STAIRCASE, CHATEAU DE MONTAL

Hipped roof

Conical spire

Turret

Eaves with oversailing fascias and fillets

Loophole

Cornice with fascias and ogee moldings

Rib vault

Column

Second-floor landing

Conical corbel

First-floor landing

Flight of stairs

Lesene

Pier supporting flight of stairs

Handrail

Pier supporting first-floor landing

Riser

Tread

CAMPANILE, CHURCH OF ST. EUSTACHE, PARIS, FRANCE, 1532-1640

Weather vane

Orb

Fish-scale tile

Hemispherical dome

Semicircular torus molding

Fillet

Weathering

Plain fascia

Ogee molding

Small architrave

Archivolt

Volute

Plain fascia

Cavetto molding

Emphasized keystone

Capital

Cincture

Fillet

Zinc plating

Square column

GLOBE THEATER, LONDON, BRITAIN, 1599

Hipped roof

Timber-framed hut housing windlass

Turret

Ornamental paneling

Pitched roof

Music gallery

Ornamental paneling with concave brace decoration

Balustrade

Balcony stage

Stage cover

Light curtain

Thatched roof

Door to dressing-rooms

Loft used as storage room

Box (gentlemen's room)

Window stage

Upper gallery (twopenny gallery)

Outer wall

Railing

Middle gallery

Post supporting bay window

Upper-gallery support

Stage-door

Lower gallery

Standing room

Bench

Round pillar (stage post)

Square, carved base

Study (inner stage) with traverse (crossing)

Platform stage

Low balustrade

Paling

Door to tiring house

Partition separating galleries from boxes

Baroque and neoclassical 1

THE BAROQUE STYLE EVOLVED IN THE EARLY 17TH CENTURY in Rome. It is characterized by curved outlines and ostentatious decoration, as can be seen in the Italian church details (right). The baroque style was particularly widely favored in Italy, Spain, and Germany. It was also adopted in Britain and France, but with adaptations. The British architects Sir Christopher Wren and Nicholas Hawksmoor, for example, used baroque features—such as the concave walls of St. Paul's Cathedral and the curved buttresses of the Church of St. George in the East (see pp. 480-481)—but they did so with restraint. Similarly, the curved buttresses and volutes of the Parisian Church of St. Paul-St. Louis are relatively plain. In the second half of the 17th century, a distinct classical style (known as neoclassicism) developed in northern Europe as a reaction to the excesses of baroque. Typical of this new style were churches such as the Madeleine (a proposed facade is shown below), as well as secular buildings such as the Cirque Napoleon (opposite) and the buildings of the British architect Sir John Soane (see pp. 482-483). In early 18th century France, an extremely lavish form of baroque developed, known as rococo. The balcony from Nantes (see pp. 482-483) with its twisted ironwork and head-shaped corbels is typical of this style.

DETAILS FROM ITALIAN BAROQUE CHURCHES

SCROLLED BUTTRESS, CHURCH OF ST. MARIA DELLA SALUTE, VENICE, 1631-1682

STATUE OF THE ECSTASY OF ST. THERESA, CHURCH OF ST. MARIA DELLA VITTORIA, ROME, 1645-1652

PROPOSED FACADE, THE MADELEINE (NEOCLASSICAL), PARIS, FRANCE, 1764 (BY P. CONTANT D'IVRY)

CIRQUE NAPOLEON (NEOCLASSICAL), PARIS FRANCE, 1852 (BY J.I. HITTORFF)

EXTERIOR

Rectangular panel

Small polyhedral roof

Attached colonette

Projecting entablature

Polyhedral iron roof

Palmette

Sculpted frieze

Cornice

Pedestal

Smooth, vertical rustication

Projecting pedestal

Statue of Amazon on horseback

Hanging wreath

Smooth rustication

Dado (die)

Plinth

Eagle carrying festoons

INTERIOR

King post

Statue of Minerva

Orb

Tie beam

Painted inner roof

Brace

Polyhedral lantern

Roll molding

Projecting entablature

Strut

Straight brace

Crest

Projecting socle

Outer wall

Attached Corinthian column

Frieze painted with scenes from classical mythology

Circle (auditorium)

Finial with cavetto molding

Foliated panel

Transverse arch

Crowning cornice

Window hood-mold

Volute

Fascia

Barrel vault

Dentil

Clerestory level

Rectangular door leading to roofed space

Raised window jamb

Groin vault

Gallery level

Semi-parabolic curve

Short pilaster

Curved buttress

Cornice

Modillion (bracket)

Pier-shaped pinnacle

Architrave decorated with oversailing fascias

Semicircular arched window

Corinthian capital

Cornice

Foliated frieze

Gallery

Depressed arch

Balustrade

Small cupola

Oeil-de-boeuf ("ox-eye") window

Keystone decorated with scroll ornament

Pendentive

Archivolt

Cornice

Archivolt decorated with plain fascias

Formeret (wall rib)

Arcade level

Round arch

Arcade

Window jamb

Outer wall

Buttress

Windowsill

Round arch

Re-entrant corner

Base

Socle

Doorway connecting chapels

Side chapels | Main vessel | Side chapels

NAVE, CHURCH OF ST. PAUL-ST. LOUIS (FRENCH BAROQUE), PARIS, FRANCE, FROM 1627 (BY E. MARTELLANGE)

Baroque and neoclassical 2

ARABESQUE

Volute *Palmette*

Tendril *Cornucopia*

BAY LEAF GARLAND

Bayberry *Bay leaf*

PATERA

Petal *Rosette*

Fillet *Ovolo (quarter-round) molding*

DECORATIVE MOLDINGS FROM ENGLISH NEOCLASSICAL BUILDINGS

Raking cornice *Representation in bas-relief of conversion of St. Paul*

TRIANGULAR PEDIMENT, WEST FACADE, ST. PAUL'S CATHEDRAL

MODEL BUILT IN 1674 OF PROPOSED EXTERIOR OF ST. PAUL'S CATHEDRAL (ENGLISH BAROQUE), LONDON, BRITAIN (BY C. WREN)

Cross

Orb

Small dome

Entablature

Pedestal

Arcade

Gallery with balustrade

Lantern

Convex molding

Circular lucarne window

Dome

Plat lesene

Curved buttress

Round arch

Corinthian pilaster

Rectangular pier

Sunken lunette

Raking cornice

Plain pilaster

Pediment

Sunken panel

Attic story

Entablature

Architrave

Cornice

Small pilaster

Pedestal

Semicircular cornice

Plinth

Concave, arched niche

Attached Corinthian column

Freestanding Corinthian column

Projecting side portal

CHURCH OF ST. GEORGE IN THE EAST (ENGLISH BAROQUE), LONDON, BRITAIN, 1714-1734 (BY N. HAWKSMOOR)

SOUTH SIDE **WEST FACADE**

Fluted circular pinnacle

Fluted capital

Pierced parapet

Plain buttress

Semicircular window

Urn

Platband

Sunken panel

Octahedral dome

Octahedral turret

Round-arched window

Plain frieze

Triple keystone

East pediment

Oeil-de-boeuf ("ox-eye") window

Cornice

Semicircular apse

Lateral pilaster-strip

Emphasized keystone

Semicircular crypt window

Emphasized quoin

Plain pedestal

Square post

Label mold

Side entrance

Steeple

Cornice

Stepped archivolt

Octahedral lantern

Parapet

Square stone block

Set-back buttress

Three-tier belfry

Cornice decorated with ogee molding and fascias

Pepper-pot lantern

Finial

Broken pediment

Volute

Ionic capital

Raking cornice

Continuous hood-mold

Triple band

Platband

Dog-leg staircase set in oval stone walls

Curved buttress

Ionic twin columns

Attic of drum

Stepped tetrahedral roof

Statuette

Urn

Lantern

Entablature

Drum

Rectangular window

Twin columns

Cruciform pedestal

Arcade

Circular lucarne window

Dome

Pedestal

Stepped cornice

Triangular lesene

Cornice

Raking cornice of facade pediment

Dentil ornament

Frieze

Corinthian capital

Corinthian twin pilasters

Dado

Re-entrant

Doorway

Architrave

Rectangular vestibule

Round-arched window

Concave wall

Emphasized keystone

Crepidoma (stepped base)

Corinthian capital

Baroque and neoclassical 3

DETAILS FROM BAROQUE, NEOCLASSICAL, AND ROCOCO BUILDINGS

PORTICO, THE VYNE, HAMPSHIRE, BRITAIN, 1654 (NEOCLASSICAL)

GILT IRONWORK FROM SCREEN, PALAIS DE VERSAILLES, FRANCE, 1669-1674 (FRENCH BAROQUE)

WINDOW, PALAZZO STANGA, CREMONA, ITALY, EARLY 18TH CENTURY (ROCOCO)

ATLAS (MALE CARYATID), UPPER BELVEDERE, VIENNA, AUSTRIA, 1721 (GERMAN-STYLE BAROQUE)

BALCONY, NANTES, FRANCE, 1750-1740 (ROCOCO)

MASONRY OF A NICHE IN THE ROTUNDA (NEOCLASSICAL), BANK OF ENGLAND, LONDON, BRITAIN, 1794 (BY J. SOANE)

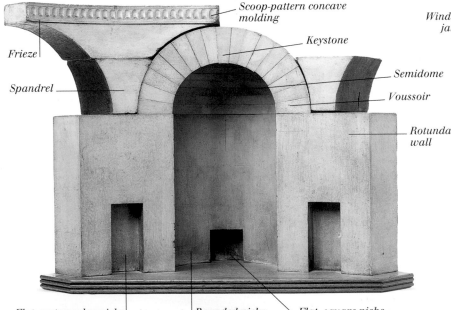

Scoop-pattern concave molding

Keystone

Frieze

Spandrel

Semidome

Voussoir

Rotunda wall

Flat, rectangular niche

Rounded niche

Flat, square niche

CORNER OF THE NEW STATE PAPER OFFICE (NEOCLASSICAL), LONDON, BRITAIN, 1830-1831 (BY J. SOANE)

Classical-style entablature

Cornice

Frieze

Architrave

Pantile (S-shaped roofing tile)

Eaves

Fascia

Scroll-shaped corbel

Curved corbel

Smooth rustication

Second-floor window

Cornice

Drip-cap

Cornice

Frieze

Window architrave

Window jamb

First-floor window

Windowsill in the form of a frieze

Ground-floor window

Splayed windowsill

Vermiculated rustication

TYRINGHAM HOUSE (NEOCLASSICAL), BUCKINGHAMSHIRE, BRITAIN, 1793-1797 (BY J. SOANE)

ROOF LEVEL (ATTIC LEVEL)

- Space for illumination above unroofed central hall
- Chimney stack
- Space above unroofed main staircase
- Oculus illuminating secondary staircase
- Flat roof
- Parapet rail
- Balustrade
- Cornice
- Baluster
- Cornice
- Attic story of convex portico

FIRST-FLOOR LEVEL (CHAMBER FLOOR)

- Upper level of central hall, open to floor below
- Main staircase
- Secondary staircase
- Abacus
- Pilaster capital
- Triangular pilaster
- Attached Tuscan twin pilasters
- First-floor story of convex portico
- Windowsill
- Bow front

GROUND-FLOOR LEVEL (PRINCIPAL FLOOR)

- Withdrawing room
- Central hall
- Main staircase
- Library and breakfast room
- Water closet (toilet)
- Eating room
- Secondary staircase
- Segmented lintel course
- Band incised with Greek-style fret ornament
- Windowsill
- Window architrave
- Window jamb
- Base
- Basement
- Plinth
- Horizontal rustication
- Vestibule (entrance hall)
- Ground-floor storey of convex portico

FACADE OF TYRINGHAM HOUSE

- Chimney stack
- Voussoir
- Basement window
- Entrance door
- Circular entrance steps

- Rail
- Baluster
- Parapet
- Balustrade
- Cornice
- Entablature
- Capital
- Shaft
- Ionic column
- Base

PROSTYLE COLONNADE

Arches and vaults

ARCHES ARE CURVED STRUCTURES used to bridge spans and to support the weight of upper parts of buildings, such as domes, as in St. Paul's Cathedral (below) and the historical temple (opposite). The voussoirs (wedge-shaped blocks) that form an arch (right) support each other and convert the downward force of the weight of the building into an outward force. This outward force is in turn transferred to buttresses, piers, or abutments. A vault is an arched roof or ceiling. There are four main types of vault (opposite). A barrel vault is a single vault, semicircular in cross-section; a groin vault consists of two barrel vaults intersecting at right angles; a rib vault is a groin vault reinforced by ribs; and a fan vault is a rib vault in which the ribs radiate from the springing point (where the arch begins) like a fan.

PARTS OF AN ARCH

Voussoir · Keystone · Crown · Abutment
Abutment · Intrados (soffit) · Extrados · Keystone · Haunch
Impost · Springing point · Intrados (soffit)
Abutment · Span · Abutment

FRONT

SIDE

ARCHES AND BASE OF DOME, ST. PAUL'S CATHEDRAL, LONDON, BRITAIN, 1675-1710 (BY C. WREN)

Inner dome · Colonnade
Pilaster · Passageway
Base · Cornice
Pendentive · Opening to passageway · Pedestal of outer dome
"Whispering Gallery"
Triangular buttress
Molded bracket
Upper arch (concealing difference in heights between main arch and minor arches)
Round arch
Semidome
Extrados
Intrados (soffit)
Upper barrel-vaulted passage opening onto side aisle
Springing point
Impost
Barrel vault
Abutment
Passage leading to side aisle
Strut built into masonry to strengthen pier (added in the 20th century)
Minor arch leading to side aisle · Main arch leading to nave · Pier · Minor arch

TYPES OF ARCH

HORSESHOE ARCH (MOORISH ARCH), GREAT MOSQUE, CORDOBA, SPAIN, 785

BASKET ARCH (SEMI-ELLIPTICAL ARCH), PALATINE CHAPEL, AIX-LA-CHAPELLE, FRANCE, 790-798

TUDOR ARCH, TOWER OF LONDON, BRITAIN, C.1086-1097

LANCET ARCH, WESTMINSTER ABBEY, LONDON, BRITAIN, 1503-1519

TREFOIL ARCH, BEVERLEY MINSTER, YORKSHIRE, BRITAIN, C.1300

TYPES OF VAULT

Transverse rib
Temporary brace
Horizontal abutment
Temporary structure used to center vault

BARREL VAULT (TUNNEL VAULT; WAGON VAULT)

Barrel vault
Voussoir
Right-angled intersection
Groin

GROIN VAULT

Transverse ridge-rib
Longitudinal ridge-rib
Transverse arch
Diagonal rib

RIB VAULT

Tierceron (secondary rib)
Ridge rib
Springing point
Concave-sided lozenge
Panel

FAN VAULT

COMPOSITE MODEL OF HISTORICAL FRENCH TEMPLE

Coved dome
Lesene
Pedestal of lantern
Archivolt decorated with plain fascias
Lantern
Series of plain fascias
Re-entrant angle
Cavetto molding
Fillet
Cornice
Plain frieze
Architrave
Ionic capital
Chamfered corner
Keystone decorated with scroll
Plain Ionic column
Shaft
Scotia
Plinth
Dado
Abutment
Dentil
Coved dome
Pedestal of dome
Entablature
Fluted Ionic column
Round arch
Cornice
Horizontal band
Twisted vertical band
Naos (cella)
Pedestal of column
Base
Intercolumniation
Ionic column with twisted vertical bands (wreaths) and horizontal bands

ENGLISH BOND BRICKWORK OF GROIN VAULT AND RIB VAULT

Right-angled intersection
Groin
Header
Stretcher
Cell of barrel vault
Springing point

EXTRADOS OF GROIN VAULT

Stretcher
Header
Cell
Extrados of diagonal rib
Springing point

EXTRADOS OF RIB VAULT

INTERIOR DECORATION OF COFFERED VAULT

Compass
Square
Hammer
Coffer (square sunken panel)
Chamfered edge
Arris molding
Mason's tools

Domes

A DOME IS A CONVEX ROOF. Domes are categorized according to the shapes of both the base and the section through the center of the dome. The base may be circular, square, or polygonal (many-sided), depending on the plan of the drum (the walls on which the dome rests). The section of a dome may be the same shape as any arch (see pp. 484-485). Various types of dome are illustrated here: a hemispherical dome, which has a circular base and a semicircular section; a saucer dome, which has a circular base and a segmental (less than a semicircle) section; a polyhedral dome, which is a dome on a polygonal base whose sides meet at the top of the dome; and an onion dome, which has a circular or polygonal base and an ogee-shaped section. Many domes have a lantern (a turret with windows) to provide light inside.

LANTERN AND UPPER DOME TIMBERING, ST. PAUL'S CATHEDRAL

DOME TIMBERING, CHURCH OF THE SORBONNE, PARIS, FRANCE, 1635-1642 (BY J. LEMERCIER)

Ogee-curved dome

Straight brace

Deeply projecting pier buttress

Cornice

Depressed hood mold

Circular lucarne window

Window zone

Floor joist

Pedestal

Hood mold

Floorboard

Waisted-oval lucarne window

Ashlar piece

Pin

Short strut

Ogee-curved window frame

Mortise and tenon joint

Principal rafter

Straight brace

Vertical post

Tie beam

Circular baseplate

Common rafter

Shaft connecting lantern and church interior

ROOF WITH LANTERN AND ONION DOME

Weather vane

Ellipsoid orb

Keeled lesene

Onion dome

Fish-scale tile

Octahedral base

Sloping roof

Oversailing fascia

Round arch

Attached pillar

Tetrahedral capital

Vertical band

Return

Window

Oversailing fascia

Torus

Fillet

Octahedral base of lantern

Lantern

Tetrahedral roof

REPRESENTATION OF DOME METALING, CHURCH OF THE SORBONNE

Cross

Orb

Square rib

Inverted ovolo (quarter-round)

Astragal

Fillet

Volute

Plain fascia

Roll molding

Round-arched window

Buttress

Volute

Ovolo (quarter-round)

Cornice

Fillet

Projecting pier buttress

Lantern

Dome on a circular base

Fish-scale tile

Inverted demi-heart torus molding

Hood mold

Waisted-oval lucarne window

Small volute

Gutter

Parapet

Small roll

Fillet

Plain fascia

Triple lesene

Semicircular torus molding

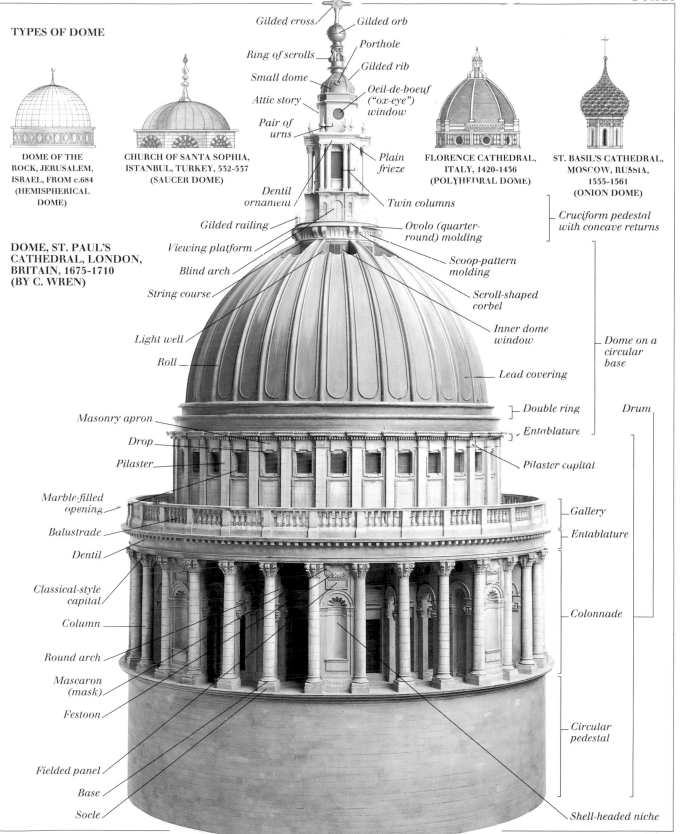

TYPES OF DOME

DOME OF THE
ROCK, JERUSALEM,
ISRAEL, FROM c.684
(HEMISPHERICAL
DOME)

CHURCH OF SANTA SOPHIA,
ISTANBUL, TURKEY, 532-537
(SAUCER DOME)

FLORENCE CATHEDRAL,
ITALY, 1420-1436
(POLYHEDRAL DOME)

ST. BASIL'S CATHEDRAL,
MOSCOW, RUSSIA,
1555-1561
(ONION DOME)

Gilded cross

Gilded orb

Ring of scrolls

Porthole

Small dome

Gilded rib

Attic story

Oeil-de-boeuf
("ox-eye")
window

Pair of
urns

Plain
frieze

**DOME, ST. PAUL'S
CATHEDRAL, LONDON,
BRITAIN, 1675-1710
(BY C. WREN)**

Dentil
ornament

Twin columns

Gilded railing

Ovolo (quarter-
round) molding

Viewing platform

Scoop-pattern
molding

Blind arch

String course

Scroll-shaped
corbel

Light well

Inner dome
window

Roll

Lead covering

Cruciform pedestal
with concave returns

Dome on a
circular
base

Masonry apron

Double ring

Drum

Drop

Entablature

Pilaster

Pilaster capital

Marble-filled
opening

Gallery

Balustrade

Entablature

Dentil

Classical-style
capital

Colonnade

Column

Round arch

Mascaron
(mask)

Festoon

Circular
pedestal

Fielded panel

Base

Socle

Shell-headed niche

487

Islamic buildings

OPUS SECTILE MOSAIC DESIGN

THE ISLAMIC RELIGION was founded by the prophet Mohammed, who was born in Mecca (in present-day Saudi Arabia) about 570 AD. During the next three centuries, Islam spread from Arabia to North Africa and Spain, as well as into India and much of the rest of Asia. The worldwide influence of Islam remains strong today. Common characteristics of Islamic buildings include ogee arches and roofs, onion domes, and walls decorated with carved stone, paintings, inlays, or mosaics. The most important type of Islamic building is the mosque—the place of worship—which generally has a minaret (tower) from which the muezzin (official crier) calls Muslims to prayer. Most mosques have a mihrab (decorative niche) that indicates the direction of Mecca. As figurative art is not allowed in Islam, buildings are ornamented with geometric and arabesque motifs and inscriptions (frequently Koranic verses).

Budlike onion dome

Depressed arch surrounding mihrab

Painted roof pavilion

Turkish crescent finial

Lotus flower pendentive

Arabic inscription

Crest

Painted minaret with censer (incense burner)

Spandrel

Series of recessed arches

Semidome

Arched niche within a niche

Mural resembling tomb

Polyhedral niche

Recessed colonettes

MIHRAB, JAMI MASJID (PRINCIPAL OR CONGREGATIONAL MOSQUE), BIJAPUR, INDIA, c.1636

Tablet flower

Shield

Herringbone pattern

Spandrel with floral design

Ogee arch

Carved stone

Undulating band

Cusp

Volute

Impost

Capital with stylized floral design

Panel with fret pattern

Band with Arabic inscriptions praising Allah (God)

Attached colonette

Jali (latticed screen) with geometrical patterns

ARCH, THE ALHAMBRA, GRANADA, SPAIN, 1333-1354

Enameled turquoise earthenware tile

Cube with chamfered corners

Trigon

Polygonal capital

Niche

Enameled white earthenware tile

Column shaft

Arabesques of stylized plants

Enameled lapis blue earthenware tile

MIHRAB WITH COLUMN, EL-AINYI MOSQUE, CAIRO, EGYPT, 15TH CENTURY

EXAMPLES OF ISLAMIC MOSAICS, EGYPT AND SYRIA

Star-shaped motif

Triangle of yellow marble

Rhombus of black marble

Stone band

Greek cross of red marble

STAR AND GREEK CROSS MOSAIC

Mosaic tessellation

Stone

Black marble

Turquoise glass

Tessera (small mosaic piece)

FRET-PATTERN MOSAIC

Greek cross of black and yellow marble

Star-shaped motif

Stone band

Rhombus of red marble

STAR AND GREEK CROSS MOSAIC

Parallelogram of black marble

Triangle of yellow marble

Rhombus of red marble

Symmetrical quadrilateral of stone

Star-shaped motif

MOSAIC OF HEXAGONS, TRIANGLES, AND SYMMETRICAL QUADRILATERALS

Hexagonal design

Band of black marble

Band of stone

HEXAGON AND BAND MOSAIC

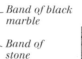

Triangle of turquoise glass

Parallelogram of mother-of-pearl

DANCETTE (ZIG-ZAG)-PATTERN MOSAIC

Symmetrical quadrilateral of black marble

Hexagon of red marble

Triangle of stone

MOSAIC OF HEXAGONS, TRIANGLES, AND SYMMETRICAL QUADRILATERALS

MARBLE TOMB OF ITIMAD-UD-DAULA, AGRA, INDIA, c.1622-1628

Kalasa finial (finial with orbs)

Padmakosa (lotus petal)

Ogee-curved roof

Chajya (deep eaves)

Balcony

Roof pavilion

Domed roof

Cusped arch

Pietra dura inlay (slices of semiprecious stone laid in sockets)

Cornice

Bracket

Spandrel decorated with arabesque

Circular top of minaret

Parapet decorated with latticework

Octahedral base of minaret

Star-pattern inlay

Sandstone plinth

Sandstone parapet decorated with latticework

Jali (latticed screen) with geometrical patterns

Depressed entrance arch

Sandstone stairway

Opus sectile mosaic (geometric mosaic) of stone, tile, glass, and enamel

South and east Asia

THE TRADITIONAL ARCHITECTURE of south and east Asia has been profoundly influenced by the spread from India of Buddhism and Hinduism. This influence is shown by both the abundance and by the architectural styles of temples and shrines in the region. Many early Hindu temples consist of rooms carved from solid rock faces. However, freestanding structures began to be built in southern India from about the eighth century AD. Many were built in the Dravidian style, like the Temple of Virupaksha (opposite), with its characteristic antarala (terraced tower), perforated windows, and numerous arches, pilasters, and carvings. The earliest Buddhist religious monuments were Indian stupas, which consisted of a single hemispherical dome surmounted by a chattravali (shaft) and surrounded by railings with ornate gates. Later Indian stupas and those built elsewhere were sometimes modified. For example, in Sri Lanka, the dome became bell-shaped, and was called a dagoba. Buddhist pagodas, such as the Burmese example (right), are multistoried temples, each story having a projecting roof. The form of these buildings probably derived from the yasti (pointed spire) of the stupa. Another feature of many traditional Asian buildings is their imaginative roof forms, such as gambrel (mansard) roofs, and roofs with angle rafters (below).

DETAILS FROM EAST ASIAN BUILDINGS

KASUGA-STYLE ROOF WITH SUMIGI (ANGLE RAFTERS), KASUGADO SHRINE OF ENJOJI, NARA, JAPAN, 12TH-14TH CENTURY

TERRACES, TEMPLE OF HEAVEN, BEIJING, CHINA, 15TH CENTURY

GAMBREL (MANSARD) ROOF WITH UPSWEPT EAVES AND UNDULATING GABLES, HIMEJI CASTLE, HIMEJI, JAPAN, 1608-1609

CORNER CAPITAL WITH ROOF BEAMS, POPCHU-SA TEMPLE, POPCHU-SA, SOUTH KOREA, 17TH CENTURY

SEVEN-STORIED PAGODA IN BURMESE STYLE, c.9TH-10TH CENTURY

Gilded band

Gilded iron hti (crown)

Dubika (mast)

Arrow motif

Torus molding with spiral carving

Decorative eaves board

Ogee-arched motif with decorative carvings

Ogee-arched motif forming horn

Hip rafter

Pentroof

Undulating molding

Engaged pillar

Arched entrance

Baluster finial

Balustrade

Rectangular window

Baluster

Pillar

Straight brace

PERFORATED STONE WINDOWS, TEMPLES OF VIRUPAKSHA AND MALLIKARJUNA, PATTADAKAL, INDIA, 8TH CENTURY

Tablet flower

Chain motif

Fret motif

Floral pattern

Leaf

Scroll motif

Sickle motif

Semicircle

DAGOBA STUPA, KANDY, SRI LANKA, c.2ND CENTURY BC–7TH CENTURY AD

Chattra (umbrella)

Hanging ornament

Chattravali (shaft)

Ring with indentations symbolizing chattras

Ornamental metalwork

Yasti (tee; pointed spire)

Harmika (stylized square railing)

Auda (bell-shaped dome)

Trimala (series of three circular courses)

Circular base

SIDE VIEW AND PLAN VIEW, TEMPLE OF VIRUPAKSHA, PATTADAKAL, INDIA, c.746

Stupica (small stupa) of the Dravidian order

Dravidian finial

Blind chataya arch

Perforated window

Gopuram finial (wagonlike finial)

Bracketed capital

Small gopuram (gate head)

Parapet

Roll cornice

Antarala (terraced tower)

Niche with statue

Gate

Panel with bas-relief carving

Pillar

Plan view

Twin pilasters

Pradakshina (circumambulatory passage around shrine)

Shrine

Shrine chamber

Niche

Gate

Mandapa (pillared hall)

The 19th century

BUILDINGS OF THE 19TH CENTURY are characterized by the use of new materials and by a great diversity of architectural styles. From the end of the 18th century, iron and steel became widely used as alternatives to wood for the framework of buildings, as in the flax-spinning mill shown here. Built in Britain in 1796, this mill exemplifies an architectural style that became common throughout the industrialized world for more than a century. The Industrial Revolution also brought mass production of building parts—a development that enabled the British architect Sir Joseph Paxton to erect London's Crystal Palace (a building made entirely of iron and glass) in only nine months, ready for the Great Exhibition of 1851. The 19th century saw a widespread revival of older architectural styles. For example, in the United States and Germany, Neo-Greek architecture was fashionable; in Britain and France, Neo-Baroque, Neo-Byzantine, and Neo-Gothic styles (as seen in the Palace of Westminster and Tower Bridge, London) were dominant.

SECTION THROUGH A FLAX-SPINNING MILL

Cast-iron wall plate
Pitched roof
Ridge
Machinery space
Verge
Gutter
Cast-iron mortise and tenon joint
Anchor joint
Inverted T-section cast-iron beam
Drain pipe
Segmentally arched brick vault
End flange
Concrete floor
Tapering part of column
Paved ground floor
Strengthened central column

FLAX-SPINNING MILL, SHREWSBURY, BRITAIN, 1796 (BY C. BAGE)

Multi-gabled roof (ridge and furrow roof)
Ridge
Furrow
Verge
Timber rafter
Cast-iron wall plate
Gutter
Gable
Drain pipe
Tapering part of column
Three courses of stretchers
Segmentally arched brick vault
Course of headers
Cast-iron mortise and tenon joint
Course of decorative headers
Tie-rod
Cast-iron cruciform column
Cast-iron lattice window
Inverted T-section cast-iron beam
Cast-iron tenon
Anchor joint
Strengthened central column
Bonded brick wall
Stone foundation
Quoin
Jamb
Gauged arch (segmental arch of tapered bricks)

CLOCK TOWER ("BIG BEN"), PALACE OF WESTMINSTER, LONDON, BRITAIN, 1836-1868 (BY C. BARRY AND A.W.N. PUGIN)

Finial

Spire

Skylight

Iron tracery

Dormer window

Cornice decorated with shields

Round arch filled with open tracery

Tetrahedral spire

Iron railing

Bell chamber

Balustrade

Small orb

Ogee tracery arch filled with trefoil

Orb

Flying buttress

Pinnacle

Spandrel

Octahedral shaft with billet decoration

Dial

Cornice

Molded corbel

Star-shaped corner buttress

Paneled field filled with tracery

Slender diagonal buttress

Narrow window

String course

Carved panel

Stepped storys

DETAILS FROM BUILDINGS IN REVIVALIST STYLES

CUPOLA, MERCHANTS' EXCHANGE, PHILADELPHIA, USA, 1832-1834 (NEO-GREEK)

SCULPTURE AND PEDIMENT, OPERA HOUSE, PARIS, FRANCE, 1861-1874 (NEO-BAROQUE)

DOMED TURRET, WESTMINSTER CATHEDRAL, LONDON, BRITAIN, 1894-1903 (NEO-BYZANTINE)

Tetrahedral spire

Finial

Spire

Finial

Cornice

High-level footbridge

Dormer head (gable) filled with blind tracery

Parapet

Parapet of balcony

Octahedral upper turret

Latticework

Heraldic shield

Archway

Cast-iron tracery

Cast-iron paneling

Wedge-shaped corbel

String course

Molded corbel

Drawbridge (bascule)

Steel brace

Stone panel

Circular turret/buttress

Archway

Pier

TOWER BRIDGE, LONDON, BRITAIN, 1886-1894 (BY H. JONES)

CRYSTAL PALACE EXHIBITION HALL, LONDON, BRITAIN, 1851 (BY J. PAXTON)

Arched facade

Longitudinal girder

Window

Cast-iron ornamental arch-plate

Semicircular barrel vault

Ridge and furrow glass roof-windows

Crest

Cast-iron trapezium

Octahedral column

Side exit

Sheet-iron louver

Strengthened support

Entrance

The early 20th century

ARCHITECTURE OF THE EARLY 20TH CENTURY is notable for radical new types of steel and glass buildings—particularly skyscrapers—and the widespread use of steel-reinforced concrete. The steel-framed skyscraper was pioneered in Chicago in the 1880s but did not become widespread until the first decades of the 20th century. As construction techniques were refined, skyscrapers became higher and higher. For example, the Empire State Building (right) of 1929-1931 has 102 storys. Many buildings of this period were constructed from lightweight concrete slabs that could be supported by cantilever beams or by pilotis (stilts), as in the Villa Savoye (below). The early 20th century also produced a great variety of architectural styles, some of which are illustrated opposite. Despite their diversity, the styles of this period generally had one thing in common: they were completely new, with few links to past architectural styles. This originality is in marked contrast to 19th-century architecture (see pp. 492-493), much of which was revivalist.

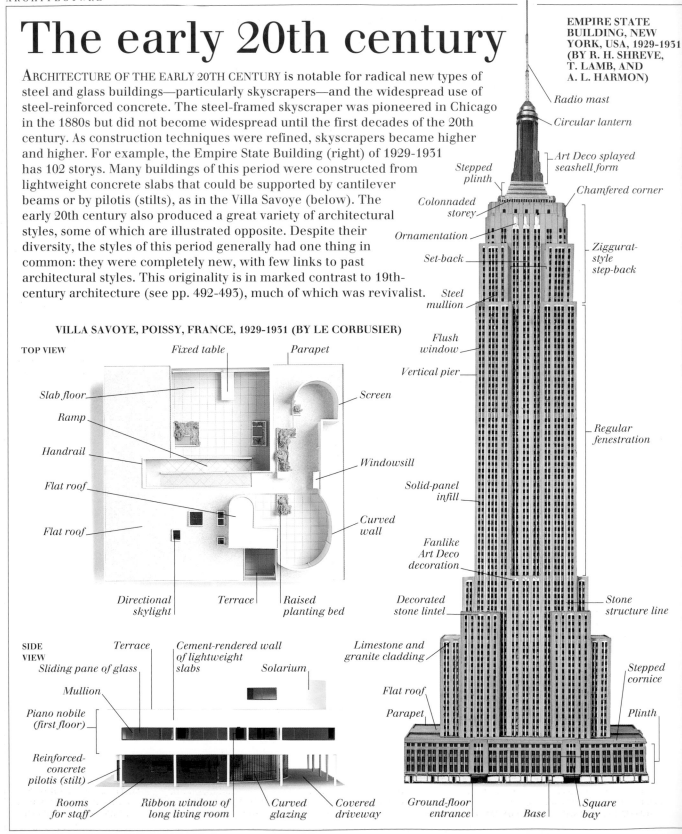

EMPIRE STATE BUILDING, NEW YORK, USA, 1929-1931 (BY R. H. SHREVE, T. LAMB, AND A. L. HARMON)

Radio mast
Circular lantern
Art Deco splayed seashell form
Stepped plinth
Chamfered corner
Colonnaded storey
Ornamentation
Ziggurat-style step-back
Set-back
Steel mullion
Flush window
Vertical pier
Regular fenestration
Solid-panel infill
Fanlike Art Deco decoration
Decorated stone lintel
Stone structure line
Limestone and granite cladding
Flat roof
Stepped cornice
Parapet
Plinth
Ground-floor entrance
Base
Square bay

VILLA SAVOYE, POISSY, FRANCE, 1929-1931 (BY LE CORBUSIER)

TOP VIEW

Fixed table
Parapet
Slab floor
Screen
Ramp
Handrail
Windowsill
Flat roof
Curved wall
Flat roof
Directional skylight
Terrace
Raised planting bed

SIDE VIEW

Terrace
Cement-rendered wall of lightweight slabs
Solarium
Sliding pane of glass
Mullion
Piano nobile (first floor)
Reinforced-concrete pilotis (stilt)
Rooms for staff
Ribbon window of long living room
Curved glazing
Covered driveway

MIDWAY GARDENS, CHICAGO, USA, 1914 (BY F. L. WRIGHT)

Flagpole

Plain coping stone

Main floor

Decorated cement frieze

Projecting balustrade

Ornamental light

Arcade

Terrace

Steps

Stage

Orchestra shell

Tiled, shallow pitched roof

Ridge

Hip

Main pavilion

Terrace

Ornamental sculpture

Stone plinth

Tiled frieze

Deep-set window

Brick pier

Stepped flat roofs

Ornamented coping stone

Terrace

Slit window

Planting bed

Cantilevered latticed shade

Flat roof

Octagonal window

EAST SIDE

NORTH SIDE

EARLY 20TH-CENTURY ARCHITECTURAL STYLES

DORMER WINDOW, STUDIO ELVIRA, MUNICH, GERMANY, 1902 (ART NOUVEAU)

AEG TURBINE HALL, BERLIN, GERMANY, 1909 (DEUTSCHER WERKBUND)

ROBIE HOUSE, CHICAGO, USA, 1909-1910 (PRAIRIE STYLE)

GRUNDTVIG CHURCH, COPENHAGEN, DENMARK, 1920 (EXPRESSIONIST)

VERTEX, CHRYSLER BUILDING, NEW YORK, USA, 1928-1930 (ART DECO)

TOWER, TOWN HALL, HILVERSUM, NETHERLANDS, 1930 (DUTCH CUBIST)

CASA DEL FASCIO, COMO, ITALY, 1932-1936 (GRUPPO SEVEN CUBIST)

MOTIF ABOVE DOORWAY, HOOVER FACTORY, LONDON, BRITAIN, 1933 (ART DECO)

Modern buildings 1

KAWANA HOUSE, JAPAN, FROM 1987 (BY N. FOSTER)

ARCHITECTURE SINCE ABOUT THE 1950s is generally known as modern architecture. One of its main influences has been functionalism—a belief that a building's function should be apparent in its design. Both the Centre Georges Pompidou (below and opposite) and the Hong Kong and Shanghai Bank (see pp. 498-499) are functionalist buildings. On each, elements of engineering and the building's services are clearly visible on the outside. In the 1980s, some architects rejected functionalism in favor of postmodernism, in which historical styles—particularly neoclassicism—were revived, using modern building materials and techniques. In many modern buildings, walls are made of glass or concrete hung from a frame, as in the Kawana House (right); this type of wall construction is known as curtain walling. Other modern construction techniques include the intricate interlocking of concrete vaults—as in the Sydney Opera House (see pp. 498-499)—and the use of high-tension beams to create complex roof shapes, such as the paraboloid roof of the Church of St. Pierre de Libreville (see pp. 498-499).

Solar panel
Concrete frame
Pile foundation
Raft
Composite cladding panel
SIDE VIEW

Rocker beam
Curtain walling
Lattice beam
Floor-beam connection
Floor
FRONT VIEW

SERVICES FACADE, CENTRE GEORGES POMPIDOU, PARIS, FRANCE, 1977 (BY R. PIANO AND R. ROGERS)

Metal-faced fire-resistant panel
Air-conditioning duct
Cooling tower
Water pipe

Grand gallery level
Main gallery levels
Library level
Administrative level
Mezzanine gallery level
Reception level

Staircase to grand hall
Electrical plant
Water-cooled fire-resistant column
Continuous glazing
Tinted glass
Services entrance

PRINCIPAL FACADE, CENTRE GEORGES POMPIDOU

Gallery space
External walkway
Electronically operated roller blind
Cooling tower
Continuous glazing
Steel lattice beam
Terrace
Main truss
Cradle support for escalator
Gerberette (cast-steel rocker beam)
Cross-bracing
Double fire escape staircase
Suspended fire-resistant glass curtain

Reinforced-concrete and steel floor plate
Double floor height
Main entrance
Glazed escalator tube
Node
Water-cooled fire-resistant steel column

Exposed "plug-in" services

Steel lattice beam
Dual air-conditioning unit for roof
Elevator
Elevator-motor room
Vertical-duct distribution zone

Metal sandwich-panel (insulating panel)
Gerberette (cast-steel rocker beam)
Rose connection
Outer tension-column
External steel-lattice mullion
Water-cooled fire-resistant cross-beam
Double fire escape staircase

Water storage tank
Cross-bracing
Open gallery floor
Water pipe
Steel-framed services column
Double cross-bracing

Modern buildings 2

HONG KONG AND SHANGHAI BANK, HONG KONG, 1981–1985 (BY N. FOSTER)

Mast

Illuminated fascia

Inverted top truss

Curved glazing

External maintenance crane

Soffit

Cockpit

Counterweight

Boom

Circular access platform

Sunshade louver

Steel column

Mullion

Face panel

Hanger

Handrail

Composite cladding panel

Top beam

Outer diagonal beam

Escalator

Outer bottom boom

Inner diagonal beam

Inner bottom boom

Fire escape staircase

Pin joint

External staircase

Refuge terrace

Double floor height

Hanger

Full-height glazing

Sun scoop

Two-story stability truss (coat hanger truss)

Glazed curtain wall

Flange

Lightweight, column-free steel and concrete floor

Vertical glazed typhoon screen

Glazed soffit

Entrance lobby

Plaza

SOUTH FACADE

Soffit

Helicopter landing pad

Navigation light

Stepped elevation

Face panel

Horizontal window

Vertical window

External maintenance crane

Cross-bracing

Service shaft

Double floor height

Sun scoop

10-floor-high atrium

Internal bridge

EAST SIDE

**CHURCH OF ST. PIERRE,
LIBREVILLE, GABON, 1990**

Lattice truss

Cross-bracing

Paraboloid roof

Concave curve

Convex curve

Tension member

Mullion

Plate connector

Rafter

Full-height glazing

Bolt

Eaves

Rendered splayed outer wall

Entrance

Reinforced plinth

Concrete shoe

Inner diagonal beam

Beam housing

Pin joint

Glulam wall plate (glued and laminated wall plate)

Tinted glass

Circular steps

Secondary hall

Main hall

**OPERA HOUSE, SYDNEY, AUSTRALIA,
1959-1973 (BY J. UTZON)**

Vaults with curved ribs

Precast concrete rib

Glass wall

Mullion

Bronze glazing bar

Main hall

Precast concrete rib segment

Ridge

Continuous glazing

Solid podium

Ribbon window

HARBOR FACADE

Vault roof constructed of chevron-shaped precast tiles

Vault over restaurant

Staircase

Solid podium

Pink cladding

Pink granite-aggregate paving slab

Main line of support

Awning

Staircase

Terrace

WEST SIDE

MUSIC

Musical notation

MUSICAL NOTATION IS ANY METHOD by which sounds are written down so that they can be read and performed by others. The present-day conventional system of notation uses a five-line stave (staff)—divided by vertical lines into sections known as bars—on which notes, rests, clefs, key signatures, time signatures, accidentals, and other symbols are written. A note indicates the duration of a sound and, according to its position on the stave, its pitch. Notes can be arranged on the stave in order of pitch to form a scale. A silence in the music is indicated by a rest. The clef, which is placed at the begininng of a stave, fixes the pitch. The key signature, which is placed after the clef, indicates the key. The time signature, placed after the key signature, shows the number of beats in a bar. Accidentals are used to indicate the raising or lowering of the pitch of a note.

ELEMENTS OF MUSICAL NOTATION

CLEFS

Treble (or G) clef

Alto (or C) clef

Bass (or F) clef

TIME SIGNATURES

Six-eight time

Three-four time

Stave (staff)

NOTES

Breve

Minim

Quaver

Semibreve

Crotchet

Semiquaver

RESTS

Breve rest

Minim rest

Quaver rest

Semibreve rest

Crotchet rest

Semiquaver rest

SCALE

C D E F G A B C

ACCIDENTALS

Sharp

Natural

Double sharp

Flat

Double flat

Key signature

EXAMPLE OF AN ORIGINAL MANUSCRIPT: THE PRODIGAL SON, ARTHUR SULLIVAN, 1869

Moderately fast and quiet

Tie (bind)

Repeat the previous bar

Treble clef

Bass clef

Four-four time (common time)

Key signature

Alto clef

Treble voice

Alto voice

Tenor voice

Bass voice

Organ part for right hand

Organ part for left hand

Organ pedal line

Instruments of the orchestra written in Italian

Bar line

Bar

Bass clef

Crotchet

FLUTES

OBOES

CLARINETS IN A

BASSOONS

HORNS IN D

TRUMPETS IN D

TIMPANI IN D AND A

Accidental sharp

Tie (bind)

Accidental natural

Unison (both clarinets play the same note)

Semibreve

Crotchet

FIRST AND SECOND VIOLINS

VIOLAS

VOICES

Slur

Crotchet rest

Semibreve rest

Accidental sharp

Piano (play softly)

Pianissimo (play very softly)

ORGAN

CELLOS

DOUBLE BASSES

Orchestras

AN ORCHESTRA IS A GROUP of musicians that plays music written for a specific combination of instruments. The number and type of instruments included in the orchestra depends on the style of music being played. The modern orchestra (also known as a symphony orchestra) is made up of four sections of instruments—stringed, woodwind, brass, and percussion. The stringed section consists of violins, violas, cellos (violoncellos), double basses, and sometimes a harp (see pp. 510-511). The main instruments of the woodwind section are flutes, oboes, clarinets, and bassoons—the piccolo, cor anglais, bass clarinet, saxophone, and double bassoon (contrabassoon) can also be included if the music requires them (see pp. 508-509). The brass section usually consists of horns, trumpets, trombones, and the tuba (see pp. 506-507). The main instruments of the percussion section are the timpani (see pp. 518-519). The snare drum, bass drum, cymbals, tambourine, triangle, tubular bells, xylophone, vibraphone, gong (tam-tam), castanets, and maracas can also be included in the percussion section (see pp. 516-517). The musicians are usually arranged in a semi-circle—strings spread along the front, woodwind and brass in the center, and percussion at the back. A conductor stands in front of the musicians and controls the tempo (speed) of the music and the overall balance of the sound, ensuring that no instruments are too loud or too soft in relation to the others.

TUBULAR BELLS

TAM-TAM (GONG)

VIBRAPHONE

XYLOPHONE

CASTANETS

TAMBOURINE

MARACAS

TRIANGLE

TRUMPETS

HORNS

CLARINETS

BASS CLARINET

HARP

SAXOPHONE

PICCOLO

SECOND VIOLINS

FIRST VIOLINS

CYMBALS SIDE DRUM BASS DRUM

TIMPANI

**EXAMPLE OF A LAYOUT OF THE
INSTRUMENTS FOR A MODERN
(SYMPHONY) ORCHESTRA**

TROMBONES

TUBA

BASSOONS

DOUBLE BASSOON

DOUBLE BASSES

FLUTES

OBOES

COR ANGLAIS

VIOLAS

Score

CONDUCTOR'S
STAND

CELLOS

505

Brass instruments

BRASS INSTRUMENTS ARE WIND INSTRUMENTS that are made of metal, usually brass. Although they appear in many different shapes and sizes, all brass instruments have a mouthpiece, a length of hollow tube, and a flared bell. The mouthpiece of a brass instrument may be cup-shaped, as in the cornet, or cone-shaped, as in the horn. The tube may be wide or narrow, mainly conical, as in the horn and tuba, or mainly cylindrical, as in the trumpet and trombone. The sound of a brass instrument is made by the player's lips vibrating against the mouthpiece, so that the air vibrates in the tube. By changing lip tension, the player can vary the vibrations and produce notes of different pitches. The range of notes produced by a brass instrument can be extended by means of a valve system. Most brass instruments, such as the trumpet, have piston valves that divert the air in the instrument along an extra piece of tubing (known as a valve slide) when pressed down. The total length of the tube is increased and the pitch of the note produced is lowered. Instead of valves, the trombone has a movable slide that can be pushed away from or drawn toward the player. The sound of a brass instrument can also be changed by inserting a mute into the bell of the instrument.

BUGLE

Brace

Tuning slide

Counterbalancing weight

SIMPLIFIED DIAGRAM SHOWING HOW A PISTON VALVE SYSTEM WORKS

Piston valves at rest

Air bypasses piston valves

PISTON VALVES AT REST

First piston valve pressed down

Second and third piston valves at rest

Air diverted through first valve slide

PISTON VALVE PRESSED DOWN

TRUMPET

Finger button

First piston valve

Spring returns piston valve to rest position

Second piston valve

Third piston valve

Holes divert air into valve slides

Little finger support

Music stand holder

Narrow, cylindrical tube

Flared bell

Cup-shaped mouthpiece

Mouthpiece receiver

Tuning slide

Tuning slide water key

First valve slide

First valve slide thumb hook

Second valve slide

Third valve slide finger ring

Third valve slide

Third valve slide water key

SECTIONS OF A TROMBONE

Flared bell

EXAMPLES OF MUTES

CUP MUTE

TENOR MUTE

ALTO MUTE

Inner tube

Outer tube of slide

Cup-shaped mouthpiece

Mouthpiece brace held by the left hand

Slide brace held by the right hand

Narrow, cylindrical tube

Water key

TROMBONE

Flared bell

Outer tube of slide

Cup-shaped mouthpiece

FLUGELHORN

Little finger support

Piston valves

Flared bell

Cup-shaped mouthpiece

Valve slide

Conical tube

HORN

Cone-shaped mouthpiece

Finger key

Rotary valves

Narrow, conical bore

Large, flared bell

CORNET

Piston valves

Little finger support

Flared bell

Cup-shaped mouthpiece

Bore widens after valves

Valve slide

TUBA

Large, flared bell

Piston valves

Cup-shaped mouthpiece

Valve slide

Wide, conical tube

507

Woodwind instruments

WOODWIND INSTRUMENTS ARE wind instruments that are generally made of wood, although some are made of metal or plastic. The sound of a woodwind instrument is produced by the vibration of air in a hollow tube. The air is made to vibrate by blowing across a blow hole—as in the flute and piccolo—or by blowing through a single reed—as in the clarinet and saxophone—or a double reed—as in the bassoon, cor anglais, and oboe. The pitch of a woodwind instrument can be changed by opening or closing holes cut into the tube of the instrument.

Bell

Double reed

Bell joint

Curved crook

Conical, wooden tube

Tenor joint

Crook

Double reed

Cylindrical, metal tube

Key

Body joint

Blow hole

Head joint

Lip plate

PICCOLO

Conical, wooden tube

Upper joint

Key

Right-hand rest

Bass joint

Key

Double reed

Cork

Upper joint

Key

Finger hole

Foot joint

Key

Mouthpiece with single reed

Ligature

Barrel joint

Body joint

Butt

Key

Middle joint

Key

Middle joint

Finger hole

Cylindrical, metal tube

Cylindrical, wooden tube

Upper joint

BASSOON

Bell joint

Bulb-shaped bell

COR ANGLAIS

Conical, wooden tube

Finger hole

Lip plate

Head joint

Key

Blow hole

FLUTE

Bell joint

Flared bell

OBOE

Bell joint

Flared bell

Middle joint

CLARINET

TENOR SAXOPHONE

Mouthpiece with single reed

Conical, metal tube

Upturned, flared bell

SECTIONS OF A TENOR SAXOPHONE

Mouthpiece with single reed

Ligature

Neck

Upper octave key

Key rod

KEYS FOR THE LEFT THUMB

Lower octave key

Key

Key

KEYS FOR THE LEFT HAND

Key rod

Key

Mother-of-pearl touchpiece (button)

Key rod

KEYS FOR THE LEFT PALM

KEYS FOR THE RIGHT HAND

Key

Key rod

MAIN BODY OF SAXOPHONE

Conical, metal tube

KEYS FOR THE RIGHT PALM

Upturned, flared bell

Tone hole

Mother-of-pearl touchpiece (button)

Tone hole

Pad made up of layers of felt and cork

Roller

Cup

Key rod

Key guard

Key

Metal center of pad reflects sound

Key guard

KEYS FOR THE RIGHT LITTLE FINGER

Padded key

KEYS FOR THE LEFT LITTLE FINGER

Key guard

Stringed instruments

STRINGED INSTRUMENTS PRODUCE SOUND by the vibration of stretched strings. This may be done by drawing a bow across the strings, as in the violin; or by plucking the strings, as in the harp and guitar (see pp. 512-513). The four modern members of the bowed string family are the violin, viola, cello (violoncello), and double bass. Each consists of a hollow, wooden body, a long neck, and four strings. The bow is a wooden stick with horsehair stretched across its length. The vibrations made by drawing the bow across the strings are transmitted to the hollow body, and this itself vibrates, amplifying and enriching the sound produced. The harp consists of a set of strings of different lengths stretched across a wooden frame. The strings are plucked by the player's thumbs and fingers—except the little finger of each hand—which produces vibrations that are amplified by the harp's sound board. The pitch of the note produced by any stringed instrument depends on the length, weight, and tension of the string. A shorter, lighter, or tighter string gives a higher note.

Scroll eye

Scroll

Peg hole

Ebony tuning pegs

Neck made of maple wood

Fingerboard

Strings

Rounded shoulder

Belly (sound board)

Waist

Sound hole

Rib

Purfling

Chin rest

Bridge

Tailpiece

Tailpiece loop fits around end pin

SECTIONS OF A VIOLIN

End pin (tail pin)

Head

Point

Stick

Horsehair

Scroll

Scroll eye

Peg box

Tuning peg

Nut

String

Fingerboard

Rounded shoulder

Purfling

Belly (sound board)

Waist

Sound hole

Bridge

Tuning adjustor

Frog

Screw

Chin rest

Tailpiece

VIOLIN BOW

VIOLIN

Crown

Tuning peg

Neck (string arm)

Shoulder

String

Sound board

Scroll

Scroll eye

Peg box

Tuning peg

Nut

Fingerboard

String

Belly (sound board)

Rounded shoulder

Pillar

Pedestal

Foot

Pedal

HARP

Belly (sound board)

Head

Point

Nut

Inward-curving stick

Horsehair

Frog

Screw

DOUBLE BASS BOW

Scroll

Scroll eye

Tuning pegs at back of peg box

Fingerboard

Sloping shoulder

Purfling

Waist

Bridge

Rib

Sound hole

Sound hole

Bridge

Scroll

Tuning peg

Scroll eye

Peg box

Nut

Fingerboard

String

Belly (sound board)

Rounded shoulder

Purfling

Waist

Bridge

Waist

Sound hole

Chin rest

Tuning adjustor

Tailpiece

VIOLA

Waist

Sound hole

Bridge

Tuning adjustor

Tailpiece

Spike

CELLO (VIOLONCELLO)

Tailpiece

Spike

DOUBLE BASS

Guitars

THE GUITAR IS A PLUCKED stringed instrument (see pp. 510-511). There are two types of guitar—acoustic and electric. Acoustic guitars have hollow bodies and six or twelve strings. Plucking or strumming the strings produces vibrations that are amplified by their hollow bodies. Electric guitars usually have solid bodies and six strings. Pick-ups placed under the strings convert vibrations into electronic signals that are magnified by an amplifier, and sent to a loudspeaker where they are converted into sounds (see pp. 520-521). Electric bass guitars are very similar in structure to electric guitars, and produce sound in the same way, but have four heavier-gage strings and play lower pitched notes.

ACOUSTIC GUITAR

String   Fret   Machine head

Hollow body

Neck   Headstock

Sound hole

Bridge

B string

G string

D string

A string

Low E string

Maker's label

Lining glued along top and bottom edge of rib

Rib

End block

Strap peg

Joint

Transverse (crosswise) strut strengthens back

Back made of two pieces of cherry wood joined together

Saddle

Bridge pin

Bridge

Binding

COMPONENTS OF AN ACOUSTIC GUITAR

Top E string

Nut

Truss rod cover

Screws

Machine heads

Headstock

Machine head

Truss rod slot

Truss rod

Fingerboard

Position marks

Fretwire slot

Fretwire

Sound hole

Bracing

Sound board made of two pieces of spruce joined together

EXAMPLES OF ACOUSTIC GUITARS

Rose

Hollow body

Sound hole

String

Machine head

Bridge

Neck   Headstock

Scratch plate

WASHBURN TWELVE-STRING

Hollow, metal body

Sound hole

Tailpiece

String

Machine head

Neck   Headstock

Resonator

DOBRO RESONATOR

EXAMPLES OF ELECTRIC GUITARS

Pick-up   Scratch plate

Solid body

String

Machine head

Bridge

Neck   Headstock

Output socket

Vibrato arm

FENDER STRATOCASTER

Pick-up   Pick-up selector

Solid body

String

Machine head

Bridge

Neck   Headstock

Scratch plate

GIBSON LES PAUL

Pick-up

Solid body

String

Machine head

Bridge

Neck   Headstock

Output socket

Scratch plate

FENDER JAZZ BASS

Keyboard instruments

KEYBOARD INSTRUMENTS are instruments that are sounded by means of a keyboard. The organ and piano are two of the principal members of the keyboard family. The organ consists of pipes which are operated by one or more keyboards and foot pedals. The pipes are lined up in rows (known as ranks or registers) on top of a wind chest. The sound of the organ is made when air is admitted into a pipe by pressing a key or pedal. The piano consists of wire strings stretched over a metal frame, and a keyboard and pedals that operate hammers and dampers. The piano frame is either vertical—as in the upright piano—or horizontal—as in the grand piano. When a key is at rest, a damper lies against the string to keep it from vibrating. When a key is pressed down, the damper moves away from the string as the hammer strikes it, causing the string to vibrate and sound a note.

ORGAN
PIPE

UPRIGHT PIANO

Muffler felt
Pressure bar
Tuning pin
Pin block
Hammer
Hammer rail
88–note keyboard
Wooden case
Keybed
Sound board
Metal frame
String
Hitch pin
Treble bridge
Bass bridge
Una corda (soft) pedal
Sostenuto pedal
Damper (sustaining) pedal

ORGAN CONSOLE

Pipe
Pedal stop
Music stand
Swell stop
Choir stop
Swell manual (keyboard)
Great stop
Great manual (keyboard)
Thumb piston
Choir manual (keyboard)
Toe piston
Pedal board
Foot pedal
Swell pedal

UPRIGHT PIANO ACTION

KEY AT REST

String
Hammer
Damper lies against string, and keeps it from vibrating
Hammer rest
Back check
Damper lever
Action lever
Jack
Capstan screw
Key released

KEY PRESSED DOWN

String
Hammer strikes string
Damper moves away from string, allowing it to vibrate
Hammer rest
Back check
Damper lever
Action lever
Capstan screw
Jack
Key pressed down

CONCERT GRAND PIANO (VIEWED FROM ABOVE)

Sound board

Bass bridge

Hitch pin

Metal frame

Single bass note string

Long bridge

CONCERT GRAND PIANO (FRONT VIEW)

Lid

String

Wooden case

Keyboard

Una corda (soft) pedal

Sostenuto pedal

Damper (sustaining) pedal

Tenor note strings (two strings for each note)

Treble note strings (three strings for each note)

Wooden case

Hammer

Tuning pin

Wrest plank

Keyboard lid

88-note keyboard

STEINWAY & SONS

NEW YORK HAMBURG

B

518422

STEINWAY

Percussion instruments

TUBULAR BELLS

PERCUSSION INSTRUMENTS are a large group of instruments that produce sound by being struck, shaken, scraped, or clashed together. Some percussion instruments—such as the gong (tam-tam), cymbals, and maracas—do not have a definite pitch and are used for rhythm and impact, and the distinctive timber (color) of their sound. Other percussion instruments—such as the xylophone, vibraphone, and tubular bells—are tuned to a definite pitch and can play melody, harmony, and rhythms. The xylophone and vibraphone each have two rows of bars that are arranged in a similar way to the black and white keys of a piano. Metal tubes are suspended below the bars to amplify the sound. The vibraphone has electrically operated fans that rotate in the tubes and produce a vibrato (wavering pitch) effect.

TEMPLE BLOCKS

Tube struck with mallet

Hollow, metal tube

Damper bar

Metal frame

Mechanism linking pedal and damper bar

Row of tubes graduated in length and pitch

Damper pedal

EXAMPLES OF MALLETS

SOFT-HEADED MALLET — Felt-covered head

HARD-HEADED MALLET — Rosewood head

HAMMER MALLET — Leather-covered head

XYLOPHONE

Row of bars graduated in length and pitch

Wooden bar struck with hard-headed mallet

Hollow, metal tube

Metal stand

GONG (TAM-TAM)

Tam-tam struck in center with soft-headed mallet

Cord

Metal frame

Rim

Large, metal disk

CYMBALS

Leather strap fits around player's hand

Pad protects hands from vibrations

Thin, convex disk of copper and tin alloy

Zildjian

SECTIONS OF A MARACA

Wooden handle

Hollow, wooden head

Lead beads

TRIANGLE

Steel rod bent into triangular shape

Steel wand

CLAVES

Hardwood sticks clashed together to give a sharp crack

CASTANETS

Cord

Hollowed wood

VIBRAPHONE

Row of bars graduated in length and pitch

Metal bar struck with soft headed mallet

MUSSER

Metal frame

Damper pedal

Metal tube containing electrically operated fan that produces vibrato (wavering pitch) effect

Electric cable

Drums

A DRUM IS A percussion instrument that consists of a drumhead, made of skin or plastic, stretched over one or both ends of a hollow vessel (the body shell). Drums are played in most parts of the world and are made in a number of different shapes and sizes. They can be divided into three groups according to the shape of the body shell: frame drums (e.g., tambourines), bowl-shaped drums (e.g., timpani), and tubular drums (e.g., congas). Drums are usually sounded by striking the drumhead with the hands or with mallets, such as a hard-headed stick. The drumhead vibrates, and its vibrations are amplified by the hollow body shell. The snare drum has wires—known as snares—stretched across the lower drumhead; the snares vibrate against the lower drumhead when the drum is played. Most drums, such as congas, do not have a definite pitch and can play only rhythms (see pp. 516-517). Other drums, such as timpani, have a definite pitch and can play melody, harmony, and rhythms. They can be tuned by adjusting the tension of the drumhead. Different types of drum can be combined together with other percussion instruments to form a drum kit. The basic components of the drum kit are bass drum, tom-toms, floor tom (tenor drum), snare drum, and cymbals.

TAMBOURINE

Crash cymbal

Tension key

DRUM KIT

Tension rod

Tom-tom

Lug

Hi-hat cymbal

Snare drum

Tripod stand

Chain

Tension screw

Felt-covered mallet

Pedal

Pedal

SNARE DRUM (VIEWED FROM BELOW)

Snare mounting

Adjustable damper

Lug

Transparent lower drumhead

Snare

Upper drumhead

Stick

Snare release lever

EXAMPLES OF STICKS

Acorn

HARD-HEADED STICK

Taper

SOFT-HEADED STICK

Felt-covered head

WIRE BRUSH

Wire bristles

Ride cymbal

Tension key

Tom-tom

Height adjustment key

Tension rod

Lug

Floor tom (tenor drum)

Tension rod

Lug

Wooden body shell

Height adjustment key

Leg

Bass drum

Rubber foot

CONGAS

Metal hoop

Drumhead

Wooden body shell

Tension rod

Tripod stand

Leg

TIMPANUM (KETTLE DRUM)

Drumhead

Tension rod

Metal hoop

Tuning gauge

Copper body shell

Strut

Tension rod

Crown

Tuning pedal

Castor

Electronic instruments

ELECTRONIC DRUMS

ELECTRONIC INSTRUMENTS generate electronic signals that are magnified by an amplifier and sent to a loudspeaker, where they are converted into sounds. Synthesizers, and other electronic instruments, simulate the characteristic sounds of conventional instruments, and also create entirely new sounds. Most electronic instruments are keyboard instruments, but electronic wind and percussion instruments are also popular. A digital sampler records and stores sounds from musical instruments or other sources. When the sound is played back, the pitch of the original sound can be altered. A keyboard can be connected to the sampler so that a tune can be played using the sampled sounds. With a MIDI (Musical Instrument Digital Interface) system, a computer can be linked with other electronic instruments, such as keyboards and electronic drums, to make sounds together or in sequence. It is also possible, using music software, to compose and play music on a home computer.

Drum pad

Height adjustment key

Tripod

HOME KEYBOARD

Power button *Volume control* *Function display* *Sequence record button* *Tone editor control*

Demonstration tune button

Modulation wheel *Multiaccompaniment system control* *Tone and rhythm pattern selector* *Key*

SYNTHESIZER

Memory card slot *Joystick* *Function display* *Edit control* *Data entry key pad*

Volume control

Sound waveform selection guide

Modulation wheel *Sound selection control* *Key*

WIND SYNTHESIZER

Keys for left hand

Mouthpiece

DIGITAL SAMPLER

WIND CONTROLLER

Keys for right hand

Contrast control

Function display

Power button

Data increment control

POWER PACK

MIDI (Musical Instrument Digital Interface) cable

SOUND MODULE

Connecting cable

Record trigger

Floppy-disk drive

Play button

Data entry key pad

Microphone input

Store button

Data entry key pad

Input connector socket

Volume control

COMPUTER WITH MIDI AND AUDIO SOFTWARE SEQUENCER

Edit control

Play button

Function display

Effect balance control

Start and stop controls

Audio clock settings

Surround sound special effect plug-in

COMPUTER DISPLAY

APPLE MACINTOSH G4 COMPUTER

Software effect plug-in

Recorded information

Virtual mixing board

CD drive

SPEAKER

KEYBOARD

MOUSE

SPEAKER

SPORTS

Soccer

GAMES INVOLVING KICKING A BALL have a long history and were recorded in China as early as 300 BC; in medieval Europe, street football was banned as a menace to the public; only in 1863 were the rules established, specifically banning carrying the ball for all players except the goalkeeper, and separating rugby from soccer. Soccer, also known as association football, is a team sport in which players attempt to score goals by passing and dribbling the ball down the field past opposing defenders, and kicking or heading the ball into the goal net, outwitting the defending goalkeeper or "goalie." Each team consists of ten outfield players (defenders, midfielders, and strikers) and a goalkeeper. Players from the opposing team may challenge the player in possession of the ball, but an illegal or foul tackle results in a penalty if a foul occurs inside the penalty area or a free kick if outside the penalty area. The round ball used in soccer is more easily controlled than the oval balls used in American, Canadian, and Australian rules football and in rugby. The result is a more "open" or flowing game which is played and watched by millions of people worldwide.

ASSISTANT REFEREE'S FLAG

Lightweight, brightly colored fabric

Handle with rubber grip

REFEREE'S EQUIPMENT

Red card

Yellow card

Referee's whistle

Stopwatch

SOCCER FIELD

150–300 ft
(46–91 m)

Goal line

Corner flag

Corner arc

Penalty area

Penalty mark

Referee

Halfway-line flag

Striker

Striker

Left midfielder

Central midfielder

Left back

Touch line

Central defender

Goal

Goalkeeper

Penalty arc

Assistant referee

Center circle

Center spot

Halfway line

Striker

Right midfielder

Right back

Central defender

Goal area

FIELD MARKINGS

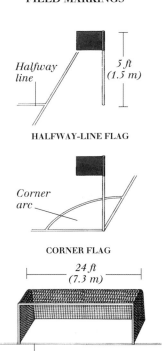

Halfway line

5 ft
(1.5 m)

HALFWAY-LINE FLAG

Corner arc

CORNER FLAG

24 ft
(7.3 m)

Goal line

GOAL

GOALKEEPER

Goalkeeper's shirt

Glove

Shin guard

Shorts

Sock

Soccer shoe

SOCCER UNIFORM

Open-neck collar

Lightweight, man-made fabric team shirt

Team logo

Manufacturer's logo

Ribbed welt

lotto

Motta

Sponsor's logo

MAKING A SOCCER BALL

Hole punched in panel for stitching

Mitre

F.I.F.A. APPROVED

MULTIPLEX

Waxed thread

Ball size number

Manufacturer's name

Edge cut to fit perfectly

5

Mitre

MULTIPLEX

8¹⁄₂–9 in (22–23 cm)

Needle

Bladder valve

Bladder made from latex rubber

Panels sewn together with ball inside out

Laminated panel

Long cotton sock

Club crest

Team shorts

Synthetic shoelace

Reebok

Interchangeable nylon stud

SOCCER SHOE

Football

IN AMERICAN AND CANADIAN FOOTBALL, the object of the game is to get the ball across the opponent's goal line, either by passing or carrying it across (a touchdown), or by kicking it between their goalposts (a field goal). An American football team has 11 players on the field at a time, although up to 40 players can appear for each side in a single game. The agile offense tries to score points, and the heavy hitting defense holds back the opposition. When in possession of the ball, a team has four chances (downs), to move it at least ten yards up the field to make a first down. The opposition gains possession if they fail, or by tackling and intercepting the ball. Canadian football is played on a larger field, with 12 men on each side. A team has only three chances, instead of four, to achieve a first down. Otherwise, the game is very similar to American football. Helmets, face masks, and layers of body padding are worn by the players for protection.

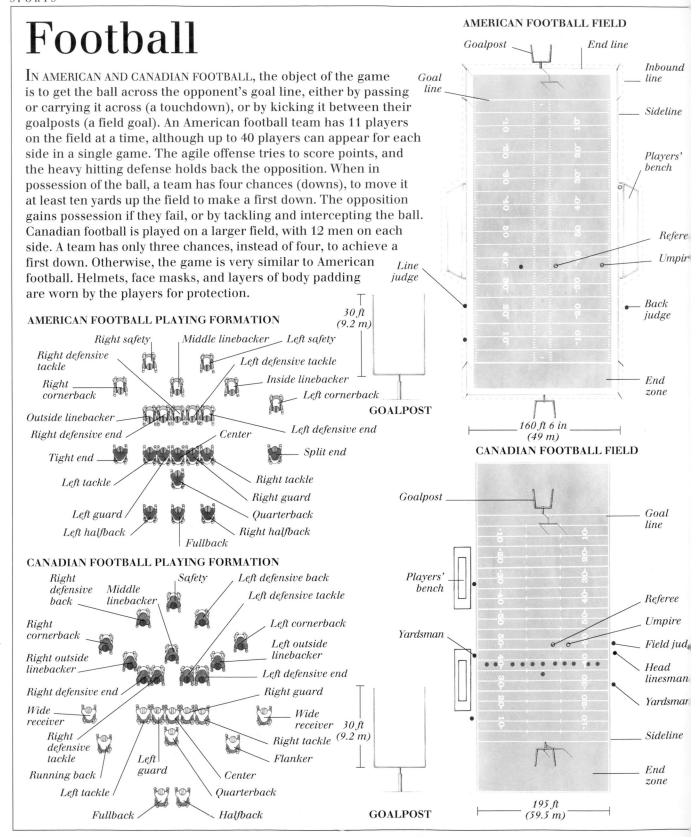

AMERICAN FOOTBALL FIELD

Goalpost

End line

Goal line

Inbound line

Sideline

Players' bench

Referee

Umpire

Back judge

End zone

160 ft 6 in (49 m)

AMERICAN FOOTBALL PLAYING FORMATION

Right safety
Middle linebacker
Left safety
Right defensive tackle
Left defensive tackle
Right cornerback
Inside linebacker
Left cornerback
Outside linebacker
Right defensive end
Center
Left defensive end
Tight end
Split end
Left tackle
Right tackle
Right guard
Left guard
Quarterback
Left halfback
Right halfback
Fullback

Line judge

30 ft (9.2 m)

GOALPOST

CANADIAN FOOTBALL FIELD

Goalpost

Goal line

Players' bench

Referee
Umpire
Field jud
Head linesman
Yardsman

Yardsman

Sideline

End zone

195 ft (59.5 m)

CANADIAN FOOTBALL PLAYING FORMATION

Right defensive back
Middle linebacker
Safety
Left defensive back
Left defensive tackle
Right cornerback
Left cornerback
Left outside linebacker
Right outside linebacker
Left defensive end
Right defensive end
Wide receiver
Right guard
Wide receiver
Right defensive tackle
Right tackle
Flanker
Running back
Center
Left guard
Left tackle
Quarterback
Fullback
Halfback

30 ft (9.2 m)

GOALPOST

PLAYER

Team logo · Helmet · Wrist pad · Player's number · Thigh pad · Pants · Tie to shoulder pads · Studded shoe

PROTECTIVE EQUIPMENT

11 in (28 cm) · Painted white ring · Lace · Brown pebbled leather · FOOTBALL

HELMET

Non-breakable plastic · Rubber-coated plastic · Shock absorber

SHOULDER PAD

Chest protector weight up to 5 lb 8 oz (2.5 kg)

RIB PADS · Strap ties onto shoulder pad

UPPER ARM PAD

BIKE

REFEREE'S SIGNALS

TIME OUT · TOUCHDOWN OR FIELD GOAL

PERSONAL FOUL · OFFSIDE OR ENCROACHMENT

HOLDING · ILLEGAL MOTION

FIRST DOWN · PASS INTERFERENCE

ELBOW PAD

Foam-sponge filling · Tail bone pad · HIP PAD

FINGERLESS GLOVE

Screw-in stud · Rigid plastic covering · THIGH PAD

FOOTWEAR · Fold-over leather tongue · PANTS · KNEE PAD

527

Australian rules and Gaelic football

VARIETIES OF FOOTBALL have developed all over the world and Australian rules football is considered to be one of the roughest versions, allowing full body tackles although participants wear no protective padding. Two teams of 18 players play on a large, oval pitch. Players can kick or punch the ball, which is shaped like a rugby ball, but cannot throw it. Running with the ball is permitted, as long as the ball touches the ground at least once every ten meters. The full backs defend two sets of posts. Teams try to score goals (six points) between the inner posts or behinds (one point) inside the outer posts. Each game has four quarters of 25 minutes, and the team with the most points at the end of the allotted time is the winner. In Gaelic football, an Irish version of soccer (see pp. 524–525), a size 5 association football is used. Each team can have 15 players on the field at a time. Players are allowed to catch, fist, and kick the ball, or dribble it using their hands or feet, but cannot throw it. Teams are awarded three points for getting the ball into the net, and one point for getting it through the posts above the crossbar. Gaelic football is rarely played outside of Ireland.

START OF PLAY

Field umpire · Center circle

SCORING

GOAL (6 POINTS)

BEHIND (1 POINT)

AUSTRALIAN RULES FOOTBALL FIELD

Goal · Goal umpire · Full back
Right full back · Left full back
Center halfback · Left halfback
Right halfback · Rover
Follower · Center square
Follower · Center circle · Left center (wing)
Right center (wing) · Field umpire
Center · Left half forward
Right half-forward · Left full forward
Center half-forward · Full forward
Right full forward · Boundary line · Goal umpire

445–610 ft (135–185 m)

21 ft (6.4 m)
Goalpost
21 ft (6.4 m)
Behind post
Behind line
Goal line
Goal square
GOALPOSTS

10 ⅞ in (27.5 cm)
Lace
SHERRIN
Leather covering
AUSTRALIAN RULES FOOTBALL

AUSTRALIAN RULES FOOTBALL SKILLS

RUNNING WITH THE BALL

KICKING

TACKLING

TAKING A MARK

PASSING THE BALL

AUSTRALIAN RULES FOOTBALL UNIFORM

Australian Football League logo

Team colors

Sleeveless team guernsey

Sock

Shorts

GAELIC FOOTBALL PITCH

Corner flag

Goalkeeper

Goal umpire

Goal area

Right fullback

Left fullback

Fullback

Right halfback

Left halfback

Center halfback

Center flag

Linesman

Linesman

Left midfielder

Right midfielder

Midfield line

Referee

Right half-forward

Left half-forward

Right full-forward

Center half-forward

Full forward

Left full-forward

260–295 ft
(80–90 m)

CONTROLLING THE BALL

SCORING IN GAELIC FOOTBALL

GOAL (3 POINTS)

POINT (1 POINT)

8 ¹/₂–9 in
(22–23 cm)

21ft
(6.4 m)

Goalpost

Crossbar

Parallelogram

GOAL

oneills
all-ireland

GAELIC FOOTBALL

Rugby

RUGBY IS PLAYED WITH AN OVAL BALL, which may be carried, thrown, or kicked. There are two codes of rugby, both played at amateur and professional levels. Rugby Union is played by two teams of 15 players. They can score points in two ways: by placing the ball by hand over the opponents' goalline (a try, scoring four points) or by kicking it over the crossbar of the opponent's goal (a conversion of a try, scoring two points; a penalty kick, scoring three points; or a dropkick, scoring three points). Rugby League developed from the Union game but is played by 13 players. In League games, a try scores four points; a conversion scores two points; a drop goal scores one point, and a penalty kick scores two points. Scrummages occur in both codes when play stops following an infringement.

RUGBY UNION SCRUMMAGE

Scrum-half
Loose-head prop
Hooker
Tight-head prop
Flanker
Flanker
Lock forward
Lock forward
Number 8

RUGBY LEAGUE SCRUMMAGE

Blind-side prop
Hooker
Open-side prop
Scrum-half
Second-row forward
Second-row forward
Loose forward

RUGBY UNION GOALPOST

18 ft (5.5 m)
Upright
Crossbar
Protective padding
9 ft 10 in (3 m)

RUGBY LEAGUE GOALPOST

5.5 m (18 ft)
Upright
Crossbar
Protective padding

RUGBY UNION FIELD

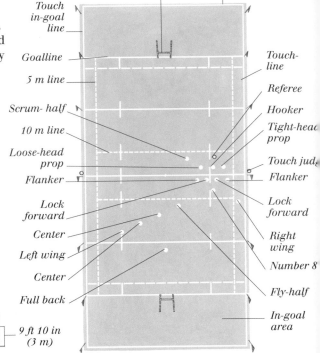

Goal
Dead-ball line
Touch in-goal line
Goalline
Touch-line
5 m line
Referee
Scrum-half
Hooker
Tight-head prop
10 m line
Touch judge
Loose-head prop
Flanker
Flanker
Lock forward
Lock forward
Center
Right wing
Left wing
Number 8
Center
Fly-half
Full back
In-goal area
225 ft (68 m) maximum

RUGBY LEAGUE FIELD

Goal
Dead-ball line
Touch in-goal line
Touch in-goal
Goal-line
Touch-line
10 m line
Hooker
Referee
Open-side prop
Touch judge
Touch judge
Blind-side prop
Second-row forward
Second-row forward
Scrum-half
Loose forward
Stand-off half
Left wing
Center
Center
Fullback
Right wing
225 ft (68 m) maximum

RUGBY SCORING AND SKILLS

GOAL

Goal line

TRY

PASS

PLACE KICK

FLYING TACKLE

Ankle support

Circular cleat

RUGBY BOOT

RUGBY UNION PLAYER

Shirt in team color

Knee high sock

Team shorts

Rugby boot

RUGBY UNION BALL

Laminated leather panel covered with textured plastic

Four-panel construction

GILBERT
REPLICA
SIZE:5
official ENGLAND replica ball

11–12 in (28–30 cm)

RUGBY LEAGUE BALL

Eight-panel construction

Laminated leather panel covered with textured plastic

TETLEY'S
GILBERT
official TETLEY replica ball
SIZE:5

11 in (28 cm)

Button-up collar

RUGBY LEAGUE SHIRT

Team crest

Short sleeve

RUGBY UNION SHIRT

GILBERT

BEDFORD BLUES

CITY

Team crest

Team color   **RUGBY SHIRTS**

Basketball

BASKETBALL IS A BALL GAME for two teams of five players, originally devised in
1890 by James Naismath for the Y.M.C.A. in Springfield, Massachusetts. The object
of the game is to take possession of the ball and score points by throwing the ball
into the opposing team's basket. A player moves the ball up and down the court by
bouncing it along the ground or "dribbling"; the ball may be passed between players
by throwing, bouncing, or rolling. Players may not run with or kick the ball, although
pivoting on one foot is allowed. The game begins with the referee throwing the ball
into the air and a player from each team jumping up to try and "tip" the ball to a
teammate. The length of the game and the number of periods played varies at
different levels. There are amateur, professional, and international rules. No game
ends in a draw. As many extra periods as necessary are played to break the tie.
In addition to the five players on court, each team has up to seven substitutes, but
players may only leave the court with the permission of the referee. Basketball is a
noncontact sport and fouls on other players are penalized by a throw-in awarded
against the offending team; a free throw at the basket is awarded when a player is
fouled in the act of shooting. Basketball is a fast-moving game, requiring both physical
and mental coordination. Skillful tactical play matters more than simple physical
strength and the agility of the players makes the game an excellent spectator sport.

BASKETBALL SKILLS

CHEST PASS

DRIBBLE

OVERHEAD PASS

LAY-UP SHOT

JUMP SHOT

LONG PASS

INTERNATIONAL BASKETBALL COURT

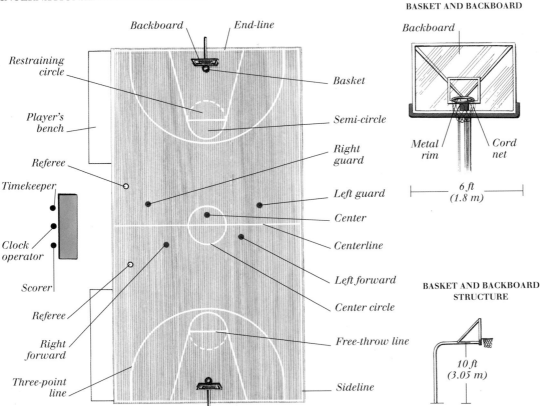

Backboard
End-line
Restraining circle
Player's bench
Referee
Timekeeper
Clock operator
Scorer
Referee
Right forward
Three-point line

Basket
Semi-circle
Right guard
Left guard
Center
Centerline
Left forward
Center circle
Free-throw line
Sideline

49 ft 3 in (15 m)

BASKET AND BACKBOARD

Backboard

Metal rim
Cord net

6 ft
(1.8 m)

BASKET AND BACKBOARD STRUCTURE

10 ft
(3.05 m)

ZONE DEFENSES

Point man

Free-throw line

1 – 2 – 2 ZONE

1 – 3 – 1 ZONE

9½–9¾ in (24–5 cm)

2 – 3 ZONE

AMERICAN BASKETBALL JERSEY

Cool, lightweight fabric

Team name

Player's number

LAKERS

32

48

BASKETBALL

Textured surface for good grip

Cushioned sole

Low heel profile

BASKETBALL SHOE

INTERNATIONAL REFEREE'S SIGNALS

TECHNICAL FOUL

INTENTIONAL FOUL

JUMP BALL

STOP CLOCK FOR FOUL

SUBSTITUTION

PERSONAL FOUL: NO FREE THROWS

TRAVELLING

ILLEGAL DRIBBLE

CHARGING WITH THE BALL

ONE FREE THROW

STOP CLOCK

Volleyball, netball, and handball

VOLLEYBALL, NETBALL, AND HANDBALL are fast-moving team sports played with balls, usually on courts with a hard surface. In volleyball, the object of the game is to hit the ball over a net strung across the center of the court so that it touches the ground on the opponent's side. The team of six players can take three hits to direct the ball over the net, although the same player cannot hit the ball twice in a row. Players can hit the ball with their arms, hands or any other part of their upper body. Teams score points only while serving. The first team to score 15 points, with a two-point margin over their opponent, wins the game. Netball is similar to basketball (see pp. 532–533), but is played on a slightly larger court with seven players instead of five. A team moves the ball toward the goal by throwing, passing, and catching it with the aim of throwing the ball through the opponents' goal net. Players are confined by their playing position to specific areas of the court. Team handball is one of the world's fastest games. Each side has seven players. A team moves the ball by dribbling, passing, or bouncing it as they run. Players may stop, catch, throw, bounce, or strike the ball with any part of the body above the knees. Each team tries to score goals by directing the ball past the opposition's goalkeeper into the net, which is similar to a soccer goal net (see pp. 524–525).

VOLLEYBALL SHOTS

OVERHAND SERVE　　SPIKE (SMASH)

UNDERHAND SERVE　　FOREARM PASS (DIG)

VOLLEYBALL KIT

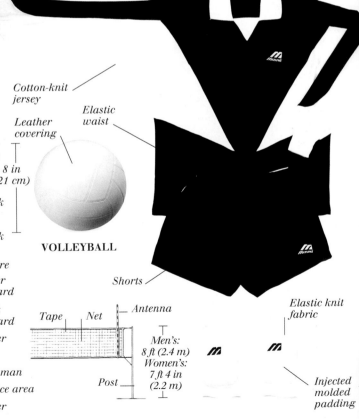

Team colors

Ribbed cuff

Cotton-knit jersey

Elastic waist

Leather covering

m (Mizuno)

Shorts

Elastic knit fabric

m (Mizuno)

Injected molded padding

KNEE PADS

VOLLEYBALL COURT

End line

Linesman

Linesman

Sideline

Players' bench

Referee

Scorer

Net

Left forward

Back zone

Left back

Linesman

29 ft 6 in (9 m)

Clear space

8 in (21 cm)

Attack zone

Attack line

VOLLEYBALL

Umpire

Center forward

Right forward

Center back

Linesman

Service area

Server

Tape　Net

Antenna

Men's: 8 ft (2.4 m)

Women's: 7 ft 4 in (2.2 m)

Post

VOLLEYBALL NET

NETBALL COURT

Mineral surface with non-slip tarmacadam coating

Goalpost

Back line

Goalkeeper

Goal circle

Defense third

Goal defense

Wing defense

Umpire

Scorer

ekeeper

Scorer

Center

Central third

Central circle

Goal attack

Transverse line

Wing attack

Goal third

Goalpost

Goal shooter

Sideline

50 ft (15.2 m)

NETBALL GOALPOST AND NET

Ring

Net

10 ft (3.5 m)

NETBALL

Rubber or leather covering

8¹/₄ in (22.4 cm)

NETBALL PASSES

CHEST PASS

UNDERARM PASS

SHOULDER PASS

BOUNCE PASS

HANDBALL COURT

Goal area

Goal

Net

Goal area line

Guide mark

Goal line

Penalty line

Free-throw line

Players' bench

Sideline

Secretary

Center line

Court referee

Timekeeper

Left wing

Right wing

Center back

Center forward

Left back

Right back

Goalkeeper

Goal-line referee

65 ft 6in (20 m)

HANDBALL

Leather covering

MEN'S: 7¹/₂ IN (18.8 CM)
WOMEN'S: 7 IN (17.5 CM)

HANDBALL SHOE

HANDBALL NET

Crossbar

6 ft 6 in (2 m)

Post

Goal line

HANDBALL SKILLS

OVERARM PASS

DRIBBLE

BOUNCE PASS

JUMP SHOT

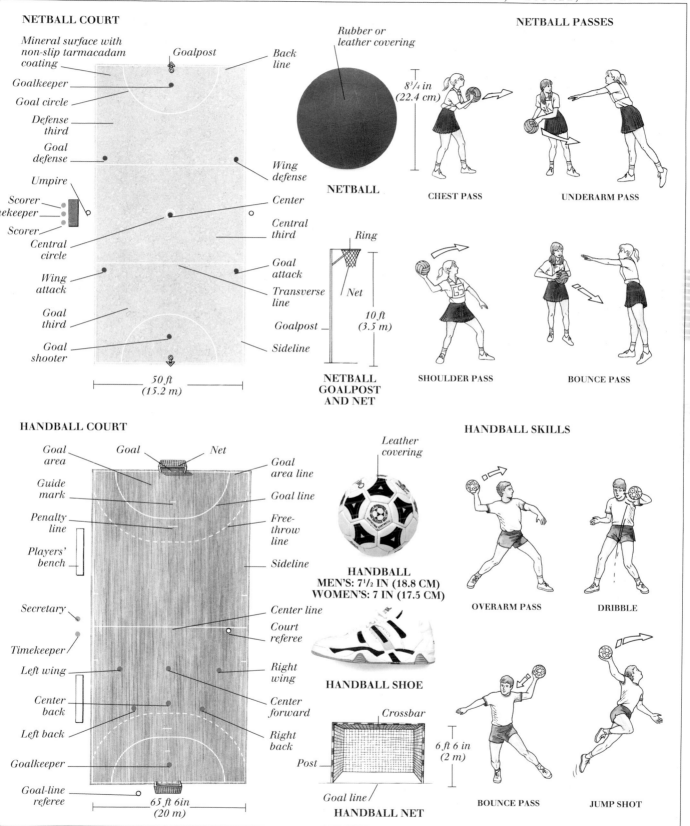

Baseball

BASEBALL IS A BALL GAME for two teams of nine players. The batter hits the ball thrown by the opposing team's pitcher, into the area between the foul lines. He then runs round all four fixed bases in order to score a run, touching or "tagging" each base in turn. The pitcher must throw the ball at a height between the batter's armpits and knees, a height which is called the strike zone. A ball pitched in this area that crosses over the home plate is called a "strike" and the batter has three strikes in which to try to hit the ball (otherwise he has "struck out"). The fielding team tries to get the batting team out by catching the ball before it bounces, tagging a player of the batting team who is running between bases with the ball, or by tagging a base before the player has reached it. Members of the batting team may stop safely at a base as long as it is not occupied by another member of their team. When the batter runs to first base, his teammate at first base must run onto second – this is called a force play. A game consists of nine innings and each team will bat once during an inning. When three members of the batting team are out, the teams swap roles. The team with the most runs wins the game.

BATTER'S HELMET

Plastic shell

Peak

Foam padding

Wire coated in strong nylon

Plastic-coated foam padding

CATCHER'S MASK

BASEBALL FIELD

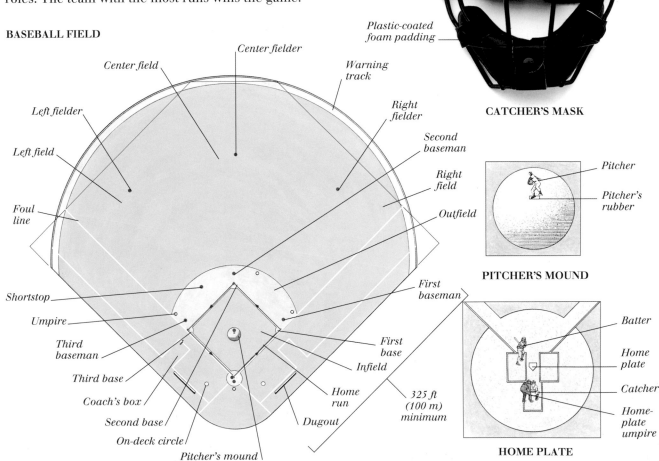

Center fielder

Center field

Warning track

Left fielder

Right fielder

Left field

Second baseman

Foul line

Right field

Outfield

Shortstop

First baseman

Umpire

First base

Third baseman

Infield

Third base

Home run

Coach's box

325 ft (100 m) minimum

Second base

Dugout

On-deck circle

Pitcher's mound

Pitcher

Pitcher's rubber

PITCHER'S MOUND

Batter

Home plate

Catcher

Home-plate umpire

HOME PLATE

MAKING A BASEBALL

Wool yarn

Rubber inner casing

Horsehide strip

Cork center

CUSHION CORK
9oz
TAIWAN
LEATHER COVER

Cooper
63

Cotton thread outer casing

Wool strand

Red outer stitching

BASEBALL EQUIPMENT

Webbed pocket

Fingers laced together

Strap

Thumb

STEERHIDE LEATHER

Palm

Leather stitching

Heel

FIELDER'S GLOVE AND BALL

PONY

Metal heel plate

AMERICAN BASEBALL SHOE

Metal toe plate

THE PITCHING SEQUENCE

THE WINDUP 1   **THE WINDUP 2**   **THE WINDUP 3**

THE WINDUP 4   **THE RELEASE**   **THE FOLLOW-THROUGH**

UMPIRING SIGNALS

BALL   **INFIELD**   **STRIKE**

FAIR BALL   **RUNNER IS SAFE**   **FOUL TIP**

Batter's helmet

Bat

Batting glove

Team shirt

Undershirt

Pants

Spiked shoe

BATTER

Hitting area

Official Baseball

Crest

3 ft 6 in (1.1 m) maximum

Handle

Knob

BAT

Cricket

CRICKET IS A BALL GAME PLAYED by two teams of eleven players on a pitch with two sets of three stumps (wickets). The bowler bowls the ball down the pitch to the batsman of the opposing team, who must defend the wicket in front of which he stands. The object of the game is to score as many runs as possible. Runs can be scored individually by running the length of the playing strip, or by hitting a ball which lands outside the boundary (six), or which lands inside the boundary but bounces or rolls outside (four); the opposing team will bowl and field, attempting to dismiss the batsmen. A batsman can be dismissed in one of several ways: by the bowler hitting the wicket with the ball ("bowled"); by a fielder catching the ball hit by the batsman before it touches the ground ("caught"); by the wicket-keeper or another fielder breaking the wicket while the batsman is attempting a run and is therefore out of his ground ("stumped" or "run out"); by the batsman breaking the wicket with his own bat or body ("hit wicket"); by a part of the batsman's body being hit by a ball that would otherwise have hit the wicket ("leg before wicket" ["lbw"]). A match consists of one or two innings and each innings ends when the tenth batsman of the batting team is out, when a certain number of overs (a series of six balls bowled) have been played, or when the captain of the batting team "declares" ending the innings voluntarily.

CRICKET STROKES

FORWARD DEFENSIVE STROKE

BACKWARD DEFENSIVE STROKE

ON-DRIVE

OFF-DRIVE

PULL

HOOK

SQUARE CUT

LEG GLANCE

POSSIBLE FIELD POSITIONS FOR AN AWAY SWING BOWLER TO A RIGHT-HANDED BATSMAN (IN RED) AND OTHER FIELD POSITIONS

Long on
Umpire
Long off
Boundary line
Bowler
Deep mid-wicket
Non-striking batsman
Mid-on
Silly mid-on
Extra cover
Forward short leg
Mid-off
Square leg
Silly mid-off
Deep square leg
Cover
Square-leg umpire
Point
Batsman
Gulley
Long leg
Third man
Leg slip
Second slip
Wicket-keeper
First slip
Fine leg
Sight screen

CRICKET PITCH

Wicket-keeper
Batsman
Wicket
Bowling crease
66 ft (20 m)
Bowler
Return crease
Umpire
Non-striking batsman

CRICKET BALL AND WICKET

Leather skin
Seam
BALL
Bail
WICKET
Stump

MAKING A BAT HANDLE

Sarawak cane

Twine wrapped around handle

Rubber strip

LAMINATING THE WOOD

BINDING THE HANDLE

MAKING A BAT BLADE

V-shaped splice

Kiln-dried willow

SEASONING THE TIMBER

Blade planed by hand

CUTTING THE SPLICE

PROTECTIVE CLOTHING

Slit in leather for greater flexibility

Padding protects knuckles from injury

Dimpled rubber improves grip

Polycarbonate shell with cloth covering

Mesh covering for ventilation

Wrist strap

Peak

Foam cheek-piece for comfort and good fit

Protective plastic ear piece

BATTING GLOVE

WICKET-KEEPER'S GLOVES

HELMET

ADDING THE HANDLE TO THE BAT

Rubber grip

Grip rolled onto handle

Shoulder of bat

Handle glued into splice

Scoop

Toe of the bat shaped

FITTING THE HANDLE

GRAY·NICOLLS

PLACEMENT POWER

Sanded and polished bat

FINISHING TOUCHES

Bat

BATSMAN

Padded glove

Cap

Wristband

White shirt

White sweater

Stripes in team colors

Thigh pad under white pants

Knee roll

Cricket shoe

Leg pad

Dimpled rubber sole

539

Field hockey, lacrosse, and hurling

ALL OVER THE WORLD, TEAM GAMES have evolved which require that a ball be struck or carried, and tossed at the end of a stick. Early forms of these games include hurling, shinty, bandy, and pelota. Field hockey is played by men and women: two teams of eleven players try to gain and keep possession of the ball and score goals by using the hockey stick to propel the ball into their opponents' goal net. Skills such as passing, pushing, or hitting the ball by slapping or lifting it in a flicking movement, and shooting at the goal are crucial. Field hockey is played indoors and outdoors on grass or synthetic fields. Lacrosse is played internationally as a 12-a-side game for women and as 10-a-side game for men. The women's field has no absolute boundaries but the men's has clearly defined sidelines and end lines. The ball is kept in play by being carried, thrown or batted with the crosse, and rolled or kicked in any direction. In men's and women's lacrosse, play can continue behind the marked goal areas. Similar skills are required in hurling – a Gaelic field game played on the same pitch as Gaelic football (see pp. 528–529), using the same goalposts and net. In hurling, the ball may be struck with or carried on the hurley and, when off the ground, may be struck with the hand or kicked. Goals (three points) are scored when the ball passes between the posts and under the crossbar; one point is scored when the ball passes between the posts and over the crossbar.

GOALKEEPER'S EQUIPMENT

Face mask

Hard shell

Air vent

HELMET

Strap

Rigid palm

Padded wrist

GAUNTLET

FIELD HOCKEY STICK AND BALL

STICK

Handle

Tape

Steam-bent ash head

Blade

Slazenger

3 ft (91 cm)

Stitched seam

$2^{3}/_{4}$–3 in (7–7.5 cm)

BALL

FIELD HOCKEY FIELD

Corner flag

Sideline

Center forward

Inside right

Right wing

Right half

Right back

Shooting circle

Goal

Penalty spot

Five yard mark

Goal line

Inside left

Left wing

Umpire

Center half

Left half

Left back

Goalkeeper

180 ft (55 m)

Protective overshoe

Padding protects toes against the hard ball

GOALKEEPER'S BOOT

Strap

7 ft (2.1 m)

FIELD HOCKEY GOAL

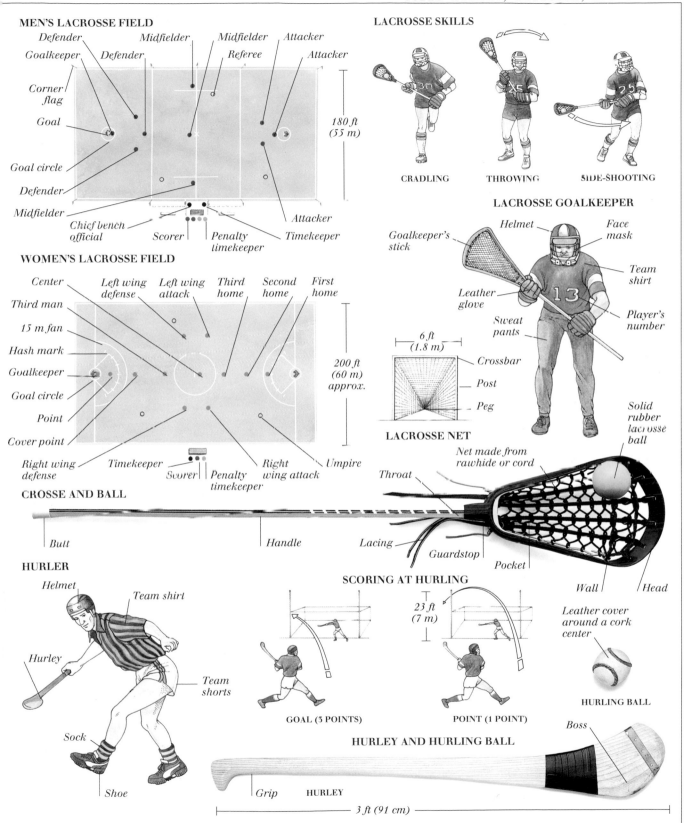

MEN'S LACROSSE FIELD

Defender
Midfielder
Midfielder
Attacker
Goalkeeper
Defender
Referee
Attacker
Corner flag
Goal
Goal circle
Defender
Midfielder
Chief bench official
Scorer
Penalty timekeeper
Attacker
Timekeeper

180 ft (55 m)

WOMEN'S LACROSSE FIELD

Center
Left wing defense
Left wing attack
Third home
Second home
First home
Third man
15 m fan
Hash mark
Goalkeeper
Goal circle
Point
Cover point
Right wing defense
Timekeeper
Scorer
Penalty timekeeper
Right wing attack
Umpire

200 ft (60 m) approx.

CROSSE AND BALL

Butt
Handle
Throat
Lacing
Guardstop
Pocket
Net made from rawhide or cord
Wall
Head

HURLER

Helmet
Team shirt
Hurley
Team shorts
Sock
Shoe

LACROSSE SKILLS

CRADLING
THROWING
SIDE-SHOOTING

LACROSSE GOALKEEPER

Goalkeeper's stick
Helmet
Face mask
Team shirt
Leather glove
13
Player's number
Sweat pants
Solid rubber lacrosse ball

6 ft (1.8 m)
Crossbar
Post
Peg

LACROSSE NET

SCORING AT HURLING

GOAL (3 POINTS)
23 ft (7 m)
POINT (1 POINT)

Leather cover around a cork center

HURLING BALL

Boss

HURLEY AND HURLING BALL

Grip
HURLEY
3 ft (91 cm)

Track and field

THE SPORTS that make up athletics are divided into two main groups: track events – which include sprinting, middle, and long distance running, relay running, hurdling, and walking – and field events which require jumping and throwing skills. Contests designed to test the speed, strength, agility, and stamina of athletes were held by the ancient Greeks over 4,000 years ago. However, the abolition of the Olympic Games in 393 AD meant that track and field events were neglected until the revival of large-scale competitions in the mid-nineteenth century. Modern stadiums offer areas reserved for the long jump, triple jump, and pole vault usually situated outside the running track. The javelin, shot, hammer, and discus are thrown within the track area. Most athletes specialize in one or two events but, in the heptathlon, women compete in seven events, held over two days: 200 m and 800 m races, 100 m hurdles, javelin, shot put, high jump, and long jump. In the decathlon, men compete in ten events over two days: 100 m, 400 m, and 1,500 m races, 110 m hurdles, javelin, discus, shot put, pole vault, high jump, and long jump.

FIELD EVENT EQUIPMENT

Steel wire

Head

Body

Swivel

HAMMER
16 LB (7 KG)

Metal rim

Center weight

Hammer handle

DISCUS
MEN'S: 4 LB 7 OZ (2 KG)
WOMEN'S: 2 LB 3 OZ (1 KG)

Rubber coating

Shot pellet filling

5 in (12.7 cm)

4 in (10 cm)

MEN'S SHOT
16 LB (7 KG)

WOMEN'S SHOT
8 LB 12 OZ (4 KG)

JAVELIN

Cord grip

Shaft

Tip

Men: 8 ft 6 in (2.6 m)
Women: 7 ft 6 in (2.3 m)

TRACK AND FIELD

Finishing post

Pole vault mat

Pole vault runway

100 m starting line

Finish line

Hammer circle

Javelin fan

Discus circle

Steeplechase water jump

Javelin runway

Lane

One lap is 400 m

Shot put fan

High jump fan

Shot put circle

High jump mat

Discus fan

Hammer fan

Triple jump takeoff board

Triple jump takeoff line

Indicator board

Triple jump runway

Long jump takeoff board

Landing area

TYPES OF SHOE

Hollow plastic tube

RELAY BATONS

Lightweight construction

Spiked sole

TRACK SHOE

Reflective side strip

Wedge heel

Air-cushioned sole

RUNNING SHOE

DISCUS THROW

Swing — *Shift* — *Twist* — *Release*

SHOT PUT

Crouch — *Shift* — *Release* *Thrust* — *Release*

HAMMER THROW

Swing — *Entry* — *Lift* — *Release*

JAVELIN THROW

Withdrawal stride — *Halfturn* — *Step* — *Drive forward* — *Release*

LONG JUMP

Takeoff — *Flight* — *Hitch kick* — *Stretch* — *Landing*

Takeoff board

TRIPLE JUMP

Takeoff — *Hop* — *Skip* — *Jump*

Takeoff board

Land on foot used for takeoff

Land on opposite foot

HIGH JUMP

Approach — *Takeoff* — *Drive* — *Arch* — *Landing*

POLE VAULT

Plant — *Takeoff* — *Hang* — *Rock-back* — *Push-pull* — *Handstand* — *Release* — *Landing*

Racket sports

PROTECTIVE EYEWEAR

THE OBJECT OF ALL RACKET SPORTS is to make shots the opponent cannot return. Games are played by two players (singles) or four players (doubles). Racket shape and size is tailored to each sport, but all rackets are constructed of wood, plastic, aluminum, or high-performance materials such as fiberglass and carbon graphite. Racket strings are usually synthetic, although natural gut is still used. Tennis is played on a court divided by a low net. Opposing players serve alternate games. At least six games must be won to gain a set, and two or sometimes three sets are needed to win a match. Tennis courts may be concrete, grass, clay, or synthetic, each surface requiring a different style of play. Badminton is an indoor sport that is played with light, flexible rackets and a birdie on a court with a high net. Players can score points only on their serve. The first to reach 15 points (11 points for women's singles) wins the game. Two games are needed to win a match. Squash and racketball are both played in enclosed courts. One player hits the ball against the front wall, and the other tries to return it before it bounces on the floor more than once. Squash rackets have smaller, rounder heads and stiffer frames than badminton rackets. International courts are wider than those in the U.S., where a much harder ball is used. Squash games are played to nine points (international) or 15 points (U.S.). In racketball, players use a ball that is larger and bouncier than a squash ball. The racketball racket is thick and sturdy, with a large head, short handle, and a strap that loops around the wrist. Points can be won only when serving, and the first player to reach 21 points wins.

TENNIS RACKET

Synthetic string
Frame
Head
Logo
Throat
Grip
Butt

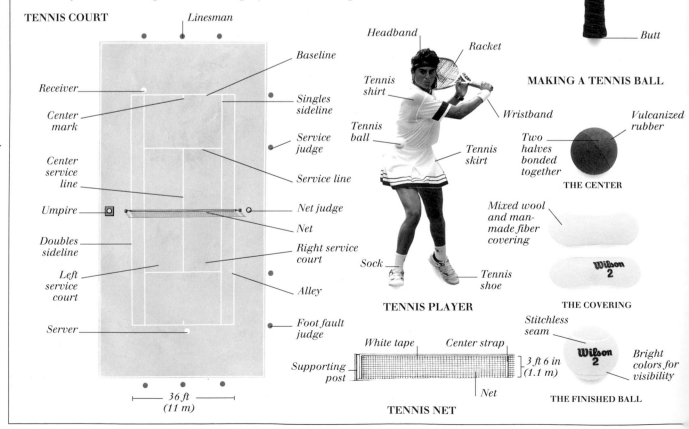

TENNIS COURT

Linesman
Baseline
Receiver
Singles sideline
Center mark
Service judge
Center service line
Service line
Umpire
Net judge
Net
Doubles sideline
Right service court
Left service court
Alley
Server
Foot fault judge

36 ft (11 m)

TENNIS PLAYER

Headband
Racket
Tennis shirt
Wristband
Tennis ball
Tennis skirt
Tennis shoe
Sock

MAKING A TENNIS BALL

Vulcanized rubber
Two halves bonded together

THE CENTER

Mixed wool and man-made fiber covering

THE COVERING

Stitchless seam
Bright colors for visibility

THE FINISHED BALL

TENNIS NET

White tape
Center strap
Supporting post
Net
3 ft 6 in (1.1 m)

BADMINTON RACKET AND SHUTTLECOCK

Synthetic string

Flexible frame

Shaft

BIRDIE

Feather crown

Handle

Cork tip

RACKET

BADMINTON COURT

Service judge

Receiver

Doubles sideline

Singles sideline

Linesman

Umpire

Net

Short service line

Server

Alley

Back boundary line

Long service line (doubles)

20 ft (6 m)

White tape

Post

5 ft (1.5 m)

Net

BADMINTON NET

SQUASH RACKET AND SQUASH BALLS

Protective strip

Frame

Synthetic strings

Logo

Open-throat head

Shaft

Handle

RACKET

SQUASH BALLS

YELLOW DOT (VERY SLOW)

WHITE DOT (SLOW)

RED DOT (FAST)

BLUE DOT (VERY FAST)

RACKETBALL RACKET, BALL, AND GLOVE

RACKET

Synthetic string

Frame

Logo

Throat

Short handle

Leather treated to make it sticky

Wrist strap

RACKETBALL

GLOVE

AMERICAN SQUASH COURT

Outer boundary line

Front wall

Service line

Side-wall line

Floor

Telltale

Half-court line

Side wall

Short line

Service box

Receiver

Server

Left service court

Right service court

18 ft 6 in (5.6 m)

INTERNATIONAL SQUASH COURT

Outer boundary line

Front wall

Service line

Tin

Floor

Side-wall line

Side wall

Short line

Service box

Half-court line

Server

Left service court

Right service court

Receiver

21 ft (6.4 m)

RACKETBALL COURT

Front wall

Side wall

Service line

Server

Service zone

Service box line

Receiving line

Service line

Center court

Floor

Receiver

20 ft (6 m)

545

Golf

GOLF BALL AND TEE

THE GAME OF GOLF was first played in Scotland some 400 years ago. Players are required to hit a ball, using a wooden or iron club, from a smooth level point or teeing ground, down the fairway, and onto a putting green where the target hole is located. The fairway is a strip of clear land along which there are natural hazards – such as ponds and streams, man-made hazards – such as bunkers (sand pits), and rough (areas of uncut grass). Championship golf courses have 18 holes. The object of the game is to hit the ball into each hole in turn, and to complete the "round" using as few strokes as possible. Players may compete individually or in teams, playing the course together in groups of two, three, or four. The two basic forms of competition are match play and stroke play. In match play, the side winning the majority of holes over a certain number of rounds wins the match. In stroke play, the winner is the player who finishes a certain number of rounds having made the fewest strokes.

GOLF BALL WITH BALATA SURFACE

Dimpled surface

Wound yarn

Liquid

Balata cover

Membrane to contain liquid

Water obstacle

Putting green

Dog-leg hole

Elevated green

Bridge

Putting green

Pond

Clubhouse

Hole

Bunker

Teeing ground

Practice area

Pathway

Rough

Fairway

AUGUSTA NATIONAL GOLF COURSE, AUGUSTA, GEORGIA

Screen of trees

A TYPICAL HOLE

Teeing ground

Water obstacle   Bridge   Fairway   Wood   Rough

546

MAKING A WOODEN CLUB

Close grain of wood

Streamlined back

Plastic insert on face

Sand, stain, and varnish finish

Persimmon wood

Slot cut for plate

Metal sole plate protects the wood

Outline of head

RAW MATERIAL

CREATING THE BASIC SHAPE

ADDING THE LEAD WEIGHT

THE FINISHED CLUB HEAD

RANGE OF WOODEN CLUBS

10 degree loft

15 degree loft

21 degree loft

DRIVER

3-WOOD

5-WOOD

30 degree loft

34 degree loft

38 degree loft

42 degree loft

46 degree loft

50 degree loft

56 degree loft

5-IRON

6-IRON

7-IRON

8-IRON

9-IRON

PITCHING WEDGE

SAND WEDGE

RANGE OF IRON CLUBS

22 degree loft

26 degree loft

3-IRON

4-IRON

GOLF ACCESSORIES

GOLF SCORE RECORD

BALL MARKERS

SCORECARD AND PENCIL

GOLF TEES

PITCHMARK REPAIRER

PRACTICE BALL

Spiked sole

LIGHTWEIGHT SHOE

Flag pole or pin

Green

Bunker (sand pit)

PUTTER, WOOD, AND IRON

WOOD

Textured vulcanized rubber grip

IRON

PUTTER

Shaped pistol grip

Stainless steel shaft

Steel shaft

Steel shaft

33 in (85 cm)

37 in (97 cm)

43 in (109 cm)

Neck

Neck

Angled neck

Face

Heel

Heel

Toe

Toe

Toe

Groove

Sole

Heel

Blade

Archery and shooting

TARGET SHOOTING AND ARCHERY EVOLVED as practice for hunting and battle skills. Modern bows, although designed according to the principles of early hunting bows, use laminates, fiberglass, dacron, and carbon, and are equipped with sights and stabilizers. Competitors in target archery shoot over distances of 100 ft (30 m), 165 ft (50 m), 230 ft (70 m), and 300 ft (90 m) for men, and 100 ft (30 m), 165 ft (50 m), 200 ft (60 m), and 230 ft (70 m) for women. The closer the shot is to the center of the target, the higher the score. The individual scores are added up, and the archer with the highest total wins the competition. Crossbows are used in match competitions over 33 ft (10 m), and 100 ft (30 m). Rifle shooting is divided into three categories: smallbore, bigbore, and air rifle. Contests take place over a variety of distances and further subdivisions are based on the type of shooting position used; prone, kneeling, or standing. The Olympic biathlon combines cross-country skiing and rifle shooting over a course of approximately 12$\frac{1}{2}$ miles (20 km). Additional magazines of ammunition are carried in the butt of the rifles. Bigbore rifles fitted with a telescopic sight can be used for hunting and running game target shooting. Pistol shooting events, using rapid-fire pistols, target pistols, and air pistols, take place over 33 ft (10 m), 82 ft (25 m), and 165 ft (50 m) distances. In rapid-fire pistol shooting, a total of 60 shots are fired from a distance of 82 ft (25 m).

CROSSBOW AND BOLT

Laminated fiberglass bow

Bolt

Bolt rest

1$\frac{3}{4}$ in (45 mm)

CROSSBOW TARGET

Sight

Stirrup held between feet when drawing bow

Hardwood laminate limb

Dacron string

Sight

MODERN BOW

Pressure button

Grip

V-bar stabilizers

Magnesium riser

Plastic fletch

Nock

Forearm guard

Finger hole

Aluminum shaft

BRACER

FINGER TAB

Strap

Wristband

ARCHER'S GLOVE

Waistband

Velcro fastening

Accessory pouch

Weight

ARCHERY EQUIPMENT

QUIVER

SMALLBORE
BIATHLON RIFLE

Rifle sight without
magnifying lens

Fore sight

Barrel

Trigger

0.22 in (5.6 m)
caliber bullet

Trigger
guard

Magazine

Extra magazine
stored in rifle butt

6 in
(155 m)

SMALLBORE
FREE RIFLE
TARGET FOR
165 FT (50 M)
RANGE

BIGBORE
HUNTING RIFLE

Bolt
handle

Bolt

Telescopic sight

Open sight

Open sight

0.3 in
(7.62 mm)
calibre
bullet

Sling fixing point

39 in
(1 m)

BIGBORE RIFLE
TARGET FOR
1000 FT (300 M)
RANGE

AIR PISTOL

Cocking
lever and
barrel

Wooden grip
shaped to fit
the hand

Piston

6 in
(155 mm)

AIR-PISTOL
TARGET FOR
33 FT (10 M)
RANGE

TARGET PISTOL

Back sight

Fore sight

Hammer

Firing
pin

Sight
pin

7³/₄ in
(197 mm)

Sight ring
attachment

Magazine

0.35 in
(9 mm)
calibre
bullet

PISTOL
TARGET FOR
60 FT (18 M)
RANGE

Trigger

Air-pistol
pellet

Nock

FIELD ARROW

Metal tip

Feathering

Wooden shaft

Straw butt

White inner
2 points

Aluminum
longrod stabilizer

Blue outer
5 points

Yellow inner 10
points (bull's-eye)

ARCHERY TARGET

Ice hockey

ICE HOCKEY IS PLAYED by two teams of six players on an ice rink, with a goal net at each end. The object of this fast, and often dangerous, game is to hit a frozen rubber puck into the opposing team's net with an ice hockey stick. The game begins when the referee drops the puck between the sticks of two players from opposing teams, who face off. The rink is divided into three areas: defending, neutral, and attacking zones. Players may move with the puck and pass it to one another along the ice, but the puck should not travel more than two zones across the rink markings. A goal is scored when the puck entirely crosses the goal-line between the posts and under the crossbar of the goal. A team may field up to 20 players although only six players are allowed on the ice at one time; substitutions occur frequently. Each game consists of three periods of 20 minutes, divided by breaks of 15 minutes.

GOALKEEPER

Helmet
Face mask
Throat protector
Butt end
Team shirt
Pants
Catch glove
Blocking pad
Goalkeeper's pad
Skate
Blade
Goalkeeper's stick
Heel
Blade

ICE HOCKEY RINK

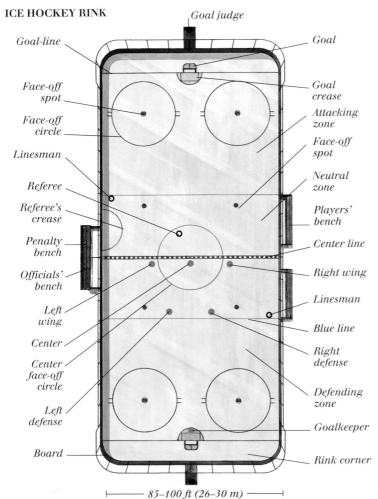

Goal judge
Goal-line
Goal
Face-off spot
Goal crease
Face-off circle
Attacking zone
Linesman
Face-off spot
Referee
Neutral zone
Referee's crease
Players' bench
Penalty bench
Center line
Officials' bench
Right wing
Left wing
Linesman
Center
Blue line
Center face-off circle
Right defense
Left defense
Defending zone
Board
Goalkeeper
Rink corner

|— 85–100 ft (26–30 m) —|

THE FACE OFF

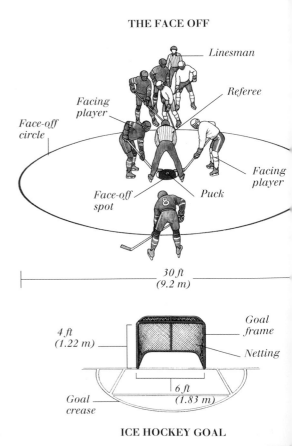

Linesman
Facing player
Referee
Face-off circle
Facing player
Face-off spot
Puck

30 ft (9.2 m)

4 ft (1.22 m)
Goal frame
Netting
6 ft (1.83 m)
Goal crease

ICE HOCKEY GOAL

GOALKEEPER'S HELMET

Customized paint

Face guard

Chin protection

PLAYER'S BODY ARMOR

Air vents

Rigid plastic shell

Manufacturer's logo

Chin strap

Foam padding

PLAYER'S HELMET

ICE HOCKEY STICKS

GOALKEEPER'S STICK

MADE IN FINLAND

OUTFIELD PLAYER'S STICK

SHOULDER AND CHEST PADDING

Shoulder padding

ELBOW PADS

TORSPO

Pro 5000

TORSPO

Pro 5000

4 ft 9 in (147 cm)

DR
Daignault - Rolland
4355M
DÉFENSE-PRO-DEFENCE

Strap

Chest padding

DR
gnault
LAND
3075N
GRAND / LARGE

TORSPO
20

Wrist protection

Heavy padding

Flexible gusset

Rigid finger cap

GLOVE

LEG PROTECTOR

Rigid plastic casing

Knee protection

16.5" 43cm CENTURION-J

Thick foam backing

Wide lower shaft

TORSPO

Thin shaft

TORSPO

Vulcanized rubber

3 in (7.62 cm)

FROZEN PUCK

Ankle support

Leg pad

Safety heel tip

Blade

SKATE

Puck stopper

15 in (39 cm)

12 1/2 in (32 cm)

Thick blade

Heel

Alpine skiing

COMPETITIVE ALPINE SKIING is divided into four disciplines: downhill, slalom, giant slalom, and super-giant slalom (Super-G). Each one tests different skills. In downhill skiing, competitors race down a slope marked out by control flags, known as "gates," and are timed on a single run only. Competitors wear crash helmets, one-piece Lycra suits, and long skis with flattened tips to minimize air resistance. Slalom and giant slalom skiers negotiate a twisting course requiring balance, agility, and quick reactions. Courses are defined by pairs of gates. Racers must pass through each pair of gates to complete the course successfully. Competitors are timed on two runs over different courses, and the skier who completes the courses in the shortest time wins. The equipment and protective guards used by slalom skiers are shown opposite. In Super-G races, competitors ski a single run that combines the technical challenge of slalom with the speed of downhill. The course requires skiers to complete medium-to-long radius turns at high speed, and contain up to two jumps. Clothing is the same as for downhill, but slightly shorter skis are used.

DOWNHILL SKIER

Ski goggles · Helmet · One-piece lycra ski suit · Wrist strap · Ski pole · Basket · Ski boot · Safety binding · Tail · Ski glove

ALPINE SKI SLOPE COURSES

Downhill start · Downhill racing control flag · Super-G start · Pine forest · Giant slalom start · Giant slalom gate · Slalom start · Slalom gate · Safety barrier · Finish line

SKI BOOT

Polyamide inner boot · Tongue · Upper cuff · Upper strap · Adjusting catch · Buckle · Power bar · Tension control · Sole · Lower shell of boot · Heel grip

SAFETY BINDING

Toe piece · Heel piece · Blind release lever · Wing · Anti-friction pad · Housing · Release adjustment screw · Base plate · Brake arm

SLALOM CLOTHING AND EQUIPMENT

GOGGLES

Elastic strap
Anti-glare lens

SLALOM HELMET

Hard nylon shell
Padding
Strap
Chin guard

SKI GLOVE

Extended cuff
Wrist strap
Rigid pad for hand protection
Double-knit wool and polyester fabric

High collar

Adjustable shoulder strap

Ribbed cuff

Zip pocket

Front zip fastening

Waterproof fabric

Cuff fits over ski boot

PADDED SKI PANTS

PADDED SWEATER

HAND GUARD

Moulded polypropylene

LEG GUARD

Tough polypropylene shell deflects the shaft of the slalom gate

Velcro strap

SLALOM SKI POLE

Wrist strap
Grip
Shock-absorbing platform under boot
Edge
Shaft
Basket

74–80 in (188–203 cm)

SLALOM SKI

Tail
Tail
Tip

Equestrian sports

EQUESTRIAN SPORTS HAVE TAKEN place throughout the world for centuries: events involving mounted horses were recorded in the Olympic Games of 642 BC. Show jumping, however, is a much more recent innovation, and the first competitions were held at the beginning of the 1900s. In this sport, horse and rider must negotiate a course of variable, unfixed obstacles, making as few mistakes as possible. Show-jumping fences consist of wooden stands, known as standards or wings, that support planks or poles. Parts of the fence are designed to collapse on impact, preventing injury to the horse and rider. Judges penalize competitors for errors, such as knocking down obstacles, refusing jumps, or deviating from the course. Depending on the type of competition, the rider with the fewest faults, most points, or fastest time wins. There are two basic forms of horse racing – flat races and races with jumps, such as steeplechase or hurdle races. Thoroughbred horses are used in this sport, because they have great strength and stamina and can achieve speeds of up to 40 mph (65 kph). Jockeys wear silks – caps and jackets designed in distinctive colors and patterns which help identify the horses. In harness racing, the horse is driven from a light, two-wheeled carriage called a sulky. Horses are trained to trot and to pace, and different races are held for each of these types of gait. In pacing races, the horses wear hobbles to prevent them from breaking into a trot or gallop. Breeds such as the Standard-bred and the French Trotter have been developed especially for this sport.

SHOW-JUMPING SADDLE

High cantle
Deep seat
Pommel
Forward-cut flap
Knee roll

SHOW-JUMPING FENCES

Standard
Foot
Plank

UPRIGHT PLANKS

Standard
Foot
Pole

UPRIGHT POLES

Back pole
Standard
Foot
Pole

TRIPLE BAR (STAIRCASE)

Standard
Pole
Foot

HOG'S-BACK

Pillar
Wooden block painted to resemble a brick

WALL

Hard hat
Browband
Throat-latch
Rein
Riding jacket
Jodhpurs
Cheek-piece
Show-jumping saddle
Hindquarters
Dock
Running martingale
Noseband
Brushing boot
Sheepskin numnah
Girth
Stirrup iron
Riding boot
Gaskin
Hock joint
Hoof
Fetlock joint
Pastern
Coronet

SHOW-JUMPING HORSE WITH RIDER

RACING SADDLE

Cut-back head

Cantle

Surcingle loop

Lightweight steel stirrup-iron

Forward-cut flap

Rawhide stirrup-leather

RACING SILKS

Plain cap

Spotted cap

Quartered cap

Plain sleeve

Plain sleeve

Striped jacket

Plain jacket

Spotted sleeve

Jacket with sash

Paddock

Finish line

Clubhouse

Grandstand

Dirt track

Home stretch

Clubhouse turn

Far turn

Grass track

Tote board

Start of straight

Barrier

Back stretch

SARATOGA RACE COURSE, SARATOGA, NEW YORK

Brow band

Rosette

Check piece

Bridle

Noseband

Driving saddle

Rein terret

Shaft

Crupper

Cap covered with racing silk

Goggles

Quartered racing silk jacket

Whip

Rubber bit-guard

Driving rein

Lightweight harness

Thimble

Girth

Seat

Over-reach boot

Belly band

Stirrup

Racing sulky

Pacing hobble

Pneumatic tire

Wheel

HARNESS RACING WITH A STANDARD-BRED HORSE

Disk covering spokes

Judo and fencing

COMBAT SPORTS ARE BASED ON THE SKILLS used in fighting. In these sports, the competitors may be unarmed – as in judo and boxing – or armed – as in fencing and kendo. Judo is a system of unarmed combat developed in the East. Translated from the Japanese the name means "the gentle way." Students learn how to turn an opponent's force to their own advantage. The usual uniform is loose white pants and a jacket, fastened with a cloth belt. The color of belt indicates the student's level of expertise, from white-belted novices to the expert black belts. Competitions take place on a mat or "shiaijo," 30 or 33 ft (9 or 10 m) square in size, bounded by "danger" and "safety" areas to prevent injury. Competitors try to throw, pin, or master their opponent by applying pressure to the arm joints or neck. Judo matches are strictly monitored, and competitors receive points for superior technique, not for injuring their opponent. Fencing is a combat sport using swords, which takes place on a narrow piste or strip 46 ft (14 m) long. Competitors try to hit specific target areas on their opponent with their sword or foil while avoiding being touched themselves. The winner is the one who scores the greatest number of hits. Fencers wear uniforms made from strong white material, which affords maximum protection while allowing freedom of movement, steel mesh masks with padded bibs to protect the fencer's neck, and a long white glove on their sword hand. Fencing foils do not have sharpened blades, and their tips end in a blunt button to prevent injuries. Three types of swords are used – foils, épées, and sabres. Official foil and épée competitions always use an electric scoring system. The sword tips are connected to lights by a long wire that passes underneath each fencer's jacket. A bulb flashes when a hit is made.

JUDO HOLDS AND THROWS

SIDE FOUR QUARTER HOLD

SINGLE WING

BODY DROP

ONE ARM SHOULDER THROW

SHOULDER WHEEL

SWEEPING LOW THROW

STOMACH THROW

KNEE WHEEL

JUDO KIT

JUDO MAT

52 ft 6 in
(16 m)

Judge

Scorer

Holding
timekeeper

Timekeeper

Danger area — Contestant

Drawstring

Contestant

Referee

Contest
area

Safety
area

Cotton
pants

Black belt — Heavy-duty
cotton jacket

FENCING STRIP

Rear limit line

46 ft (14 m)

Sabre and épéé warning line

Scorer

Electrical scoring apparatus

Center line

President

Timekeeper

On-guard line

Body wire

Reel

FENCING TARGET AREAS

SABREUR

FOILIST

EPEEIST

FENCING EQUIPMENT

Steel wire mesh

Padded bib

MESH MASK

Woven metal thread

METALLIC JACKET

Cuff

GAUNTLET

Glove

TARGET AREAS ON THE UPPER BODY

Mask

Wire mesh

Bib

Tierce

Sixte

Gauntlet

Seconde

Octave

Metallic over-jacket

Fencing shoe

Under plastron

Quinte

Quarte

Prime

Septime

Knickers

Stocking

THE SABRE

THE FOIL

Martingale

THE EPEE

Button

Blade

PARTS OF THE SWORD

Guard

Leather pad

Tang

Alternative pistol-grip handle

Brass screw

Steel foil pommel

Swimming and diving

SWIMMING GOGGLES

SWIMMING WAS INCLUDED in the first modern Olympic Games in 1896 and diving events were added in 1904. Swimming is both an individual and a team sport and races take place over a predetermined distance in one of the four major categories of stroke – freestyle (usually front crawl), butterfly, breaststroke, and backstroke. Competition pools are clearly marked for racing and anti-turbulence lane lines are used to separate the swimmers and help keep the water calm. The first team or individual to finish the race is the winner. Competitive diving is divided into men's and women's springboard and platform (highboard) events. There are six official groups of dives: forward dives, backward dives, armstand dives, twist dives, reverse dives, and inward dives. Competitors perform a set number of dives and after each one a panel of judges awards marks according to the quality of execution and the degree of difficulty.

STYLES OF DIVES

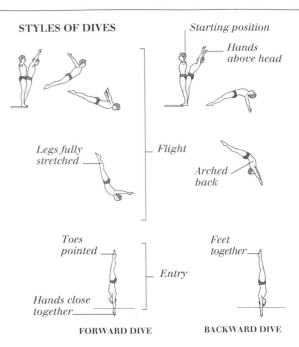

Starting position

Hands above head

Legs fully stretched

Flight

Arched back

Toes pointed

Entry

Feet together

Hands close together

FORWARD DIVE

BACKWARD DIVE

SWIMWEAR

Latex rubber molds to shape of head

CAPS

Rubber-covered wire

NOSE CLIP

Molded rubber

EARPLUG

High neckline

Man-made stretch fabric

Drawstring

High-cut leg

Strong seam

SWIMSUIT

TRUNKS

SWIMMING POOL

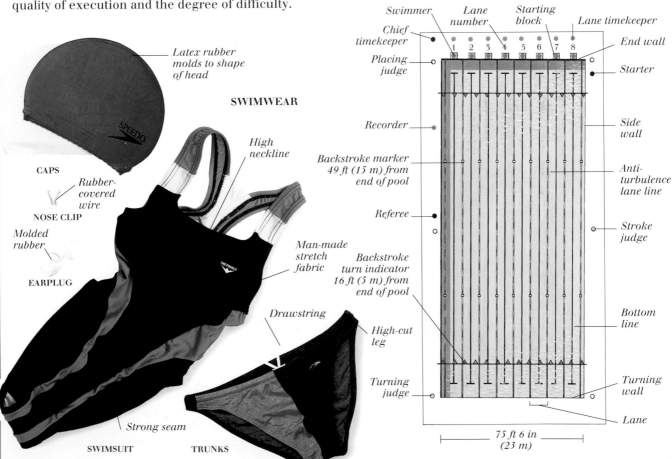

Swimmer

Lane number

Starting block

Lane timekeeper

Chief timekeeper

Placing judge

End wall

Starter

Recorder

Side wall

Backstroke marker 49 ft (15 m) from end of pool

Anti-turbulence lane line

Referee

Stroke judge

Backstroke turn indicator 16 ft (5 m) from end of pool

Bottom line

Turning judge

Turning wall

Lane

75 ft 6 in (23 m)

Perfectly steady armstand

Arms spread wide apart

Pike position

Height of dive

Pike position

Hands touch toes

Arms and legs align throughout flight and entry

Body and legs straighten for flight and entry

Shoulders fall backward for vertical entry

Feet lift up for straight entry

ARMSTAND DIVE

TWIST DIVE

REVERSE PIKE DIVE

INWARD PIKE DIVE

FRONT CRAWL

Flutter kick

Arm pulls like a paddle

Arrowlike position

Body rolls on a central axis

FULL BODY STRETCH

LOWER ARM PULL

STREAMLINED ARM ENTRY

SIDE-TO-SIDE BODY ROLL

BREASTSTROKE

Straight leg

Knees together

Elbows tucked in

Arm fully extended

BODY GLIDE

DOUBLE ARM PULL

SQUEEZING THE WATER

FROG KICK

BACKSTROKE

Little finger enters first

Arm comes up straight

Recovering hand

Shoulder exits water first

BODY ROLL

PULLING THROUGH

STRAIGHTENING OUT

SHOULDER LIFT

BUTTERFLY

Palm turned outward

Legs ready to kick down

Head clears the water

Shoulders power the stroke

CATCHING THE WATER

DOUBLE ARM PULL

KICKING DOWN

WHOLE BODY UNDULATION

Kayaking, rowing, and sailing

WATERBORNE SPORTS are as varied as the crafts used. There are two disciplines in rowing; sweep rowing, in which each rower has one oar, and sculling, in which rowers use two oars. There are a number of different Olympic and competitive rowing events for both men and women. The number of rowers and weight classes vary. Some rowing events use a coxswain; a steersman who does not row but directs the crew. Kayaks are used in straight sprint and slalom races. Slalom races take place over a course consisting of 20 to 25 gates, including at least six upstream gates. In yacht racing, competitors must complete prescribed courses, organized by the race committees, in the shortest possible time, using sail power only. Olympic events include classes for keel boats, dinghies, catamarans, and windsurfers.

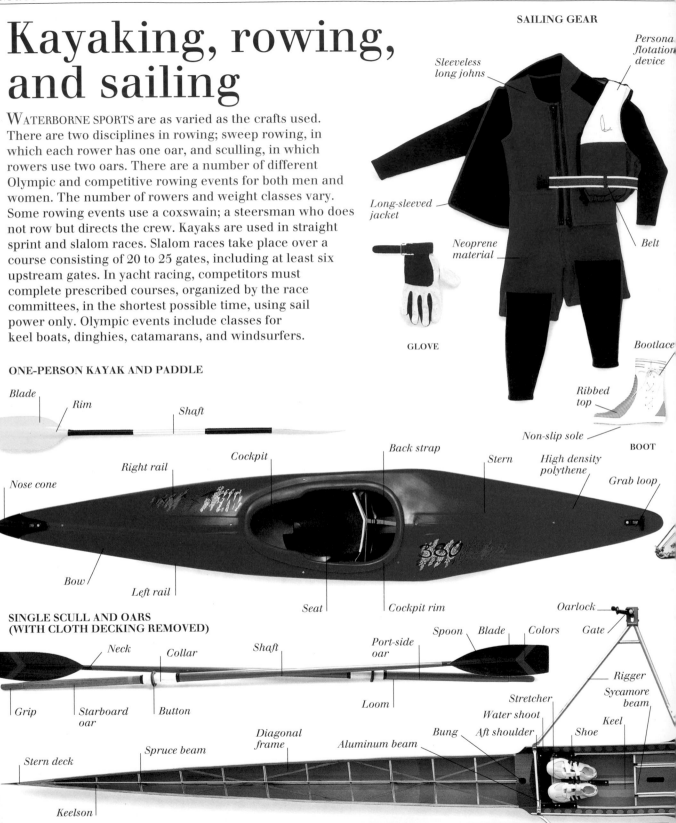

SAILING GEAR

Sleeveless long johns

Personal flotation device

Long-sleeved jacket

Neoprene material

Belt

GLOVE

Bootlace

Ribbed top

Non-slip sole

BOOT

ONE-PERSON KAYAK AND PADDLE

Blade

Rim

Shaft

Right rail

Cockpit

Back strap

Stern

High density polythene

Grab loop

Nose cone

Bow

Left rail

Seat

Cockpit rim

SINGLE SCULL AND OARS (WITH CLOTH DECKING REMOVED)

Oarlock

Spoon   Blade   Colors   Gate

Neck   Collar   Shaft   Port-side oar

Rigger

Sycamore beam

Grip   Starboard oar   Button   Loom

Stretcher

Water shoot

Bung   Aft shoulder

Keel

Shoe

Stern deck

Spruce beam   Diagonal frame   Aluminum beam

Keelson

PERSONAL FLOTATION DEVICE

Backstrap/rescue strap

Reinforced seam

Neck opening

Whistle

Topping-up valve

Lanyard

Waistband

SAILING DINGHY

Mast

Boom

Rudder

Mainsheet

Standing rigging

Spreader

Bow

Stern

Tiller

Hiking strap

Centerboard

Cockpit

Shroud

Jib fairlead

Non-slip deck surface

Sliding track

Wheel

Sliding seat

Main deck

Saxboard

Wheel spacer

Hatch

Breakwater

Bowball

Bowclip

SCULLS

DOUBLE SCULL

SINGLE SCULL

SWEEP-ROWING BOATS

FOUR WITHOUT COXSWAIN

PAIR WITH COXSWAIN

PAIR WITHOUT COXSWAIN

EIGHT

FOUR WITH COXSWAIN

Angling

ANGLING MEANS FISHING WITH A ROD, reel, line, and lure. There are several different types of angling: freshwater coarse angling, for members of the carp family and pike; freshwater game angling, for salmon and trout; and sea angling, for sea fish such as flatfish, bass, and mackerel. Anglers use a variety of methods of catching fish. These include bait fishing, in which bait (food to allure the fish) is placed on a hook and cast into the water; fly fishing, in which a natural or artificial fly is used to lure the fish; and spinning, in which a lure that looks like a small fish revolves as it is pulled through the water. The angler uses the rod, reel, and line to cast the lure over the water. The reel controls the line as it spills off the spool and as it is wound back. Weights may be fixed to the line so that it will sink. Swivels are attached to prevent the line from twisting. When a fish bites, the hook must become embedded in its mouth and remain there while the catch is reeled in.

Keeper ring

Drag spindle

Handgrip

Disk drag

Drag washer

Disk spring

Gear retainer

Dual click gear

Retaining screw

Check pawl cover

Check pawl

Check slide

Check spring

REELS

Plate-nut

Spool-release button

Reel foot (reel scoop)

Click mechanism

Mechanical brake

Side plate

Centrifugal brake

Spool

Handle

Star drag

Level-wind system

BAITCASTER

Line

Handgrip

Reel

Unskirted spool

Reel foot (reel scoop)

Handle

Tension nut (drag adjustment)

Ratchet (anti-reverse device)

Bail arm

SPINNING REEL

HOOKS, SWIVELS, AND WEIGHTS

Eye

Shank

Gap

ANATOMY OF A HOOK

Bend

Throat

Point

Barb

TREBLE HOOK

ABERDEEN HOOK

REVERSED BEND HOOK

EXAMPLES OF BARREL SWIVELS

HILLMAN ANTI-KINK WEIGHT

FLY ROD AND REEL

Intermediate ring

TIP SECTION

Reel seat

Screw locking nut

Tip-top

Butt cap

Disk drag housing

Reel foot (reel scoop)

Line

Drag knob screw

Butt extension

Release lever

Spool screw

DragonFly 100

Disc Drag

Clicker plate

Drag knob

Spool cover

Line guide

Release spring

Spool-release button

ARTIFICIAL FLIES

DUNKELD WET FLY

Line guide cover

Body

Cheek

Tail

Head

Retaining screw

Hackle

Ribbing

Handle

ARTIFICIAL LURES

DEVON MINNOW

Fin

Eye

Treble hook

Swivel

Tulip mount

DEER HOPPER DRY FLY

Front hackle

Eye

Tail

JOINTED PLUG

Hook

Adjustable vane

Joint

Head

Wing

Treble hook

THE MODERN WORLD

Personal computer

PERSONAL COMPUTERS (PCs) fall into two main types: IBM-compatible PCs, known simply as PCs, and Apple Macintosh PCs, known as "Macs." They differ in the way files and programs, and the user's access to them, are organized, and programs must be tailored for each type. However, in most other respects, PCs and Macs have much in common. Both contain microchips, or integrated circuits, that store and process data. The "brain" of any PC is a chip known as the central processing unit (CPU), which performs mathematical operations in order to run program instructions and receive, store, and output data. The most powerful CPUs today perform over a billion calculations a second. Data can be input via CDs and other storage media, as well as via modems. Highly portable laptop PCs are also in widespread use. Most PCs are able to communicate with many other devices, from video cameras (see pp. 582–83) to personal digital assistants (see pp. 568–69).

APPLE POWER MAC G4 DUAL PROCESSOR

Liquid crystal display (LCD)

System unit

Keyboard

Mouse

REAR VIEW OF SYSTEM UNIT

Lockable cover latch

Headphone socket

Modem port

Speaker socket

Ethernet network

Firewire ports

Universal serial bus (USB) ports

Access covers for PCI expansion slots

FRONT VIEW OF SYSTEM UNIT

Carrying handle

CD/DVD drive

Cooling vent

Zip expansion bay

Power socket

Cooling vent

Security lock port

Power button

Reset button

Speaker

COMPONENTS OF APPLE POWER MAC G4 DUAL PROCESSOR

Carrying handle

Case

Power supply

Cooling fan

Hard disk drive

PCI expansion slots

Legal information

Motherboard

Backup battery

Processor card

HP PAVILION DV9000 NOTEBOOK

Liquid crystal display (LCD)

Left touchpad button

Right touchpad button

Touchpad scroll zone

Optical drive

Express card slot

SIDE VIEW OF HP PAVILION DV9000 NOTEBOOK

External monitor port

Network port

Digital media slot

Security lock port

S-video port

Expansion port

Modem port

Parallel printer ports

Universal serial bus (USB) port

Video card

Processor heat sink

Processor cooling fan

Modem

Internal power cable

Headphone socket

Temperature warning

Hand-held computer

PERSONAL DIGITAL ASSISTANTS (PDAs), or hand-held computers, are among the many small electronic devices that were first developed during the last years of the 20th century. Some PDAs have integral keyboards, and these are larger and heavier than their keyboardless counterparts, which can be easily held in one hand. The latter employ a combination of touch-screen technology and handwriting-recognition programs to receive instructions and data. In order to write data into the PDA screen with a stylus, users must usually learn to use a special alphabet that the computer understands. The contents of a PDA's memory need to be regularly backed up on to a PC. Besides basic functions, such as address book, calendar, and note pad, PDAs are increasingly absorbing elements of other devices, such as MP3 players (see pp. 586–587), Global Positioning System (GPS) receivers (see pp. 590–591), and cellphones (see pp. 588–589). Some can also access email and the Internet. A related product is the e-book reader, which uses "electronic paper" to mimic the appearance of ink and normal paper, providing a more comfortable reading experience. The screen reflects light, as does normal paper, and so can be read outside in daylight.

PALM M500 PDA

Power button/ backlight control/light-emitting diode (LED) indicator

Backlit liquid crystal display (LCD)

Applications launcher icon

Menu icon

Writing area

Calculator icon

Zoom in/out icon

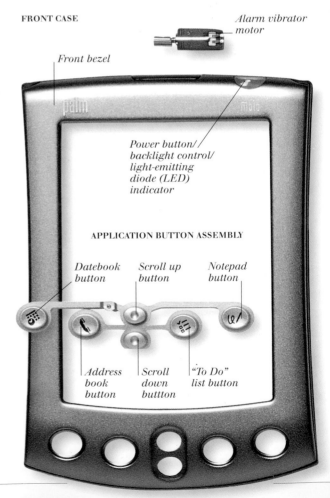

FRONT CASE

Alarm vibrator motor

Front bezel

Power button/ backlight control/ light-emitting diode (LED) indicator

APPLICATION BUTTON ASSEMBLY

Datebook button

Scroll up button

Notepad button

Address book button

Scroll down buttton

"To Do" list button

IREX ILIAD E-BOOK READER

Flipbar page turner

Book title

Connect key

Electronic paper display

Books archive key

Documents archive key

Notes key

Previous key

Confirm key

Next key

News archive key

Headphone connector

On/off switch

Travel hub connector

BOTTOM VIEW OF PALM M500 PDA

Datebook button

Scroll down butttton

"To Do" list button

Front case

Rear case

Address book button

HotSync™ connector

Notepad button

REAR CASE

Rear bezel

Accessory locator

Assembled in Hungary

HotSync™ connector slot

COMPONENTS OF A PALM M500 PDA

EXPANSION CARD

MAIN CIRCUIT BOARD

Reset button

Expansion card slot

Connectors

Power socket

Printed circuit board (PCB)

Writing tip

Underside of screen

STYLUS

BACK OF LCD ASSEMBLY

Rechargeable battery

Manufacturing code

Power supply to circuit board

Screen connector socket

PDA MOUNTED ON CRADLE

HotSync™ connector

Screen connector

palm

HotSync™ cradle provides connection to PC

Liquid crystal display (LCD) circuit board

Connector

HotSync™ button

Flatbed scanner

SCANNERS CONVERT physical images into electronic form, allowing them to be sent over the internet, displayed on a website, stored on a computer, and manipulated using specialized software. Scanners work by detecting and analyzing light reflected from an opaque image, such as a photographic print. Some can also scan photographic transparencies by analyzing light that has passed through the image. Flatbed scanners contain a unit, called the scan head, that contains a lamp, mirrors, a lens, and an array of CCDs (Charge-Coupled Devices). The carriage passes beneath the image; the lamp shines light onto or through the original; the mirrors reflect the light onto the lens, which focuses it onto the CCD array. Each CCD detects the brightness of light from a particular pixel (picture element) along a horizontal strip and converts this data into an electric signal. For color images, the light is usually passed through red, green, and blue filters and then directed to the CCD array so that it can be broken down into its component colors. This information is then converted to digital form. The quality of the image depends on its resolution, measured in dpi (Dots Per Inch).

EPSON PERFECTION 1650 SCANNER

Integrated transparency unit (TPU)

Glass plate

Start button and indicator light

Photo print button

Scan to email button

Scan to Web button

Power supply cable

Reflective document mat

Direct current (DC) inlet

TPU connector port

Lock

Inverter board

Lamp power supply connector

Shield plate

Panel board connector

Cover support

FILM AND SLIDE HOLDER

35mm-slide holder

35mm film strip holder

HOW A FLATBED SCANNER WORKS

Original image (photograph or artwork)

Lens focuses light onto CCD array

Glass plate

Lamp

The electronic image is converted to digital form and transmitted to a computer

Light beam is reflected from the original to a series of mirrors

Carriage is moved beneath the original by a stepper motor in a rapid series of tiny steps

CCD array builds up electric charges that vary according to the brightness of the light beam

UNDERSIDE OF SCAN HEAD COVER

COMPONENTS OF AN
EPSON PERFECTION
1650 SCANNER

TPU connector

Hinge

LID ASSEMBLY

*Underside of
lamp housing*

Glass plate

*Lens
assembly*

*Universal serial
bus (USB) port*

Ferrite core

*Integrated
transparency
unit (TPU)*

*Scan
head*

*Reflective
document
mat*

Mirror

FCC cable

*Carriage
shaft*

*FCC cable
slot*

UNDERSIDE OF COVER

Finger recess

*Underside
of control
panel*

OVERHEAD VIEW

*Idler
pulley*

*Control panel
circuit board*

THE EFFECT OF SCANNING AT DIFFERENT RESOLUTIONS

Pixel

15 DPI
Lowest resolution at
which you may scan.

72 DPI
Used for websites
and screen images.

300 DPI
Used for printing
books and magazines.

Airbus 380

CROSS-SECTION OF FUSELAGE

THE AIRBUS A380 WAS CONCEIVED in the early 1990s to compete with, and if possible replace, the Boeing 747. Work began in earnest on what was then called the A3XX in 1994. Its maiden flight was in April 2005. The A380's shape is subtly molded to minimize drag from its ovoid fuselage. The structure makes extensive use of composite materials, such as thermoplastics and GLARE (aluminum and fiberglass). Its four huge engines, the most powerful ever used on a plane, are surprisingly quiet. When carrying 550 passengers, it is claimed that the A380 will use only 3⁄5 gallon (2.9 liters) of fuel per passenger per 60 miles (100 km).

INTERIOR VIEW OF BUSINESS CLASS CABIN

Galley area

Personal lighting

Concealed lighting

Storage locker

Window blind

Reclining seat

Seat control panel

Aisle

folding foot rest

Obstruction light

Swept titanium fan blades

Vertical tailplane

GLARE upper fuselage

Horizontal tailplane

Company logo

Wing landing gear

FRONT VIEW

Split rudder for yaw control

Jupp-Reeselet winglet

Upper deck windows

Overwing emergency exit

A380

F-WWOW

APU exhaust

Horizontal tailplane

Tailcone fairing

Aft door

Belly fairing

Flap track fairings

Body landing gear

SIDE VIEW

INTERIOR VIEW OF GALLEY

Counter

Bar area

Storage unit

Nonslip flooring

COCKPIT

Engine warning display

Overhead control panel

Sun blind

Windshield

Folding table with integral keyboard

Primary flight display

Navigation display

Onbourd information terminal

Rudder pedal

Fly-by-wire side stick

Pylon forward fairing

Wing leading edge

Pilot's seat

Headrest

Flap track fairings

Air intake duct

Navigation light

Cursor control device (CCD)

Multifunction display

Seatbelt attachment point

System display

Power levers

Antenna

Fuselage

Upper deck passenger door

Main deck passenger door

Flightdeck door

Flightdeck windshield

A380 AIRBUS

Wing landing gear

Engine cowling

Sculpted wing-root fairing

Main deck windows

Nose landing gear

Inkjet printer

INKJET PRINTERS EXPEL ink droplets from hundreds of tiny jets, or nozzles, onto a medium, such as paper, to print an image. Each droplet corresponds to a single pixel (picture element). Black-and-white printers use only black ink, while color printers overprint combinations of the printing colors (cyan, yellow, magenta, and black) to create a full color range. The printhead containing the nozzles moves sideways across the paper, creating a line of pixels, before the paper moves slightly forward so the next line can be printed. Two basic methods are used to eject ink: thermal, in which ink is heated to form an expanding bubble that expels a droplet from the nozzle, and piezoelectric, in which an electric current expands a crystal causing it to push out the ink droplet. The printer shown here can print digital photographs directly from a memory card.

EPSON STYLUS PHOTO 895 COLOR INKJET PRINTER

Printer cover
Color ink-cartridge clamp
Black ink-cartridge clamp
Output tray
Output tray extension
Carriage drive belt
Settings display
Settings control panel
Power button
PC card adapter
Ink-cartridge replacement button
Roll paper manipulation button
Maintenance button

OVERHEAD VIEW WITH OUTER CASING REMOVED

Paper hopper
Head data cable support
Preview monitor socket
Motor assembly
Paper thickness adjust lever
Color ink-cartridge clamp
Spur gear
Head data cable
Paper output stacker
Black ink-cartridge clamp

Ink outlet hole
Color ink cartridge
Ink outlet hole
Black ink cartridge

INK CARTRIDGES

EPSON
PCMCIA adapter

PC CARD ADAPTER

PAPER FEED COMPONENTS

Attachment clip

ROLL PAPER HOLDER ADAPTER

ROLL PAPER HOLDER

Attachment clip

PAPER SUPPORT

OVERHEAD VIEW OF CASING

Left edge guide

Sheet feeder

Right edge guide

Printer cover

Preview monitor slot

Settings display

Photo select button

Cancel button

Start print button

Processing light

Setting select buttons

HOW A PIEZOELECTRIC INKJET PRINTHEAD WORKS

Uncharged piezoelectric crystal

Ink reservoir

Firing chamber

INKJET NOZZLE

Charged crystal expands, increasing pressure in reservoir

Ink droplet forced out of firing chamber by increased pressure in reservoir

DROPLET EJECTED

Ink sucked into reservoir by lowered pressure

Uncharged crystal contracts, lowering pressure in reservoir

CHAMBER REFILLED

The Internet

THE INTERNET CONSISTS OF TENS of thousands of computer networks linked together to form one huge global network, allowing any computer on one network to communicate with any computer on another. The two main services used on the Internet are email and the World Wide Web. Email allows text messages to be sent–along with attached computer files, images, or video clips, for example–to other computers on the Internet. The Web consists of billions of pages made up of digital files that are stored on computers across the world and can be viewed using a Web browser. The Web also provides interactive access to various services, for example banking and shopping.

Sender's Internet service provider (ISP) directs message into the Internet

Recipient's ISP receives message and stores it until retrieved by the recipient

Telephone line

Server guides message to its intended destination

HOW EMAIL WORKS

Screen displays email program

EMAIL SENDER

Modem encodes and sends message via the telephone line

Window controls

Inbox folder

Drafts folder

Sent mail folder

Deleted items folder

Junk mail folder

Personalized mail folder

Message display area

EMAIL ADDRESS

User name　*Domain name*

anna@merlin.provider.co.uk

Separator　*Country code*

EMAIL PROGRAM

Delete mail button　*Reply button*　*New mail button*

Sender's name　*Reply all button*　*Get mail button*

Search field

Font menus button

Font color button

DK (588 messages)

| | | | | | | | Q | |
| Delete | Junk | Reply | Reply All | Forward | New | Get Mail | Search | |

• ◆ From	Subject	Date Received	
Redwell, Laragh	FW: Birds BD153 templates	6 July 2006	12:26
St Louis, Susan	RE: Templates	6 July 2006	12:26
van Zyl, Miezan	Visual Dictionary	6 July 2006	10.07
Stradins, Ina			
van Zyl, Miezan			
St Louis, Susan			
Gilbert, Richard (DK)			
Farrow, Stephanie			
Upadhyay, Shefali			
St Louis, Susan			
Farrow, Stephanie			
van Zyl, Miezan			
St Louis, Susan			
Upadhyay, Shefali			
Upadhyay, Shefali			
Stradins, Ina			
St Louis, Susan			
Stradins, Ina			
Farrow, Stephanie			
St Louis, Susan			
St Louis, Susan			
van Zyl, Miezan			
Farrow, Stephanie			

New Message

| Send | Chat | Attach | Address | Fonts | Colors | Save As Draft |

To:
Cc:
Bcc:
Subject:

Signature: None

From: Ina Stradins
Subject: RE: Bird samples
Date: 7 July 2006 15:43:2
To: Hugh Schermuly
Return-Path: <Ina.Stradins@uk.d
Received: from punt3.mail.den
Fri, 07 Jul 2006 14:x
Received: from [194.217.242.2
1FyrYL-2W2knw-07
Received: from [80.82.96.144]

Save as draft button

Add address button

Add attachments button

Chat selector button

Send button

Address options button

Message area

EMAIL RECIPIENT

Modem

Email program on screen displays received message

Computer with email program installed

Mouse

Web browser displaying item link

RSS (REALLY SIMPLE SYNDICATION) FEEDS

Site icon

Feed name

Feed list

Pull-down edit menu button

News reader window

News item summary

Search field

Feed add button

STREAMED INTERNET VIDEO ON-SCREEN DISPLAY

Window controls

Program name

Window shade button

Screen

File status indicator

Seek bar

Rewind button

Play/pause button

Stop button

Previous file button

Next file button

Media guide button

Volume slider

Fast forward button

STREAMED INTERNET RADIO ON-SCREEN DISPLAY

Program display

Elapsed time display

Window controls

Status indicator

Pause/play control

Volume control

WEB PAGES

Browser menu with navigation buttons

Universal Resource Locator (URL), or web page address

Home page

Rollover button provides links to subsidiary page

Search field

Navigation area contains links to other parts of the site

Subsidiary page

Hyperlink text allows direct access to another web page or website

UNIVERSAL RESOURCE LOCATOR (URL) ADDRESS

Prefix

Page locator

http://www.dk.com/store_select.asp

Main website address

Electronic games

VIDEO GAMES HAVE BEEN around since the early 1970s. They are played on PCs, arcade machines, on TV using a home console, and on portable hand-held consoles. Players use devices such as joysticks and control pads with buttons to control movement and action on screen. The latest generation of consoles uses motion sensor technology to allow players to manipulate objects on screen by simply moving the controller. The game itself is stored in the form of digital information on CD, DVD, or microchip–which may be integral or stored in a removable cartridge–or on an internal hard disk. A central processing unit (CPU) (see pp. 566–567) is needed to process commands from the players, while specialized graphics chips are used to process the complex mapping and texturing functions that make modern games appear so realistic.

RIDGE RACER, FOR PSP

KAMEO: ELEMENTS OF POWER, FOR XBOX 360

COMPONENTS OF A SONY PSP

FRONT COVER ASSEMBLY

Right shoulder button

Square button

Triangle button

Action buttons actuator pad

X button

Circle button

Ribbon power cable

Ribbon data cable

LCD panel flexible wiring circuit

Wiring circuit shield

SONY PSP

Left shoulder button

Liquid crystal display (LCD)

Right shoulder button

Directional buttons pad

Action buttons pad

Memory stick access LED window

Power LED window

Wireless local-area network access LED window

Hold LED window

Analog thumb stick

Home button

Volume down button

Volume up button

Brightness adjustment button

Select button

Start button

Tone adjustment button

Liquid crystal display (LCD) panel

Button array

Button contact pad

AUDIO REMOTE CONTROL UNIT

Stereo audio jack

Remote control audio connector plug

Remote control printed circuit board

Front cover

Volume up button

Center play/pause/ forward/back button

Hold switch

Integrated circuit

Volume down button

Rear cover

Contact pad

HEADPHONE
ASSEMBLY

SONY PLAYSTATION 3

CONSOLE

Dual mold
top cover

Headphone
housing

In ear
headphone

Left shoulder
button

Piezo
speaker

Analogue
control stick

Action
buttons pad

CONTROLLER

Directional
buttons

Directional
buttons
actuator pad

Blu-ray drive
bay

Analog
thumb stick

BATTERY

Directional
buttons pad

USB port

Felt
washer

Motion sensor
on/off button

Select
button

Analog stick
printed wire
board

Removable
hard drive

Lithium-ion
rechargeable
battery

Battery
compartment
cover

MICROSOFT XBOX360

CONSOLE

Cooling
vent

Shoulder button
actuator pad

Wireless
sensor

Shoulder
button frame

Memory
unit port

Disc tray

Frame

Shoulder
button contact

Integrated
circuit

Optical
pickup

Internal power
connector

Shoulder button
ribbon cable

Guide
button

WiFi
antenna

External
power
connector

Connect
button

Speaker

Action
buttons

Universal
Media Disk (UMD)
drive traverse motor

UMD drive
ribbon cable

REAR PANEL AND
CIRCUIT BOARD

Button
contact
pad

"Ring of fire"
(online and game
status indicator)

Directional
buttons

CONTROLLER

Digital camera

FOR MORE THAN 200 YEARS, CAMERAS recorded pictures as chemical changes in silver-containing substances, on a strip of flexible, celluloid film. The digital camera records pictures in electronic form. At its heart is a specialized integrated circuit known as a charge-coupled device (CCD). This has millions of microunits known as pixels. It works in the opposite way to a miniature computer or TV screen. Instead of electric signals making pixels shine, when light hits a pixel it generates a tiny electrical signal, according to the light's color and brightness. The signals from the CCD's millions of pixels are analogue: they vary continuously in a wavelike fashion. They are converted by a microchip to digital codes of numbers, represented as on-off electronic pulses. The digital signals are processed and fed both to the in-camera memory chip, which holds a temporary version, and the memory stick, which can be removed to download its contents into a computer or television. The rest of the camera is similar to the traditional design.

FRONT VIEW OF SONY CYBER-SHOT DSC-P1 DIGITAL CAMERA

Program mode selector
Light level sensor
Viewing window objective lens aperture
Memory stick and battery recess
Finger grip
Flash unit
Lens cover
Lens bezel

LENS ZOOM AND FOCUS

CCD ribbon connector
CCD window
Lens mounting bracket
CCD board
CCD microchip
Drive gear access hole
Locating pin
Achromatic multilens
Lens inner barrel (zoom/focus)
Flash unit aperture
Viewing window objective lens aperture
Cyber-shot
SONY
SONY LENS / OPTICAL
Finger grip

FRONT PANEL

Zoom motor
0988
Drive pin

HOW A DIGITAL CAMERA WORKS

CCD turns light into electronic signals
Lens focuses light
Light from scene
Analogue signals
Analogue to digital converter microchip
Microprocessor
Digital signals
LCD screen
Memory stick
In-camera memory chip

REAR VIEW

Program selector
Macro button
Flash button
Viewing window
Screen display button
Program mode selector
Lens zoom in/out toggle
Cover for USB and recharger jack sockets
Speaker
On-screen menu selector
Image viewing screen
Screen light on/off
Volume up/down toggle

SONY

UNDERSIDE OF TOP PANEL

Shutter button
Display screen aperture
Program mode selector
Power on/off slider

Power on light
Display screen
Program mode selector control
Ribbon socket connector
Microphone

DISPLAY SCREEN AND TOP PANEL CIRCUIT BOARD

MEMORY STICK

Plastic body containing memory chip
Contact array

Fixed objective lens
Dual sliding zoom lens

VIEWING WINDOW ASSEMBLY

FRONT VIEW (COVER REMOVED)

Ribbon connector

Ribbon connector

INSIDE VIEW OF BACK PLATE ASSEMBLY

Memory stick and battery recess
Universal serial bus (USB) socket
Recharger jack socket
Zoom control microchip
CCD connector socket
Main ribbon loom socket

Universal serial bus (USB) plug

USB socket access hole
Image screen processor microchip
Rear of image viewing screen

BASE PLATE

Tripod screw socket

Digital video camera

A VIDEO CAMERA, OR CAMCORDER, records a scene as a sequence of 25 still images per second, along with sound. It comprises a camera to capture light from the scene, a viewfinder through which the scene may be viewed, a screen on which the recorded scene may be viewed, charge-coupled devices (CCDs) to convert the visual data into an electric signal, and a means of storing the signal. Digital video cameras convert the signal into digital form—a series of separate measurements of the initial analogue (continuously varying) signal. They record the digital signal on tape, hard disk, or DVD. Digital recordings can be copied accurately, whereas analogue recordings tend to "fade" with each copy.

SONY DIGITAL HANDYCAM

Accessory shoe

Viewfinder

Lock

Power switch

Memory stick slot

Cassette compartment lid

Liquid crystal display (LCD) panel

Battery release

Battery

SCREEN ASSEMBLY

LEFT SIDE ASSEMBLY

REAR ASSEMBLY

Ribbon connector

Underside of touch panel

Start/stop button

Power switch

Rear cabinet

Battery lock

Printed circuit board (PCB)

Power supply wiring

Power clip

Digital video jack cover

Outer cover

LCD panel open button

LCD circuit board

Ribbon connector

TAPE READER

Tape reading head

Cassette drive wheel

Microchip

Focus ring

Liquid crystal display (LCD) panel

Accessory shoe

Viewfinder

Start/stop button

Headphone jack

Memory stick slot

Viewfinder

Battery

Power cable

MAIN CIRCUIT BOARD

VIDEO CASSETTE

Video tape — *Outer case*

TOP ASSEMBLY

Ribbon connector

Microphone block

Microphone cover

Shoe accessory

LENS AND VIEWFINDER ASSEMBLY

Focus ring

Printed circuit board (PCB)

Viewfinder lens

Viewfinder sleeve

Viewfinder ring

Lens cap

CASSETTE COMPARTMENT ASSEMBLY

Frame

Cassette compartment cover

Base plate

Eject knob

Tripod mount

RIGHT SIDE ASSEMBLY

Speaker

A/V jack

MIC jack

Ribbon connector

Memory stick connector

Memory stick

Video jack

Cabinet underside

Video port cover

Memory stick slot

FRONT ASSEMBLY

Ribbon connector

Light-emitting diode

Window accessory

Cover front

Super nightshot control

Backlight control

Nightshot control

Photo control

Zoom control

Speaker

Display/ touch panel button

Focus ring

Focus control

Memory stick eject button

Handle attachment

Lens

Recording light

Home cinema

HOME CINEMA REPLICATES a real movie theater using visuals from a plasma wide-screen and surround sound from strategically sited loudspeakers. The source for sound and vision is a DVD (Digital Versatile Disc). Its player uses standard CD (Compact Disc) digital technology, but with a higher density of laser-read microscopic pits – more than 20 billion such pits in multi-level spiral tracks that, stretched out, would extend nearly 25 miles (40 km). Emerging technologies include Blu-ray and HD DVD, both of which fit much more data on their discs than standard DVDs, allowing High Definition video files to be stored. It is hard for the human ear to discern the direction of low-pitched sounds, so these emanate from a central bass speaker, often built into or below the screen unit. High-pitched sounds, the direction of which is easier to detect, emanate from mid- and high-frequency speakers positioned around the viewer. Plasma screens use fluorescent tube ("strip-light") technology. Tiny three-cell pixels, each about one millimeter across, contain red, green and blue phosphor chemicals and a gas mix. Where electric pulses coincide for a split second in the criss-cross matrix of wire electrodes, the gas energizes and emits ultraviolet light, which in turn makes the phosphor glow.

SONY BDZ_S77 BLU-RAY RECORDER

Display panel

Remote control

Control panel and disc tray cover

HOW SURROUND SOUND WORKS

DVD player under screen

Woofer (bass unit)

Plasma screen

Front left sound channel

Front right sound channel

Rear left sound channel

Region of most realistic sound reception

Rear right sound channel

WIDE-SCREEN PLASMA DISPLAY

Mid-gray bezel

Damped anti-shock swivel base

16:9 (width:height) screen proportions fit human field of vision

HOW A PLASMA SCREEN WORKS

Rear dielectric sandwich

Rear panel

Phosphor lining cell

Rear energized electrode

Front dielectric sandwich

Rear un-energized electrode

Red cell

Green cell

Cell barrier

Blue cell (glowing)

Pixel boundary

Inert gas in cell

Front energized electrode

Main screen

Anti-glare screen surface

Front un-energized electrode

INTERNAL VIEW OF SONY DAV-S300

AC electricity supply cord

Internal fuse overload protection

Voltage reduction and regulation circuits

Power transistors

Power transistor heat sink (dissipator)

DVD/CD drive turntable

DVD/CD laser-reader (within compartment)

Enclosed DVD/CD compartment

DVD/CD sliding tray

Tweeter speaker connectors

Woofer speaker connector

VCR (video cassette recorder) connections

Radio tuner antenna socket (FM)

Internal radio tuner antenna (AM)

Video input/output circuit board

Tuner settings memory microchip

Tuner/amplifier link cables

DVD/CD processor microchip

Display screen and control circuits

Display screen

Ribbon connectors transfer DVD/CD signals

Control buttons

Enter button activates menu choices

Volume control

Access slot in tray for reading underside of DVD/CD

FRONT VIEW

AC power on/off switch

DVD/CD sliding tray

Vibration-reducing damper foot

Remote control sensor

Display screen

Radio tuner FM/AM selector

Muting button

DVD/CD control buttons

Volume control

Headphones socket

Power button

Sleep button

TV power button

Function button

Display button

Previous/next track buttons

Play button

Enter button

DVD display button

Volume control

REMOTE CONTROL

Personal music and video

THE FIRST BATTERY-DRIVEN PORTABLE source of sound and music was the transistor radio of the 1950s. In the 1970s, the magnetic audio cassette tape allowed recordings to be played on portable tape players. Also, new metal alloys permitted the tiny but high-power magnets needed for lightweight earphones. In the 1980s, compact discs brought music into the digital era. Sony's MD, or minidisc, introduced re-recordable CDs that used magnetic and optical technology. From the mid 1990s, music could be stored in all-electronic digital form in a microchip, usually in the MP3 file format. These files can be transferred between devices and via the Internet. Today, a variety of portable media gadgets can record, play, and store video, photographs, and music in electronic form.

HARD DISK DRIVE COMPONENTS

Platter separating ring

Platter securing ring

Hard disk drive platter

HARD DISK DRIVE

Disc spindle motor

Head actuator

Actuator axis

Hard drive connector

Head position stepping motor

Magnetic read/write hea[d]

ARCHOS AV500 MOBILE VIDEO RECORDER

Remote control infrared sensor

Accelerate down button

Play/pause /resume button

Accelerate up button

Forward/ reverse, volume control, and directional buttons

Stop/escape/ off button

Up action button

Select action button

Down action button

Liquid crystal display (LCD) screen

Hard disk drive retaining clip

Hard disk drive connector

LTP400WQ-F02-00S

400WQ-F01

LTP400WQ-F02 REV.3

SCREEN AND BUTTON PANELS

LCD interface electronics

Flexible connector

Cable retract button

TELEVISION DOCKING POD

Pod case

APPLE iTUNES AND iPOD NANO

Play/pause button

Change visualizer settings button

iTUNES SCREEN

Create playlist button

Open equalizer window button

LCD interface buffer chip

LCD connector

Loudspeaker

Microphone

USB device connector

Crystal oscillator

USB computer connector

CIRCUIT BOARD AND REAR PANEL

Multi-connect jack

Power smoothing capacitor

MPEG-4 decoder chip

Switch

Switch assembly connector

Power supply inductor

Now Playing
9 of 12
The Journey
Fatboy Slim
Palookaville
3:37   -0:59

Display screen

Click wheel

Previous/rewind button

Menu button

Next/fast-forward button

Select/enter button

Play/pause button

iPOD NANO

Serial memory storage and time/date chip

Back-up battery

Programmable input/output (IO) chip

Digital signal microprocessor (DSP) chip

Dynamic random access memory (DRAM) chip

INTERCONNECTING CABLES

Scart adapter

Phono socket

USB adapter

Infrared transmitter

Top of recorder unit

HARD DISK DRIVE TRAY

Hard disk drive cover

Hard disk drive securing bracket

Right channel audio plug

Left channel audio plug

Video plug

USB plug

USB adapter

Cell- and smartphones

IN THE EARLY 1990S, THE MOBILE PHONE (or cellphone) was a rare luxury, but in recent years, it has outsold almost every other electrical gadget—as a professional tool, domestic convenience, and even a fashion accessory. Cellphones have also generally shrunk in size, due to improvements in rechargeable batteries, which now store more electricity for longer in a smaller package, and to smaller, more efficient electronics that use less electricity. A "cellphone" is basically a low-power radio receiver-transmitter, plus a tiny microphone to convert sounds into electrical signals, and a small speaker that does the reverse. When the cellphone is activated, it sends out a radio pulse that is answered by nearby mast transmitter-receivers. The phone locks onto the clearest signal and uses this while within range (the range of each transmitter is known as a cell). The phone continuously monitors signal strength and switches to an alternative transmitter when necessary. The phone's liquid crystal display (LCD) shows numbers, letters, symbols, and color pictures. Newer models have a larger screen for more complex color images, and commonly incorporate a camera, radio, and MP3 functionality. Smartphones, which are increasingly widespread, contain additional software and more may be bolted on. Smartphones typically offer Internet and email access, PDA-like functions (see pp. 568–569), and may even contain GPS navigation software.

NOKIA N93

Speaker · Secondary (videoconferencing) camera lens · Left (top) softkey · Display · Right (bottom) softkey · Light sensor · Infrared port · LED flash · System connector cover · Lanyard anchor · Camera lens · MiniSD (Secure Digital) card slot cover · Charging port

SIM CARD

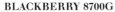

Microprocessor chip

REAR PLASTIC HOUSINGS

Loudspeaker · Battery door · Spring contacts for battery connection

BLACKBERRY 8700G

New message indicator · Scroll wheel · Shortcut key · End key · Delete key · Enter key · Shift key · Symbol key · Send/make call key · Alt key · Number lock key

HOW A CELLPHONE WORKS

Phone locks onto signals from local mast within home cell

Caller sends call signal to nearest cell tower

Recipient's land-line phone (fixed at wall socket or cordless with base-set) emits ring tone

Cells are smaller in areas where many calls occur simultaneously (cities, suburbs)

Phone out of signal range– no reception

Activated phone auto-switches to signals from next cell as it moves across cell boundary

Landlines (or tower-to-tower links) carry phone signals to local exchange

Local cellphone network exchange

Main telephone network exchange

Signals forwarded to non-cellphone

Recipient's cellphone emits ring tone

Signals forwarded to relevant cell for transmission

COMPONENTS OF A BLACKBERRY 8700G

Front plastic housing

Front speaker aperture

Screen lens

Keypad button aperture

FACIA

Rigid keypad mounting

KEYPAD ASSEMBLY

Mute button

SIM (Subscriber Identity Module) card holder

Navigation trackwheel

Escape/back button

Vibration alert motor

FRONT OF MAIN CIRCUIT BOARD

Front speaker connection

Headset socket

Microphone connection

QWERTY keypad

REAR OF MAIN CIRCUIT BOARD

Power button

Power button microswitch

Headset socket

Headset socket/ USB socket bezel

User-definable softkey

USB (Universal Serial Bus) socket

Internal antenna

Conductive pads for battery spring contacts

Active TFT (Thin Film Transistor) display

Keypad contact

Lithium-ion battery

Positive terminal

Negative terminal

BATTERY

Global positioning system

THE GLOBAL POSITIONING SYSTEM (GPS) is a network of 24 navigation satellites orbiting the Earth that people can use to pinpoint their position. The satellites orbit at a height of 12,500 miles (20,000 kilometers). A GPS receiver picks up signals from any of these satellites that are above the horizon. It uses information in each signal to work out how far away it is from the satellite. It can calculate its position on the Earth's surface when it has information from at least three satellites. A basic GPS receiver shows the latitude and longitude of its position on its screen. A more advanced receiver shows the position on a digital map. Some receivers display extra information, such the distance that has been traveled and the average speed of the vehicle in which the receiver is installed.

Cigarette lighter adapter and speaker cable

Antenna

GARMIN STREET PILOT III GPS

Page key

On/off and screen control button

Enter key

Quit key

Rocker pad

Menu key

Speak key

Find key

Route key

Zoom keys

Liquid crystal display (LCD) screen

HOW GPS WORKS

Satellite 1

Satellite 2

The receiver takes a reading of its distance from two satellites. The receiver is located along the plane where the two resultant spheres meet

Earth

Satellite 3

A signal from a third satellite defines two positions on that plane. The position on the Earth's surface is read as the correct location

IN-CAR MOUNTING BRACKET ASSEMBLY

MOUNTING BRACKET

QUICK-RELEASE BASE

Locking lever

Release catch

Ratcheted base

GARMIN GPS V

Speaker plug

Power plug

Adjustable antenna

Power backlight key

Rocker keypad

COMPONENTS OF A GARMIN STREET PILOT III GPS

Data plug

Antenna

Liquid crystal display (LCD) screen

Memory battery

Data plug socket

Main printed circuit board (PCB)

Rear case

USB PROGRAMMER ASSEMBLY

Shielded receiver

Data cartridge

Universal serial bus (USB) programmer

Front case

Liquid crystal display (LCD) assembly

Underside of control pad

SPARE FUSES

Vacuum cleaner

IN A CONVENTIONAL VACUUM CLEANER, an electric motor spins a fan that sucks in air carrying dust and debris. The air is forced through tiny pores in a dust bag, trapping most particles. In the 1990s, James Dyson's dual cyclone "bagless" design did away with the dust bag—and the reduced airflow caused by clogging of its pores. An electrically-driven fan creates a partial vacuum within the machine. Air is forced at more than 60 miles per hour past a rotating brush that loosens dirt. The airflow passes along the wand and hose to the outer part of a cylinder-shaped bin. As the air whirls around at 180 miles per hour (like a miniature hurricane or cyclone), centrifugal force flings larger particles outward, to fall to the bin's base. The air then passes through perforations into the cone-shaped, narrower inner bin, where a second cyclone spins even faster, almost 600 miles per hour, flinging off even smaller particles. The now almost-clean air exits via two microporous filters.

Wand handle and brushbar controls

Upper wand

Lower wand

Motorized brushbar floor tool

CYCLONE ASSEMBLY

Air intake from hose

Inner cyclone cone

DYSON DC05 MOTORHEAD

Air exit to bin/cyclone cover

Hose electricity connector

Hose slider

WASHABLE PRE-MOTOR FILTER

Microporous filter

Bin upper seal seating

Perforated shroud

Bin handle clip

Central retaining screw

Hose slider seating

Hose electricity supply

Post-motor micropore filter

Filter rim casing

DUST COLLECTION BIN

Inner bin fin

Bin upper seal

Bin base

Bin handle

Bin lower seal

Inner bin dust collection area

Polycarbonate plastic bin body

Bin cover retaining clip

OVERHEAD VIEW OF DYSON DC05 MOTORHEAD

Suction reduction control

On/off and brushbar motor control

Hose cuff electrical link

Flexible hose shrouding

Tool or wand cuff

Accessory holder

Electricity connector to brushbar motor

Hose base

Main motor casing

Hinged bin/cyclone cover

Air intake to bin/cyclone cover

Bin cover retaining clip

dyson

Bin cover handle

Motor air intake

Wheel guard and flex rewind

Main wheel

ACCESSORIES

Tool/brushbar connector

Nozzle

Textured scraper

STAIR TOOL

CREVICE TOOL

Brush tool articulation

Wand telescopic link

UPHOLSTERY BRUSH

WAND

Flexible hose shrouding

MOTORIZED BRUSHBAR FLOOR TOOL

Wand/handle connector

Handle connector

Brushbar drive motor cover

Roller

Sole plate roller

Brushbar drive belt cover

Rotating brushbar

Sole plate

Iron and washer-dryer

IN THE DAYS BEFORE WASHING MACHINES, laundry was done by hand—washed in a barrel, squeezed in a roller-mangle, hung on a line, and smoothed with an iron heated on the hob or stove. In the 1880s electrically heated irons were one of the first home electrical appliances. Today's iron still applies heat, sometimes moistened with steam, to dampen and flatten garment fibres. Machines with electric heaters and motors took the strain out of washing from the 1910s. Up to the 1960s, three machines were needed to wash, spin, and dry. Now clothes are swirled in a rotating ribbed tub of hot water, then spun fast to throw off most of the water, before slowly tumbling in electrically heated air to dry—all in one appliance.

FRONT VIEW OF A MIELE WASHER-DRYER

Detergent tray

Control panels

Door

Filter access flap

COMPONENTS OF A STEAM IRON

Steam control knob

Spray nozzle aperture

Spray barrel

Spray pump

Spray nozzle

Nose

Steam barrel

Steam release activator

Nose

Temperature and steam control dial

Handle

Water tank

Soleplate surround

Heating elements

Pilot light

Mains spade contacts

Earth wire

Pilot light supply wire

SIDE VIEW OF STEAM IRON

Flex kink guard

Steam control knob

Spray and steam knobs

Temperature and steam control dial

Water tank

Soleplate

Securing screw mounting

Heel moulding

Mains flex clamp

Mains supply lead

Mains flex

COMPONENTS OF A MIELE WASHER-DRYER

Waste-water antisiphon pipe hook

Detergent tray holder

Water inlet valves

Drum suspension springs

Water inlet hose

Water inlet connector

Waste-water pipe

Detergent tray recess

Control panel

Control panel wiring

Water inlet pipe

Drum and door seal

Drum inlet elbow

Stainless steel rotating drum

Door catch with safety cutout

Filter seal

Door metal cap

Fluff filter impeller

Door porthole

Drain tap

Detergent tray

Fabric softener section

Filter screw cover

Door wiring loom

Water softener dial

Filter

Hinged front panel

Tray front

Miele

Water hardness adjustment and filter flap lever

Microwave combination oven

CONVENTIONAL OVENS use electrically warmed elements or a flame to heat food. In a microwave oven heat energy is created by electromagnetic waves produced by a magnetron and led by waveguides into the oven compartment. These microwaves cannot pass through the compartment's metal casing, being reflected within and spread evenly by a fan. But they do pass through most types of plastic, ceramics, and glass. Therefore platters or containers made from these materials are suitable for use in microwave ovens. A combination oven also has conventional heating elements, to grill and "brown" in the traditional fashion, either alone or in conjunction with microwaves.

MICROWAVE COMBINATION OVEN

Turntable rotator

Door lock

Display screen

Control panel

Metal cook/grill tray (non-microwave)

Rollers

Under-turntable roller ring (non-microwave)

Glass cooking turntable

Metal turntable cover (non-microwave)

Metal grill/griddle (non-microwave)

HOW MICROWAVES HEAT FOOD

Oxygen atom

Hydrogen atom

Each water molecule in food has two hydrogen atoms and one oxygen atom

Water molecules spin with energy from microwaves

Microwaves make water molecules vibrate

Friction from spinning molecules creates heat

SIDE VIEW OF MICROWAVE COMBINATION OVEN

Magnetron assembly

Waveguide

Voltage regulators

Wiring loom

Grounding wire to case and chassis

Door

Fan electricity supply

Control panel circuitry

Main fan

Magnetron cooling fan

Rigid metal chassis

Voltage transformers

Door safety cut-out mechanism

Thermal/electrical insulation

Low-voltage supply for control circuits

Mains electrical lead

Circuit board plug

Electricity supply to magnetron

High-voltage magnetron supply

TOP VIEW OF MICROWAVE COMBINATION OVEN

Waveguide backing

Heating element cover

Heating element terminal cover

Electric heating elements

Oven compartment casing

Outer casing fitment

Microwave-proof door seals

Door

Thermal/electrical insulation

Overheat cut-out sensor supply

Chassis ground terminal

Voltage stabilizer

Magnetron assembly

Voltage circuitry

Control panel front

BACK VIEW OF MICROWAVE COMBINATION OVEN

Main fan electrical supply

Magnetron cooling fan

Magnetron cooling fan mounting

Magnetron perforated heat sink (dissipates warmth)

Electrical supply cable

Thermal/electrical insulation

Fan transformer

Vibration-reducing fan mounting

Cooling perforations for heating elements

Back of oven compartment

Fan dust shield

Main fan (scatters microwaves and circulates hot air)

Rear chassis plate

Toaster

MOST ELECTRIC TOASTERS not only grill slices of bread, they also pop them up when ready. While the slices rest on a spring-loaded rack, electric heating elements toast the bread. At the same time, a bimetallic strip heats and expands. One of the two metals in this strip expands more quickly than the other, causing the strip to curve. As it bends, it completes an electrical circuit and activates an electromagnet. The magnet attracts a catch, releasing the spring that holds the rack down in the toaster. The elements switch off, and the toasted slices pop up.

Terminal connections

Ejector bracket

Time switch

Variable time control knob

Selector switch

Screw

Screw

Switch end casting

Crumb tray

End baffle plate

Screw

Screw

Ground connection point

Cordset entry point

End element connecting link

End element

Foot

End element wire guard

Baseplate

Screw

Washer

Power supply cord

Strain release

Ejector knob

Screw

Spring

Nut

Ejector bracket

Plain end casting

Switch end casting

Stainless steel cover

Selector switch

Ejector assembly

Ejector knob

Variable time control knob

Center element wire cage

Foot

Inner cage assembly

Crumb tray

Fixing screw

Screw

Foot

End baffle plate

Screw

Element retaining stop

Plain end casting

Foot

Screw

Nut

Washer

Stainless steel cover

Screw

Element connecting link

Nut

Center element

End element

Washer

Screw

End element wire guard

Drills

THE ELECTRICALLY POWERED MOTOR OF A POWER DRILL, cooled by a fan, turns a shaft at high speed. The shaft connects, in turn, to a system of gears that rotates a chuck even faster. Clamped by the chuck, a sharp bit cuts out the hole, and at the same time the bit's screw-shaped grooves channel the waste out of the hole. For drilling hard materials, many power drills have a hammer mechanism: when this is operated a ratchet in the gearcase causes the chuck and bit to pound in and out as they drill. A hand drill, although slower and less forceful than a power drill, is easier to control. For cutting wide holes, carpenters often prefer a brace-and-bit. This acts like a lever: the bowed handle of the brace moves a larger distance than the bit, turning the bit with extra force.

MOTOR ASSEMBLY

Commutator

Armature

Armature spindle

Fan

Motor case

Field coils

Motor case

Motor case

Spring

Brush

Screw

Washer

Lead wire

Brush holder

Electromagnetic induction capacitor

Top insert blank

Hammer mechanism actuator

Screw hole

Chuck key holder

Switch

Screw

Trigger position

Hammer actuator position

Gearcase position

Motor position

INTERNAL VIEW OF HOUSING COVER

Lock button

On/off trigger

Washer

Spring

TRIGGER MECHANISM

Cable

GEAR MECHANISM

Thrust plate

Ratchet mechanism

Spindle

Gearcase cover

Chuck key

Jaw

Bit

Gearcase

Washer

Thrust washer

Gearcase cover screw

Chuck key pilot hole

POWER DRILL

Hammer mechanism actuator

Chuck

On/off trigger

Chuck key holder

Cable

Gearcase screw

HAND DRILL

Screw hole

Main handle

Turning handle

Side handle

Drive wheel

Pinion

Chuck

Jaw

Drill bit

EXTERNAL VIEW OF HOUSING COVER

Air intake slot

Air exhaust slot

Housing cover screw

BRACE-AND-BIT

Quill

Head

Crank

Handle

Ratchet

Chuck

Jaw

Drill bit

House of the future

HOUSES IN THE FUTURE are likely to be more environmentally friendly and energy-efficient than older dwellings, by making better use of materials and intelligent control systems. The Integer house was designed by Cole Thompson Associates, Bree Day Partnership, and Paul Hodgkins Associates, and built in conjunction with the Building Research Establishment in the UK. One of its key features is a large sun room that warms one side of the house. Extensive use is made of recycled, natural, and renewable materials and energy. The walls are made from timber and insulated with fiber from recycled newspaper; wastewater from the bathrooms is saved and used to flush the toilets; and a wind turbine and solar panels contribute some of the electricity requirements. Many elements were prefabricated off-site for ease of construction. The Integer house uses only half the energy and a third less water than a traditionally built house.

WALL CONSTRUCTION

Cellulose fiber insulation

Vertical batten

Plasterboard

Vertical batten

Red cedar boarding

Noggin

Baseboard

Breather paper

Floating floor

Cables and ducting

Wooden boarding

SIDE AND REAR VIEW OF THE INTEGER HOUSE

Single-glazed sun room

Gutter collects rainwater for use in the yard

Composter for recycling kitchen waste

FRONT VIEW OF THE INTEGER HOUSE

Turfed roof helps to regulate temperature

Passive stack vents from bathroom

Automatic louvers cool sun room

Small windows reduce heat loss

Red cedar walls that do not require painting or staining

Intelligent electronic door-lock

Hatch for home deliveries

ROOF CONSTRUCTION

Sedum turf

Mineral wool

Timber trellis

Root-proof membrane

Polyurethane insulation

Vapor barrier

Plywood roof deck

FM and TV antenna feeds into an integrated multimedia network

Photovoltaic panel generates electricity

Solar collector heats water

Security light

Automatic louvers to cool sun room

Window to upper floor home office

Timber bay window to living and dining area

Earth bank insulates lower floor

Blinds that open and close automatically in response to sunshine

SUN ROOM INTERIOR

Renewable energy

RENEWABLE ENERGY COMES from sources that do not become depleted as we use the energy. When a fossil fuel such as coal is burned, it is gone forever, but a renewable source remains available no matter how much is used. The tides, waves, flowing water, sunlight, and the wind are all renewable sources of energy. Wind and water energy are captured by a device called a turbine. The turbine spins and drives an electricity generator. Energy from sunlight, or solar energy, is changed into electricity in two main ways. One uses mirrors to concentrate solar energy and magnify its heating effect which is used to change water into steam to drive turbines. Photovoltaic cells change sunlight directly into electricity. A cell is made from two layers of silicon. One gives out electrons (negative particles) and the other receives them. Sunlight knocks electrons out of atoms where the two layers meet, separating them from the positive particles. The electrons are attracted to one layer of the cell, the positive particles to the other layer. Electrons are naturally attracted to the positive particles, but to come together again, the electrons must flow out of the cell, through an external electric circuit, or load, and back to the other side of the cell, creating a charge. The cell supplies electric current for as long as light keeps falling on it.

VESTAS V47 WIND TURBINE

Blade

Blade pitch control

Hub controller

Aerodynamic hub cover

Blade hub

Blade bearing

Rotor lock

TIDAL POWER

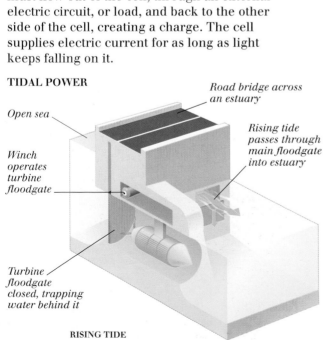

Road bridge across an estuary

Open sea

Rising tide passes through main floodgate into estuary

Winch operates turbine floodgate

Turbine floodgate closed, trapping water behind it

RISING TIDE

Turbine floodgate opened by winch allows trapped water to flow out to the open sea

Main floodgate closed as tide falls

Escaping water drives turbine

FALLING TIDE

Gearbox

Oil cooler

Generator

Anemometer

Wind vane

Service crane

Hydraulic unit

Electronic controller

Yaw ring

Yaw control

WIND TURBINES IN A WIND FARM

HOW A GENERATOR WORKS

N polarity magnet

Wire coil rotates inside magnet

Wind or water flow through turbine rotates shaft

S polarity magnet

Slip ring collects current from coil

Carbon brush collects current from slip ring

Proximity to magnet causes electric current to flow through coil

FIRST HALF TURN

N polarity magnet

Coil makes half a turn

S polarity magnet

Direction of current reverses every half turn owing to proximity to opposite polarity magnet

SECOND HALF TURN

SOLAR POWER

Antireflective coating

Glass

Sunlight

Contact grid

N-type silicon

Junction

P-type silicon

Back contact grid

Electrons flow out of cell

Electric current powers external load

Light knocks electrons out of atoms

Electrons flow back to cell

HOW A PHOTOVOLTAIC CELL WORKS

Solar cell containing photovoltaic cells

Power lead-out wires

Waterproof cable connector

SOLAR PANEL

Cloning technology

IN A LIVING CELL THE GENETIC MATERIAL DNA (deoxyribonucleic acid) contains thousands of units called genes that carry instructions for development, growth, and repair of the living creature. During normal reproduction, half the mother's genetic material contained in an egg cell joins with half the genetic material from the father carried in a sperm cell, to form a unique new genome (set of genes) for a new life. During the early stages of embryo development, the fertilized egg divides into stem cells, which have the potential to become specialized into the hundreds of cell types in a body. Through therapeutic cloning, stem cells can be produced in a laboratory. It is hoped that in the future this technology can be used to grow new tissue that can be transplanted back into the donor to treat illness, without the tissue being rejected. Rejection is when the body recognizes a transplanted part as "foreign" because it has different genes, and tries to destroy it. In another form of cloning, performed experimentally using animals, genetic material from a donor animal has been inserted into an egg from another animal that has been emptied of its own genetic material, to produce an animal genetically identical to the donor.

NORMAL REPRODUCTION

Spare cells from egg development

Nucleus with mother's genetic material

Egg cell membrane

Egg cell

Polar body (spare genetic material) forms as part of final egg cell division

THERAPEUTIC CLONING

Nucleus with mother's genetic material

Egg cell with polar body

Zona pellucida (outer casing of egg cell)

Fragments of DNA stain as dark "bar code" bands

GEL IMAGE SHOWING DNA PROFILE

"Plug" of zona removed

Suction through micro-pipette holds egg steady

Gentle suction through micro-needle

Micro-needle inserted through egg cell membrane

Zona plug discarded

Polar body removed

Egg genetic material in nucleus removed

Discarded parts no longer needed

Egg cell provides conditions for multiplication

Zona (casing)

Egg cell

Egg cell nucleus containing genetic material

GENETIC MATERIAL REMOVED FROM EGG

"Enucleated" egg cell (lacks nucleus with genetic material)

Stem cells (unspecialized or undifferentiated cells) collected from donor

Donor genetic material introduced into egg cell

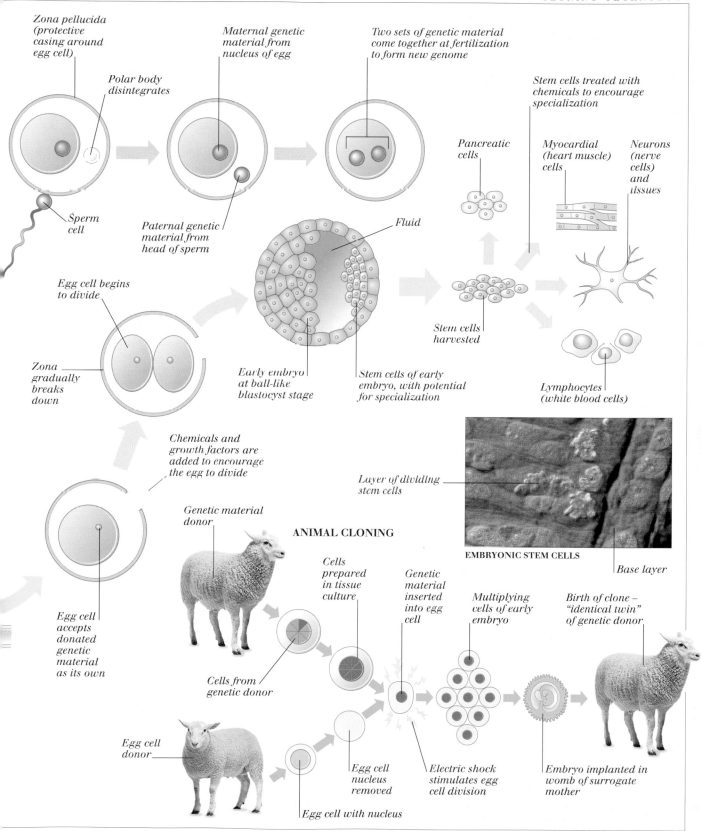

Zona pellucida (protective casing around egg cell)

Polar body disintegrates

Maternal genetic material from nucleus of egg

Two sets of genetic material come together at fertilization to form new genome

Stem cells treated with chemicals to encourage specialization

Pancreatic cells

Myocardial (heart muscle) cells

Neurons (nerve cells) and tissues

Sperm cell

Paternal genetic material from head of sperm

Fluid

Stem cells harvested

Lymphocytes (white blood cells)

Egg cell begins to divide

Zona gradually breaks down

Early embryo at ball-like blastocyst stage

Stem cells of early embryo, with potential for specialization

Chemicals and growth factors are added to encourage the egg to divide

Genetic material donor

Cells prepared in tissue culture

Genetic material inserted into egg cell

Multiplying cells of early embryo

Birth of clone – "identical twin" of genetic donor

ANIMAL CLONING

Layer of dividing stem cells

EMBRYONIC STEM CELLS

Base layer

Egg cell accepts donated genetic material as its own

Cells from genetic donor

Egg cell donor

Egg cell nucleus removed

Egg cell with nucleus

Electric shock stimulates egg cell division

Embryo implanted in womb of surrogate mother

Robots

ROBOTS ARE MACHINES THAT CAN carry out a variety of tasks on their own, with little or no human control. Most robots are mechanical arms used to build things in factories. The end of the robot's arm can be fitted with different tools for gripping, drilling, cutting, welding, and painting. Robot toys have become popular, too. They incorporate sensors that respond to sounds and sometimes touch. Some of them can even understand spoken words. The Aibo robot dog can understand 100 voice commands. Scientists are also trying to create more advanced, human-like robots that can see, hear, learn, and make their own decisions. Cog, a robot that has been progressively developed at the Massachusetts Institute of Technology since the 1990s, is one of these "humanoid" robots.

CAR-BUILDING ROBOTS

Vehicle body

Welding tool

INDUSTRIAL ROBOTS

Arm up-down joint

Wrist joints

End effector

KAWASAKI INDUSRIAL ROBOT

Arm rotation joint

Arm out-in joint

Floor-mounted base

Kawasaki

ELEMENTS OF ROBOT ACTION

CENTRAL PROCESSING UNIT (CPU)

Information from sensors

Pre-programed instructions

Information from sensors interpreted by CPU to modify actions

SENSORS

| LIGHT |
| SOUND |
| TOUCH |
| PROXIMITY |
| SMELL |
| TASTE |

MECHANICAL ACTIONS

Face light emitting diodes (LEDs)

Mode indicator

Stereo microphone

Movable tail

Rear back sensor and LED

Middle back sensor and LED

Front back sensor and LED

Head distance sensor

Color 350,000-pixel camera

Mouth

Movable chin touch sensor

Movable ear

SONY AIBO ENTERTAINMENT ROBOT DOG

Infrared chest distance sensor

AIBOne

Paw sensor

COG HUMANOID ROBOT

Right eye pan
motor

Left eye pan
motor

Motor
cabling

Peripheral
view

Foveal
view

Left

Right

Eye tilt motor

Cable to
off-board
computer

**VIEWS FROM COG'S FOUR
CAMERA EYES**

Foveal
camera
"eye"

Peripheral
camera
"eye"

Neck roll motor

Neck tilt motor

Touch-sensitive
fingertips

Sensor signal
boards

Torso frame

Shoulder
motor

Sensor
cables

Series elastic
actuator
(for wrist motor)

Elbow motor

Torso roll motor

High-performance microscopes

OPTICAL MICROSCOPES FORM a magnified image by using lenses to bend light. Some optical microscopes used in industry and research are designed for observing particular materials, such as living cells. They produce magnifications of up to about 1,000. Electron microscopes produce magnifications of as much as 1.5 million. Their images are formed by means of electrons focused by magnetic lenses. There are two main types: scanning electron microscopes (SEMs) scan electrons back and forth across the surface of a specimen; transmission electron microscopes (TEMs) transmit electrons through a thin slice of the specimen.

FEI TECNAI G² TRANSMISSION ELECTRON MICROSCOPE

TEM IMAGE OF A VIRUS

OPTICAL MICROSCOPE IMAGE OF DYING NERVE CELLS

Video camera

Right eyepiece

Filter turret

Objective lens

Manipulator

Left eyepiece

Manipulator

Specimen

Specimen stage

Electron gun housing

Evacuated column

Condenser aperture

Condenser housing

Objective lens and specimen stage

Objective aperture

Imaging system housing

Vacuum valve

Detector

Binocular eyepieces

Viewing screen

OLYMPUS BX51W1 OPTICAL MICROSCOPE

HOW A TEM WORKS

Electron gun

Electron stream

Aperture plate

Aperture creates electron beam

Condenser focuses electron beam

Specimen stage

Specimen

Objective lens refocuses image formed by electron beam

Specimen airlock

Projector lens enlarges and projects the image

Phosphor imaging screen glows when hit by electrons to create the image

Binocular eyepieces

Cooling device

Camera

Screen

Image controls

Mouse

Keyboard

HITACHI S-3500II SCANNING ELECTRON MICROSCOPE

Evacuated column

Image controls

Screen

Vacuum pump cubinet

S-3500H

Keyboard

HOW A SEM WORKS

Electron stream

Electron gun

Aperture plate

Aperture creates electron beam

Scanning coils direct electron beam across the specimen

Condenser lens focuses primary electron beam

Screen

Objective lens refocuses electron beam

Specimen stage

Electron detector assembly

Secondary electrons from the specimen surface

Specimen surface hit by primary electrons

Underside of caterpillar body

Caterpillar foot

SEM IMAGE OF A CATERPILLAR

Space telescope

SPACE TELESCOPES ORBIT THE EARTH hundreds of miles above the ground, their instruments collecting light from stars and galaxies. Telescopes in space have a clearer view than those on Earth, because they are unaffected by the Earth's atmosphere, which absorbs or distorts much of this radiation. There are a variety of types of space telescopes designed to observe different types of light. The Hubble Space Telescope observes infrared, ultraviolet, and visible light. It can detect objects that are 100 times fainter than those any telescopes on Earth can see. When this 242-ton (11,000-kilogram), 50-foot (13-meter) long telescope was launched by the Space Shuttle in 1990, it was found that its primary mirror was faulty and its images were blurred. Astronauts installed extra optics to correct the problem in 1993.

IMAGES TAKEN FROM HUBBLE

Pillar of gas

CONE NEBULA

VIEW FROM COLUMBIA SPACE SHUTTLE

Space shuttle remote manipulator system (robot arm)

Solar array

Axial instrument unit

Central deflector

High-gain radio antenna

Rotating joint

Crew handrail

Aft shroud

Guidance control sensor

7.9-foot (2.4-m) primary mirror

Aperture door mounting

Light shield

13-inch (33-cm) secondary mirror

Secondary baffle

Epoxy resin frame

Crew handrail

Aperture

Aperture door

Door hinge

Aluminium shield

Light shield

EXPLODED VIEW OF HUBBLE SPACE TELESCOPE

Hydrogen gas emissions

Young star

"WHIRLPOOL" GALAXY

"Tadpole" galaxy

DRACO CONSTELLATION

Newly formed stars

OMEGA NEBULA

"Spirograph" nebula

LEPUS CONSTELLATION

COSTAR device slot

Batteries

Space shuttle remote manipulator system (robot arm)

Space shuttle astronaut

COSTAR corrective optical device

Space shuttle astronaut

Interstellar cloud remains

PLEIADES STAR CLUSTER

Young star – LL Ori

GREAT NEBULA, ORION

High-gain radio antenna for communication with satellites

Aperture door acts like a camera lens cap

Aperture allows light into the mirror housing

HUBBLE SPACE TELESCOPE

Primary mirror housing

Solar array supporting arm

Solar array collects solar power for operating instruments

Light shield blocks out peripheral light

Thermal insulation to protect against extremes of temperature

Crew handrail for astronauts to hold during maintenance operations

Solar array

Aft shroud

Crew handrail

High-gain radio antenna

Probing the Universe

SPACE PROBES HAVE VISITED every planet in the Solar System except Pluto. They take photographs and gather data that cannot be collected using Earth-based equipment. Some probes fly past or orbit around planets or moons, while others land. Two Voyager space probes flew past most of the outer planets in the 1970s and 1980s. Two Viking spacecraft landed on Mars in 1976. The Magellan spacecraft orbited Venus from 1989 and mapped its surface. The Pathfinder spacecraft landed on Mars in 1997 and released a rover vehicle to explore the surface. The Mars Exploration Rover (MER) Mission landed two rovers in 2003. The Cassini space probe reached Saturn in 2004, and in 2005, its mini-probe, Huygens, landed on one of its moons, Titan, and became the first probe to land on a moon of another planet.

A MAP OF JUPITER'S VAST MAGNETIC FIELD PRODUCED BY CASSINI'S INSTRUMENTS

DIONE, ONE OF SATURN'S MOONS, ORBITING ABOVE THE "A" RING

High-gain antenna

Sun sensor

Helium tank

Visible amd infrared spectrometers

Remote sensing pallet

Wide-angle camera

Radio-isotope thermoelectric generator

Magnetometer

Fields and particles intruments

Huygens mini probe

Attitude control thruster

Main engines

Propulsion module

Heat shield

Reaction wheel

Lower equipment module

CASSINI SPACE PROBE AND HUYGENS MINI-PROBE

PANORAMIC VIEW OF TITAN TAKEN AS HUYGENS DESCENDED

THE ROCK-STREWN SURFACE OF TITAN, PHOTOGRAPHED BY HUYGENS

Panoramic camera (Pancam)

Navigation camera (Navcam)

COBBLESTONES LYING IN TROUGHS BETWEEN DUST RIPPLES ON THE MARTIAN SURFACE, PHOTOGRAPHED BY ROVER "OPPORTUNITY"

Pancam mast assembly

Low dain antenna

Thruster cluster

Heat shield

Propellant tank

Star scanner

Cruise stage

Backshell

Cruise electronics module

MARS EXPLORATION ROVER SPACECRAFT

Ultra-high frequency (UHF) antenna

Magnet array

Rover equipment deck

High gain antenna

Third stage motor

Delta II launch vehicle second stage

Solar array

Aft bogie

Bogie wheel strut

Front hazard avoidance camera

Aft rocker

Warm electronics box

Forward rocker

Instrument deployment device

Rocker deployment actuator

MARS EXPLORATION ROVER (MER)

Aluminum wheel

Political map of the world

This map depicts the political boundaries of the world's nations. There are currently 193 independent countries in the world – a marked increase from the 82 that existed in 1950. With the trend toward greater fragmentation, this figure is likely to increase. There are also some 60 overseas dependencies still in existence, with various forms of local administration, but all belonging to a sovereign state. The largest country in the world is the Russian Federation, which covers 6,592,800 sq. mi. (17,075,400 sq. km), while the smallest is the Vatican City, covering 0.17 sq. mi. (0.44 sq. km). Under the Antarctic Treaty of 1959, no countries are permitted to have territorial claims in Antarctica.

ABBREVIATIONS	
AFGH.	Afghanistan
ALB.	Albania
AUT.	Austria
AZ. OR AZERB.	Azerbaijan
B. & H.	Bosnia & Herzegovina
BELG.	Belgium
BELO.	Belorussia
BOTS.	Botswana
BULG.	Bulgaria
CAMB.	Cambodia
C.A.R.	Central African Republic
CRO.	Croatia
CZ. REP.	Czech Republic
DOM. REP.	Dominican Republic
EST.	Estonia
HUNG.	Hungary
KYRG.	Kyrgyzstan
LAT.	Latvia
LIECH.	Liechtenstein
LITH.	Lithuania
LUX.	Luxemburg
MACED.	Macedonia
MOLD.	Moldavia
NETH.	Netherlands
NETH. ANT.	Netherlands Antilles
PORT.	Portugal
ROM.	Romania
RUSS. FED.	Russian Federation
SERB. & MON.	Serbia & Montenegro
SLVK.	Slovakia
SLVN.	Slovenia
S.M.	San Marino
SWITZ.	Switzerland
TAJ.	Tajikistan
THAI.	Thailand
TURKMEN.	Turkmenistan
U.A.E.	United Arab Emirates
UZBEK.	Uzbekistan
VAT. CITY	Vatican City
ZIMB.	Zimbabwe

Time zones

The world is divided into 24 time zones, measured in relation to 12 noon Greenwich Mean Time (GMT), on the Greenwich Meridian (0°). Time advances by one hour for every 15° longitude east of Greenwich (and goes back one hour for every 15° west), but the system is adjusted in line with administrative boundaries. Numbers on the map show the number of hours that must be added to, or subtracted from GMT to calculate the time in each zone. Thus, the eastern US (–5) is 5 hours behind GMT.

TYPES OF CALENDAR

GREGORIAN
The 365-day Gregorian calendar was introduced by Pope Gregory XIII in 1582 and is now in use throughout most of the Western world. Every four years (leap year) an extra day is added. Below are the names of the months (and number of days).

January (31)	July (31)
February (28, 29 in leap years)	August (31)
	September (30)
March (31)	October (31)
April (30)	November
May (31)	December (31)
June (30)	

JEWISH
The Jewish calendar is a lunar calendar adapted to the solar year. It normally has 12 months but in leap years, which occur seven times in every cycle of 19 years, there are 13 months. The years are calculated from the Creation (which is placed at 3761 BC); the months are Nisan, Iyyar, Sivan, Thammuz, Ab, Elul, Tishri, Hesvan, Kislev, Tebet, Sebat, and Adar, with an intercalary month (First Adar) being added in leap years.

MUSLIM
The Muslim calendar is based on a year of 12 months, each month beginning roughly at the time of the new moon. The months are Muharram, Safar, Rabi'I, Rabi'II, Jumada I, Jumada II, Rajab, Sha'ban, Ramadan, Shawwal, Dhu l-Qa'dah, and Dhu l-Hijja.

CHINESE
The Chinese calendar is a lunar calendar, with a year consisting of 12 months. Intercalary months are added to keep the calendar in step with the solar year of 365 days. Months are referred to by a number within a year, but also by animal names that, from ancient times, have been attached to years and hours of the day.

Useful data

UNITS OF MEASUREMENT

METRIC UNIT	EQUIVALENT
Length	
1 centimeter (cm)	10 millimeters (mm)
1 meter (m)	100 centimeters
1 kilometre (km)	1,000 metres
Mass	
1 kilogram (kg)	1,000 grams (g)
1 tonne (t)	1,000 kilograms
Area	
1 square centimeter (cm²)	100 square millimetres (mm²)
1 square meter (m²)	10,000 square centimeters
1 hectare	10,000 square meters
1 square kilometer (km²)	1,000,000 square meters
Volume	
1 cubic centimeter (cc)	1 milliliter (ml)
1 liter (l)	1,000 milliliters
1 cubic meter (m³)	1,000 liters
Capacity (liquid and dry measures)	
1 centiliter (cl)	10 milliliters (ml)
1 deciliter (dl)	10 centiliters
1 liter (l)	10 deciliters
1 decaliter (dal)	10 liters
1 hectoliter (hi)	10 decaliters
1 kiloliter (kl)	10 hectoliters

IMPERIAL UNIT	EQUIVALENT
Length	
1 foot (ft)	12 inches (in)
1 yard (yd)	3 feet
1 rod (rd)	5.5 yards
1 mile (mi)	1,760 yards
Mass	
1 dram (dr)	27.344 grains (gr)
1 ounce (oz)	16 drams
1 pound (lb)	16 ounces
1 hundredweight (cwt) (long)	112 pounds
1 hundredweight (cwt) (short)	100 pounds
1 ton (long)	2,240 pounds
1 ton (short)	2,000 pounds
Area	
1 square foot (ft²) (in²)	144 square inches
9 square feet	1 square yard (yd²)
1 acre	4,840 square yards
1 square mile	640 acres
Volume	
1 cubic foot	1,728 cubic inches
1 cubic yard	27 cubic feet
Capacity (liquid and dry measures)	
1 fluidram (fl dr)	60 minims (min)
1 fluid ounce (fl oz)	8 fluidrams
1 gill (gi)	5 fluid ounces
1 pint (pt)	4 gills
1 quart (qt)	2 pints
1 gallon (gal)	4 quarts
1 peck (pk)	2 gallons
1 bushel (bu)	4 pecks

NUMBER SYSTEMS

ROMAN	ARABIC
I	1
II	2
III	3
IV	4
V	5
VI	6
VII	7
VIII	8
IX	9
X	10
XI	11
XII	12
XIII	13
XIV	14
XV	15
XX	20
XXI	21
XXX	30
XL	40
L	50
LX	60
LXX	70
LXXX	80
XC	90
C	100
CI	101
CC	200
CCC	300
CD	400
D	500
DC	600
DCC	700
DCCC	800
CM	900
M	1,000
MM	2,000

METRIC - IMPERIAL CONVERSIONS

TO CONVERT	INTO	MULTIPLY BY
Length		
Centimeters	inches	0.3937
Meters	feet	3.2810
Kilometers	miles	0.6214
Meters	yards	1.0940
Mass		
Grams	ounces	0.0352
Kilograms	pounds	2.2050
Tonnes	long tons	0.9843
Tonnes	short tons	1.1025
Area		
Square centimeters	square inches	0.1550
Square meters	square feet	10.7600
Hectares	acres	2.4710
Square kilometers	square miles	0.3861
Square meters	square yards	1.1960
Volume		
Cubic centimeters	cubic inches	0.0610
Cubic meters	cubic feet	35.3100
Capacity		
Liters	pints	2.1134
Liters	gallons	0.2642

IMPERIAL - METRIC CONVERSIONS

TO CONVERT	INTO	MULTIPLY BY
Length		
Inches	centimeters	2.5400
Feet	meters	0.3048
Miles	kilomecentimeters	1.6090
Yards	meters	0.9144
Mass		
Ounces	grams	28.3500
Pounds	kilograms	0.4536
Long tons	tonnes	1.0160
Short tons	tonnes	0.9070
Area		
Square inches	square centimeters	6.4520
Square feet	square meters	0.0929
Acres	hectares	0.4047
Square miles	square kilometers	2.5900
Square yards	square meters	0.8361
Volume		
Cubic inches	cubic centimeters	16.3900
Cubic feet	cubic metrers	0.0283
Capacity		
Pints	litres	0.4732
Gallons	litres	4.4049

RULES OF ALGEBRA

EXPRESSION	COMMENTS	EXPRESSION BECOMES
a + a	Simple addition	2a
a + b = c + d	Subtract b from either side	a = c + d – b
ab = cd	Divide both sides by b	a = cd ÷ b
(a + b) (c + d)	Multiply terms in parentheses	ac + ad + bc + bd
a^2 + ab	Use parentheses	a(a + b)
$(a + b)^2$	Expand terms in parentheses	$a^2 + 2ab + b^2$
$a^2 - b^2$	Difference of two squares	(a + b)(a – b)
1/a + 1/b	Find common denominator	(a + b)/ab
a/b ÷ c/d	Dividing by a fraction is the same as multiplying by its reciprocal	a/b × d/c

POWERS OF TEN USED WITH SCIENTIFIC UNITS

FACTOR	NAME	PREFIX	SYMBOL
10^{18}	quintillion	exa-	E
10^{15}	quadrillion	peta-	P
10^{12}	trillion	tera-	T
10^{9}	billion	giga-	G
10^{6}	million	mega-	M
10^{3}	thousand	kilo-	k
10^{2}	hundred	hecto-	h
10^{1}	ten	deca-	da
10^{-1}	one tenth	deci-	d
10^{-2}	one hundredth	centi-	c
10^{-3}	one thousandth	milli-	m
10^{-6}	one millionth	micro-	μ
10^{-9}	one billionth	nano-	n
10^{-12}	one trillionth	pico-	p
10^{-15}	one quadrillionth	femto-	f
10^{-18}	one quintillionth	atto-	a

Note: The American system of numeration for denominations above one million is used in this book. In this system, each of the denominations above one billion (1,000 millions) is 1,000 times the preceding one.

BIOLOGY SYMBOLS

SYMBOL	MEANING
○	female individual (used in inheritance charts)
□	male individual (used in inheritance charts)
♀	female
♂	male
x	crossed with; hybrid
+	wild type
F_1	offspring of the first generation
F_2	offspring of the second generation

TEMPERATURE SCALES

To convert from Fahrenheit to Celsius: $C = (F - 32) \times 5 \div 9$
To convert from Celsius (C) to Fahrenheit (F): $F = (C \times 9 \div 5) + 32$
To convert from Celsius to Kelvin (K): $K = C + 273$
To convert from Kelvin to Celsius: $C = K - 273$

Fahrenheit	-4	14	32	50	68	86	104	122	140	158	176	194	212
Celsius	-20	-10	0	10	20	30	40	50	60	70	80	90	100
Kelvin	253	263	273	283	293	303	313	323	333	343	353	363	373

PHYSICS SYMBOLS

SYMBOL	MEANING
α	alpha particle
β	beta ray
γ	gamma ray; photon
ε	electromotive force
η	efficiency; viscosity
λ	wavelength
μ	micro-; permeability
ν	frequency; neutrino
ρ	density; resistivity
σ	conductivity
c	velocity of light
e	electronic charge

SCIENTIFIC NOTATION

NUMBER	NUMBER BETWEEN 1 AND 10	POWER OF TEN	SCIENTIFIC NOTATION
10	1	10^1	1×10^1
150	1.5	$10^2 (= 100)$	1.5×10^2
274,000,000	2.74	$10^8 (= 100,000,000)$	2.74×10^8
0.0023	2.3	$10^{-3} (= 0.001)$	2.3×10^{-3}

MATHEMATICAL SYMBOLS

SYMBOL	EXPLANATION
+	addition
–	subtraction
×	multiplication
÷	division
=	equals
≠	does not equal
>	greater than
<	less than
≥	greater than or equal to
≤	less than or equal to
∞	infinity
%	percent
π	pi (3.1416)
°	degree
≈	is approximately equal to
∠	angle
∥	parallel to
Σ	summation
u,u	vectors
f(x)	function
!	factorial
√	square root
$\mathscr{E}$	universal set
A ∩ B	intersection
A ∪ B	unison
A ⊂ B	subset
∅	null set

CHEMISTRY SYMBOLS

SYMBOL	MEANING
+	plus; together with
–	single bond
•	single bond; single unpaired electron; two separate parts or compounds regarded as loosely joined
=	double bond
≡	triple bond
R	group
X	halogen atom
Z	atomic number

TRIGONOMETRY

Angle A (degrees)	sin A	cos A	tan A
0	0	1	0
30	1/2	$\sqrt{3}/2$	$1/\sqrt{3}$
45	$1/\sqrt{2}$	$1/\sqrt{2}$	1
60	$\sqrt{3}/2$	1/2	$\sqrt{3}$
90	1	0	∞

Shapes: Plane

Two-dimensional shapes are termed plane (or flat) shapes. Plane shapes constructed with straight sides, as illustrated here, are called polygons. They are categorized according to the number of sides they have – for example, three-sided polygons are known as triangles. A polygon that has sides of equal length and internal angles of equal size, such as a square, are said to be regular.

SCALENE TRIANGLE
A triangle (three-sided polygon) with no equal sides or angles.

ISOSCELES TRIANGLE
A triangle with only two sides and two angles equal.

RIGHT-ANGLED TRIANGLE
A triangle with one angle as a right angle (90°).

EQUILATERAL TRIANGLE
A regular triangle. All angles are 60°.

SQUARE
A regular quadrilateral. All angles are 90°.

RHOMBUS
A quadrilateral with all sides equal and two pairs of equal angles.

RECTANGLE
A quadrilateral with four right angles and opposite sides of equal length.

PARALLELOGRAM
A quadrilateral with two pairs of parallel sides.

TRAPEZIUM
A quadrilateral with one pair of parallel sides.

PENTAGON
A five-sided polygon. A regular pentagon is shown above.

HEXAGON
A six-sided polygon. A regular hexagon is shown above.

OCTAGON
An eight-sided polygon. A regular octagon is shown above.

AREAS AND PERIMETERS

The formulae for calculating the areas and perimeters of simple plane shapes were devised by Classical Greek mathematicians.

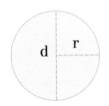

CIRCLE
r = radius
d = diameter = 2 × r

Circumference = 2 × π × r
Area = π × r²
(π = 3.1416)

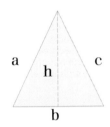

TRIANGLE
Height = h
Sides = a, b, c

Perimeter = a + b + c
Area = ½ × b × h

RECTANGLE
Sides = a, b

Perimeter = 2 × (a + b)
Area = a × b

Shapes: Solid

Three-dimensional shapes are known as solid shapes, and include spheres, cubes, and pyramids. A solid shape with a polygon at each face is called a polyhedron.

Volume refers to the amount of space that a solid object occupies. Its surface area is the sum of the area of each of its faces.

TETRAHEDRON
A four-sided polyhedron. A regular tetrahedron is shown.

CUBE
A regular hexahedron. All sides are equal and all angles are 90°.

OCTAHEDRON
A polyhedron with eight sides.

CYLINDER
Surface area =
$2 \times \pi \times r \times h + 2\pi r^2$
Volume $= \pi \times r^2 \times h$

Height = h
Radius = r

PRISM
A polyhedron of constant cross-sections in planes perpendicular to its longitudinal axis.

PYRAMID
A polygonal base and triangular sides that meet at a point.

TORUS
A doughnut-like, ring shape.

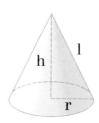

CONE
Surface area =
$\pi \times r \times l + \pi r^2$
Volume $= \frac{1}{3} \times \pi \times r^2 \times l$

Height = h
Radius = r
Side = l

SPHERE
A round shape, as in a ball or an orange.

HEMISPHERE
Formed when a sphere is cut exactly in half.

SPHEROID
An egg-shaped solid object whose cross-section is a circle or an ellipse.

CONE
An elliptical or circular base with sides tapering to a single point.

RIGHT CYLINDER
A tube-shaped, solid figure. A right cylinder has parallel faces.

HELIX
A twisted curve. The distance moved in one revolution is its pitch.

RECTANGULAR BLOCK
Surface area =
$2 (a \times b + b \times c + a \times c)$
Volume $= a \times b \times c$

Sides = a, b, c

Index

624

626

657

Acknowledgments

Dorling Kindersley would like to thank (in order of sections):

The Universe
(consultant editors – Sue Becklake, Gevorkyan Tatyana Alekseyevna):
John Becklake; the Memorial Museum of Cosmonautics, Moscow; The Cosmos Pavilion, Moscow; The United States Space and Rocket Centre, Alabama; Broadhurst, Clarkson and Fuller Ltd; Susannah Massey

Prehistoric Earth
(consultant editors – William Lindsay, Martyn Bramwell, Dr Ralph E. Molnar, David Lambert):
Dr Monty Reid, Andrew Neuman, and the staff of the Royal Tyrrell Museum of Palaeontology, Drumheller, Alberta; Dr Angela Milner and the staff of the Department of Palaeontology, the Natural History Museum, London; Professor W. Ziegler and the staff, in particular Michael Loderstaedt, of the Naturmuseum Senckenburg, Frankfurt; Dr Alexander Liebau, Axel Hunghrebüller, Reiner Schoch, and the staff of the Institut und Museum für Geologie und Paläontologie der Universität, Tübingen; Rupert Wild of the Institut für Paläontologie, Staatliches Museum für Naturkunde, Stuttgart; Dr Scheiber of the Stadtmuseum, Nördlingen; Professor Dr Dietrich Herm of Staatssammlung für Paläontologie und Historische Geologie, München; Dr Michael Keith-Lucas of the Department of Botany, University of Reading; Richard Walker; American Museum of Natural History, New York

Plants
(consultant editor – Richard Walker):
Diana Miller; Lawrie Springate; Karen Sidwell; Chris Thody; Michelle End; Susan Barnes and Chris Jones of the EMU Unit of the Natural History Museum, London; Jenny Evans of Kew Gardens, London; Kate Biggs of the Royal Horticultural Society Gardens, Wisley, Surrey; Spike Walker of Microworld Services; Neil Fletcher; John Bryant of Bedgebury Pinetum, Kent; Dean Franklin

Animals
(consultant editor – Richard Walker):
David Manning's Animal Ark; Intellectual Animals; Howletts Zoo, Canterbury; John Dunlop; Alexander O'Donnell; Sue Evans of the Royal Veterinary College, London; Dr Geoff Potts and Fred Frettsome of the Marine Biological Association of the United Kingdom, Plymouth; Jeremy Adams of the Booth Museum of Natural History, Brighton; Derek Telling of the Department of Anatomy, University of Bristol; the Natural History Museum, London; Andy Highfield of the Tortoise Trust; Brian Harris of the Aquarium, London Zoo; the Invertebrate Department, London Zoo; Dr Harold McClure of the Yerkes Regional Primate Research Center, Emory University, Atlanta, Georgia; Nielson Lausen of the Harvard Medical School, New England Regional Primates Research

Centre, Southborough, Massachusetts; Dr Paul Hopwood of the Department of Veterinary Anatomy, University of Sydney; Dean Franklin

The Human Body
(consultant editors – Dr Frances Williams, Dr Fiona Payne, Richard Cummins FRCS):
Derek Edwards and Dr Martin Collins, British School of Osteopathy; Dr M.C.E. Hutchinson of the Department of Anatomy, United Medical and Dental Schools of Guy's and St Thomas' Hospitals, London. Models – Barry O'Rorke (Bodyline Agency) and Pauline Swaine (MOT Model Agency)

Geology, Geography, and Meteorology
(consultant editor – Martyn Bramwell):
Dr John Nudds of the Manchester Museum, Manchester; Dr Alan Wooley and Dr Andrew Clark of the Natural History Museum, London; Graham Bartlett of the National Meteorological Library and Archive, Bracknell; Tony Drake of BP Exploration, Uxbridge; Jane Davies of the Royal Society of Chemistry, Cambridge; Dr Tony Waltham of Nottingham Trent University, Nottingham; staff of the Smithsonian Institute, Washington; staff of the United States Geological Survey, Washington; staff of the National Geographic Society, Washington; staff of Edward Lawrence Associates (Export Ltd), Midhurst; John Farndon; David Lambert

Rail and Road
Rail (consultant editor – John Coiley)
Michael Ashworth of the London Transport Museum

Road (consultant editors – David Burgess-Wise, Hugo Wilson)
The National Motor Museum, Beaulieu; Alf Newell of Renault UK Ltd; David Suter of Cheltenham Cutaway Exhibits Ltd; Francesca Riccini of the Science Museum, London. Signore Amadelli of the Museo dell' Automobile Carlo Biscaretti di Ruffia; Paul Bolton of the Mazda MCL Group; Duncan Bradford of Reg Mills Wire Wheels; John and Leslie Brewster of Autocavan; David Burgess-Wise; Trevor Cass of Garrett Turbo Service; John Corbett of The Patrick Collection; Gary Crumpler of Williams Grand Prix Engineering Ltd; Mollie Easterbrooke and Duncan Gough of Overland Ltd; Arthur Fairley of the Vauxhall Motor Company; Paul Foulkes-Halbard of Filching Manor Motor Museum; Frank Gilbert of I. Wilkinson and Son Ltd; Paolo Gratton of Gratton Museum; Colvin Gunn of Gunn and Son; Judy Hogg of Ecurie Bertelli; Milton Holman of Dream Cars; Ian Matthews of IMAT Electronics; Eric Neal of Jaguar Cars Ltd; Paul Niblett, Keith Davidson, Mark Reumel, and David Woolf of Michelin Tyre plc; Doug Nye; Kevin O'Keefe of O'Keefe Cars; Seat UK; Ian Whitley, Raj Johal and Andy Faiers of the Honda Institute; Roger Smith; Jim Stirling of Ironbridge Gorge Museum, Staffordshire; Jon Taylor; Doug Thompson; Martyn Watkins of Ford Motor Company Ltd; John Cattermole, Customer Services Manager at London Northern Buses; F. W. Evans Cycles Ltd; Trek UK Ltd (Bicycle); Sam Grimmer; Colin Uttley

Physics and Chemistry
(consultant editor – Jack Challoner)

Sea and Air
Sea (consultant editors – Geoff Hales and Harvey B. Loomis):
David Spence, Gillian Hutchinson, David Topliss, Simon Stephens, Robert Baldwin, Jonathan Betts, all of the National Maritime Museum, London; Ian Friel; Simon Turnage of Captain O.M. Watts of London Ltd; Davey and Company Ltd, Great Dunmow; Avon Inflatables Ltd, Llanelli; Musto Ltd, Benfleet; Peter Martin of Spencer Rigging Ltd, Southampton; Peter Rowson of Ratseys Sailmakers, Southampton; Swiftech Ltd, Wallingford; Colin Scattergood of the Barrow Boat Company Ltd, Colchester; Professor J.S. Morrison of the Trireme Trust, Cambridge; The Cutty Sark Maritime Trust; Adrian Daniels of Kelvin Hughes Marine Instruments, London; Arthur Credland of Hull City Council Museums and Art Galleries; The Hull Maritime Society; Gerald Clark; Peter Fitzgerald of the Science Museum, London; Alec Michael of HMB Subwork Ltd, Great Yarmouth, and Ray Ward of the OSEL Group, Great Yarmouth; Richard Bird of UWI, Weybridge; Walker Marine Instruments, Birmingham; The International Sailing Craft Association; The Exeter Maritime Museum; Jane Wilson of the Trinity Lighthouse Company, London; The Imperial War Museum Collections; Thorn Security Ltd; Michael Bach

Air (consultant editor – Bill Gunston):
Aeromega Helicopters, Stapleford; Aero Shopping, London; Avionics Mobile Services Ltd, Watford; Roy Barber and John Chapman of the RAF Museum, Hendon; Mitch Barnes Aviation, London; Mike Beach; British Caledonian Flight Training Ltd; Fred Coates of Helitech (Luton) Ltd; Michael Cuttell and CSE Aviation Ltd, Oxford; Dowty Aerospace Landing Gear, Gloucester; Guy Hartcup of the Airship Association; Anthony Hooley, Chris Walsh, and David Cord of British Aerospace Regional Aircraft Ltd; Ken Huntley of Mid-West Aero Engines Ltd; Imperial War Museum, Duxford; The London Gliding Club, Dunstable; Musée des Ballons, Calvados; Noel Penny Turbines Ltd; Andy Pavey of Aviation Scotland Ltd; Tony Pavey of Thermal Aircraft Developments, London; the Commanding Officer and personnel of RAF St Athan; the Commanding Officer and personnel of RAF Wittering; The Science Museum, London; Ross Sharp of the Science Museum, Wroughton; The Shuttleworth Collection; Skysport Engineering; Mike Smith; Solar Wings Ltd, Marlborough; Julian Temple of Brooklands Museum Trust Ltd; Kelvin Wilson of Flying Start

Architecture
(consultant editor – Alexandra Kennedy):
Stephen Cutler for advice and text; Gavin Morgan of the Museum of London, London; Chris Zeuner of the Weald and Downland Museum, Singleton, Sussex; Alan Hills and James Putnam of the British Museum, London; Dr Simon Penn and Michael Thomas of the Avoncroft Museum of Buildings, Bromsgrove,

Worcestershire; Christina Scull of Sir John Soane's Museum, London; Paul Kennedy and John Williamson of the London Door Company, London; Lou Davis of The Original Box Sash Window Company, Windsor; Goddard and Gibbs Studios Ltd, London, for access to stained glass windows; The Royal Courts of Justice, Strand, London; Charles Brooking and Peter Dalton for access to the doors and windows in the Charles Brooking Collection, University of Greenwich, Dartford, Kent; Clare O'Brien of the Shakespeare Globe Trust, Shakespeare's Globe Museum, Bear Gardens, Southwark, London; Ken Teague of the Horniman Museum, London; Canon Haliburton, Mike Payton, Ken Stones, and Anthony Webb of St Paul's Cathedral, London; Roy Spring of Salisbury Cathedral; Reverend Gillean Craig of the Church of St George in the East, London; the Science Museum, London; Dr Neil Bingham; Lin Kennedy of Historic Royal Palaces; Katy Harris of Sir Norman Foster and Partners; Production Design, Thames Television plc, London; Dominique Reynier of Le Centre Georges Pompidou, Paris; Denis Roche of Le Musée National des Monuments Français, Paris; Franck Gioria and students of Les Compagnons du Devoir, Paris, for access to construction models; Frank Folliot of Le Musée Carnavalet, Paris; Dr Martina Harms of Hessische Landesmuseums, Darmstadt; Jefferson Chapman of the University of Tennessee, Knoxville, for access to the model of the Hypostyle Hall, Temple of Amon-Re; staff of the Palazzo Strozzi, Florence; staff of the Sydney Opera House, Sydney; staff of the Empire State Building, New York, Nick Jackson; Ann Terrell

The Visual Arts
(consultant editor – Pip Seymour):
Rosemary Simmons; Michael Taylor of Paupers Press, London; Tessa Hunkin and Emma Biggs of Mosaic Workshop, London; John Tiranti, Jonathan Lyons of Alec Tiranti Ltd, London; Chris Hough; Dr Ashok Roy; Satwinder Sehmi of Alphabet Soup, London; Phillip Poole of Cornelissens, London; George Weil and Sons Ltd, London; The National Gallery, London; Chris Webster of the Tate Gallery, London; China Art Cultural Centre, London; London Graphic Centre, London; A.P. Fitzpatrick, London; Flowers Graphics, London; Intaglio Printmaker, London; Falkiner Papers, London; Edgar Udny and Co, London; John Green

Music
(consultant editor – Susan Sturrock):
Boosey and Hawkes Music Publishers Ltd, London, for permission to reproduce extract from The Prodigal Son by Arthur Sullivan; The Bass and Drum Cellar, London; Empire Drums and Percussion, London; Argents (part of World of Music), London; Bill Lewington Ltd, London; Frobenius organ at Kingston Parish Church, Surrey; Yamaha-Kemble Music (UK) Ltd, Tilbrook, Milton Keynes; Yamaha Atelier, London; Akai (UK) Ltd, Hounslow, Middlesex; Casio Electronics Co. Ltd, London; Roland (UK) Ltd, Fleet, Hampshire; Richard Schulman; Andy Brown of Musictrack

Sports
The Sports Council Information Centre, London; The British Olympic Games Committee; Brian Crennell of Black's Leisure Group (First Sport); Lillywhites of Piccadilly, London; Mitre Sports International Ltd, Huddersfield; David Bloomfield of the Football Association; Denver Athletics Ltd, Norfolk; Greg Everest and Keith Birley of the British League of Australian Rules Football; Peter McNally of the Gaelic Athletic Association; Jeremy Garman of James Gilbert Ltd.; Rex King of the Rugby Football Union, Twickenham; Neil Tunnicliffe and John Huxley of the Rugby Football League, Leeds; Wayne Patterson of the Basketball Hall of Fame, Springfield, Connecticut; Brian Coleman of the English Basketball Association; All American Imports, Northampton; George Bulman of the English Volleyball Association; Julie Longdon of Mizuno Mallory (UK) Ltd; Juliet Stanford of the All-England Netball Association; Jeff Rowland of the British Handball Association; Cally Melin of Adidas UK Ltd; Patrick Donnely of the Baseball Hall of Fame, Cooperstown, New York; Ian Lepage and Stephen Barlow of the Hockey Association, Milton Keynes; Alison Taylor and Anita Mason of the All England Women's Lacrosse Association, Birmingham; David Shuttleworth of the English Lacrosse Union; Les Barnett and Jock Bentley of the British Athletic Federation Ltd, Birmingham; Mike Gilks of the Badminton Association of England; Gurinder Purewall for advice on archery; Chris McCartney of the US Archery Association; Geoff Doe of the National Smallbore Rifle Association, Bisley, Surrey, for information and reference material on shooting; Fagan Sports Goods Distributors, Surrey; Konrad Bartelski for advice on skiing; The British Ski Federation, Edinburgh; Mike Barnett of Snow and Rock of London; Sally Spurway of Mast-Co. Ltd, Reading; Sarah Morgan for advice on equestrian sports; Steve Brown and the New York Racing Association Inc, New York; Danrho of London; Alan Skipp and James Chambers of the Amateur Fencing Association, London; Carla Richards of the US Fencing Association; Hamilton Bland and John Dryer of the Amateur Swimming Association, Loughborough; Cotswold Camping Ltd, London; Tim Spalton of Glyn Locke (Racing Shells) Ltd, Chalgrove; Terry Friel of the US Rowing Association; House of Hardy; Leeda Fishing Tackle

The Modern World
John Lewis, Brent Cross, for the loan of products for photography; Apple Computers UK; Palm Inc.; Epson UK; Naynesh Mistry of Brother UK; Nintendo; Sony UK; Nokia Mobile Phones Ltd; Sony Ericsson; Tony Broad of Garmin Europe; Dualit Ltd; Black and Decker Ltd; James Honour of the Buildings Research Establishment; Craig Anders of Cole Thompson Associates; Vestas Wind Systems; Bryan Adams of MIT; Dr Julian Heath of *Microscopy and Analysis*; Fei UK Ltd; Steve Parker; Ian Graham

PHOTOGRAPHY:
M. Alexander; Peter Anderson; Colin Bowling; Charles Brooks; Jane Burton; Peter Chadwick; Simon Clay; Gordon Clayton; John Coiley; Andy Crawford; Geoff Dann; Philip Dowell; John Downs; Mike Dunning; Torla Evans; David Exton; Paul Forrester; Robert and Anthony Fretwell of Fretwell Photography Ltd.; Philip Gatward; Steve Gorton; Anna Hodgson; Gary Kevin; J. Heseltine; Cyril Laubscher; John Lepine; Lynton Gardiner (American Museum of Natural History, New York); Steve Gorton; Michelangelo Gratton; Judith Harrington; Peter Hayman; Anna Hodgson; Colin Keates; Gary Kevin; Dave King; Bob Langrish; Brian D.Morgan; Nick Nicholls; Nick Partitt; Tim Parmenter and Colin Keates (Natural History Museum, London); Tim Ridley; Dave Rudkin; Philippe Sebert; James Stevenson; Clive Streeter; Harry Taylor; Matthew Ward; Jerry Young

PHOTOGRAPHIC ASSISTANCE:
Kevin Zak; Gary Ombler

ILLUSTRATORS:
Julian Baum; Rick Blakeley; Kuo Kang Chen; Karen Cochrane; Simone End; Ian Fleming; Roy Flooks; Mark Franklin; David Gardner; Will Giles; Mick Gillah; David Hopkins; Selwyn Hutchinson; Mei Lim; Linden Artists; Nick Loates; Chris Lyon; Kathleen McDougall; Coral Mula, Sandra Pond, Dave Pugh; Colin Rose; Graham Rosewarne; John Temperton; Halli Verrinder; John Woodcock; Chris Woolmer

MODEL MAKERS:
Roby Braun; David Donkin; Morrison Frederick; Gordon Models; John Holmes; Graham High and Jeremy Hunt of Centaur Studios; Richard Kemp; Kelvin Thatcher; Paul Wilkinson

ADDITIONAL DESIGN ASSISTANCE:
Stefan Morris; Ulysses Santos; Suchada Smith

ADDITIONAL EDITORIAL ASSISTANCE:
Helen Castle; Colette Connolly; Camela Decaire; Nick Harris; Andrea Horth; Stewart McEwen; Damien Moore; Melanie Tham

INDEX: Kay Wright; Lynn Bresler